TEACHERS' EDITION
to accompany

BASIC MODERN MATHEMATICS

ROBERT E. EICHOLZ

Ball State University

PHARES G. O'DAFFER

Ball State University

Consulting authors

CHARLES F. BRUMFIEL

The University of Michigan

MERRILL E. SHANKS

Purdue University

ADDISON-WESLEY PUBLISHING COMPANY, INC.

PALO ALTO, CALIFORNIA

ADDISON-WESLEY PUBLISHING COMPANY, INC.
Reading, Massachusetts · Palo Alto · London
Dallas · Atlanta

School Division Office:
3220 Porter Drive, Palo Alto, Cailfornia 94304

Foreword

Reflecting much of the thinking and findings of leading educators, psychologists, and mathematicians over the past decade, *Basic Modern Mathematics* coordinates proven teaching techniques and the latest developments in learning theory with the precise concepts of modern mathematics. In this series, we provide for the necessary mastery of basic number skills, presenting the material in a way that communicates the exciting, creative side of mathematics. At every stage, students are encouraged to seek out and discover ideas for themselves, to look for interesting patterns and relationships, and to develop their own generalizations. New and fascinating topics are explored not only for their own mathematical value but also to create interest and stimulate students to put forth their best efforts.

Our point of view is that basic skills are not to be presented as a body of uninteresting, unrelated facts that must be learned as a necessary preliminary to the important applications of arithmetic and mathematics in the later years. Rather, mathematics is to be presented as it really is, a dynamic subject which holds extreme fascination and interest for students. Drill for the mastery of skills must be used carefully and, primarily, as a follow up to the introduction of concepts which are approached through an understanding of the over-all structure of mathematics.

The chief tool of the student in a curriculum built around the mastery of isolated facts and techniques is a good memory; the student is most highly rewarded for passive acceptance of that to which he is exposed. The impact of recent cultural, political, and technological revolutions highlights the inadequacies of this traditional approach to the teaching of mathematics —an approach that stresses mastery of skills before understanding of concepts has been achieved. Recognizing these inadequacies, some of the best minds of our time have contributed to the revision of our mathematics curriculum. Vast amounts of talent, time, and money have been expended. The judgments which come from every source, from every experimental project, from every corner of the country, are much the same: students must from the beginning be exposed to the structure of mathematics; they find concepts intensely interesting; they can discover and make use of patterns and relationships; they can think creatively and analytically; they are stimulated by and interested in new mathematical topics; and the learning process is shorter and more effective when based upon a conceptual approach that emphasizes the discovery and understanding of ideas.

Basic Modern Mathematics is written from this modern point of view. In the presentation of basic addition, subtraction, multiplication, and division facts, attention is focused upon *how* these facts may be deduced from certain basic concepts relating to sets and from understanding of the counting process. The *interrelationships between the facts of mathematics*, rather than the facts themselves, command primary attention.

As the relationships between the so-called basic facts are examined, attention is directed toward certain fundamental principles that will serve later to unify the study of advanced mathematics.

In any arithmetic program that brings students to proper levels of understanding and skills, there must be much problem solving and adequate practice for development of speed and accuracy. This series provides a sufficient number of practice pages to meet the objectives of competence in computation and in the solving of word problems. But, above all, *Basic Modern Mathematics* is designed to provide students with opportunities to think mathematically and to create imaginative methods for attacking mathematical problems.

This series provides the more capable students with material which is both challenging and stimulating; it also provides the average and slower students a far more realistic approach to mathematics than has been the case in the past. No matter what level or amount of mathematics will be required by future occupations and interests, all pupils will have greater success in meeting their mathematical needs if they have studied mathematics in a curriculum which stresses logical reasoning, patterns, structure, and skills rather than one that emphasizes skills alone. The abilities to think, to reason, and to attack new problems will remain with the pupils long after mechanical skills have faded from memory.

The very essence of *Basic Modern Mathematics* is reflected in the beliefs to which we are dedicated: that there are fundamental mathematical concepts which can be isolated and set forth with sharpness and clarity, and which, when understood by the learner, provide him with powerful tools for extending his knowledge; that students at every level should be encouraged to think, to question, and to seek understanding; that to each generation must be passed on a certain body of knowledge sifted out from the thousands of years of civilization behind us; that the creativity each new generation brings into the universe must not be dulled by forcing upon our students patterns of thought which have served us well in the past but which may be inadequate for the future.

Mathematics can be taught in this spirit. At every stage in the learning of mathematics the discovery of new relationships can be a delight. It is in this educational philosophy that this series has been written.

About The Teachers' Edition

An orientation section to familiarize you with the content, the mathematics, and the instructional program for the complete year.

The main body of the teaching suggestions, with chapter notes to orient you to the objectives of each chapter, and complete lesson notes for each page of the text.

The complete students' text is reproduced in full color, with answers, in this teachers' edition. Thus, you may have before you at all times, in one book, both the page being studied by the students and the pertinent manual and answer material.

Throughout the manual, page numbers in roman type (000) refer to pages in the pupils' text, and page numbers in italic type (000) refer to pages in the manual.

The Program

Contents

Chapter 4 (pages 82–113 in the text)

Multiplication
Groups of equivalent sets
Number line
Repeated addition
Skip counting
Product sets
Facts through 81
Multiplication table
Logic
Basic principles
Word problems
Geometry lesson 4/Angles and triangles

Chapter 5 (pages 114–133 in the text)

Division
Division concepts
Number of equivalent sets
Number in a set
Inverse relation
Repeated subtraction
Number line
Basic facts (for products through 81)
Word problems

Chapter 6 (pages 134–155 in the text)

Measurement
Length
arbitrary units
inches and centimeters
to nearest half unit
Area
counting squares
approximation
Volume
counting cubes
liquid

Chapter 7 (pages 156–175 in the text)

> *Basic Principles*
> > Order (commutative) principle, addition and multiplication
> > Grouping (associative) principle, addition and multiplication
> > Zero and one principles, addition and multiplication
> > Multiplication-addition (distributive) principle
> > Word problems
> > Geometry lesson 5/Right angles

Chapter 8 (pages 176–207 in the text)

> *Multiplying*
> > Use of multiplication-addition principle
> > Estimation
> > Inequalities
> > One-digit multiplication (with carrying)
> > Two-, three-, and four-digit factors
> > Word problems
> > Geometry lesson 6/Right triangles and rectangles

Chapter 9 (pages 208–245 in the text)

> *Dividing*
> > Estimation
> > Inverse relation
> > Repeated subtraction
> > Inequalities
> > Logic
> > Long-division process (one-digit divisor)
> > Word problems
> > Geometry lesson 7/Quadrilaterals

Chapter 10 (pages 246–259 in the text)

> *Number Theory*
> > Even and odd numbers
> > Multiples and factors
> > Common factors and greatest common factors
> > Prime numbers
> > Clock (modular) arithmetic

Chapter 11 (pages 260–293 in the text)

Fractions
Fractions and number pairs
Fractions and measurement
Fractions and segments
Fractions and sets
Fractions and parts of an object
Equivalent fractions
Sets of equivalent fractions
A check (definition) for equivalent fractions
Lower, higher, and lowest terms
Improper fractions
Mixed numerals
Word problems

Chapter 12 (pages 294–326 in the text)

Rational Numbers
Fractions and numbers
On the number line
Names for rational numbers
Equality of rational numbers
Inequalities for rational numbers
Rational numbers greater than one
Addition of rational numbers (intuitive)
Whole numbers and rational numbers
Use in linear measurement
Word problems

Supplementary Exercises (pages 329–352 in the text)

The pages of the text are reproduced, with answers, in this teachers' edition and with them appears the main body of teaching suggestions, called Chapter and Page Lesson Notes. For each chapter of the text, notes are provided to orient you to the contents and objective of the chapter, and these are followed by detailed lesson notes for each page of that chapter. Mathematics sections are included to provide understanding of the concepts presented and to provide detailed explanation whenever a mathematical topic new to the students is introduced.

Two suggestions for utilization of the Chapter and Page Lesson Notes are offered. (1) Read them carefully and consider each point in terms of the objectives for the lesson and the over-all objectives of the chapter. (2) Do *not* allow them to stifle your own effective teaching methods and creative efforts.

It is not possible, or even desirable, to write directions for the teacher which will fit every teacher in every situation. Treat the notes merely as suggestions to be implemented by your own resourcefulness, and adjust preparation activities to the students' abilities and your own proven teaching techniques. Although teaching modern mathematics may be new to you, teaching students is your specialty. The day-to-day handling of your class and each individual in it cannot and should not be dictated to you in a manual.

We have assumed that the students know all addition and subtraction facts through 18. You will notice, however, that there is considerable review of addition and subtraction concepts as well as a review of these basic facts. Much of the early review in the text devotes considerable time to the basic concepts and ideas underlying *seemingly* trivial factual information. However, as the students proceed to explore more difficult concepts, you will notice that covering these basic concepts early in the student's experience will pay great dividends.

The concepts and facts of multiplication are introduced and work is provided leading toward basic understanding and mastery.

You will notice that in the development of subtraction and division facts considerable emphasis is placed upon the student's ability to think of differences as missing addends and quotients as missing factors. While we intend that the students gain facility at finding differences and quotients, it is hoped that this will come through thinking about the inverse operation.

Of course, the "Exercises for Experts" found scattered through the text are not to be considered an integral part of the development of the mathematics for the text. These exercises are to be used primarily as enrichment and as stimulus to arouse the interest and enthusiasm of the class.

Throughout the text you will find many starred exercises. These, along with other enrichment features in the text, are intended to provide a maximum challenge for all the students in your class. Certainly, the slower students will be challenged to the limit of their ability, and it is hoped that these enrichment features will also provide a maximum challenge for the more able students.

Of course, you must exercise considerable caution and discretion in assigning enrichment exercises to your entire class. You will need to take particular care in helping the students understand that they may attempt the starred exercises, but that they should not be discouraged if they are unable to work them. From time to time the less able students might successfully complete the easier of the starred exercises. When this does happen, they should get a considerable boost in enthusiasm from this successful experience.

Periodically throughout the year you may find it helpful to have additional exercises to supplement those provided in the body of the text. Supplementary exercises have been prepared and are found in the back of the students' text (they are reproduced with answers in the back of this manual). The supplementary exercises can be used for those students who will clearly benefit from the extra practice, as diagnostic or test material or as review exercises.

One of the key features of presenting mathematics as a structured system is to develop a topic and pursue it until you have reached a certain plateau with regard to that particular topic.

• *Evaluation*

Because the over-all objectives differ, evaluation in the modern program presents a problem different from that of traditional programs. Traditional objectives center around techniques and skills, and, certainly, the mastery of facts and computational rules readily lends itself to testing. It is not an easy matter to judge students' progress when the chief points of emphasis are upon ideas, thinking, and understanding.

A sound evaluation of the progress of a student in a modern program must be based on daily observations. An occasional testing situation has value, but day-to-day observations of the activities, both written and oral, constitute the most effective means of evaluation.

No pages in the students' text are designated specifically as test pages; however, most pages are in a sense evaluation or test sheets. This does not mean that you need to correct every paper and record all grades; it does mean that you should constantly observe the oral and written activities of the students. You should be alert to the thinking process employed by the student in deriving oral and written answers. The student who must think of just one fraction at a time is much less mature mathematically than the student who can recognize a single number idea as stemming from a set of equivalent fractions. Yet it is possible that both students respond with the correct answers.

The chapter reviews can be used as chapter tests or as your guide for preparing tests. When one of your chief goals for a given page is evaluation and testing, there is no need to interject a competitive element into the situation by announcing that a test is being given. Simply prepare the class for the lesson and exercise extra care in seeing that each member works the page independently.

This, of course, is one of the guiding philosophies behind the development of *Basic Modern Mathematics*. You will particularly notice this philosophy in the development of some fairly intense sections of work. That is, once a topic is introduced, it is explored in considerable detail. However, every effort has been made in developing these materials to provide interesting activities to relieve the intensity of certain long sections. Treat these relief materials with a light touch.

You are encouraged to give the students every opportunity to think and express themselves. Much of the value from a program such as this is found in allowing the students this communication. Hard and fast rules are avoided wherever possible. Students are encouraged at every stage to reason and to express themselves concerning their findings. Of course, this cannot be done in a random fashion, and a certain amount of guidance is necessary both from you and from the materials in the text. However, at every stage you should be alert to providing opportunities for the class to discuss mathematical concepts which may have come out of certain bodies of material in the text.

• *Time Schedule*

We do not intend to provide a rigid time schedule for you to follow throughout the year. We merely suggest that the program is designed to be covered on the basis of about one pair of pages per day throughout the school year. There is, of course, leeway which will allow you to adjust your schedule for days of school missed and to devote extra time to certain pages. Naturally, the leading factors in any time schedule are the abilities and motivation of the students.

Chapter
and
Page
Lesson Notes

Contents

Objectives of Chapter 1

To provide a thorough understanding of place-value concepts

To introduce hundreds, thousands, and millions

To review and extend work with inequalities

Without an understanding of place value, there is no hope of teaching with any comprehension the algorithms of arithmetic and decimal notation. For this reason, the concepts of place value are treated carefully in this first chapter.

We begin this chapter by using two-digit numerals to present some basic place-value ideas. Following this brief review, hundreds and thousands are introduced and explored carefully. Following the work with thousands, the students are given many opportunities to work with place-value concepts in identifying the number represented by a given digit in a symbol and in working with inequalities.

Although the inequality symbols are not used in this chapter, the ideas are explored and used to focus attention upon place-value concepts. When a student is asked to write the larger of two numbers on his paper and when the symbols for these numbers differ in only the hundreds place, the student is led automatically to see that one number has more hundreds than the other and, thus, is greater than the other.

At this time, the meaning of individual places in the place-value system is not carried beyond the thousands place. To introduce five-digit and six-digit numbers, we simply point out that the three digits in the fourth, fifth, and sixth places name the number of thousands. This procedure facilitates arriving at the meaning of large numbers with minimum effort. This also facilitates the reading of large numbers. The same idea is carried through in introducing millions. The students are told that the digits in the seventh, eighth, and ninth places simply tell the number of millions. We feel that it is more important to get quickly to the reading of large numbers than it is to focus attention upon each individual place after the fourth. The more able students may recognize quickly that the fifth place is the 10,000 place, and so on, but it is not a point that is stressed in this work. These places will be stressed later in the program.

Following the introduction of millions, the students are given an opportunity to work with large numbers in meaningful situations.

Mathematics of Chapter 1

The *digits* are the symbols 0, 1, 2, 3, 4, 5, 6, 7, 8, and 9. A *numeral* is any symbol that stands for a number. Thus the symbol *4* is a digit and it is also a numeral. The symbol *57* consists of two digits and is a numeral for the number fifty-seven.

Correct usage of the words *number, numeral,* and *digit* is often quite awkward. For example, one might ask a student to write the "number" 1486, or one might refer to this as a "four-digit number." These, of course, are abuses of the language. You do not write the *number,* nor does the *number* have four digits. You write the *symbol* or the *numeral,* and it is the symbol or the numeral that has four digits. However, both of the above expressions are acceptable since the students will no doubt understand that you mean write the symbol for this number on the chalkboard and that when you call it a four-digit number you are referring to the symbol which is used to represent this number.

Certain abuses of the number-numeral terminology are clearly objectionable. You would not want to ask the students to *add the digits or numerals* 37 and 52. We *add* numbers; we *write* digits and numerals.

The important thing to remember in number-numeral terminology is to keep your language simple and meaningful. Whenever there is doubt as to whether you should say number or numeral, say *number.* Also, you should avoid making an issue of these words. If a student points at his paper and says that that is the number 57, do not criticize or correct this remark. Students have an intuitive grasp of the difference between number and numeral; a lengthy discussion of these ideas may serve only to confuse something which was previously clear.

When we write the symbol 4357, the numerals 4, 3, 5, and 7 stand for 4000, 300, 50, and 7, respectively. This illustrates an important property of our numeration system: the utilization of place value. Place value simply means that the number a digit represents depends upon the place it occupies in the symbol.

Another important fact, which simplifies our calculations and makes it easy to learn arithmetic, is that we can represent any number by using only ten symbols, 0, 1, 2, 3, 4, 5, 6, 7, 8, 9. Each of these digits used by itself represents a single number; it is only when we write symbols for numbers greater than nine that a given digit may stand for two or more numbers. Thus in 636, one 6 stands for 600, and the other stands for 6.

The place-value scheme that we utilize has a base of ten. Base ten means that we group by tens. That is, given a collection of objects, we might ask how many disjoint groups of ten can be formed. Consider the set of dots shown in the illustration; we see that there are three groups of ten and eight left over.

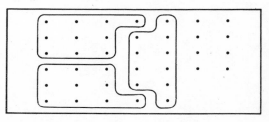

The importance of place value is evident when we attempt to write the numeral for this number of dots. Instead of writing "3 groups of ten and 8 more," we simply write "38" and agree that the digit in the "second place" (3 in this case) is to represent groups of ten.

Of course, when working with larger numbers, we must group the groups of ten by tens. We then have groups of 10 tens, each of which we call one hundred. For example, we might have a set of objects grouped as follows: 5 groups of one hundred, 3 groups of ten, and 7 more; we write 537.

Teaching Chapter 1

Although the students should be able to grasp abstract ideas from pictures shown on the printed page, use of demonstration materials plays an important role in the presentation of place-value concepts. You should use sets freely to illustrate the concepts of the early pages of the chapter.

When hundreds and thousands are introduced, you may find it helpful to introduce different-sized boxes or paper bags with the numerals *100* and *1000* written on them. For example, you could show two large and three small paper bags, four bundles of ten, and five pencils. Tell the students to imagine that the large paper bags each contain 1000 and the smaller paper bags each contain 100. From this they can visualize the number illustrated by your demonstration.

It is important in this chapter that the students become accustomed to distinguishing between the words *digit* and *numeral*. They should recognize that when you talk about a digit you mean *one* of the symbols (0, 1, 2, 3, 4, 5, 6, 7, 8, 9) and that when you talk about a numeral you mean *any* symbol that stands for a number.

In the lessons covering numbers having more than four digits, the vocabulary problem increases. It is not easy for students at this level to read large numbers. However, if you make it clear to the students that the three digits in the fourth, fifth, and sixth places name the thousands and that the three digits in the seventh, eighth, and ninth places name the millions, they should recognize quickly that reading large numbers is no more difficult than recognizing whether the number is in the millions or the thousands.

You should not expect all members of your class to master reading large numerals. However, all students should understand the elementary place-value concepts.

Plan to spend a maximum of 2½ weeks on the chapter, but attempt to cover it in two weeks.

The chapter review should serve as a yardstick for evaluating the students' progress in this chapter. However, keep in mind that the most important items to evaluate are found in the early lessons of the chapter. The reading and comparison of very large numbers should be considered as enrichment rather than as more important items of the chapter. Recognition of the place-value concepts in two- and three-digit numbers must be the first item in your evaluation of the students' progress for this chapter.

There are many lessons containing review material on place value throughout the remainder of the text. This will give those students who have not completely mastered the ideas of this chapter an opportunity to attain a better understanding of them as they move through the program.

The word-problem pages on the odometer, mountain peaks, and planets provide stimulating activities for work with large numbers. Do not expect all students to be able to work all of the problems on these pages. You may choose to treat much of the material on these word-problem pages as class-discussion activity. However, in handling these pages, do not deny your faster students an opportunity to explore the problems by themselves.

Emphasize the fact that the number for which a given digit stands depends upon its place in the numeral. This idea is brought out in the table by showing that the 5 stands for four different numbers according to its position in the given numeral.

When the students have completed reading and studying this material, give them an opportunity to ask questions.

Chapter 1 PLACE VALUE

Grouping by tens

Using place value, we can write the numeral for any whole number with only the digits

0, 1, 2, 3, 4, 5, 6, 7, 8, 9.

A digit may stand for different numbers. What the digit stands for depends on its place or position in the numeral. Here is an example.

2 3 4 5 ⟶ The 5 stands for 5 ones (5).
4 2 5 3 ⟶ The 5 stands for 5 tens (50).
3 5 4 2 ⟶ The 5 stands for 5 hundreds (500).
5 3 2 4 ⟶ The 5 stands for 5 thousands (5000).

Here are some examples to help you think about the grouping by tens in the place-value system.

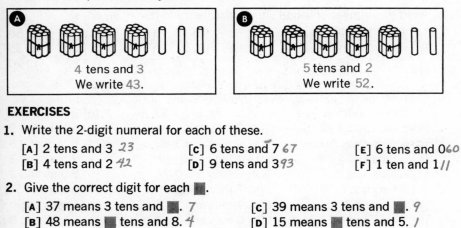

4 tens and 3
We write 43.

5 tens and 2
We write 52.

EXERCISES

1. Write the 2-digit numeral for each of these.
   [A] 2 tens and 3 *23*   [C] 6 tens and 7 *67*   [E] 6 tens and 0 *60*
   [B] 4 tens and 2 *42*   [D] 9 tens and 3 *93*   [F] 1 ten and 1 *11*

2. Give the correct digit for each ▓.
   [A] 37 means 3 tens and ▓. *7*   [C] 39 means 3 tens and ▓. *9*
   [B] 48 means ▓ tens and 8. *4*   [D] 15 means ▓ tens and 5. *1*

1

Teaching Page 1

PURPOSE

To build an understanding of place value for two-digit numerals

To stress grouping by tens

MATHEMATICS

In this lesson, grouping by tens is emphasized by showing pictures of bundles of ten with a certain number left.

The exercises at the bottom of page 1 (e.g., "37 means 3 tens and 7") provide a way of talking about the numerals that points out that the very concept of place value is centered around the marks that we put on paper. When we discuss the meaning of a given numeral with regard to

place value, we are actually concerned with the digits and their position with respect to other digits. The concept of the number does not enter into place-value notation. Thus the entire study of place value merely involves agreements with regard to the writing of symbols.

PREPARATION

Exhibit a group of pencils or similar objects and give the students an opportunity to group these objects by ten and then write the symbol for this number of objects. This should be done without the aid of counting beyond ten. For example, you might exhibit a set of 57 pencils and have students form groups of ten until you have five groups of ten with seven left over; then have someone write the numeral 57 on the board.

17

Give the class an opportunity to study the chart. Then discuss several lines of the chart with them. Stress the four headings, "We see (the bundles)," "We think (about the number of tens)," "We write (the numeral)," and "We say (the word)." Some students may need to review the names given in the table.

Encourage all the students to participate in answering the oral exercises.

2-digit numerals

We see	We think	We write	We say
	2 tens	20	twenty
	3 tens	30	thirty
	4 tens	40	forty
	5 tens	50	fifty
	6 tens	60	sixty
	7 tens	70	seventy
	8 tens	80	eighty
	9 tens	90	ninety

ORAL EXERCISES

1. Read the number. Then tell how many tens and how many ones.

[A] 63 [D] 57 [G] 96 [J] 60 [M] 17 [P] 11 [S] 48 [V] 50
[B] 47 [E] 21 [H] 85 [K] 51 [N] 21 [Q] 10 [T] 80 [W] 35
[C] 39 [F] 16 [I] 43 [L] 30 [O] 78 [R] 99 [U] 27 [X] 70

2. Give the correct number for each of these.

[A] 6 tens and 5 *65*   [I] 8 tens and 3 *83*   [Q] 7 tens and 0 *7*
[B] 5 tens and 9 *59*   [J] 3 tens and 6 *36*   [R] 4 tens and 9 *4*
[C] 4 tens and 2 *42*   [K] 4 tens and 3 *43*   [S] 8 tens and 5 *8*
[D] 5 tens and 4 *54*   [L] 1 ten and 0 *10*   [T] 7 tens and 3 *7*
[E] 6 tens and 2 *62*   [M] 2 tens and 9 *29*   [U] 9 tens and 2 *9*
[F] 3 tens and 0 *30*   [N] 7 tens and 1 *71*   [V] 1 ten and 5 *15*
[G] 1 ten and 3 *13*   [O] 7 tens and 7 *77*   [W] 8 tens and 0 *80*
[H] 4 tens and 6 *46*   [P] 6 tens and 0 *60*   [X] 6 tens and 8 *6*

Teaching Pages 2 and 3

● **PURPOSE**

To focus further attention on two-digit place value
To review the number names twenty *through* ninety
To introduce 100

● **MATHEMATICS**

Once the concept of grouping by tens is mastered, it is not hard for the students to understand the meaning of two-digit numerals. Extending this idea to include groups of 10 tens is slightly more difficult, but it utilizes the same

Hundreds

Ten	10 tens
	one hundred
	one hundred
	one hundred

EXERCISES

1. Draw a set of one hundred dots (10 rows of ten).
Now draw a set of thirty dots (3 rows of ten).
Now draw a set of seven dots.
You have drawn one hundred thirty-seven dots.

2. Did you need to count higher than 10 to draw the dots in exercise 1? *No*

3. Draw a set of one hundred twenty-three dots.
Do not count higher than 10.

4. Which set of dots has more, the blue or the black? *the black*

5. How many more does one set have than the other? *10 more*

Ask the class to study the chart at the top of the page. As you discuss each frame of the chart, stress that 100 is 10 tens. The illustrations are so arranged that the students can make the transition from 1 ten to 10 tens by counting groups of ten.

Instruct the students to work the exercises on their own. Follow this with a discussion in which the class is given a chance to ask questions.

concept. That is, one must recognize that when ten groups of ten are obtained, the grouping is extended to groups of 100. Of course, this extension of grouping by tens continues on through the place-value scheme. For this reason the progression from two-digit to three-digit numerals is an important phase for a thorough understanding of place-value ideas.

PREPARATION

The chief point of emphasis in preparing for this lesson is to stress that ten groups of ten is one group of 100. To do this you can exhibit sets of pencils, or other suitable objects, in groups of 40, 50, or 80. Have the students bundle these sets into groups of ten and write the appropriate numeral on the chalkboard. Complete the demonstration by exhibiting a group of 100 for the students to group by tens. When they have finished, write the numeral *100* on the chalkboard and explain that this is 10 tens and that the *1* in the third place represents one group of 100. Stress also that we think of this numeral as a 10 (or *one, zero*) in the tens place, which points out that 100 is 10 tens.

When discussing the table at the top of the page, have the students count the sets of 100, the sets of ten, and the number of ones. Explain how the numeral represents this number of dots.

Have the class do the first set of exercises orally. After a student reads the number, have him tell the number of hundreds, tens, and ones, For example, in exercise 1 of the oral exercises, the student would read, "Two hundreds, seven tens, and eight ones." This provides experience and reinforcement of the idea of placement of the digit with respect to the number it represents.

Following the oral exercises, direct the students to work the rest of the exercises on their own. After they have finished, allow time for reading and discussing the answers.

3-digit numerals

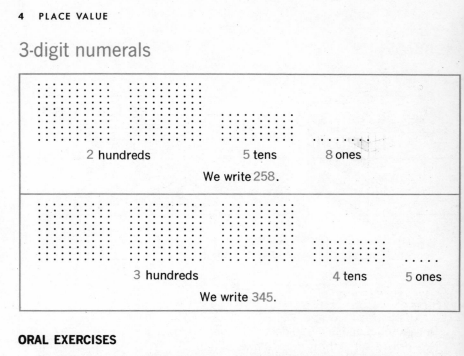

2 hundreds   5 tens   8 ones
We write 258.

3 hundreds   4 tens   5 ones
We write 345.

ORAL EXERCISES

Read the number. Then tell how many hundreds, tens, and ones.

1. 278	**4.** 923	**7.** 318	**10.** 704	**13.** 707	**16.** 864
2. 346	**5.** 765	**8.** 640	**11.** 900	**14.** 770	**17.** 297
3. 512	**6.** 492	**9.** 380	**12.** 506	**15.** 437	**18.** 485

EXERCISES

1. Write the numeral. (*h* stands for hundreds and *t* for tens.)

   [A] 3 *h*, 2 *t*, and 6 *326*   [D] 6 *h*, 0 *t*, and 1 *601*   [G] 6 *h*, 2 *t*, and 7 *76*
   [B] 4 *h*, 7 *t*, and 2 *472*   [E] 3 *h*, 2 *t*, and 0 *320*   [H] 1 *h*, 0 *t*, and 0 *010*
   [C] 6 *h*, 5 *t*, and 0 *650*   [F] 3 *h*, 0 *t*, and 0 *300*   [I] 7 *h*, 6 *t*, and 5 *7*

2. Give the missing digit.

   [A] 384 means 3 hundreds, ▉ tens, and 4 ones. *8*
   [B] 659 means ▉ hundreds, 5 tens, and 9 ones. *6*
   [C] 518 means 5 hundreds, 1 ten, and ▉ ones. *8*
   [D] 304 means ▉ hundreds, 0 tens, and 4 ones. *3*
   [E] 760 means 7 hundreds, 6 tens, and ▉ ones. *0*
   [F] 927 means 9 hundreds, ▉ tens, and 7 ones. *2*

Teaching Pages 4 and 5

• PURPOSE

To strengthen understanding of three-digit numerals
To introduce 1000
To build an understanding of four-digit numerals

• MATHEMATICS

Once a transition has been made from tens to hundreds, extending the idea of place value to thousands is little more than a formality. If students understand that 100 is ten groups of ten, they should easily be able to extend this to an understanding that 1000 is ten groups of 100.

• PREPARATION

Since the number of objects required for providing demonstrations of four-digit numerals is prohibitive, other devices must be utilized to give the students a feeling for the meaning of 1000. You can have the students pretend that certain containers hold 1000 objects each. Then you can have them think about 10 such containers or one large container holding 1000 objects. Once the students have been given this understanding of 1000 as 10 hundreds, you

Thousands

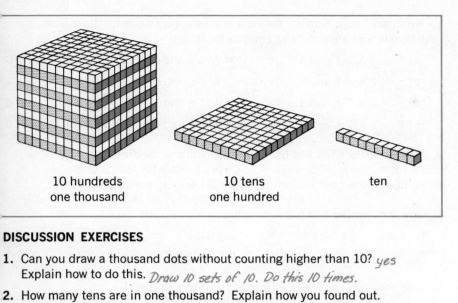

10 hundreds
one thousand

10 tens
one hundred

ten

DISCUSSION EXERCISES

1. Can you draw a thousand dots without counting higher than 10? *yes*
Explain how to do this. *Draw 10 sets of 10. Do this 10 times.*

2. How many tens are in one thousand? Explain how you found out.
100.   To draw 1000 dots, you would make 100 sets of 10.

For 1 thousand, 3 hundreds, 2 tens, and 6, we write   1326.

For 6 thousands, 4 hundreds, 7 tens, and 5, we write   6475.

For 8 thousands, 2 hundreds, 0 tens, and 7, we write   8207.

ORAL EXERCISES

Read the number. Then tell how many thousands, hundreds, tens, and ones.

1. 7264	**5.** 1635	**9.** 9025	**13.** 8340	**17.** 9216	**21.** 3210
2. 8315	**6.** 7986	**10.** 8840	**14.** 2600	**18.** 7007	**22.** 1000
3. 9126	**7.** 8204	**11.** 7602	**15.** 5000	**19.** 6000	**23.** 9020
4. 8427	**8.** 3716	**12.** 9100	**16.** 8083	**20.** 5080	**24.** 8003

can illustrate a given four-digit numeral by exhibiting a large bag with "1000" written on it, several small bags with "100" written on them, a few bundles of 10 objects, and a few objects left over. You should repeat this demonstration to illustrate various four-digit numerals.

During these discussions and demonstrations, you should continue to stress that 100 is 10 tens, and that 1000 is 100 tens or 10 hundreds.

Give the class an opportunity to study the figure at the top of the page. Re-emphasize that 100 is 10 tens and that 1000 is 10 hundreds.

Work through the discussion exercises with the class. Exercise 1 may present a particular problem, since it may be difficult for the students to express how to draw 1000 dots without counting higher than ten. However, a great deal of value can be derived from a discussion of this type. Elicit from the students that they can draw ten dots and then can continue drawing ten more dots until they have ten sets of ten. Then they can do this ten times and be quite sure that they would have 1000 dots without having counted beyond ten. This idea should be summarized before going to the next exercise.

Exercise 2 may already have been answered. However, it is important that the students have an opportunity to express this idea in their own words. Elicit responses such as, "There are 10 tens in 100 and 10 hundreds in 1000 so we know that there are 100 tens in 1000."

Following the discussion exercises, have the class read the material in the table that follows. In each case, have the students read the number of thousands, hundreds, tens, and ones and then read the numeral. For example, for the first entry in the table the students should say, "1 thousand, 3 hundreds, 2 tens, and 6 ones" and then read, "one thousand three hundred twenty-six."

Following this, move on to the oral exercises. In exercise 1, the students should read, "seven thousand two hundred sixty-four," and then say, "There are 7 thousands, 2 hundreds, 6 tens, and 4 ones."

Give the students an opportunity to work the exercises. When they have finished, allow time for checking answers and any questions the students may have.

Emphasize for the students that they can think of place-value concepts rather than addition and subtraction for working exercises 3, 4, 5, and 6. That is, by simply thinking of place value and skip-counting concepts they can easily answer the questions without reference to addition or subtraction concepts.

Place-value exercises

1. Write the 4-digit numeral for each of these. (*th* stands for thousands, *h* stands for hundreds, and *t* stands for tens.)

   [A] 6 *th*, 5 *h*, 2 *t*, and 4   6524
   [E] 9 *th*, 4 *h*, 0 *t*, and 0   9400
   [I] 6 *th*, 0 *h*, 8 *t*, and 0   6080

   [B] 1 *th*, 2 *h*, 3 *t*, and 9   1239
   [F] 9 *th*, 0 *h*, 0 *t*, and 0   9000
   [J] 4 *th*, 5 *h*, 0 *t*, and 2   4502

   [C] 9 *th*, 4 *h*, 2 *t*, and 1   9421
   [G] 1 *th*, 1 *h*, 1 *t*, and 1   1111
   [K] 7 *th*, 3 *h*, 5 *t*, and 6   7356

   [D] 9 *th*, 4 *h*, 2 *t*, and 0   9420
   [H] 1 *th*, 0 *h*, 0 *t*, and 0   1000
   [L] 3 *th*, 2 *h*, 0 *t*, and 0   3200

2. The numerals 6325 and 6425 differ only in the hundreds place. Which number, 6325 or 6425, has more hundreds? Which of the two numbers is larger? How much larger is one than the other?
   6425 is 100 larger than 6325.

3. Give the number that is 10 more than

   [A] 25 35   [C] 468 478   [E] 841 851   [G] 3168 3178   [I] 595 605

   [B] 68 78   [D] 725 735   [F] 1425 1435   [H] 9256 9266   [J] 307 317

4. Give the numbers that are 10 less than those in exercise 3.
   15   458   831   3158   585
   58   715   1415   9246   297

5. Give the number that is 100 more than

   [A] 256 356   [C] 4682 4782   [E] 8417 8517   [G] 3168 3268   [I] 2927 3027

   [B] 682 782   [D] 7256 7356   [F] 1425 1525   [H] 3426 3526   [J] 4036 4136

6. Give the numbers that are 100 less than those in exercise 5.
   156   4582   8317   3068   2827
   582   7156   1325   3326   3936

7. What number is 10 more than 5? What number is 100 more than 5? What number is 1000 more than 5? 15, 105, 1005

8. From each pair of numbers, choose the larger.

   [A] 6254   [D] 1728   [G] 4321   [J] 4200
       6354   1720   4391   4070

   [B] 8321   [E] 3256   [H] 7192   [K] 1283
       7321   3259   7092   1279

   [C] 5280   [F] 2999   [I] 5300   [L] 3260
       5281   3000   5200   3209

Teaching Pages 6 and 7

- **PURPOSE**

  To reinforce the place-value concepts developed thus far

- **PREPARATION**

  Conduct a short discussion period to review the place-value concepts developed to this point. You can use the exercises on pages 6 and 7 to guide you in your review lesson. During this review, provide the students with experiences in working with abbreviations like those in exercise 1 on page 6 so that they will have been exposed to these abbreviations prior to working the exercises.

9. Rearrange these numbers from smallest to largest. *(See answers at right.)*

[A] 689, 52, 1683, 100

[B] 3429, 516, 8154, 275

[C] 5654, 5454, 5154, 5954

[D] 8276, 8216, 8246, 8236

[E] 7920, 7918, 7921, 7919

[F] 5278, 5280, 5279, 5281

[G] 6498, 6500, 6499, 6501

[H] 3999, 3998, 4000, 4001

10. Give the next 3 numbers for each of these sequences.

[A] 289, 290, 291, *292, 293, 294*

[B] 566, 567, 568, *569, 570, 571*

[C] 1298, 1299, 1300, *1301, 1302, 1303*

[D] 4380, 4390, 4400, *4410, 4420, 4430*

[E] 7256, 7356, 7456, . . . *7556, 7656, 7756*

[F] 3173, 3183, 3193, . . . *3203, 3213, 3223*

[G] 6496, 6497, 6498, . . . *6499, 6500, 6501*

[H] 2995, 2996, 2997, . . . *2998, 2999, 3000*

11. In each numeral below, one of the digits is blue. Give the number for which that digit stands. For example, in exercise A the 7 stands for 700.

[A] 6728 *700* [C] 4286 *80* [E] 7106 *100* [G] 9457 *9000* [I] 4037 *0*

[B] 4325 *4000* [D] 9515 *5* [F] 8732 *700* [H] 1260 *0* [J] 5208 *0*

12. Find the missing digits for each of these.

[A] 6721 means ▧ hundreds, 6 thousands, 1 one, ▧ tens.

[B] 4362 means 4 thousands, ▧ tens, ▧ hundreds, 2 ones.

[C] 7820 means 2 tens, ▧ hundreds, 0 ones, ▧ thousands.

[D] 5207 means ▧ hundreds, ▧ tens, 5 thousands, 7 ones.

[E] 6431 means 1 one, 6 thousands, ▧ tens, ▧ hundreds.

[F] 2803 means 2 thousands, ▧ tens, ▧ hundreds, 3 ones.

[G] 4076 means ▧ tens, 0 hundreds, ▧ ones, 4 thousands.

[H] 8030 means 0 ones, ▧ thousands, ▧ hundreds, 3 tens.

13. Think about the number 8253. Now answer these questions.

[A] What number is 100 and 10 more than 8253? *8363*

[B] What number is 1000 and 3 less than 8253? *7250*

[C] What number is 253 less than 8253? *8000*

[D] What number is 8000 less than 8253? *253*

[E] What number is 8000 and 50 less than 8253? *203*

Instruct the class to work the exercises. Allow time at the end for checking papers and answering any questions the students may have.

If the less able students are given an opportunity to work exercise 13, it should be pointed out to them that this exercise is more difficult than some of the others and that they should not be discouraged if they are unable to arrive at the correct answers.

Answers, exercise 9, page 7

[A] 52, 100, 689, 1683

[B] 275, 516, 3429, 8154

[C] 5154, 5454, 5654, 5954

[D] 8216, 8236, 8246, 8276

[E] 7918, 7919, 7920, 7921

[F] 5278, 5279, 5280, 5281

[G] 6498, 6499, 6500, 6501

[H] 3998, 3999, 4000, 4001

Have the students work the exercises on their own. Since some students may experience difficulty in reading and interpreting the exercises, you should move around the class and give assistance as necessary. If any of the exercises give particular difficulty to a large number of students, stop and discuss with the class the problem involved; then have the students again proceed on their own.

Exercise 6 is considerably more difficult than the rest and should be used primarily as enrichment for the more able students.

Reading the odometer

EXERCISES

1. When Jim's family left home, the odometer on their car looked like this. ➡️ ⟨9⟩⟨7⟩⟨6⟩⟨5⟩

   Jim saw this sign. *REDTOWN 100 MILES* What did the odometer read when they were in Redtown? **9865**

2. West Road had markers every 10 miles. When the car turned onto West Road, the odometer looked like this. ➡️ ⟨1⟩⟨0⟩⟨2⟩⟨4⟩⟨0⟩

   Jim counted 10 markers. He surprised his sister Nancy by telling her what the number on the odometer was without looking. What did the odometer read? **10,340**

3. At Wood City the odometer looked like this. ➡️ ⟨1⟩⟨0⟩⟨7⟩⟨8⟩⟨4⟩

   At River City the odometer looked like this. ➡️ ⟨1⟩⟨0⟩⟨7⟩⟨9⟩⟨4⟩

   How far is it from Wood City to River City? **10 miles**

4. Logtown is 100 miles farther from Jim's house than Fish Hook is.

   JIM'S HOUSE   FISH HOOK   100 MILES   LOGTOWN

   The odometer looked like this at Fish Hook. ➡️ ⟨1⟩⟨1⟩⟨0⟩⟨6⟩⟨5⟩

   What do you think the odometer read at Logtown? **11,165**

5. The toll road had black markers every 100 miles. When the car turned onto the toll road the odometer looked like this. ➡️ ⟨1⟩⟨2⟩⟨0⟩⟨4⟩⟨3⟩

   100 MILES   100 MILES   TOLL ROAD

   What will the odometer read after the car goes past 10 black markers? **13,043**

★ 6. When Jim arrived home the odometer looked like this. ➡️ ⟨1⟩⟨3⟩⟨8⟩⟨9⟩⟨7⟩

   How far did Jim and his family travel on their vacation? **4132 miles**

Teaching Pages 8 and 9

• PURPOSE

To utilize concepts of place value in a real-life situation

To strengthen skills in working with word problems

To provide stimulus for the work in this chapter

To strengthen understanding of the place-value concepts developed thus far

• PREPARATION

Your preparation activities for this lesson are essentially taken care of by the review exercises in the previous lesson. However, you will want to explain the meaning of five-digit numerals to the students. So far, their work has been restricted to numbers less than 10,000. You can accomplish this simply by giving them several exercises involving four-digit numbers and then exhibiting on the chalkboard sev-

ow many beads?

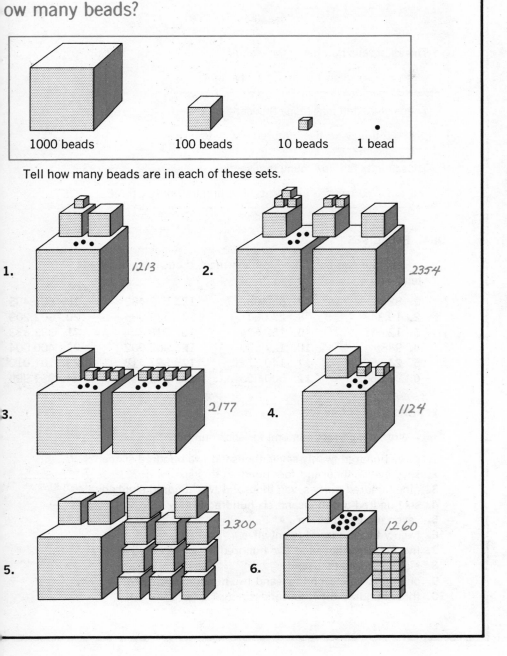

Tell how many beads are in each of these sets.

1. *1213*

2. *2354*

3. *2177*

4. *1124*

5. *2300*

6. *1260*

Have the students study the figure at the top of the page. Remind them that they are to think of the large box as containing 1000 beads; the middle-sized box, 100 beads; and the small box, 10 beads. Notice with them that the little dots are to be thought of as one bead each.

Now give the students an opportunity to write the correct numeral for the beads in exercise 1. When they have finished, exhibit the correct answer on the chalkboard and give the students an opportunity to ask questions and discuss this answer with respect to the drawing in the book.

Direct the students to complete the page. When they have finished, go back and discuss each exercise.

eral five-digit numerals. Have the class read the five-digit numerals. This will present little difficulty since the comma separating the thousands and hundreds should readily indicate to the students that a numeral such as 13,897 is read as, "thirteen thousand, eight hundred ninety-seven."

As a preparation activity for the exercises on page 9, label three different-sized boxes or bags "1000," "100," and "10," according to their size. Have available a collection of ten beads. Ask the students to imagine that the large bags contain 1000 beads, and so on. Exhibit various collections of these bags with a few single beads and have the students tell how many beads. Each time, write the numeral on the chalkboard and emphasize the number of thousands, the number of hundreds, the number of tens, and the number of ones.

Give the class an opportunity to study the examples at the top of the page. Discuss each example and have the students read the numbers aloud. Follow this by having the students take turns reading the large numbers given in the oral exercises.

Instruct the class to do the exercises at the bottom of the page. As a follow-up, discuss the exercises and exhibit the correct numerals on the chalkboard.

Answers, oral exercises, page 10

1. 8 *th*, 2 *h*, 6 *t*, 4 *o*
2. 19 *th*, 3 *h*, 4 *t*, 8 *o*
3. 12 *th*, 6 *h*, 1 *t*, 5 *o*
4. 9 *th*, 4 *h*, 8 *t*, 5 *o*
5. 24 *th*, 6 *h*, 5 *t*, 2 *o*
6. 91 *th*, 8 *h*, 6 *t*, 0 *o*
7. 58 *th*, 4 *h*, 0 *t*, 3 *o*
8. 27 *th*, 0 *h*, 6 *t*, 4 *o*
9. 152 *th*, 6 *h*, 3 *t*, 4 *o*
10. 127 *th*, 5 *h*, 0 *t*, 0 *o*
11. 140 *th*, 3 *h*, 7 *t*, 2 *o*
12. 500 *th*, 5 *h*, 0 *t*, 0 *o*
13. 672 *th*, 4 *h*, 8 *t*, 3 *o*
14. 529 *th*, 0 *h*, 0 *t*, 6 *o*
15. 318 *th*, 8 *h*, 6 *t*, 4 *o*
16. 902 *th*, 9 *h*, 0 *t*, 2 *o*
17. 587 *th*, 4 *h*, 1 *t*, 8 *o*
18. 70 *th*, 0 *h*, 7 *t*, 0 *o*
19. 601 *th*, 4 *h*, 8 *t*, 5 *o*
20. 902 *th*, 2 *h*, 0 *t*, 9 *o*
21. 333 *th*, 3 *h*, 3 *t*, 3 *o*
22. 400 *th*, 0 *h*, 0 *t*, 4 *o*
23. 101 *th*, 0 *h*, 1 *t*, 0 *o*
24. 999 *th*, 9 *h*, 9 *t*, 9 *o*

5- and 6-digit numerals

This digit tells how many thousands. ⟶ 7628

seven thousand six hundred twenty-eight

These digits tell how many thousands. ⟶ 36,584

thirty-six thousand five hundred eighty-four

These digits tell how many thousands. ⟶ 418,293

four hundred eighteen thousand two hundred ninety-three

ORAL EXERCISES

Read the number. Then tell how many thousands, hundreds, tens, and ones. *(See answers at left.)*

1. 8264	7. 58,403	13. 672,483	19. 601,485
2. 19,348	8. 27,064	14. 529,006	20. 902,209
3. 12,615	9. 152,634	15. 318,864	21. 333,333
4. 9485	10. 127,500	16. 902,902	22. 400,004
5. 24,652	11. 140,372	17. 587,418	23. 101,010
6. 91,860	12. 500,500	18. 70,070	24. 999,999

EXERCISES

Write the correct numeral for each number.

1. three hundred twenty-seven thousand two hundred sixteen *327,216*
2. seventy-five thousand four hundred fifty-six *75,456*
3. nine hundred thirty-seven thousand two hundred eighty-one *937,281*
4. six hundred two thousand six hundred twenty *602,620*
5. seven thousand seven *7007*
6. twenty-five thousand twenty-five *25,025*
7. five hundred thousand five hundred *500,500*
8. eight hundred thousand *800,000*
9. one hundred eleven thousand two hundred twenty-two *111,222*
10. three hundred fifty thousand ninety *350,090*

Teaching Pages 10 and 11

● **PURPOSE**

To introduce five- and six-digit numbers

● **MATHEMATICS**

In the place-value scheme, a problem occurs when one gets into five-digit and six-digit numerals. Each place is given a new name through the fourth place (the first place is the ones place, the second is the tens, the third is the hundreds, and the fourth is the thousands). However, no new names are used after the thousands place until one gets to the seventh place, where we give the name *millions*. Of course, it could be claimed that the fifth place is called the ten thousands place and the sixth place is called the hundred thousands place; however, the term *thousands* still applies to these two places. In these beginning lessons, we do not call attention to these special names for the fifth and sixth places; rather, we call attention to the fact that three places (the fourth, fifth, and sixth) name the number of thousands.

Of course, the naming of places other than the first three occurs in blocks of three for all other extensions of the place-value system through millions, billions, etc. By focusing attention on three places at this point, we are able to simplify for the students the reading of large numbers.

One million

EXERCISES

1. Give the next 3 numbers for each of these.

[A] 500	[B] 950	[C] 5000	[D] 9500
600	960	6000	9600
700	970	7000	9700
800	*980*	*8000*	*9800*
900	*990*	*9000*	*9900*
1000	*1000*	*10,000*	*10,000*

[E] 50,000	[F] 95,000	[G] 500,000	[H] 950,000
60,000	96,000	600,000	960,000
70,000	97,000	700,000	970,000
80,000	*98,000*	*800,000*	*980,000*
90,000	*99,000*	*900,000*	*990,000*
100,000	*100,000*	*1,000,000*	*1,000,000*

2. Write the numeral for each of these.

[A] nine hundred thousand *900,000*   [C] nine hundred ninety-nine thousand *999,000*

[B] ten hundred thousand *1,000,000*   [D] one thousand thousand *1,000,000*

3. [A] What number is 1 more than 99? *100*

[B] What number is 1 more than 999? *1000*

[C] What number is 1 more than 9999? *10,000*

[D] What number is 1 more than 99,999? *100,000*

[E] What number is 1 more than 999,999? *1,000,000*

One million ——————————→ 1,000,000

We can think of one million in different ways:

One million is a thousand thousand.

1,000,000

One million is ten hundred thousand.

1,000,000

Have the students complete the exercises on their own. When they have finished, focus particular attention on the box at the bottom of the page and the number 1,000,000. Stress the fact that one million is a thousand thousands and that it is ten hundred thousands.

PREPARATION

Exhibit on the chalkboard several four-digit numerals for the students to read. Now exhibit a five-digit numeral and give the students an opportunity to read this. Many of them will know how this should be read. However, emphasize that the two digits in front of the comma, or to the left of the comma, name the number of thousands.

(In this book, the comma will generally be used only in numerals of five or more digits. Occasionally, a comma is used in a four-digit numeral to illustrate a certain point or to be uniform with regard to other numerals.)

Following the work with five-digit numerals, exhibit some six-digit numerals and again give the students an op-

portunity to guess how each numeral should be read. Be sure to focus attention on the fact that the three digits in the fourth, fifth, and sixth places name the number of thousands.

During this preparation, do not mention the number or the numeral for 1,000,000. Page 11 is designed to lead the students to this number, and you can follow page 11 with a discussion of the number 1,000,000.

Have the class study and read aloud the examples at the top of the page. Do the oral exercises as a class activity. Follow this by giving the students an opportunity to work the exercises at the bottom of the page. Allow time for discussion of the exercises.

7-, 8-, and 9-digit numerals

This digit tells how many millions. ——————→ 5,684,971

five million six hundred eighty-four thousand nine hundred seventy-one

These digits tell how many millions. ——————→ 56,742,314

fifty-six million seven hundred forty-two thousand three hundred fourteen

These digits tell how many millions. ——————→ 612,524,600

six hundred twelve million five hundred twenty-four thousand six hundred

ORAL EXERCISES

Read the numbers.

1. 2,364,827	7. 37,618,425	13. 18,000,000	19. 73,006,043
2. 15,927,865	8. 764,867,351	14. 18,000,018	20. 25,025,025
3. 327,786,934	9. 761,804,700	15. 600,000,000	21. 250,250,250
4. 926,418,321	10. 605,315,080	16. 314,000,000	22. 4,004,004
5. 75,642,872	11. 700,600,300	17. 726,800,000	23. 999,999,999
6. 9,672,183	12. 50,050,670	18. 500,500,000	24. 628,473,856

EXERCISES

1. In each part below, some of the digits are underlined. For these digits, tell how many thousands or how many millions.

[A] 268, 542, 716 *542 th*   [E] 5, 123, 426 *5 m*   [I] 93, 000, 000 *0 t*

[B] 413, 624, 981 *413 m*   [F] 78, 203, 654 *203 th*   [J] 482, 600, 0006

[C] 76, 235, 651 *235 th*   [G] 56, 521, 000 *521 th*   [K] 482, 600, 000 *t*

[D] 82, 343, 612 *82 m*   [H] 93, 000, 000 *93 m*   [L] 700, 652, 000 *7*

Teaching Pages 12 and 13

- **PURPOSE**

To introduce seven-, eight-, and nine-digit numbers

- **PREPARATION**

Conduct a brief review on the reading of four-, five-, and six-digit numbers. Then write a seven-digit number on the chalkboard and give the students an opportunity to discover how this should be read. Provide several other seven-digit examples for the students to read. Now introduce an eight-digit numeral, and again give the class an opportunity to discover how this should be read. Next, introduce nine-digit numbers with several examples.

2. Write the correct numeral for each number name.

[A] thirty-two million four hundred ninety-six thousand one hundred fifty-three *32,496,153*

[B] six hundred million seven hundred eighty-three thousand nine hundred ∧ *600,783,900*

[C] five million six hundred thousand one hundred fifty *5,600,150*

[D] forty million three hundred fifty-six thousand seven hundred *40,356,700*

[E] forty million three hundred fifty-six thousand twenty *40,356,020*

[F] eight million five hundred thousand one hundred sixteen *8,500,116*

[G] eight million seventy thousand one hundred sixteen *8,070,116*

[H] six million six thousand six *6,006,006*

3. Write the number that is

[A] one thousand more than 6,281,573. *6,282,573*

[B] one million more than 6,281,573. *7,281,573*

[C] one hundred thousand more than 6,281,573. *6,381,573*

[D] two million more than 1,164,285. *3,164,285*

[E] four thousand less than 164,285. *160,285*

[F] sixty thousand less than 164,285. *104,285*

[G] one hundred thousand less than 164,285. *64,285*

[H] one million more than 164,285. *1,164,285*

[I] one million less than 1,164,285. *164,285*

4. Think carefully before you answer each question.

[A] How many hundreds make a thousand? *10*

[B] How many thousands make a million? *1000*

5. For each pair of numbers below, write the larger one on your paper.

[A] 357,286	257,286	[G] 99,999,999	100,000,000
[B] 5,357,286	5,257,286	[H] 900,000,000	798,978,896
[C] 42,761	32,761	[I] 727,000,999	727,001,000
[D] 8,942,761	8,932,761	[J] 8,200,900	8,201,000
[E] 327,156,924	387,156,924	[K] 15,156,789	15,156,790
[F] 54,020,009	54,020,010	[L] 92,609,300	92,610,300

Have the students work the exercises. Allow time at the end for reading answers and discussing the exercises. In the discussion of exercise 3, emphasize the ideas of place value and counting rather than those of addition and subtraction.

Give the students an opportunity to read the material on the page and study the table. Have them discuss the various entries in the table and attempt to pronounce some of the names and the locations of the mountains. As an additional exercise in the reading of large numbers, have the class read the various heights given in the table.

Mountain peaks in North America

Mt. McKinley, Alaska

The first three mountains in the table are the highest in North America. There are other mountain peaks in North America higher than the remaining mountains listed in the table, but none is as high as the first three.

Name	Place	Feet
McKinley	Alaska	20,320
Logan	Canada	19,850
Citlaltepetl	Mexico	18,700
King	Canada	17,130
Steele	Canada	16,440
Bona	Alaska	16,420
Wood	Canada	15,880
Bear	Alaska	14,850
Whitney	California	14,495
Elbert	Colorado	14,431
Rainier	Washington	14,410
Lincoln	Colorado	14,284

Teaching Pages 14 and 15

- **PURPOSE**

    To provide a realistic situation in which the students use large numbers and make comparisons which rely largely on place-value ideas

    To provide additional experiences in working with word problems

After the students have completed the page, discuss each exercise. Particularly emphasize those exercises which focus attention on place-value concepts. For example, the altitudes of some mountain peaks differ only in one or two places, and you can use the examples to further strengthen understanding of place value.

EXERCISES

1. What mountain peak in the table is more than 17,000 feet and less than 18,000 feet? *King*

2. What mountain peak in the table is between 15,000 feet and 16,000 feet? *Wood*

3. How many peaks in the table are less than 16,000 feet? *6*

4. How many peaks in the table are more than 15,000 feet? *7* How many are more than 14,000 feet? *12*

5. If an airplane flies at 17,000 feet, over how many of these peaks could it fly? *8*

6. Which mountain peaks are more than 14,400 feet and less than 14,500 feet? *Rainier, Elbert, Whitney*

7. How much higher is Mount Steele than Mount Bona? *20 feet*

8. How much higher is Mount Elbert than Mount Rainier? *21 feet*

9. Mount Hubbard (not given in the table) is 100 feet higher than Mount Bear. How high is Mount Hubbard? *14,950 feet*

10. How much higher is Mount Wood than Mount Bear? *1030 feet*

PREPARATION

Conduct a class activity in which the students compare several pairs of large numbers. You might exhibit on the chalkboard two 5-digit numbers and ask the class to tell which number is larger. Repeat this with several examples.

Give the students an opportunity to study the illustration at the top of the page. Have them read the number of miles from each planet to the sun. Point out that the distance from the sun varies for each planet. The distances given are between the greatest and the least for each planet.

Following this, ask the students to work the first six exercises. When they have finished, discuss each one. Treat the introduction of billion and trillion at the bottom of the page primarily as enrichment and not as material to be mastered by all members of the class.

The oral exercises should prove to be a stimulating activity for the more able students.

Planets

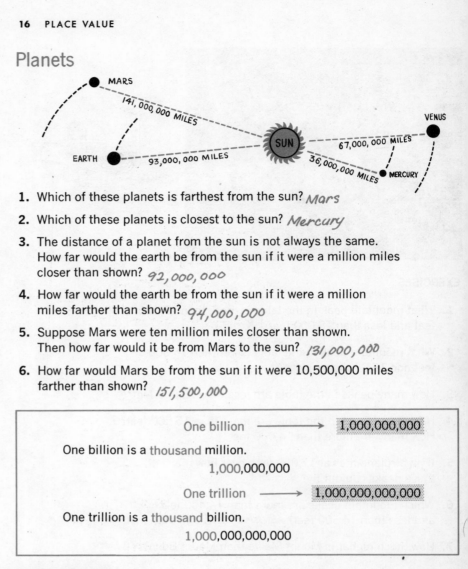

1. Which of these planets is farthest from the sun? *Mars*

2. Which of these planets is closest to the sun? *Mercury*

3. The distance of a planet from the sun is not always the same. How far would the earth be from the sun if it were a million miles closer than shown? *92,000,000*

4. How far would the earth be from the sun if it were a million miles farther than shown? *94,000,000*

5. Suppose Mars were ten million miles closer than shown. Then how far would it be from Mars to the sun? *131,000,000*

6. How far would Mars be from the sun if it were 10,500,000 miles farther than shown? *151,500,000*

One billion ⟶ 1,000,000,000

One billion is a thousand million.
1,000,000,000

One trillion ⟶ 1,000,000,000,000

One trillion is a thousand billion.
1,000,000,000,000

★ ORAL EXERCISES

Read the numbers.

1. 52,387,268,491

2. 478,291,096,503

3. 7,836,403,728,500

4. 928,304,067,392,530

Teaching Pages 16 and 17

● PURPOSE

To provide another experience in working with and comparing large numbers

To provide a set of exercises as a review or evaluation

● PREPARATION

Write on the chalkboard several large numbers and ask the class to list these numbers in order. Focus attention on the place-value concepts shown by having the students

Chapter review

ORAL EXERCISES

Read the numbers.

1. 56,218	**7.** 3,493,206	**13.** 735,654	**19.** 562,394
2. 275,654	**8.** 567,285,431	**14.** 8,008,008	**20.** 2765
3. 3,428,317	**9.** 34,364,521	**15.** 8,080,080	**21.** 901,318
4. 86,379,435	**10.** 176,349,821	**16.** 8,800,800	**22.** 76,542,012
5. 47,600	**11.** 35,350,035	**17.** 111,111,111	**23.** 201,302,405
6. 547,600	**12.** 600,000,000	**18.** 7,654,392	**24.** 504,203,102

EXERCISES

1. Give the correct number for each of these. *(See answers at right.)*

[A] In 347, the 4 stands for ▓.   [G] In 4,373,654, the 7 stands for ▓.
    (Answer: 40)

[B] In 6418, the 4 stands for ▓.   [H] In 5,718,304, the 5 stands for ▓.

[C] In 926, the 6 stands for ▓.   [I] In 123,619, the 2 stands for ▓.

[D] In 7286, the 7 stands for ▓.   [J] In 305,651, the 0 stands for ▓.

[E] In 48,354, the 8 stands for ▓.   [K] In 27,354,683, the 2 stands for ▓.

[F] In 68,024, the 0 stands for ▓.   [L] In 528,764,318, the 5 stands for ▓.

2. Write the correct numeral for each of these.

[A] six hundred twenty-eight thousand three hundred fifteen *628,315*

[B] six million two hundred thirty-eight thousand *6,238,000*

[C] seven hundred eighteen million *718,000,000*

[D] five hundred million five hundred thousand five hundred *500,500,500*

[E] eight million eight thousand eight *8,008,008*

3. Write the correct numeral for each of these.

[A] 10 tens *100*   [D] 1000 tens *10,000*

[B] 10 hundreds *1000*   [E] 1000 hundreds *100,000*

[C] 100 hundreds *10,000*   [F] 1000 thousands *1,000,000*

DIRECTIONS PAGE 17

This lesson may be treated primarily as a chapter review, or you may choose to use it as an evaluation in testing the students' achievement for the chapter. If you do use it as a chapter review, you can use the exercises on this page as a guide for designing your evaluation instrument.

Answers, exercise 1, page 17

[A] 40
[B] 400
[C] 6
[D] 7000
[E] 8000
[F] 0
[G] 70,000
[H] 5,000,000
[I] 20,000
[J] 0
[K] 20,000,000
[L] 500,000,000

read the number of ones, tens, hundreds, etc. Following this, pick a particular digit from each number and have one member of the class tell the number that that digit stands for.

During this preparation period, be sure to give the students an opportunity to ask questions concerning any topics in the chapter with which they have had particular difficulty.

Teaching
Geometry Lesson 1

- **PURPOSE**

  To introduce the circle

  To provide experiences in drawing circles with a compass

  To introduce the concept of families of circles through a point

  To introduce the concept of the regions of a plane, inside and outside, associated with a circle

A formal definition of circle is not provided. However, by showing a picture of a circle with the two regions (inside and outside) illustrated in different colors, we are able to define intuitively the concept of circle and the center of the circle. The students should be made aware that we think of the circle as the black outline only and that it is quite distinct from the inside of the circle (which contains the center point and is one region of the plane) and the outside of the circle (another region of the plane).

The students are not expected to master a great deal of factual material in these geometry lessons. The intention is to provide interesting experiences in working with geometric ideas. Of course, some amount of factual material will be retained by the students; however, in evaluating students' progress in the geometry lessons, keep in mind that retention of all facts presented is not an objective.

In this lesson, we begin by giving students experiences in drawing circles with a compass. Following this, they are given an opportunity to draw various families of circles through a given point.

- **MATHEMATICS**

In the study of geometry, our point of view is that there are two kinds of geometry: physical geometry and mathematical geometry. Physical geometry is the geometry of the drawing board or of the physical world. Mathematical geometry is an abstract mathematical system that unfolds from a set of undefined objects and assumptions about these objects. Of course, physical geometry provides an excellent model and motivation for the development of mathematical geometry. While, in theory, one could completely separate mathematical geometry from any dependence upon the physical world, such a development would hardly be practical, at least in an early study of geometry.

The early lessons primarily present the geometry of the physical world. Thus the black outline shown on the paper can be called a circle or square. Later it will be pointed out that the black mark is a picture or model of an idea existing in our minds. Such abstractions need not be presented in this early study of geometry.

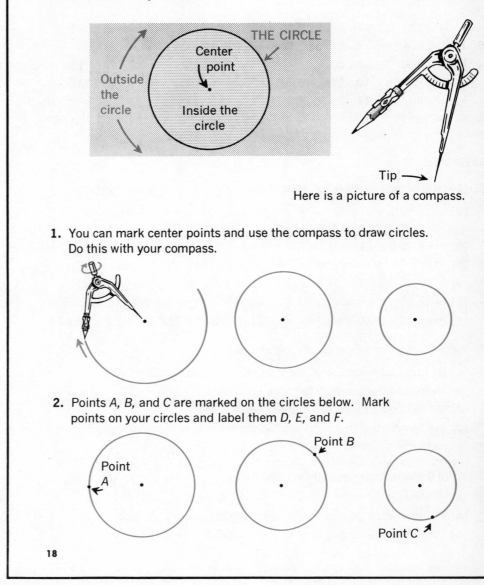

GEOMETRY - Lesson 1

Circles and points

THE CIRCLE

Center point

Outside the circle

Inside the circle

Here is a picture of a compass.

Tip →

1. You can mark center points and use the compass to draw circles. Do this with your compass.

2. Points *A*, *B*, and *C* are marked on the circles below. Mark points on your circles and label them *D*, *E*, and *F*.

Point A

Point B

Point C

18

3. Draw 5 circles of different sizes.

4. Mark a point on each circle. Label these points *A, B, C, D,* and *E*. It is easy to mark a **point** on a **circle**. Can you draw a **circle** through a **point**?

5. Mark a point *A* on your paper. Draw 6 different circles through this point.

Here are some interesting ways to draw circles through points.

6. [A] Mark a point on your paper. Use your ruler to draw a line that goes through this point.

[B] Now draw 6 different-sized circles through the point. Do this by putting the tip of your compass at different places **on the line.**
(See figure above.)

[C] Do this again. This time make 2 of the circles the same size.
(See figure below.)

7. [A] Mark a point on your paper. Use your compass to draw a circle with this point as the center.

[B] Now draw 6 circles through this point. Do this by putting the tip of your compass at different places **on the circle.**

[C] Are all the circles the same size? *yes*

[D] Do this again. Each time, put the tip of your compass **where the circles meet** (for example, at point *A* in the picture).

6[C]

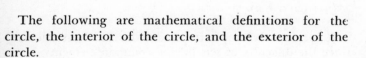

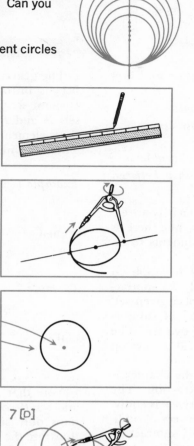

Discuss with the class the diagrams shown at the top of the page. Emphasize in particular that the circle is the black outline of the figure, that the gray is the outside of the circle, and that the blue is the inside of the circle. Notice with the students the center point of the circle.

Call attention to the picture of the compass and have the students get out their compasses. Now read with the students the remainder of the page and have them follow through with the suggested activities.

The suggested activities on page 19 can be treated as a class activity; however, avoid giving students the correct answers during the discussion period. As far as possible, allow the students every opportunity to think creatively as they work through this lesson.

Throughout the presentation of this lesson, encourage all the class to participate in a discussion and elaboration of the ideas being presented.

The following are mathematical definitions for the circle, the interior of the circle, and the exterior of the circle.

A circle with center *O* and radius *r* is the set of all points *A* such that the length of *OA* is equal to *r*.

The interior of the circle is the set of all points *B* such that the length of *OB* is less than *r*.

The exterior of the circle is the set of all points *C* such that the length of *OC* is greater than *r*.

These ideas are shown to the students in an intuitive way through the use of color in the illustration. In this lesson, the students are asked to draw families of circles through a given point. The mathematical definition of a point lying on a circle is simply taken from the definition of circle. That is, if a point *X* is on the circle, then *X* is one of the points *A* given in the definition above.

Objectives of Chapter 2

To focus attention on the concepts of addition and subtraction

To provide experiences in working with equations

To improve skills with addition and subtraction facts with sums through 18

To provide experiences in working with word problems

To focus attention on the inverse relationship between addition and subtraction

The bulk of this chapter is devoted primarily to exploring addition and subtraction concepts, but there is sufficient practice material to enable the students to review the basic addition and subtraction facts.

The opening pages of the chapter focus attention on the four equations (two addition facts and two subtraction facts) associated with each break-up of a given set.

Following this, a different interpretation of subtraction is explored through the comparison of two sets. The number line is brought in as an additional aid to develop understanding of addition-subtraction concepts.

One of the chief points of emphasis in the chapter is the relationship between addition and subtraction. The students are led to see that finding the difference is equivalent to finding a missing addend. The mastery of addition facts is stressed more than mastery of subtraction facts, since it is possible to arrive at subtraction facts through knowledge of addition facts.

Next, the commutative and associative (order and grouping) principles are introduced for addition. Following this introduction, the two principles are quickly generalized to the idea that when adding three or more numbers, one can rearrange the addends in any convenient way. A basic reliance is made on the associative principle of addition for finding sums greater than ten. For example, in finding the sum $7 + 5$, the 5 is broken into $3 + 2$. Then, using the associative principle, the 7 and the 3 are grouped to get $10 + 2$, or 12. This is essentially the chief tool the student is given to find sums greater than ten. Of course, we work quickly toward mastery of these sums once this idea has been explored.

Following this development of sums, additional emphasis is given to the relationship between addition and subtraction, and then differences associated with sums 11 through 18 are explored. This is done both by focusing attention on the idea of a missing addend and by doing a subtraction in two parts. (As an example of two-part subtraction, for the difference $15 - 7$, the 7 is broken into $5 + 2$ so that $15 - 5 = 10$ and $10 - 2 = 8$, or $(15 - 5) - 2 = 8$.) In this way, the students are given two methods for finding differences associated with sums 11 to 18. However, the primary emphasis is on thinking about subtraction in terms of finding a missing addend.

Mathematics of Chapter 2

The general concept of the sum of two cardinal numbers is introduced through the union of disjoint sets. Disjoint sets have no common elements. The union of sets A and B, denoted by $A \cup B$, is the set containing those elements that are in A, or in B, or in both A and B. The following examples illustrate this definition.

Example 1. Consider two sets A and B as follows:

$$A = \{m, n, o, p\}, \qquad B = \{p, q, r\},$$

then

$$A \cup B = \{m, n, o, p, q, r\}.$$

Example 2. Consider two sets R and S as follows:

$$R = \{1, 2, 3\}, \qquad S = \{15, 16\},$$

then

$$R \cup S = \{1, 2, 3, 15, 16\}.$$

Note that in example 1 set A contains four elements and set B contains three elements, whereas $A \cup B$ contains only six elements. Clearly, example 1 does not illustrate the addition concept. Consider now example 2, where set R contains three elements and set S contains two elements. This time the union of these sets, $R \cup S$, contains five elements, which illustrates the idea we choose to call addition. These examples should emphasize the importance of the word *disjoint* in the following definition for the sum of two cardinal numbers.

Consider two cardinal numbers, a and b, and disjoint sets, A and B, from these cardinal numbers. The cardinal number of the union of the sets A and B is the sum of the cardinal numbers a and b (written $a + b$).

It is relatively simple to present this idea to students, since the difficulty of sets having common elements does not occur. For example, when one puts two sets together, the sets are usually grouped in such a way that there are no common elements. For the students, forming the union of two sets merely requires pushing the objects together into one group.

We define subtraction in two basic ways: in terms of sets and in terms of addition. Removing objects from a given set is a clear, concrete method for introducing subtraction. Closely related to the idea of "take away" is the "comparison" idea of subtraction. A careful analysis of the definition below will show, in fact, that subtraction encompasses both the idea of "take away" and the idea of comparing two sets.

Let a and b be any two cardinal numbers such that $a > b$ or $a = b$. Choose sets A and B from a and b, respectively. There is a subset S of A that is equivalent to B. The difference of a and b (written $a - b$) is the cardinal number of the set of objects in A other than those in S.

The following diagram illustrates this definition for cardinal numbers five and three.

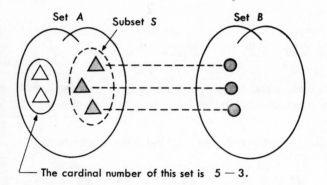

The cardinal number of this set is $5 - 3$.

From this illustration, we obtain the subtraction equation $5 - 3 = 2$.

The definition and the illustration show clearly why subtraction is used to compare two sets. On the other hand, it is not quite as clear how the removal of objects from a given set relates to this definition.

Using the illustration, we point out that the objects to be removed from set A to explain "take away" could be those in the dotted ring. This set was chosen to match one-to-one with set B. However, using the "take-away" procedure, we would say that set B consists of the numbers one, two, and three, and we would count objects "one, two, three" in set A and take them away. Thus, in the "take-away" procedure, set B becomes an abstraction containing the counting numbers up to and including the number of objects we wish to remove. The idea of "take away" is merely a special case of the more general concept of subtraction associated with comparison of sets.

Now let us investigate a definition of subtraction in terms of addition.

Let a, b, and c be whole numbers such that $a + b = c$. The number a is the difference $c - b$, and the number b is the difference $c - a$. In symbols,

$$a = c - b, \qquad b = c - a.$$

According to this definition of subtraction, there are two subtraction equations associated with each addition equation. There is some advantage, however, to associating only one subtraction equation with a given addition equation. For example, we like to think of $5 + 3$ as an expression for adding three to five, and $8 - 3$ as an expression for subtracting three from eight. Then it is useful to link the two equations,

$$5 + 3 = 8 \qquad \text{and} \qquad 8 - 3 = 5.$$

For this type of example, we say that adding three and subtracting three undo each other, since we start with five, add three, and get eight and we then subtract three from eight, and are back to five again. In general, if a, b, and c are whole numbers such that $a + b = c$, we link the two equations,

$$a + b = c \qquad \text{and} \qquad c - b = a.$$

This is the inverse relation for addition and subtraction.

Teaching Chapter 2

Since the students have had many experiences in working with sets to illustrate addition and subtraction, there is little need now to make a great play on set demonstrations for union or putting together of sets to illustrate addition or the taking apart or taking away of objects to illustrate subtraction.

The material of the chapter is simple enough that most of the students will be able to master the ideas and skills without resorting to manipulative activities.

Depending upon the background of the class, you may be able to cover this chapter in less than three weeks. However, if the students are weak in the basic addition and subtraction skills, you may need to extend this to $3\frac{1}{2}$ or four weeks.

When evaluating students' achievement, it is quite difficult to arrive at an accurate judgment of whether or not they *understand the concepts* of addition and subtraction. Evaluation of students' understanding is best done on a daily observation basis. To learn whether or not the students have mastered the basic addition and subtraction facts is quite simple and straightforward. Thus, you should prepare your evaluation in such a form as to cover the concepts involved and the skills required in this chapter. You can use the chapter review for evaluation or as a guide in designing your chapter test.

You will note that mastery of the basic addition and subtraction facts is one of the objectives of this chapter. However, do not attempt to dwell on this objective until *every* student knows the facts. Do work toward mastery for most of the students and then continue to help the slower students with the facts as you proceed through the text.

Of course, a certain amount of drill is essential, but you should avoid an excessive amount of flash-card or straight paper-work drill. This will serve only to discourage the less able students and bore the more able students. Attempt to intersperse drill sessions with more exciting activities.

Have the students read the material at the top of the page and identify the obvious break-up of the set into three triangles and four circles. Call attention to the four equations listed below this set. Have the class discuss how the set break-up helps them think about four equations.

Before the students begin the exercises at the bottom of the page, draw their attention to the fact that the four sets shown in exercise 1 refer to the four equations above. When the students have completed exercise 1, check their answers to be sure they see the relationship between the set diagrams and the equations.

Have the students do exercise 2 on their own. Discuss the exercises when they have finished. The answers given for exercise 2 depend on a left-to-right orientation. For example, equation [A] could be matched with set picture E if we read (or think) right to left.

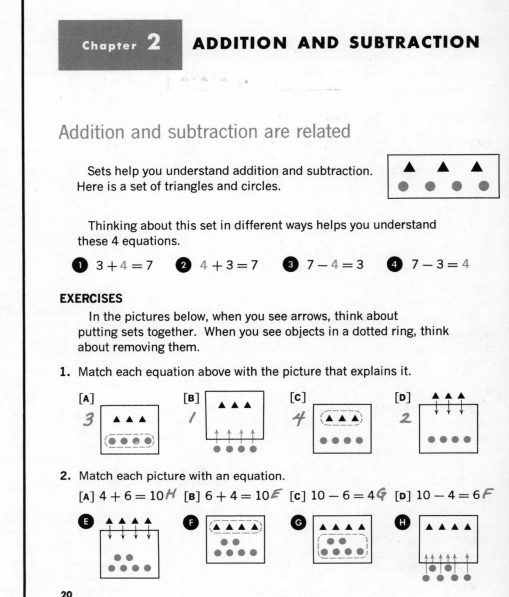

Chapter **2** ADDITION AND SUBTRACTION

Addition and subtraction are related

Sets help you understand addition and subtraction. Here is a set of triangles and circles.

Thinking about this set in different ways helps you understand these 4 equations.

1 $3 + 4 = 7$ **2** $4 + 3 = 7$ **3** $7 - 4 = 3$ **4** $7 - 3 = 4$

EXERCISES

In the pictures below, when you see arrows, think about putting sets together. When you see objects in a dotted ring, think about removing them.

1. Match each equation above with the picture that explains it.

[A] *3* [B] *1* [C] *4* [D] *2*

2. Match each picture with an equation.

[A] $4 + 6 = 10$ *H* [B] $6 + 4 = 10$ *E* [C] $10 - 6 = 4$ *G* [D] $10 - 4 = 6$ *F*

E **F** **G** **H**

20

Teaching Pages 20 and 21

• **PURPOSE**

To develop addition and subtraction concepts simultaneously

To focus attention on the union of sets and its relation to addition

To focus attention on the "take-away" idea associated with subtraction

To introduce equations

• **MATHEMATICS**

Page 20 illustrates that with each break-up of a given set one can arrive at two addition and two subtraction equations. At the top of the page a set is shown consisting of three triangles and four circles. Then, in the first exercise arrows and dotted rings are used to demonstrate for the students how one can think about the given set in four different ways and thus arrive at four different equations. Of course, this demonstration is concerned with the more formal aspect of set union and subsets.

EXERCISES

1. Write 4 different equations for each set. *(see answers at right.)*

[A]   [B]   [C]   [D]

2. Answer the questions about the sets.

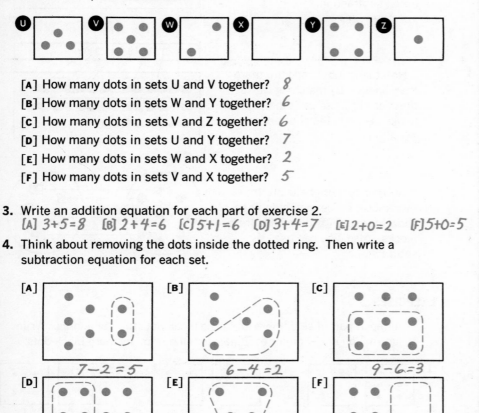

U   V   W   X   Y   Z

[A] How many dots in sets U and V together? *8*

[B] How many dots in sets W and Y together? *6*

[C] How many dots in sets V and Z together? *6*

[D] How many dots in sets U and Y together? *7*

[E] How many dots in sets W and X together? *2*

[F] How many dots in sets V and X together? *5*

3. Write an addition equation for each part of exercise 2.

[A] *3+5=8*   [B] *2+4=6*   [C] *5+1=6*   [D] *3+4=7*   [E] *2+0=2*   [F] *5+0=5*

4. Think about removing the dots inside the dotted ring. Then write a subtraction equation for each set.

[A]   *7−2=5*

[B]   *6−4=2*

[C]   *9−6=3*

[D]   *12−5=7*

[E]   *5−5=0*

[F]   *6−0=6*

DIRECTIONS PAGE 21

Instruct the students to work the exercises on their own. When they have finished, allow time for checking papers and answering questions.

Answers, exercise 1, page 21

[A] $4 + 2 = 6$
$6 - 2 = 4$
$2 + 4 = 6$
$6 - 4 = 2$

[B] $3 + 2 = 5$
$5 - 2 = 3$
$2 + 3 = 5$
$5 - 3 = 2$

[C] $8 + 5 = 13$
$13 - 5 = 8$
$5 + 8 = 13$
$13 - 8 = 5$

[D] $7 + 4 = 11$
$11 - 4 = 7$
$4 + 7 = 11$
$11 - 7 = 4$

Although our basic definition of addition in terms of sets makes no apparent distinction between $3 + 4$ and $4 + 3$, this distinction can be made for the students by showing one set being put with another, or vice versa.

PREPARATION

Show the class a set of five objects and write the numeral 5 on the chalkboard. Then put with these five objects four more objects and beside the 5 write "+ 4." Have the students complete the equation, $5 + 4 = 9$. Now remove four of the objects and write the equation, $9 - 4 = 5$.

Point out to the class that you began with five, added four, then subtracted four, and you are back to five again. Repeat this demonstration beginning with a set of four and putting a set of five with it.

Follow this with a demonstration of the four equations associated with a given breaking apart of a set. For example, you might exhibit a set of eight objects and break this set into a set of five and a set of three. Have the students participate in finding the four equations:

$$5 + 3 = 8, \qquad 3 + 5 = 8, \qquad 8 - 3 = 5, \qquad 8 - 5 = 3.$$

Read and study the material at the top of the page with the students. As you discuss each pair of sets, call attention to the lines that match some objects in one set with all the objects in the other set. Point out the dotted ring around those objects in the one set that are matched with all the objects in the other set. Explain that the dotted ring helps them think of subtraction. Call attention also to the equation associated with the pair of sets.

Following a discussion of this material, have the students do the six exercises at the bottom of the page. When they have finished, provide ample opportunity for review. During the discussion, you can exhibit one exercise on the chalkboard and show the matching involved to determine how many more one set has than another.

Comparing sets

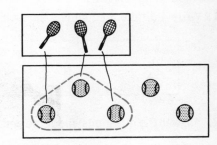

How many more tennis balls are there than rackets? You can draw matching lines to show that the answer is **2**. Also, you can think about subtraction.

$$5 - 3 = \boxed{n}\ 2$$

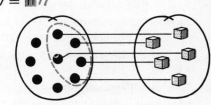

How many more caps are there than hooks? By matching we see there are **11** more caps than hooks. Here is the subtraction equation.

$$18 - 7 = \boxed{n}\ 11$$

How many more balls are there than blocks? The matching lines show there are **4** more balls than blocks. Also, you can use subtraction.

$$9 - 5 = \boxed{n}\ 4$$

EXERCISES

For each pair of sets, there are more black dots than blue dots. Write a subtraction equation for each pair to tell how many more black dots.

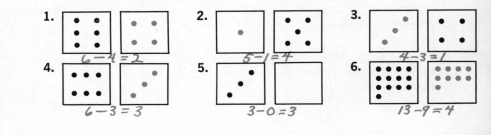

1. $6 - 4 = 2$ 2. $5 - 1 = 4$ 3. $4 - 3 = 1$

4. $6 - 3 = 3$ 5. $3 - 0 = 3$ 6. $13 - 9 = 4$

Teaching Pages 22 and 23

- **PURPOSE**

  To develop an understanding of subtraction with regard to the comparison of sets

  To provide word-problem experiences

- **MATHEMATICS**

  In this lesson subtraction is related directly to the abstract definition for subtraction in terms of sets. The comparison of sets by matching lines demonstrates for the stu-

Collecting shells

Nan collects shells. She also collects facts about shells. Page 1 in her notebook looked like this. →

Notebook page:

Knife handles are made from shells.

Buttons are made from shells.

Some shells are used to make roads.

Some windows are made of shells instead of glass.

Some people use shells for money.

Some shells are very pretty.

Tree-snail shells

1. Nan collected 5 tree-snail shells and 3 clam shells. How many more tree-snail shells does she have than clam shells? *2*

2. Nan and Jill went to the beach to look for shells. Nan placed her shells in a row like this. → Jill placed her shells like this. →

   [A] Who had more shells? [B] How many more?
   Nan; 2 more

3. Nan found 9 mussel shells near the pond. She gave 4 of them to Jill. How many did Nan have left? *5*

4. Nan wants pictures of her shells. She has 10 different snail shells. She has pictures of 7 of them. How many more pictures does she need? *3*

5. Nan took 10 colored shells to school. She had 3 colored shells at home. She had fewer colored shells at home than at school. How many fewer? *7*

★ 6. Nan picked out 5 white shells. She put some blue paint on 3 of them. Then she could see white on only 3 of the 5 shells. On how many could she see both blue and white? *1 (2 shells all blue, 2 shells all white, 1 shell blue and white)*

Read the first paragraph with the class, and study with them the notebook page shown. Ask them to work the first exercise. When they have finished, read the correct answer and exhibit the proper subtraction equation on the chalkboard. Encourage a discussion of how this equation relates to the idea in exercise 1. If you think it necessary, repeat this procedure for exercise 2. Then have the students complete the page.

Treat exercise 6 primarily as enrichment for the more able students. Since this exercise is quite difficult to visualize, you might actually have some of the students paint shells (or shell drawings) in the manner described. Such a demonstration will certainly be necessary for understanding by less able students.

---

dents the idea that subtraction is used to find out how many more or how many fewer one set has than another. The matching lines enable the students to determine by quick examination that one set contains more than another set.

PREPARATION

Exhibit on a demonstration table a set of 12 objects and a set of eight objects which are easily distinguished from the 12. You might use a set of 12 erasers and a set of eight pieces of chalk. Ask the question, "How many more erasers are there than pieces of chalk?" and have one of the

students match each eraser with a piece of chalk by placing them side by side. After the matching has been completed, the students readily see that four erasers are left over. Write on the chalkboard the equation $12 - 8 = 4$. Repeat this activity until the students have thoroughly grasped how subtraction is related to comparison of sets.

Discuss with the students the number-line illustrations at the top of the page. When the students have completed the exercises, read and discuss the correct answers. If necessary, write several of the exercises on the chalkboard.

Addition and subtraction on the number line

The number line helps you think about addition and subtraction.

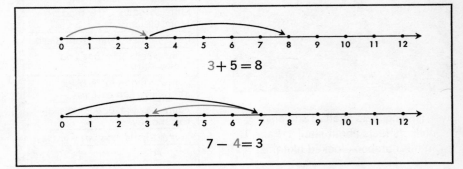

$3 + 5 = 8$

$7 - 4 = 3$

EXERCISES

1. Give the missing number in the equation for each number line.

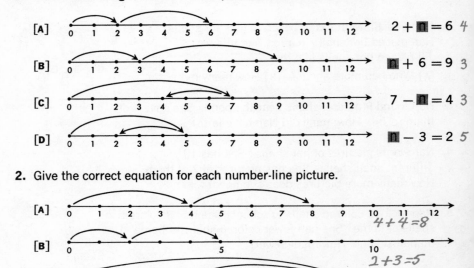

[A] $2 + \blacksquare = 6$ *4*

[B] $\blacksquare + 6 = 9$ *3*

[C] $7 - \blacksquare = 4$ *3*

[D] $\blacksquare - 3 = 2$ *5*

2. Give the correct equation for each number-line picture.

[A] *4+4=8*

[B] *2+3=5*

[C] *9-5=4*

[D] *8-6=2*

Teaching Pages 24 and 25

- **PURPOSE**

To reintroduce the number line

To utilize the number line to demonstrate concepts of addition and subtraction

- **MATHEMATICS**

This lesson treats the number line primarily as a physical device for showing the order of the set of whole numbers. Below is a model of the number line.

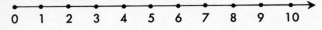

Notice that certain points on the number line are labeled with whole numbers. The distance between each point (the unit distance) is the same. We can find points on the number line which do not represent whole numbers, that is, points representing fractional or negative numbers. (The students, of course, are not yet ready to consider such numbers.) The number line could point in any direction, but it is conventional to have it in a horizontal position with the numbers, represented by points, progressing from left to right. The arrow is to indicate that the number line has no end point in that direction. There is no arrow to the left of zero because the students will not be concerned with negative numbers at this time.

3. Write an equation for each number-line picture.

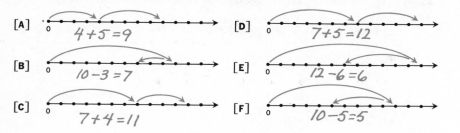

[A] $4+5=9$ [D] $7+5=12$

[B] $10-3=7$ [E] $12-6=6$

[C] $7+4=11$ [F] $10-5=5$

4. Draw a 6-inch line on your paper. Starting at the 0 dot, mark dots each half inch and label them as shown.

Now use arrows to show the sum $5 + 6$.

5. Draw a number line for each part below. Show the sum or difference by using arrows.

[A] $6 + 3$ [C] $11 - 9$ [E] $8 + 3$ [G] $11 - 3$

[B] $10 - 2$ [D] $12 - 2$ [F] $3 + 8$ [H] $6 + 4$

6. Write an equation for each part of exercise 5.

[A] $6+3=9$ [B] $10-2=8$ [C] $11-9=2$ [D] $12-2=10$ [E] $8+3=11$ [F] $3+8=11$ [G] $11-3=8$ [H] $6+4=10$

7. Draw a number line and show the sum $2 + 2 + 2 + 2 + 2 + 2$.

8. Draw a number line and show the sum $3 + 3 + 3 + 3$.

★**9.** Write an equation for each number-line picture.

[A] $5+0=5$

[B] $8-8=0$

> **Exercise for Experts**
>
> There is no largest number.
> The last one can't be found.
> Just add me to get the next.
> There is no upper bound. _one_
> _____
> I'm a little bitty number.
> So very small indeed.
> If you add me to another,
> A change you cannot read.
>
> WHO AM I? _zero_

Have the students do the exercises. Allow time for discussion after they have finished.

The riddles are fairly simple, and all students should be given an opportunity to think about the ideas presented. Be sure that one student does not give away the answer and ruin the other student's opportunity to discover the correct response.

Addition and subtraction equations are shown by jumps on the number line. For example, in the figure at the top of page 24, the combination $3 + 5$ is shown by a jump from 0 to 3 followed by a jump of five units to the right. The combination $7 - 4$ is shown by a jump from 0 to 7 followed by a jump of four units to the left.

With these basic ideas concerning operations on the number line, the students are expected to show certain number-line manipulations and to relate them to equations. In exercises such as 2B and others, some of the points on the number line are unlabeled and the students must count the distance of the jump to decide what numbers are involved.

• **PREPARATION**

Draw a number line on the chalkboard. Show jumps on this number line to illustrate several addition and subtraction equations. Have the students participate by drawing the arrows and writing the equations. You should at this time plan to have the students practice two procedures: writing equations associated with given jumps on the number line and showing the jumps on the number line for a given equation.

Read and study with the students the material preceding the exercises. Stress the words *addend* and *sum* as you discuss the material.

Have the students work the exercises at the bottom of the page. You may need to give them additional instructions for working exercise 1. Explain that for exercise 1A they are to find the sum $0 + 6$ and that on their papers they should write the sum 6 for part A. Now, observe with the students that B in the table is the sum $2 + 5$ and that C is the sum $2 + 8$. Be sure that they have written 7 as the answer to B and 10 as the answer to C.

Now have them complete the table and remaining exercises on the page.

As students read and discuss the answer, ask them to point out addends and sums. Encourage them to use these words.

Answers, exercise 1, page 26

[A]	6	[H]	7
[B]	7	[I]	9
[C]	10	[J]	6
[D]	5	[K]	9
[E]	7	[L]	10
[F]	9	[M]	9
[G]	10		

Addends and sums

The numbers we add are called addends. The answer is called the sum.

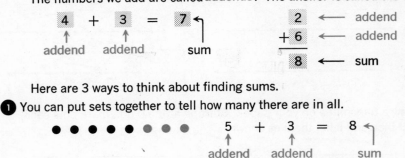

Here are 3 ways to think about finding sums.

1 You can put sets together to tell how many there are in all.

$$5 + 3 = 8$$
addend addend sum

When one addend is 5 and the other addend is 3, the sum is 8.

2 You can use the number line or counting.

$$4 + 2 = 6$$
addend addend sum

3 You can use facts you already know.
Since $3 + 3 = 6$, you know that $3 + 4 = 7$.

EXERCISES

1. Give the sum for each gray square.
(see answers at left.)

+	0	1	2	3	4	5	6	7	8	9
0							[A]			
1										
2						[B]		[C]		
3			[D]	[E]	[F]					
4					[G]					
5			[H]	[I]						
6	[J]		[K]							
7			[L]							
8	[M]									
9										

2. Find the sums.

[A] 6
+3
9

[B] 6
+4
10

[C] 5
+4
9

[D] 6
+2
8

[E] 7
+3
10

[F] 4
+6
10

[G] 4
+3
7

[H] 4
+5
9

[I] 3
+7
10

[J] 5
+5
10

[K] 2
+8
10

[L] 5
+2
7

3. Solve the equations.

[A] $5 + 4 = \blacksquare$ 9 [D] $\blacksquare + 4 = 9$ 5

[B] $\blacksquare + 7 = 10$ 3 [E] $\blacksquare + 6 = 10$ 4

[C] $2 + \blacksquare = 8$ 6 [F] $2 + \blacksquare = 9$ 7

Teaching Pages 26 and 27

• **PURPOSE**

To introduce the words addend *and* sum

To provide experience in working with an addition table

To provide an interesting discovery activity leading toward mastery of addition facts

• **PREPARATION**

Exhibit on the chalkboard a small addition table like the one illustrated at the left.

Have the students assist you in filling in the entries. Explain to them that they begin with a number in the first

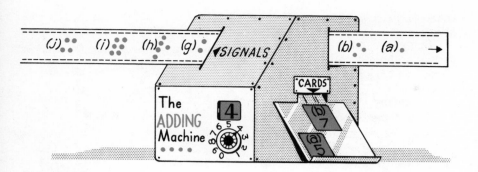

EXERCISES

1. Look at the machine and answer the questions.

[A] What cards will the machine put out for signals (g), (h), (i), and (j)? *(g)6, (i)10, (h)9, (j)8*

[B] Suppose you change to an "Adding 2" machine. What cards will it put out for signals (g) through (j)? *(g)4, (h)7, (i)8, (j)6*

[C] What cards will an "Adding 3" machine put out for signals (g) through (j)? *(g)5, (h)8, (i)9, (j)7*

[D] What cards will an "Adding 8" machine put out for signals (g) through (j)? *(g)10, (h)13, (i)14, (j)12*

2. The "Adding 5" machine puts out this card: 9
What signal went into the machine? *4*

3. Give what should go in each gray space in the table.

	Machine	Signal	Card
[A]	Adding 5	· · ·	*8*
[B]	Adding 5	· · ·	8
[C]	Adding 5	· · ·	8
[D]	Adding 3	· · · · ·	*8*
[E]	Adding 6	: :	*10*
[F]	Adding 2	· · · · · ·	8
[G]	Adding 0	: : :	*6*
[H]	Adding 0	· · ·	3
[I]	Adding 4	: : :	10
[J]	Adding 6	· · ·	9
[K]	Adding 1	: : : : :	10
[L]	Adding 4	· · ·	*7*

column and then add to it a number from the top row. Be sure they understand in which box they should put the sum of the two numbers.

+	0	1	2	3	4
0					
1					
2					
3					
4					

Study and discuss the "Adding-4 Machine" pictured at the top of the page. Notice with the class that signal (a) is one dot and that the machine adds four to one and then puts out card (a), labeled 5; that signal (b) is three dots and that the machine adds four to three getting 7 and then puts out card (b), labeled 7. Also point out that the dial on the "Adding-4 Machine" is turned to 4. You might remark that later we'll think of turning the dial to other numbers.

Treat the work on this page as a game. You and the students are to decide what the machine will do in various situations.

Now give the students an opportunity to work exercise 1. If you prefer, you can treat this primarily as a discussion exercise. However, be sure that the students have an opportunity to work some of the exercises on their own. A discussion session for reading answers and answering questions should follow each part of exercise 1. As soon as the students have become accustomed to working with the machine, allow them to complete the page on their own.

Exercise 3 may require some additional instruction. Notice with the class that for exercise 3A they are to find what the card will read when the signal 3 is put into an "Adding-5 Machine." Thus, they should think of $5 + 3$ to find that the card should read 8.

For part 3B, point out that it is an "Adding-5 Machine" and that the card reads 8. Now ask the students what signal the machine should be given so that the sum turned out is 8.

Proceed to exercise 3c and notice with the class that with the signal 3 and the sum 8 they are to discover the number to which the machine is dialed, that is, they should discover that this would be an "Adding-5 Machine."

Following this brief introduction, give the students an opportunity to complete the table.

Read and study the material at the top of the page with the students. Give particular emphasis to the fact that they can find differences by looking for missing addends.

Direct the students to work exercises 1 and 2 on their own. When they have finished, stress that in exercise 1 they first found a missing addend and then a difference and that these turned out to be the same number in each case.

For exercise 2, have the students check their answers by giving addition equations. For example, in exercise 2A, the students should notice that since $4 + 4 = 8$, $8 - 4 = 4$.

Differences and missing addends

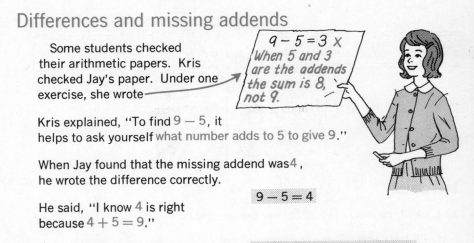

Some students checked their arithmetic papers. Kris checked Jay's paper. Under one exercise, she wrote

*9 − 5 = 3 X
When 5 and 3
are the addends
the sum is 8,
not 9.*

Kris explained, "To find $9 - 5$, it helps to ask yourself what number adds to 5 to give 9."

When Jay found that the missing addend was 4, he wrote the difference correctly.

$$9 - 5 = 4$$

He said, "I know 4 is right because $4 + 5 = 9$."

Then Jay wrote this rule in his notebook:

We can find **DIFFERENCES** by looking for **MISSING ADDENDS**.

EXERCISES

1. Find the differences by finding the missing addends

[A] $\blacksquare + 4 = 7$ 3
$7 - 4 = \blacksquare$ 3

[B] $\blacksquare + 3 = 10$ 7
$10 - 3 = \blacksquare$ 7

[C] $4 + \blacksquare = 9$ 5
$9 - 4 = \blacksquare$ 5

[D] $\blacksquare + 6 = 10$ 4
$10 - 6 = \blacksquare$ 4

[E] $4 + \blacksquare = 8$ 4
$8 - 4 = \blacksquare$ 4

[F] $\blacksquare + 4 = 5$ 1
$5 - 4 = \blacksquare$ 1

[G] $\blacksquare + 5 = 10$ 5
$10 - 5 = \blacksquare$ 5

[H] $6 + \blacksquare = 9$ 3
$9 - 6 = \blacksquare$ 3

[I] $\blacksquare + 1 = 7$ 6
$7 - 1 = \blacksquare$ 6

[J] $\blacksquare + 0 = 8$ 8
$8 - 0 = \blacksquare$ 8

[K] $7 + \blacksquare = 10$ 3
$10 - 7 = \blacksquare$ 3

[L] $3 + \blacksquare = 9$ 6
$9 - 3 = \blacksquare$ 6

2. Use addition facts to help you find these differences.

[A] $8 - 4 = \blacksquare$ 4
[B] $10 - 9 = \blacksquare$ 1
[C] $9 - 4 = \blacksquare$ 5
[D] $7 - 4 = \blacksquare$ 3

[E] $10 - 4 = \blacksquare$ 6
[F] $10 - 8 = \blacksquare$ 2
[G] $7 - 7 = \blacksquare$ 0
[H] $7 - 1 = \blacksquare$ 6

[I] $6 - 2 = \blacksquare$ 4
[J] $9 - 7 = \blacksquare$ 2
[K] $9 - 3 = \blacksquare$ 6
[L] $5 - 2 = \blacksquare$ 3

Teaching Pages 28 and 29

- **PURPOSE**

  To emphasize further the relationship between addition and subtraction

  To focus attention on the fact that finding a difference is equivalent to finding a missing addend

  To work toward mastery of subtraction combinations associated with sums of ten or less

- **MATHEMATICS**

  This lesson stresses the point that finding a difference is equivalent to finding a missing addend. Of course, this idea is directly related to the meaning or definition of subtraction. That is, when we define subtraction, we define the number

  $$a - b$$

  as the number that adds to b to give a. That is,

  $$(a - b) + b = a.$$

  Of course, this is the idea that to find the difference $a - b$, we find the number that adds to b to give a.

  There is nothing particularly new about this approach to subtraction. Students have long been taught to check their subtraction problems by addition. However, using this missing-addend approach to find differences may be new. We intend that students memorize the addition combinations but not the subtraction combinations since

When you want to find the difference, think about finding the missing addend. You might think like this:

$$\begin{array}{r} 7 \\ -3 \\ \hline 4 \end{array}$$
Because $4 + 3 = 7$,
I know 4 is the answer.

3. Find the differences by finding the missing addends.

| [A] $\begin{array}{r}10\\-6\\\hline 4\end{array}$ | [B] $\begin{array}{r}10\\-3\\\hline 7\end{array}$ | [C] $\begin{array}{r}8\\-2\\\hline 6\end{array}$ | [D] $\begin{array}{r}9\\-4\\\hline 5\end{array}$ | [E] $\begin{array}{r}4\\-2\\\hline 2\end{array}$ | [F] $\begin{array}{r}10\\-4\\\hline 6\end{array}$ |

| [G] $\begin{array}{r}6\\-3\\\hline 3\end{array}$ | [H] $\begin{array}{r}7\\-3\\\hline 4\end{array}$ | [I] $\begin{array}{r}5\\-5\\\hline 0\end{array}$ | [J] $\begin{array}{r}9\\-7\\\hline 2\end{array}$ | [K] $\begin{array}{r}5\\-2\\\hline 3\end{array}$ | [L] $\begin{array}{r}10\\-2\\\hline 8\end{array}$ |

| [M] $\begin{array}{r}9\\-3\\\hline 6\end{array}$ | [N] $\begin{array}{r}8\\-1\\\hline 7\end{array}$ | [O] $\begin{array}{r}6\\-0\\\hline 6\end{array}$ | [P] $\begin{array}{r}9\\-2\\\hline 7\end{array}$ | [Q] $\begin{array}{r}8\\-4\\\hline 4\end{array}$ | [R] $\begin{array}{r}5\\-3\\\hline 2\end{array}$ |

| [S] $\begin{array}{r}9\\-5\\\hline 4\end{array}$ | [T] $\begin{array}{r}10\\-7\\\hline 3\end{array}$ | [U] $\begin{array}{r}10\\-5\\\hline 5\end{array}$ | [V] $\begin{array}{r}10\\-8\\\hline 2\end{array}$ | [W] $\begin{array}{r}7\\-4\\\hline 3\end{array}$ | [X] $\begin{array}{r}7\\-2\\\hline 5\end{array}$ |

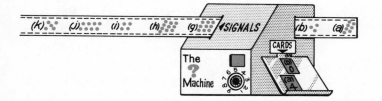

4. [A] What does this machine do?
Subtracts 3

[B] Show the cards the machine will put out for signals (g), *6* (h), *7* (i), *5* (j), and (k). *2*

[C] If this were a "Subtracting 2" machine, what cards would it put out for signals (a), *5* (b), *1* (g), *7* (h), *8* (i), *2* (j), *6* (k)? *3*

5. Solve the equations.
[A] $7 - \blacksquare = 3$ *4*
[B] $\blacksquare - 6 = 2$ *8*
[C] $\blacksquare - 5 = 5$ *10*
[D] $\blacksquare - 4 = 4$ *8*
[E] $\blacksquare - 2 = 8$ *10*
[F] $9 - \blacksquare = 7$ *2*
[G] $10 - \blacksquare = 4$ *6*

Have the students work the exercises. Allow time for discussion after the students have completed the page.

It may be necessary to provide some discussion and explanation for exercise 4. Give the students considerable freedom in discussing what they think this machine does. If someone guesses wrong and says, for example, that the machine is an adding machine, have the other students tell what numbers they think would come out if it were an adding machine.

---

by having a thorough knowledge of addition combinations, the students quickly can arrive at given subtraction combinations. Later, this same method will be pursued further by treating quotients as missing factors.

● **PREPARATION**

Write on the chalkboard the equation $3 + \square = 9$. Have a student come to the chalkboard and write the correct numeral in the box. Read with the students, "$3 + 6 = 9$." Now, immediately under this equation, exhibit the equation $9 - 3 = \square$. Again have a student come to the chalkboard and write the correct solution to this equation. Continue with similar pairs of equations until they discover that they can find differences by finding the missing addend, or by thinking about missing addends.

Present the class with several subtraction equations without the accompanying addition equations. In each case, stress that to find the difference the students should think about finding a missing addend. Following the solution of each subtraction equation, exhibit the corresponding addition equation.

Instruct the students to work exercises 1 through 4. Treat exercise 5 as enrichment for your more able students.

The riddles given in the "Exercise for Experts" may be considered enrichment, but give all the students an opportunity to read them and think about them. Most students will be able to understand a riddle once the correct answer is given. However, caution the students against giving away answers before everybody has had an opportunity to discover them.

---

30 ADDITION AND SUBTRACTION

Let's Review

- ADDITION
- SUBTRACTION
- MULTIPLICATION
- DIVISION
- MEASUREMENT
- PLACE VALUE
- INEQUALITIES
- PRINCIPLES

1. Find the sums and differences.

[A]	8 +2 = 10	[B]	6 +3 = 9	[C]	9 −4 = 5	[D]	7 +1 = 8
[E]	9 −3 = 6	[F]	6 −5 = 1	[G]	2 +5 = 7	[H]	5 +5 = 10
[I]	10 −4 = 6	[J]	7 −3 = 4	[K]	6 +4 = 10	[L]	10 −1 = 9
[M]	4 +4 = 8	[N]	7 −5 = 2	[O]	10 −6 = 4	[P]	0 +6 = 6
[Q]	4 +5 = 9	[R]	10 −3 = 7	[S]	10 −7 = 3	[T]	3 +5 = 8

2. [A] What number is 100 more than 9628? *9728*

[B] What number is 1000 less than 12,259? *11,259*

[C] What number is 1,000,000 more than 7,265,348? *8,265,348*

[D] What number is 1,000,000 less than 68,256,379? *67,256,379*

[E] What number is 6000 more than 61,250? *67,250*

[F] What number is 60,000 more than 1,000,000? *1,060,000*

3. For each pair of numbers, write the larger one on your paper.

[A] 5,286,704
   5,486,704

[B] *293,685,428*
   293,684,999

[C] 100,972,364
   101,972,364

4. Write the correct numeral for each.

[A] sixty-eight million five hundred two thousand one hundred fifteen *68,502,115*

[B] two hundred million eight hundred *200,000,800*

[C] nine hundred thousand two *900,002*

★**5.** Write the word name for 100,100,100. *one hundred million one hundred thousand one hundred*

Exercise for Experts

Addition is my dearest friend.
We never fuss or fight.
When I am done,
He comes and checks
To see that I am right. *subtraction*

I think I'm big until I spy
So many numbers larger than I.
My name has a one
And zeros galore. *one million*
Seven digits in all, not one more.

If I'm not right, I'll take no blame.
When I'm between, *equal sign*
They're just the same.

WHO AM I?

Teaching **Pages 30 and 31**

● **PURPOSE**

To provide a review of the material previously covered

To provide word-problem experiences

Treasure map

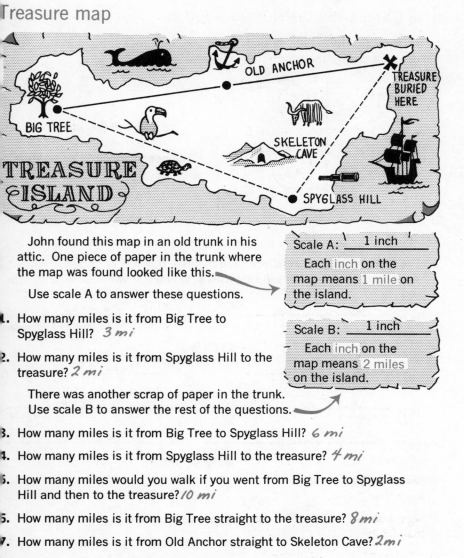

John found this map in an old trunk in his attic. One piece of paper in the trunk where the map was found looked like this.

Use scale A to answer these questions.

Scale A: ____1 inch____
Each inch on the map means 1 mile on the island.

1. How many miles is it from Big Tree to Spyglass Hill? *3 mi*

2. How many miles is it from Spyglass Hill to the treasure? *2 mi*

Scale B: ____1 inch____
Each inch on the map means 2 miles on the island.

There was another scrap of paper in the trunk. Use scale B to answer the rest of the questions.

3. How many miles is it from Big Tree to Spyglass Hill? *6 mi*

4. How many miles is it from Spyglass Hill to the treasure? *4 mi*

5. How many miles would you walk if you went from Big Tree to Spyglass Hill and then to the treasure? *10 mi*

6. How many miles is it from Big Tree straight to the treasure? *8 mi*

7. How many miles is it from Old Anchor straight to Skeleton Cave? *2 mi*

8. How far is it from Skeleton Cave to Spyglass Hill? *1 mi*

9. Which is farther from Big Tree, Spyglass Hill or the treasure? How much farther? *Treasure is 2 mi farther.*

For these exercises the students will need a ruler to make the appropriate measurements on their maps.

Ask the students to study the map and read the material that precedes the exercise set. Discuss the meaning of scale A with respect to the map. Help the students see that to find how far certain distances are on the island they must measure on the map to determine how many inches.

Give the students an opportunity to work exercises 1 and 2. When they have finished, conduct a discussion of these exercises.

Now read and discuss the material concerning scale B. Point out that when they use scale B, each inch on the map means two miles on the island. Have the students complete the remaining exercises. Allow time for checking papers and any discussion which might accompany the exercises.

PREPARATION

Provide a short oral practice session in working with basic addition and subtraction combinations for sums of ten or less.

Follow this with a brief review of place-value concepts and reading of large numbers.

Study and discuss the material at the top of the page with the class. Then, instruct the students to work the exercises at the bottom of the page. Following completion of the exercises, give the students an opportunity to check their own papers.

The order principle for addition

These 4 pictures help show that changing the order of two addends does not change the sum.

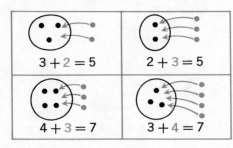

3 + 2 = 5   2 + 3 = 5

4 + 3 = 7   3 + 4 = 7

We call this idea:

The **ORDER** principle for addition.

EXERCISES

1. The number lines in exercise **A** show that $2 + 5 = 5 + 2$.
What do the number lines in exercises **B, C,** and **D** show?

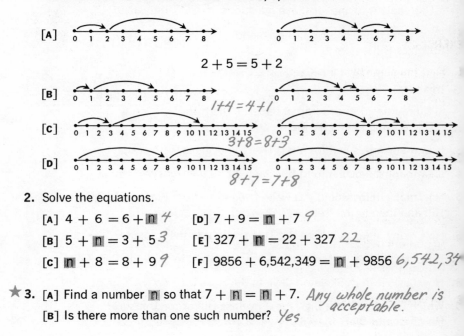

[A] $2 + 5 = 5 + 2$

[B]   *1 + 4 = 4 + 1*

[C]   *3 + 8 = 8 + 3*

[D]   *8 + 7 = 7 + 8*

2. Solve the equations.

[A] $4 + 6 = 6 + \boxed{n}$ *4*   [D] $7 + 9 = \boxed{n} + 7$ *9*

[B] $5 + \boxed{n} = 3 + 5$ *3*   [E] $327 + \boxed{n} = 22 + 327$ *22*

[C] $\boxed{n} + 8 = 8 + 9$ *9*   [F] $9856 + 6,542,349 = \boxed{n} + 9856$ *6,542,34*

★ 3. [A] Find a number $\boxed{n}$ so that $7 + \boxed{n} = \boxed{n} + 7$. *Any whole number is acceptable.*
[B] Is there more than one such number? *Yes*

Teaching Pages 32 and 33

• **PURPOSE**

To introduce the order principle for addition
To introduce the grouping principle for addition

• **MATHEMATICS**

We give the formal statements for the order and grouping principles for addition. The commutative, or order, principle for addition is stated as follows:
For any whole numbers a and b,
$$a + b = b + a.$$

The associative or grouping principle for addition is stated as follows:
For any whole numbers a, b, and c,
$$(a + b) + c = a + (b + c).$$

These ideas are given here as generalizations in an abstract sense. The principles are presented to the students through numerical examples that enable them to arrive at generalizations of the main concepts: we can change the order of the two addends and still get the same sum; for any addition of three numbers, we can change the grouping and still get the same sum.

The grouping principle for addition

Think about 3 addends in a special order.   4   3   2

How shall we add if we do not change the order?

We could add these first.		We could add these first.
4 3 2	or	4 3 2
(4 + 3) + 2		4 + (3 + 2)
We think: 7 + 2, the sum is 9.		We think: 4 + 5, the sum is 9.

We may group the first two addends or the last two addends and still get the same sum.

We call this idea: The **GROUPING** principle for addition.

EXERCISES

1. Find the sums by using the grouping shown. Do not change the order.

[A] 1 5 2 *8*   [C] 1 5 2 *8*   [E] 2 4 1 *7*   [G] 2 4 1 *7*

[B] 3 4 2 *9*   [D] 3 4 2 *9*   [F] 5 3 2 *10*   [H] 5 3 2 *10*

2. The last two addends are grouped in the problems below. By changing the grouping, you can find the same sum more easily.

[A] 7 + (3 + 5) *15*   [E] 78 + (2 + 6) *86*   [I] 999 + (1 + 235) *1235*

[B] 8 + (2 + 7) *17*   [F] 8 + (2 + 6) *16*   [J] 99 + (1 + 532) *632*

[C] 6 + (4 + 8) *18*   [G] 4 + (6 + 3) *13*   [K] 6 + (4 + 8321) *8331*

[D] 59 + (1 + 7) *67*   [H] 5 + (5 + 3) *13*   [L] 7 + (3 + 8,267,529)
                                                              8,267,539

3. Solve these equations.

[A] (5 + 3) + ■ = 5 + (3 + 2) *2*   [B] (■ + 29) + 67 = 48 + (29 + 67) *48*

Read the material at the top of the page with the students. Have them work the exercises. When they have finished, have each student check his own paper as you read the answers. Allow time for questions and discussion.

Notice in particular that the easy way to work exercise 2 is to use the grouping principle. For example, in exercise 2A, changing the grouping gives $(7 + 3) + 5$ instead of $7 + (3 + 5)$. In this way, we have $10 + 5$ rather than $7 + 8$. All these exercises are designed to encourage the students to change the grouping before finding the sum.

PREPARATION

Conduct a short oral session, such as the following, in which you give one student pairs of equations. First ask, "What is the sum of four and three?" When the student responds, "Seven," ask "What is the sum of three and four?" Continue this until the students see that the answer is the same in each case.

Next, exhibit several equation pairs that show the idea of the grouping principle. For example, you might show this pair of equations on the chalkboard:

$$(4 + 3) + 2 = n \qquad 4 + (3 + 2) = n$$

Provide several pairs of equations similar to this and have the students solve the equations, so they will see that the grouping does not affect the sum.

Call everyone's attention to the first column in the chart. Tell the students that in this column they are to think about the sum of three numbers, 2, 3, and 4, but they are to think about adding the 2 and the 4 first. In parts A and B the 2 and the 4 are given first, but in different order. In parts C and D the 2 and 4 are given last, again in a different order. When the students discover that each of these sums is nine, move to the second column.

Explain that in the second column the students are to think about adding the 4 and the 3 first.

Continue the discussion for the third column. Encourage the students to participate in the discussion of these ideas.

Some of the more able students may become bored with this lengthy discussion for these three addends and comment, "Well, it doesn't matter how we do it; we always get nine." However, far more than indicating boredom, such a comment would indicate that these students have achieved the objective of this lesson: they have generalized the order and grouping principles into the principle of rearranging addends in any way that is convenient.

Following your discussion, have the students do the exercises. Allow time for checking papers and answering any questions which may arise.

Rearranging addends

Think about 3 addends.   2 4 3

When we change the **order** of the addends, we get the same sum.

When we **group** the addends differently, we get the same sum.

When we use these principles together, we begin by adding any two numbers.

We could add these first. We could add these first. We could add these first.

2 4 3	2 4 3	2 4 3
[A] $(2+4)+3$	[E] $2+(4+3)$	[I] $(2+3)+4$
[B] $(4+2)+3$	[F] $2+(3+4)$	[J] $4+(2+3)$
[C] $3+(2+4)$	[G] $(4+3)+2$	[K] $(3+2)+4$
[D] $3+(4+2)$	[H] $(3+4)+2$	[L] $4+(3+2)$

EXERCISES

1. Find each sum in the chart above. *All the sums are 9.*

2. Addends: 3 5 1
   We could add the first two addends and write $(3+5)+1=9$.
   Which addends do we add first when we write

   [A] $5+(3+1)=9$?   [C] $3+(5+1)=9$?   [A] *3 and 1*   [C] *5 and 1*
   [B] $1+(5+3)=9$?   [D] $(1+5)+3=9$?   [B] *5 and 3*   [D] *1 and 5*

3. Solve the equations.

   [A] $(2+3)+5=$ ▨ *10*   [G] $5+(3+2)=$ ▨ *10*
   [B] $2+(3+5)=$ ▨ *10*   [H] $(5+3)+2=$ ▨ *10*
   [C] $2+(5+3)=$ ▨ *10*   [I] $(3+5)+2=$ ▨ *10*
   [D] $(2+5)+3=$ ▨ *10*   [J] $3+(5+2)=$ ▨ *10*
   [E] $(5+2)+3=$ ▨ *10*   [K] $3+(2+5)=$ ▨ *10*
   [F] $5+(2+3)=$ ▨ *10*   [L] $(3+2)+5=$ ▨ *10*

Teaching Pages 34 and 35

- **PURPOSE**

  To arrive at a generalization of the order and grouping principles

- **MATHEMATICS**

  This lesson involves a simple but important step in the mathematics of this program. The fact that we can change the order and the grouping of numbers in addition permits any rearrangement that is convenient for three or more addends.

  Since three numbers can be ordered six ways and since each of these orderings can be grouped in two ways, three

addends such as a, b, and c can be ordered and grouped in 12 ways:

1. $(a+b)+c$ 5. $(c+a)+b$ 9. $(b+c)+a$
2. $a+(b+c)$ 6. $c+(a+b)$ 10. $b+(c+a)$
3. $a+(c+b)$ 7. $c+(b+a)$ 11. $b+(a+c)$
4. $(a+c)+b$ 8. $(c+b)+a$ 12. $(b+a)+c$

One can proceed down this list and verify the equality of these expressions by alternately applying the grouping and order principles for addition. Even without this complete list, we can prove the equality of any two of these expressions by using the order and grouping principles. To show that

$$c+(b+a)=b+(c+a),$$

we offer two different proofs.

Since we can change **order** and **grouping** and still get the same sum, we may **add any two** numbers first. We could think like this to find 6 + 3 + 4.

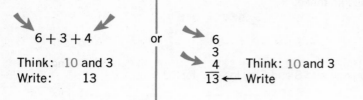

6 + 3 + 4   or

Think: 10 and 3
Write: 13

6
3
4
‾‾‾
13 ← Write

Think: 10 and 3

4. Find the sums. Look for tens.

[A] 7 + 3 + 2 *12*   [D] 5 + 6 + 5 *16*   [G] 6 + 3 + 1 *10*   [J] 10 + 0 + 8 *18*

[B] 7 + 2 + 3 *12*   [E] 4 + 6 + 9 *19*   [H] 5 + 2 + 8 *15*   [K] 2 + 5 + 2 *9*

[C] 9 + 8 + 1 *18*   [F] 7 + 8 + 2 *17*   [I] 8 + 5 + 2 *15*   [L] 3 + 5 + 5 *13*

5. Find the sums.

[A]	[B]	[C]	[D]	[E]	[F]	[G]	[H]	[I]
8	4	4	8	7	9	8	6	4
2	2	8	4	5	9	2	0	6
+4	+8	+2	+2	+3	+1	+8	+4	+9
14	*14*	*14*	*14*	*15*	*19*	*18*	*10*	*19*

6. Find the sums. Look for tens.

[A] 2 + 8 + 3 + 4 *17*   [C] 2 + 3 + 4 + 8 *17*   [E] 4 + 3 + 3 + 6 *16*

[B] 2 + 3 + 8 + 4 *17*   [D] 4 + 6 + 3 + 3 *16*   [F] 7 + 4 + 3 + 5 *19*

7. Find the sums.

[A]	[B]	[C]	[D]	[E]
9	8	5	6	6
7	2	7	4	7
1	3	3	7	4
+2	+1	+2	+3	+3
19	*14*	*17*	*20*	*20*

When we use the **order** and **grouping** principles together to find sums:

> We can **ARRANGE** the addends in any way and still get the same **SUM**.

Have the students read and study the material at the top of the page and then complete the exercises.

When the students have finished these exercises and their answers have been checked, call particular attention to the statement at the bottom of the page, "We can arrange the addends in any way and still get the same sum."

Supplementary exercises, Set 1 (page 329), Set 3 (page 330), and Set 5 (page 331), may be assigned as necessary beyond this page.

First proof: $c + (b + a) = (c + b) + a$ grouping principle

               $= (b + c) + a$ order principle

               $= b + (c + a)$ grouping principle

Second proof: $c + (b + a) = (b + a) + c$ order principle

               $= b + (a + c)$ grouping principle

               $= b + (c + a)$ order principle

Another important idea in this lesson is that the grouping principle allows the omission of parentheses from expressions involving the sum of three numbers. Since we can group these numbers in any convenient way, the expression will be just as meaningful without parentheses (we will get the same sum regardless of how we consider the grouping). Of course, this leads to the additional step of rearranging the numbers in the absence of parentheses.

● **PREPARATION**

Center your preparation activities around a discussion of the chart at the top of page 34.

Read and study with the students the material at the top. Call particular attention to the way 5 is broken into 2 and 3 so that the 2 can be put with 8 to get 10.

Have the students complete the page. When they have finished, allow time for discussion of the exercises.

Sums between 10 and 19

You can use what you have learned about grouping to find sums like these.

$$8 + 5$$
$$7 + 4$$
$$9 + 6$$

You can add 8 and 5 by looking for 10.

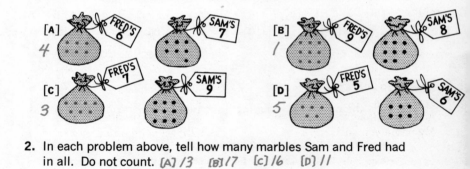

Explain why 5 is written as 2 + 3 in this example.

8 + 5
↓
8 + 2 + 3

5 is written as 2+3 so that 2 can be added to 8 to make 10.

Think: 10 and 3
Write: 13

EXERCISES

1. Tell how many of Sam's marbles Fred needs to make 10.

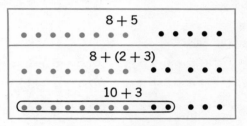

[A] 4   [B] 1   [C] 3   [D] 5

2. In each problem above, tell how many marbles Sam and Fred had in all. Do not count. [A] *13* [B] *17* [C] *16* [D] *11*

Teaching Pages 36 and 37

- **PURPOSE**

  To review and extend sums greater than ten by using the grouping principle

- **MATHEMATICS**

  Below we give an example of how the grouping principle is used to arrive at sums greater than ten.

$$7 + 5 = 7 + (3 + 2)$$
$$= (7 + 3) + 2$$
$$= 10 + 2$$
$$= 12$$

3. Solve the equations.

[A] $8 + ■ = 10$ *2* [D] $6 + ■ = 10$ *4* [G] $■ + 6 = 10$ *4* [J] $■ + 4 = 10$ *6*

[B] $5 + ■ = 10$ *5* [E] $4 + ■ = 10$ *6* [H] $■ + 9 = 10$ *1* [K] $■ + 5 = 10$ *5*

[C] $7 + ■ = 10$ *3* [F] $9 + ■ = 10$ *1* [I] $■ + 7 = 10$ *3* [L] $■ + 8 = 10$ *2*

4. Solve the equations.

[A] $5 = ■ + 2$ *3* [D] $6 = ■ + 2$ *4* [G] $6 = 3 + ■$ *3* [J] $8 = 4 + ■$ *4*

[B] $9 = ■ + 4$ *5* [E] $8 = ■ + 5$ *3* [H] $8 = 6 + ■$ *2* [K] $5 = 3 + ■$ *2*

[C] $7 = ■ + 4$ *3* [F] $7 = ■ + 2$ *5* [I] $9 = 3 + ■$ *6* [L] $6 = 1 + ■$ *5*

5. Find the missing numbers.

[A] $7 + 6 = 7 + (■ + 3)$ *3* [G] $9 + 3 = 9 + (1 + ■)$ *2*

[B] $9 + 5 = 9 + (■ + 4)$ *1* [H] $7 + 4 = 7 + (3 + ■)$ *1*

[C] $8 + 4 = 8 + (■ + 2)$ *2* [I] $8 + 5 = 8 + (2 + ■)$ *3*

[D] $6 + 5 = 6 + (■ + 1)$ *4* [J] $6 + 6 = 6 + (4 + ■)$ *2*

[E] $7 + 5 = 7 + (■ + 2)$ *3* [K] $8 + 7 = 8 + (2 + ■)$ *5*

[F] $8 + 6 = 8 + (■ + 4)$ *2* [L] $9 + 7 = 9 + (1 + ■)$ *6*

6. Find the missing numbers.

[A] $7 + 6 = 10 + ■$ *3* [E] $7 + 5 = 10 + ■$ *2* [I] $8 + 5 = 10 + ■$ *3*

[B] $9 + 5 = 10 + ■$ *4* [F] $8 + 6 = 10 + ■$ *4* [J] $6 + 6 = 10 + ■$ *2*

[C] $8 + 4 = 10 + ■$ *2* [G] $9 + 3 = 10 + ■$ *2* [K] $8 + 7 = 10 + ■$ *5*

[D] $6 + 5 = 10 + ■$ *1* [H] $7 + 4 = 10 + ■$ *1* [L] $9 + 7 = 10 + ■$ *6*

7. Find each sum by thinking first about how much needs to be added to one number to make 10.

[A] $8 + 3$ *11* [D] $8 + 4$ *12* [G] $8 + 5$ *13* [J] $8 + 8$ *16* [M] $3 + 9$ *12* [P] $7 + 9$ *16*

[B] $9 + 2$ *11* [E] $7 + 5$ *12* [H] $9 + 4$ *13* [K] $9 + 9$ *18* [N] $5 + 7$ *12* [Q] $6 + 8$ *14*

[C] $7 + 6$ *13* [F] $9 + 6$ *15* [I] $7 + 7$ *14* [L] $7 + 4$ *11* [O] $6 + 8$ *14* [R] $5 + 6$ *11*

Exercise for Experts

I'm not so very big,
Just over 33.
Add some fives together,
My name you soon will see. *35*

I'm a little over 16
And less than 22.
If you'll just start adding sixes,
My name will come to you. *18*

WHO AM I?

DIRECTIONS PAGE 37

Give the students an opportunity to work these exercises on their own.

Note the organization of exercises 3, 4, 5, and 6. In exercise 3 the students are asked how much is needed to go with a certain number to make 10. In exercise 4 the students break apart numbers in much the same way as they will be doing to find sums of 10. In exercise 5 the students must again break apart numbers; however, the notation is slightly different, and attention is focused upon getting a combination to make ten. Exercise 6 is essentially the same set of exercises as exercise 5. Exercise 7 contains many of the combinations from exercise 6. Be sure to stress for exercise 7 that the students should begin by taking enough of the second number to combine with the first number to make ten.

Following the completion of exercise 7, give the students an opportunity to solve the two riddles.

Notice in this example that we need to use only the grouping principle and the concept of place value to arrive at this sum.

PREPARATION

Exhibit on the chalkboard the sum $7 + 5$. Now show on a demonstration table a set of seven and a set of five. Have a student come to the front and put enough of the set of five with the set of seven to make ten. Write the corresponding equations on the chalkboard:

$$7 + 5 = 7 + (3 + 2) = (7 + 3) + 2.$$

Observe with the students that the 5 is broken into 3 and 2 to get enough to go with 7 to make 10. Now complete the equation. If necessary, provide several set demonstrations for other sums. Each time, elicit from the students the response that they must take enough of one number to put with the other to make ten.

Instruct the students to work the exercises on their own. Allow time for a discussion of the exercises and checking papers.

In particular, focus attention on exercise 3 and the ideas involved here. The students should be helped to see how the answer to the second addition equation can be obtained from the information given in the first addition equation. This is of particular importance since this method will be used later in developing a mastery of multiplication combinations.

Supplementary exercises, Set 2 (page 329) and Set 6 (page 331), may be assigned as necessary beyond this page.

Exercises

1. Find the missing numbers.

[A] $7 + 7 = 10 + \blacksquare$ *4*   [E] $7 + 8 = 10 + \blacksquare$ *5*   [I] $8 + 5 = 10 + \blacksquare$

[B] $6 + 5 = 10 + \blacksquare$ *1*   [F] $6 + 9 = 10 + \blacksquare$ *5*   [J] $5 + 8 = 10 + \blacksquare$

[C] $9 + 6 = 10 + \blacksquare$ *5*   [G] $4 + 8 = 10 + \blacksquare$ *2*   [K] $4 + 9 = 10 + \blacksquare$

[D] $8 + 7 = 10 + \blacksquare$ *5*   [H] $9 + 4 = 10 + \blacksquare$ *3*   [L] $3 + 7 = 10 + \blacksquare$

2. Find the sums.

[A]	[B]	[C]	[D]	[E]	[F]	[G]	[H]
4 +4 = 8	5 +2 = 7	4 +3 = 7	2 +8 = 10	6 +3 = 9	9 +4 = 13	7 +6 = 13	8 +1 = 9

[I]	[J]	[K]	[L]	[M]	[N]	[O]	[P]
0 +9 = 9	6 +1 = 7	3 +3 = 6	4 +6 = 10	7 +2 = 9	9 +8 = 17	7 +7 = 14	2 +7 = 9

[Q]	[R]	[S]	[T]	[U]	[V]	[W]	[X]
4 +2 = 6	6 +6 = 12	5 +5 = 10	8 +3 = 11	7 +8 = 15	6 +7 = 13	5 +3 = 8	8 +8 = 16

3. Read each exercise carefully. Then give the sum.

[A] Because $4 + 4 = 8$, we know that $4 + 5 = \blacksquare$. *9*

[B] Because $7 + 7 = 14$, we know that $7 + 6 = \blacksquare$. *13*

[C] Because $5 + 5 = 10$, we know that $5 + 6 = \blacksquare$. *11*

[D] Because $6 + 6 = 12$, we know that $6 + 7 = \blacksquare$. *13*

[E] Because $9 + 9 = 18$, we know that $9 + 8 = \blacksquare$. *17*

[F] Because $8 + 8 = 16$, we know that $8 + 9 = \blacksquare$. *17*

[G] Because $6 + 6 = 12$, we know that $6 + 5 = \blacksquare$. *11*

[H] Because $7 + 7 = 14$, we know that $6 + 8 = \blacksquare$. *14*

[I] Because $8 + 8 = 16$, we know that $7 + 9 = \blacksquare$. *16*

[J] Because $6 + 6 = 12$, we know that $5 + 7 = \blacksquare$. *12*

4. Give the sums.

[A]	[B]
3 4 +5 = 12	5 3 +7 = 15

[C]	[D]
5 1 +9 = 15	5 4 +6 = 15

[E]	[F]
3 2 +6 = 11	8 0 +9 = 17

5. Solve the equations.

[A] $3 + 2 + 4 + 5 = \blacksquare$ *14*   [D] $(3 + 5) + (2 + 6) = \blacksquare$ *16*

[B] $1 + 2 + 3 + 4 = \blacksquare$ *10*   [E] $\blacksquare + (3 + 6) = 10$ */*

[C] $(3 + 4) + (5 + 4) = \blacksquare$ *16*   [F] $8 + \blacksquare = 14$ *6*

Teaching Pages 38 and 39

● **PURPOSE**

To provide more experiences in working with sums greater than ten

To provide experiences in looking for patterns and drawing conclusions from given data

To focus additional attention on finding the difference by thinking of a missing addend

● **PREPARATION**

Conduct a short oral practice for combinations greater than 10. If necessary, give additional set demonstrations and exhibit some of the equations on the chalkboard. Emphasize during this session the idea of breaking apart one number so that part of it combines with the other number to make ten.

Getting the class ready for page 39 is more a matter of preparing them for an attitude rather than worrying

Finding differences when you know addends

You can find differences if you can find missing addends.

$$9 - 5 = \blacksquare \qquad \blacksquare + 5 = 9$$

These numbers are the same.

EXERCISES

1. Read carefully. Then find the difference.

[A] Because 6 + 7 = 13, we know that 13 − 7 = $\blacksquare$. *6*

[B] Because 8 + 7 = 15, we know that 15 − 8 = $\blacksquare$. *7*

[C] Because 9 + 5 = 14, we know that 14 − 5 = $\blacksquare$. *9*

[D] Because 8 + 6 = 14, we know that 14 − 6 = $\blacksquare$. *8*

[E] Because 9 + 7 = 16, we know that 16 − 9 = $\blacksquare$. *7*

2. Read carefully. Then find the difference.

[A] Because 48 + 37 = 85, we know that 85 − 37 = $\blacksquare$. *48*

[B] Because 76 + 88 = 164, we know that 164 − 76 = $\blacksquare$. *88*

[C] Because 57 + 19 = 76, we know that 76 − 19 = $\blacksquare$. *57*

[D] Because 95 + 83 = 178, we know that 178 − 83 = $\blacksquare$. *95*

3. Read carefully. Then find the missing number.

[A] To find 15 − 7, it helps to think 7 + $\blacksquare$ = 15. *8*

[B] To find 17 − 9, it helps to think 9 + $\blacksquare$ = 17. *8*

[C] To find 14 − 6, it helps to think 6 + $\blacksquare$ = 14. *8*

[D] To find 12 − 7, it helps to think 7 + $\blacksquare$ = 12. *5*

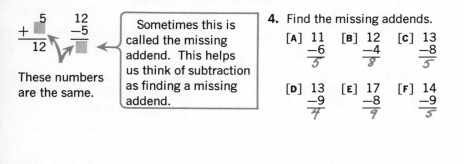

Sometimes this is called the missing addend. This helps us think of subtraction as finding a missing addend.

These numbers are the same.

4. Find the missing addends.

[A] 11
−6
5

[B] 12
−4
8

[C] 13
−8
5

[D] 13
−9
4

[E] 17
−8
9

[F] 14
−9
5

Give the students an opportunity to work the exercises on the page. Allow time for checking papers and answering any questions the students may have.

about any particular background of skills or knowledge. Hopefully, in this and the lessons which follow, we will be able to lead the students to think about finding differences as finding a missing addend. Certainly some of your students will not want to relinquish the take-away idea with regard to subtraction. However, you should attempt to prepare those who are ready for acceptance of the ideas presented in this lesson. The importance of this will be even more evident when the students are exposed to divi-

sion concepts later in the book. In having students master division facts, we place heavy emphasis upon their ability to think of finding the quotient as finding a missing factor in a multiplication equation.

Give the students an opportunity to work the exercises. When they have finished, discuss the diagram at the bottom of the page.

Another way to find differences

These exercises will help you think about another way to find differences.

EXERCISES

1. Solve the equations.

[A] $15 - 5 =$ ▦ *10*   [E] $11 -$ ▦ $= 10$ *1*   [I] $14 -$ ▦ $= 10$ *4*

[B] $17 - 7 =$ ▦ *10*   [F] $15 -$ ▦ $= 10$ *5*   [J] $16 -$ ▦ $= 10$ *6*

[C] $12 - 2 =$ ▦ *10*   [G] $13 - 3 =$ ▦ *10*   [K] $17 -$ ▦ $= 10$ *7*

[D] $13 -$ ▦ $= 10$ *3*   [H] $12 -$ ▦ $= 10$ *2*   [L] $18 -$ ▦ $= 10$ *8*

2. The numbers subtracted are given in blue. Make sure the answers are correct. For each exercise, tell how much was subtracted in all.

[A] $(15 - 5) - 2 = 8$ *7*   [D] $(15 - 5) - 1 = 9$ *6*   [G] $(13 - 3) - 4 = 6$ *7*

[B] $(17 - 7) - 2 = 8$ *9*   [E] $(17 - 7) - 2 = 8$ *9*   [H] $(16 - 6) - 3 = 7$ *9*

[C] $(12 - 2) - 3 = 7$ *5*   [F] $(14 - 4) - 4 = 6$ *8*   [I] $(16 - 6) - 1 = 9$ *7*

3. Solve the equations.

[A] $15 - 5 =$ ▦ *10*   [D] $14 - 4 =$ ▦ *10*   [G] $15 - 5 =$ ▦ *10*

    $(15 - 5) - 2 =$ ▦ *8* $(14 - 4) - 5 =$ ▦ *5* $(15 - 5) - 4 =$ ▦

    $15 - 7 =$ ▦ *8* $14 - 9 =$ ▦ *5* $15 - 9 =$ ▦ *6*

[B] $13 - 3 =$ ▦ *10*   [E] $17 - 7 =$ ▦ *10*   [H] $18 - 8 =$ ▦ *10*

    $(13 - 3) - 3 =$ ▦ *7* $(17 - 7) - 2 =$ ▦ *8* $(18 - 8) - 1 =$ ▦

    $13 - 6 =$ ▦ *7* $17 - 9 =$ ▦ *8* $18 - 9 =$ ▦ *9*

[C] $16 - 6 =$ ▦ *10*   [F] $12 - 2 =$ ▦ *10*   [I] $13 - 3 =$ ▦ *10*

    $(16 - 6) - 1 =$ ▦ *9* $(12 - 2) - 6 =$ ▦ *4* $(13 - 3) - 5 =$ ▦

    $16 - 7 =$ ▦ *9* $12 - 8 =$ ▦ *4* $13 - 8 =$ ▦ *5*

You can find differences such as $15 - 7$ by doing two easy subtractions in place of a harder one.

$$\begin{array}{r} 15 \\ -5 \\ \hline 10 \\ -2 \\ \hline 8 \end{array}$$

$15 - 7$

← Subtracting 7 →

$15 - 7 = 8$

$(15 - 5) - 2 = 8$

Teaching Pages 40 and 41

- **PURPOSE**

  To consider another method for finding differences

  To provide practice in finding sums and differences

- **MATHEMATICS**

  The fact that one can subtract a given number from another number by doing it in parts is intuitively obvious. However, as demonstrated by the statement below concerning the general case, it is a fairly difficult mathematical concept.

Finding sums and differences

1. Find the differences.

[A] $12 - 4 =$ ▨ *8*   [D] $14 - 5 =$ ▨ *9*   [G] $16 - 9 =$ ▨ *7*   [J] $17 - 8 =$ ▨ *9*

[B] $11 - 5 =$ ▨ *6*   [E] $14 - 7 =$ ▨ *7*   [H] $13 - 6 =$ ▨ *7*   [K] $12 - 7 =$ ▨ *5*

[C] $13 - 6 =$ ▨ *7*   [F] $15 - 8 =$ ▨ *7*   [I] $11 - 8 =$ ▨ *3*   [L] $13 - 9 =$ ▨ *4*

2. Find the sums and differences. Use any method you choose.

[A] 8 +2 = *10*	[B] 9 −6 = *3*	[C] 8 +7 = *15*	[D] 7 +6 = *13*	[E] 12 −3 = *9*	[F] 14 −6 = *8*	[G] 7 +8 = *15*	[H] 8 +0 = *8*
[I] 13 −4 = *9*	[J] 13 −5 = *8*	[K] 6 +6 = *12*	[L] 17 −7 = *10*	[M] 18 −9 = *9*	[N] 6 +8 = *14*	[O] 5 +5 = *10*	[P] 7 +3 = *10*
[Q] 10 −4 = *6*	[R] 10 +8 = *18*	[S] 9 +7 = *16*	[T] 15 −7 = *8*	[U] 8 +8 = *16*	[V] 9 +9 = *18*	[W] 16 −6 = *10*	[X] 14 −9 = *5*

3. Jane and Brenda played a game. Try to solve their puzzles.

$n + 6 = 10$ $n = ?$

[A] I'm thinking of a number. If you add 6 to it, you get 10. What is the number? *4*

[B] I'm thinking of a number. If you add it to 4, you get 8. What is the number? *4*

[C] I'm thinking of a number. If you add 3 to it and then add 2, you get 10. What is the number? *5*

[D] I'm thinking of a number. If you subtract 5 from it, you get 10. What is the number? *15*

[E] If you subtract 6 from a number and then subtract 2, you get 8. What is the number? *16*

★[F] I'm thinking of a number. If you add it to itself and then add 4, you get 10. What is the number? *3*

4. Solve the equations.

[A] $14 -$ ▨ $= 6$ *8*   [D] ▨ $- 6 = 9$ *15*   [G] ▨ $- 9 = 4$ *13*   [J] $10 -$ ▨ $= 7$ *3*

[B] $5 + 8 =$ ▨ *13*   [E] ▨ $+ 6 = 11$ *5*   [H] $6 +$ ▨ $= 10$ *4*   [K] $2 +$ ▨ $= 10$ *8*

[C] $17 -$ ▨ $= 10$ *7*   [F] $8 +$ ▨ $= 15$ *7*   [I] ▨ $+ 8 = 17$ *9*   [L] ▨ $+ 9 = 13$ *4*

For all whole numbers a, b, and c such that $a > b + c$ or $a = b + c$,

$$a - (b + c) = (a - b) - c.$$

Here is an example of this generalization.

$$12 - 7 = 12 - (2 + 5)$$
$$= (12 - 2) - 5$$

Since this generalization is never presented to the students, there will be little or no problem concerning the idea of subtracting in parts.

● PREPARATION

Give the students an opportunity to work this page on their own. Allow time for checking papers.

Supplementary exercises, Set 4 (page 328) and Set 7 (page 330), may be assigned as necessary beyond this page.

Conduct a short oral practice session using problems similar to those in exercise 1 on page 40.

Follow this by doing several exercises similar to those in exercise 3 on page 40. Write these on the chalkboard and explain to the students that they are to think about subtracting in parts. Using exercise 3A as an example, you might begin by writing on the chalkboard $15 - 7$. Point out to the students that they are to think about subtracting 7 in parts. That is, first they subtract 5, getting 10; then they subtract 2, getting 8. Thus, they see that $15 - 7 = 8$.

Work the first few short-story exercises as a class activity. Following this, have the students complete the page. Allow time at the end of the lesson for checking papers and a discussion of the stories.

Short stories

1. 11 balloons.
3 blew away. How many left? *8*

2. 5 girls with balloons.
9 girls without.
How many girls? *14*

3. Jumping contest.
9 grasshoppers. 7 crickets.
How many in all? *16*

4. 5 merit badges.
Need 14 in all.
How many more needed? *9*

5. 13 wins.
6 losses. How many
more wins than losses? *7*

6. 13 balloons.
Stick 8 with a pin.
How many left? *5*

7. 8 cats. 13 monkeys. How
many more monkeys than cats? *5*

8. 9 points scored. 16 points
needed to win the game. How
many more points must be
scored? *7*

9. 10 fingers. 10 toes. How
many more fingers than toes? *0*

10. 16 flies. 7 frogs.
Each frog gets a fly.
How many flies are left? *9*

11. 8 girls. 8 shoes. How many
more shoes do they need? *8*

12. 12 peanuts.
Ate 2 and drank milk. Ate 5
more. How many left? *5*

13. 12 peanuts.
Ate 2 and drank milk. Ate 5
more. How many eaten in all? *7*

14. Caught 17 fish.
9 too small so threw them back.
How many left? *8*

15. 14 boys.
6 hats.
How many fewer hats than boys? *8*

16. Had 15 cents. Spent 5 cents,
and then spent 3 cents. How
much left? How much spent? *7, 8*

17. Caught 12 butterflies. 7 got
away. How many left? *5*

18. 17 papers.
Want to sell all but 10.
How many must be sold? *7*

19. Gave 8 valentines.
Received 17 valentines. Gave
how many fewer than received? *9*

20. 13 newspapers. Sold 3 to
women, and then sold 4 to men.
How many customers? *7*
How many papers left? *6*

Teaching Pages 42 and 43

- **PURPOSE**

  To provide word-problem experiences

  To provide experience in looking for patterns and drawing conclusions from given data

- **PREPARATION**

  You might have the students play several "guess-the-rule" games in preparation for the exercises on page 43.

Guess–the–rule games

When Jane said 3, Tom answered 5.
When Jane said 8, Tom answered 10.
When Jane said 5, Tom answered 7.
When Jane said 2, what did Tom answer? *4*
What rule do you think Tom was using? *Add 2*

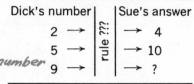

Sue thought of a rule.
When Dick said 2, Sue answered 4.
When Dick said 5, Sue answered 10.
Dick said 9. What did Sue answer? *18*
What rule do you think Sue was using?
Double the number

Dick's number	rule ???	Sue's answer
2 →		→ 4
5 →		→ 10
9 →		→ ?

When Nancy said 3, Mike answered 2.
When Nancy said 8, Mike answered 2.
When Nancy said 12, Mike answered 2.
When Nancy said 0, Mike answered 2.
What do you think Mike answered when
Nancy said 50? What rule do you think
Mike was using? *Always answer 2*

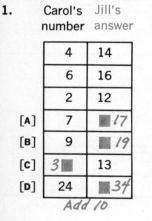

EXERCISES

Study the tables carefully. Guess the rule, then give what you think
should go in each ▦.

1.

Carol's number	Jill's answer
4	14
6	16
2	12
[A] 7	▦ *17*
[B] 9	▦ *19*
[C] *3* ▦	13
[D] 24	▦ *34*

Add 10

2.

Cindy's number	Nan's answer
8	1
7	0
10	3
[A] 9	▦ *2*
[B] *13* ▦	6
[C] *15* ▦	8
[D] *17* ▦	10

Subtract 7

★3.

Cathy's number	Susan's answer
2	0
4	0
3	1
5	1
8	0
[A] 6	▦ *0*
[B] 11	▦ *1*

If even, answer 0.
If odd, answer 1.

DIRECTIONS **PAGE 43**

Do the first exercise concerning
Jane and Tom as a class activity.

When this is completed and the
students have discovered the rule,
give them a chance to study the
second exercise and write the rule
on their papers. Have someone
give the correct answer. Discuss the
various ways that they could use the
facts given to arrive at this answer.

Repeat this procedure for the exercise concerning Nancy and Mike.

Now give the students an opportunity to work the three exercises
at the bottom of the page. Exercise
3 is much more difficult than the
first two. Caution the students
about the difficulty and ask them to
consider it carefully. Do not allow
them to become discouraged in attempting to find the rule. Most of
the students will understand exercise 3 once the rule is given. However, you should be sure that your
more able students have adequate
time to discover the rule on their
own.

As you study each section of this page with the class, point out the relationship between the picture of the student and the function machine. Note with them that the function machine is simply a way to describe what we do when we work with these ideas. The input corresponds to our taking a number and applying the function rule to it, and the output corresponds to our answer.

The function game

Study the pictures to see how the function machine works.

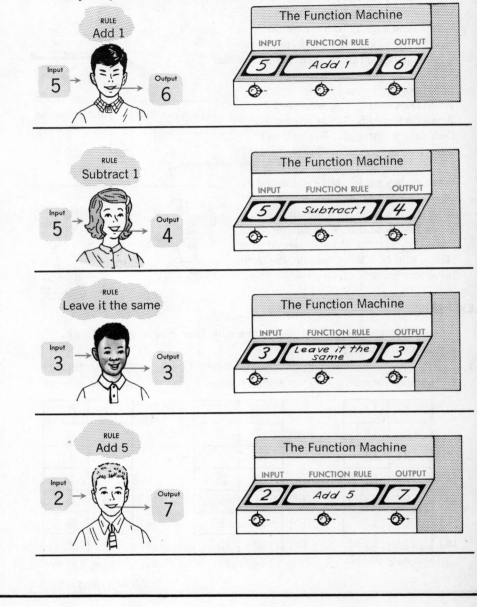

Teaching Pages 44 and 45

- **PURPOSE**

  To provide an interesting discovery activity which lends itself to further practice in working with the combinations

  To introduce informally the concept of a function

- **MATHEMATICS**

  The concept of a function is one of the most important ideas in mathematics, yet it can be presented on an intuitive basis. Rather than present a precise mathematical definition of function, we give examples and point to some significant features.

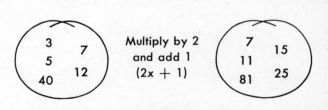

Set A	Rule	Set B
3 7 5 40 12	Multiply by 2 and add 1 (2x + 1)	7 15 11 81 25

If we take a number from set *A*, say 7, and apply the rule, we get exactly one number in set *B*. Hence, we get the set of pairs,

(3, 7), (7, 15), (5, 11), (12, 25), and (40, 81).

One vital feature of these pairs is that for each first number, *there is only one second number*.

EXERCISES

Think about the function machine and tell what you think should go in each gray space.

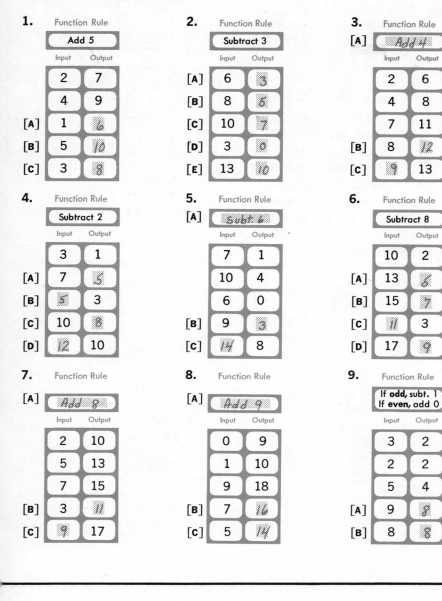

Have the students read the directions and work the first exercise. Discuss the function rule and the three correct answers.

Now have them do exercises 2 and 3. When they complete these exercises, read all the correct answers. Be sure that the students see that the rule for exercise 3 is "add 4." Now have the students complete the page. Discuss each exercise when they finish.

Here is another example.

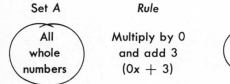

Set A	Rule	Set B
All whole numbers	Multiply by 0 and add 3 $(0x + 3)$	3

Some of the pairs of numbers are,

$$(17, 3), \quad (2, 3), \quad (1, 3), \quad (0, 3), \quad (285, 3), \ldots$$

Notice that although every second number is 3, it still remains true that given any first number, we get *only one second number* (in this case, 3).

In summary, we have a set and a rule for each function. When we apply the rule to an element of the set, we get just *one* answer. Thus for each function we have a set of ordered pairs, no two of which have the same first number.

● **PREPARATION**

Think of a rule such as "add 2." Tell the students they are to give you various numbers, you are going to apply your rule to these, and they have to guess the rule. Suppose a student gives you the number five. You say "seven." Another student gives you the number two; you say "four." Do this until several students discover your rule. Now try it with a different rule. Avoid subtraction since the students could give you a smaller number than the number you are subtracting. Vary the procedure by letting the students take your place as "rule thinker."

Give the students an opportunity to work these exercises on their own. When they have finished, allow time for class discussion.

Answers, exercise 3, page 46

[A] tens
[B] thousands
[C] hundreds

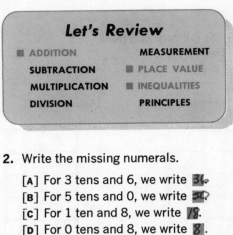

Let's Review

■ ADDITION   MEASUREMENT
SUBTRACTION   ■ PLACE VALUE
MULTIPLICATION   ■ INEQUALITIES
DIVISION   PRINCIPLES

2. Write the missing numerals.

[A] For 3 tens and 6, we write 36.
[B] For 5 tens and 0, we write 50.
[C] For 1 ten and 8, we write 18.
[D] For 0 tens and 8, we write 8.
[E] 60 means 6 tens and 0.
[F] For 1 ten and 0, we write 10.
[G] For 7 tens and 4, we write 74.
[H] 28 means 2 tens and 8.
[I] 46 means 4 tens and 6.

3. Give the missing words.
(See answers at left.)
[A] In 1847, the 4 means four _?_.
[B] In 6253, the 6 means six _?_.
[C] In 2584, the 5 means five _?_.

4. Solve the equations.

[A] $63 = 60 + \blacksquare$ *3*
[B] $10 + 7 = \blacksquare$ *17*
[C] $60 + 2 = \blacksquare$ *62*
[D] $18 = \blacksquare + 8$ *10*
[E] $70 = 70 + \blacksquare$ *0*
[F] $15 = 10 + \blacksquare$ *5*
[G] $80 + 0 = \blacksquare$ *80*
[H] $30 + 4 = \blacksquare$ *34*
[I] $67 = \blacksquare + 7$ *60*
[J] $60 + \blacksquare = 65$ *5*

1. In the pictures below there are 10 dots in each ring. Without counting, give the number of dots in each box.

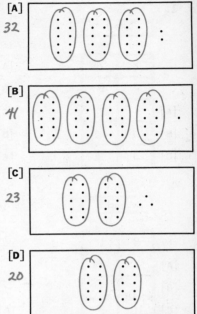

[A]
32

[B]
41

[C]
23

[D]
20

5. In each pair, which number is larger?

[A] (62,429)
    62,197
[B] 28,315
    (30,000)
[C] (126,418)
    109,348
[D] 9999
    (10,000)
[E] 6,354,681
    (6,364,681)

Teaching Pages 46 and 47

● **PURPOSE**

To provide a cumulative review
To provide a chapter review

● **PREPARATION**

Certainly, in addition to many other key concepts provided in this chapter, the students should know the basic addition and subtraction combinations. Most of the students can get by very adequately by knowing only the addition combinations and then figuring out subtraction

Chapter review

(see answers at right.)

1. Write 2 addition and 2 subtraction equations for each set.

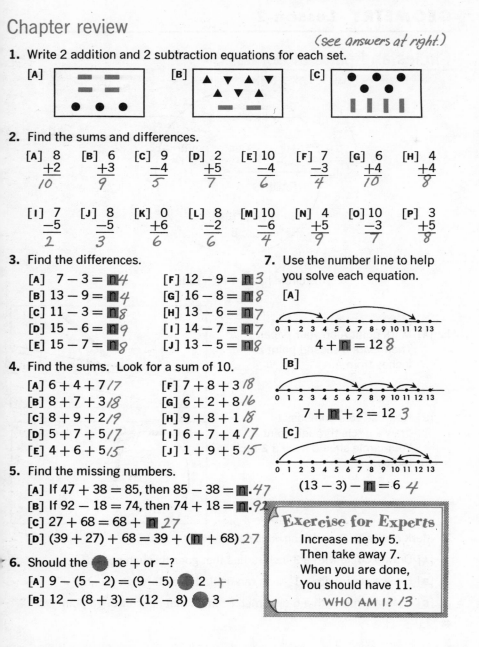

[A]   [B]   [C]

2. Find the sums and differences.

[A] 8 +2 = 10   [B] 6 +3 = 9   [C] 9 −4 = 5   [D] 2 +5 = 7   [E] 10 −4 = 6   [F] 7 −3 = 4   [G] 6 +4 = 10   [H] 4 +4 = 8

[I] 7 −5 = 2   [J] 8 −5 = 3   [K] 0 +6 = 6   [L] 8 −2 = 6   [M] 10 −6 = 4   [N] 4 +5 = 9   [O] 10 −3 = 7   [P] 3 +5 = 8

3. Find the differences.

[A] $7 - 3 = \blacksquare$ 4   [F] $12 - 9 = \blacksquare$ 3
[B] $13 - 9 = \blacksquare$ 4   [G] $16 - 8 = \blacksquare$ 8
[C] $11 - 3 = \blacksquare$ 8   [H] $13 - 6 = \blacksquare$ 7
[D] $15 - 6 = \blacksquare$ 9   [I] $14 - 7 = \blacksquare$ 7
[E] $15 - 7 = \blacksquare$ 8   [J] $13 - 5 = \blacksquare$ 8

4. Find the sums. Look for a sum of 10.

[A] $6 + 4 + 7$ 17   [F] $7 + 8 + 3$ 18
[B] $8 + 7 + 3$ 18   [G] $6 + 2 + 8$ 16
[C] $8 + 9 + 2$ 19   [H] $9 + 8 + 1$ 18
[D] $5 + 7 + 5$ 17   [I] $6 + 7 + 4$ 17
[E] $4 + 6 + 5$ 15   [J] $1 + 9 + 5$ 15

5. Find the missing numbers.

[A] If $47 + 38 = 85$, then $85 - 38 = \blacksquare$. 47
[B] If $92 - 18 = 74$, then $74 + 18 = \blacksquare$. 92
[C] $27 + 68 = 68 + \blacksquare$ 27
[D] $(39 + 27) + 68 = 39 + (\blacksquare + 68)$ 27

6. Should the ⬤ be + or −?

[A] $9 - (5 - 2) = (9 - 5)$ ⬤ 2 +
[B] $12 - (8 + 3) = (12 - 8)$ ⬤ 3 −

7. Use the number line to help you solve each equation.

[A]
$4 + \blacksquare = 12$ 8

[B]
$7 + \blacksquare + 2 = 12$ 3

[C]
$(13 - 3) - \blacksquare = 6$ 4

Exercise for Experts

Increase me by 5.
Then take away 7.
When you are done,
You should have 11.

WHO AM I? 13

DIRECTIONS PAGE 47

You may choose to use this as an evaluation page or as a chapter review. In either case, after the page is completed, you should take the opportunity to go over the page carefully with the class and stress any points with which they have had difficulty.

You may treat the riddle at the bottom of the page primarily as enrichment material for the more able students. However, all of the students should be given an opportunity to attempt the riddle. Most of them will understand the concepts involved once the correct answer is given.

Supplementary exercises, Set 8 (page 332), may be assigned as necessary beyond this page.

Answers, exercise 1, page 47

[A] $4 + 3 = 7$
$7 - 3 = 4$
$3 + 4 = 7$
$7 - 4 = 3$

[B] $7 + 2 = 9$
$9 - 2 = 7$
$2 + 7 = 9$
$9 - 7 = 2$

[C] $5 + 4 = 9$
$9 - 4 = 5$
$4 + 5 = 9$
$9 - 5 = 4$

combinations by thinking about missing addends. This, of course, is most acceptable. Therefore, one of the things you will want to do in preparation for this lesson is to give the students a short oral practice session on the basic addition and subtraction combinations of the chapter. Following this you should select several key concepts and review these ideas with the students. Again, attempt to determine those points with which the students have had difficulty and to place particular stress upon the concepts involved in these points.

In preparing for page 46, provide the class with a short practice session involving concepts of place value and a short review of some basic measurement ideas.

Teaching
Geometry Lesson 2

- **PURPOSE**

  To continue work with circles and points

  To introduce the concept of radius

  To introduce the concept of a family of circles through two given points

  The primary emphasis of this lesson is to study the family of circles through two given points. Another important item is the introduction of the concept of a radius of a circle. This concept should be fairly simple for the students.

  Following the introduction to radius, the students are given an opportunity to discover ways of drawing a circle through two given points. It is hoped that some students will make interesting discoveries in these initial activities before they are given the suggestion of folding the paper in order to arrive at circles containing the two points.

- **MATHEMATICS**

  If two different points lie on one circle, it is clear from the definition of radius that these two points are the same distance from the center point. Thus, to draw a circle through two given points, we must choose a center point which is equidistant from the two given points. Of course, in geometry this would suggest the perpendicular bisector of the segment connecting the two points. The illustration below shows this clearly.

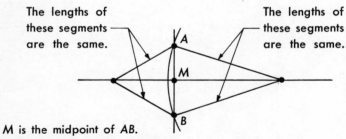

The lengths of these segments are the same. —— The lengths of these segments are the same.

M is the midpoint of AB.
The lines intersect at right angles.

GEOMETRY - Lesson 2

Circles and pairs of points

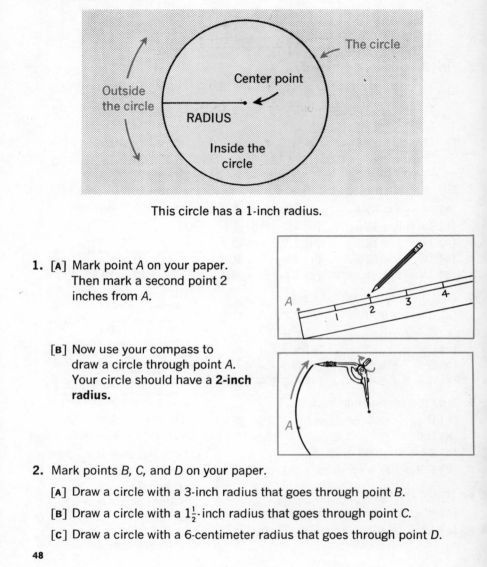

This circle has a 1-inch radius.

1. **[A]** Mark point *A* on your paper. Then mark a second point 2 inches from *A*.

   [B] Now use your compass to draw a circle through point *A*. Your circle should have a **2-inch radius**.

2. Mark points *B*, *C*, and *D* on your paper.

   [A] Draw a circle with a 3-inch radius that goes through point *B*.

   [B] Draw a circle with a $1\frac{1}{2}$-inch radius that goes through point *C*.

   [c] Draw a circle with a 6-centimeter radius that goes through point *D*.

48

The figure gives two examples of the fact that a point on the line is the same distance from *A* as it is from *B*. This, of course, is true of any point on this line. Clearly, if any point *on this line* is used as the center point of a circle through *A*, then that circle will also contain *B*. These ideas are not introduced formally. Rather, they are presented as an intuitive discovery without formal language or constructional problems. For example, the students are led to discover how, by folding the paper in a specified way, they can find the perpendicular bisector of the line segment connecting two points.

3. Use your centimeter ruler to measure

[A] the radius of the circle
with center *E*,   *1 cm*

[B] the radius of the circle
with center *F*,   *2 cm*

[C] the radius of the circle
with center *G*,   *3 cm*

[D] the radius of a circle that has
center *H* and goes through
point *P*.   *6 cm*

It is easy to draw a circle through **one** point. Can
you draw a circle that goes through **two** points?

4. Draw 2 points on your paper.
Now try to draw some circles
that go through both points.

If your drawing looks like this, you
are close but not close enough.

Here is a way to draw a circle through 2 points without guessing.

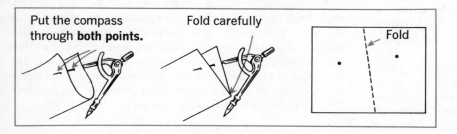

Put the compass through **both points.**	Fold carefully	Fold

5. Mark 2 points on your paper. Draw a circle through the points as
shown above. Put the tip of your compass at different places on
the fold, and draw 10 different-sized circles through the 2 points.
(See figure below)

6. Draw the circle that goes through the 2 points of exercise 5 and has
the smallest possible radius. Where did you put the tip of your compass?
(See figure below.)

Although there are several important mathematical concepts in this lesson, the students should not be expected to
master all these ideas. As with the first geometry lesson,
this lesson should be treated quite informally and primarily as an exploration of some of the interesting features
in geometry. With this in mind, you will want to allow
considerable time for exploration and discussion activities
in connection with the presentation of this lesson.

DIRECTIONS

PAGES 48 and 49

Begin by having the students
study the figure at the top of page
48. Emphasize for the class the
word *radius* and then explain that
the circle pictured has a radius of
one inch.

Following this, give the students
an opportunity to do exercise 1. If
they need additional practice, you
might have them draw a circle with
a 1½- or 4-inch radius.

Have the students complete exercise 2 and discuss the ideas.

After the students have completed exercise 3, guide them carefully in a discussion of the ideas in
exercise 4. Point out that they are
seeking a method which will permit
them to draw a circle through two
given points. Have the students
follow the directions for the paper-
folding activity to obtain a line for
the center of all the circles containing the two given points. When the
students have completed this have
them draw the 10 circles indicated
in exercise 5.

Exercise 6 is of special significance and should be approached in
the spirit of exploration. Give all
the students an opportunity to
work this exercise, but take care
that the slower students do not become discouraged.

Following an exploration period
for exercise 6, you should show the
correct solution, or have one of the
students show the correct solution.

Answers, exercises 5 and 6, page 49

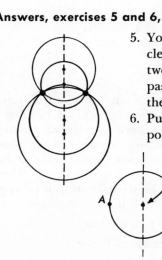

5. You can continue drawing circles of different sizes through
two points by placing the compass tip at different points on
the fold.

6. Put the compass tip at the midpoint of segment *AB*.

Objectives of Chapter 3

To develop skill in addition (with and without carrying)

To develop skill in subtraction (with and without borrowing)

To provide word-problem experiences

To provide work with coins

To develop skill in reasoning

To maintain addition and subtraction concepts

The initial pages of the chapter are designed to cover work with collections of coins and to prepare the students for addition involving numbers of two-digits or more. Many pages provide problem sequences that help develop the students' reasoning abilities. With this introduction, the students work through a carefully organized sequence of pages which lead them to discover the method of column addition for two-digit numbers. Subtraction is then related to addition, and subtracting in columns is explored. The remainder of the chapter develops ideas associated with carrying and borrowing.

Although the primary objective in this chapter is a careful development of addition and subtraction processes, it must be noted that a large portion of the material is oriented to thought-provoking activity. This is designed to lead the students to a better understanding of the mathematical concepts and the relation of these concepts to the complete development.

Mathematics of Chapter 3

Rearranging addends is most important in developing the addition algorithm. If all the order and grouping ideas basic to such a problem were shown, the number of steps would be impractical. However, by utilizing a generalization of the order and grouping principles, we can reduce the number of steps.

Below are steps for two-digit addition similar to those presented to the students.

$$23 + 64 = (20 + 3) + (60 + 4)$$
$$= (20 + 60) + (3 + 4)$$
$$= 80 + 7$$
$$= 87$$

We rely heavily on the relationship between addition and subtraction in developing subtraction of two-digit numbers. By pointing out that finding a difference is the same as finding a missing addend, we present the idea that because we can add in columns we can subtract in columns.

The mathematical concepts associated with this process are quite difficult. Consider the following example.

$$75 - 23 = (70 + 5) - (20 + 3)$$
$$= ((70 + 5) - 20) - 3$$

From this set of equations, it is intuitively obvious that if we want to subtract 23 $(20 + 3)$, we must subtract both the 20 and the 3. The mathematics associated with this idea (shown below) often is confused with the grouping principle for addition.

For all whole numbers a, b, and c such that $b > c$ or $b = c$,

$$(a + b) - c = a + (b - c).$$

Certainly, in this situation it is not at all surprising that we can first add and then subtract or first subtract and then add. The following examples illustrate the simplicity of this idea.

$$7 + (3 - 2) = (7 + 3) - 2$$
$$3 + (6 - 6) = (3 + 6) - 6$$
$$4 + (8 - 3) = (4 + 8) - 3$$

The significance of a discussion of such a simple concept becomes evident when expanding or generalizing the idea. It is tempting to think that regrouping can be used in any case involving addition and subtraction, but this is not true. Note that in the examples above the grouping is changed, but the operation signs remain the same. However, if the subtraction precedes the addition (left to right), equality does not hold:

$$7 - (3 + 2) \neq (7 - 3) + 2.$$

(Note that again the operation signs are not altered; only the grouping is changed.) Of course, you can see that the equality does not hold because the expression $7 - (3 + 2)$ indicates that the sum $3 + 2$ is to be subtracted. Hence,

$$7 - (3 + 2) = (7 - 3) - 2.$$

Note also that

$$(7 - 3) + 2 = 7 - (3 - 2).$$

We now investigate the mathematics of a simple exercise in carrying:

$$
\begin{array}{r}
28 \\
+64 \\
\hline
92
\end{array}
\qquad
\begin{aligned}
28 + 64 &= (20 + 8) + (60 + 4) \\
&= (20 + 60) + (8 + 4) \\
&= 80 + 12 \\
&= 80 + (10 + 2) \\
&= (80 + 10) + 2 \\
&= 90 + 2 \\
&= 92
\end{aligned}
$$

Up to the expression $80 + 12$, we used the same procedures as we did for sums like $23 + 64$. For $80 + 12$, we write 12 as $10 + 2$ and regroup (carry) to complete the problem.

An intermediate step is introduced to develop a short form for adding two 2-digit numbers. The example below shows how the two processes are related and illustrates how students are taught to understand the final algorithm. The hand-lettered numerals illustrate the relation between the processes.

Intermediate Step	Final Algorithm
28	28
+64	+64
12	*92*
80	
92	

We offer here a discussion of a simple exercise involving borrowing.

$$\begin{array}{r} {}^{2}\cancel{3}{}^{1}4 \\ -6 \\ \hline 28 \end{array}$$

$$34 - 6 = (30 + 4) - 6$$
$$= (20 + 14) - 6$$
$$= 20 + (14 - 6)$$
$$= 20 + 8$$
$$= 28$$

In the previous subtraction exercises, subtraction in the ones column was possible without regrouping or borrowing; this is impossible in this case, since 6 is greater than 4. So $30 + 4$ is regrouped as $20 + 14$ and 6 is subtracted from 14.

Teaching Chapter 3

The initial work on the use of coins is designed to assist students in understanding the ideas involved in adding two-digit numbers. For this reason, you should limit the use of coins primarily to dimes and pennies. When the students combine various collections of coins, focus attention on putting the sets of dimes together and putting the sets of pennies together. For example, if you combine a set of two dimes and four pennies with a set of three dimes and five pennies, the set of two dimes should be put with the set of three dimes and the four pennies with the five pennies. At first, avoid situations in which carrying occurs. Later, you will want to combine sets of coins such as two dimes and four pennies with three dimes and eight pennies so that the students will see that 10 pennies can be thought of as one dime and that the collection can be thought of as six dimes and two pennies rather than as five dimes and 12 pennies.

Grouping objects by ten will prove most useful in developing understanding of the place-value concept in carrying and borrowing. Such demonstrations should accompany early discussions of the addition and subtraction processes.

Although the concept of "greater than" and "less than" has arisen frequently in previous chapters, we have reserved formal introduction of the symbols to this chapter. Of course, the students have already been exposed to the use of these symbols in previous mathematics courses.

Your time schedule will depend somewhat upon the background of the students. If the students have a strong background, plan to cover this material in about four weeks. You should not devote more than five weeks to the chapter.

There is little to be said about evaluating the students' proficiency in the addition and subtraction algorithms. A test for such evaluation is easily prepared. However, much of this chapter is devoted to the thought processes and reasoning necessary to understand the algorithms. Therefore, you will want to consider, as part of your evaluation of the students' progress in this chapter, a daily observation of their ability to think and reason about these concepts.

An important part of this lesson should come in your discussion of the exercise. Point out to the students the place-value concepts involved in arriving at the value of the collections in the table. For example, in exercise A you should help the students see that two dimes and four pennies is much the same as two tens and four, or 24, in our place-value system.

Chapter **3**   **ADDING AND SUBTRACTING**

Pennies and dimes

What is the value of each collection below?

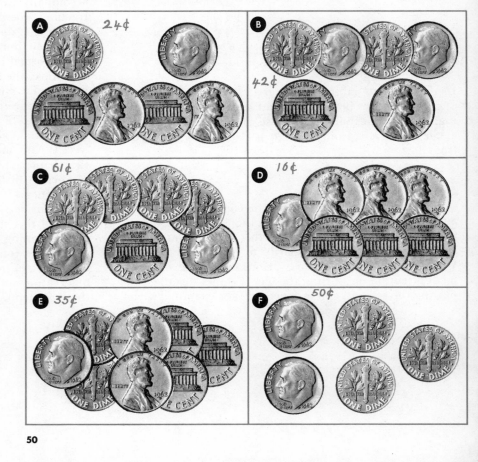

50

Teaching Pages 50 and 51

- **PURPOSE**

    To provide experiences in working with coins
    To provide readiness for two-digit addition and subtraction

- **PREPARATION**

    Have the students work with collections of dimes and pennies. At this point, in order to avoid any situation of carrying or borrowing, do not use collections which make a total of ten or more pennies.

EXERCISES

1. For each part, tell which collection on page 50 has the greater value.

[A] A or B   [c] E or F   [E] B or E   [G] C or E

[B] C or D   [D] C or F   [F] A or D   [H] B or F

2. Give the value of each of the two coin collections together.

[A] A and B 66¢   [D] B and D 58¢   [G] D and F 66¢   [J] A and F 74¢

[B] A and C 85¢   [E] B and E 77¢   [H] A and D 40¢   [K] C and E 96¢

[c] C and D 77¢   [F] A and E 59¢   [I] D and E 51¢   [L] E and F 85¢

3. Which pair of collections has the greater value?

[A] A and B together or C and D together

[B] A and C together or B and D together

[c] A and E together or B and D together

[D] A and F together or C and D together

[E] B and F together or C and E together

[F] A and C together or B and E together

4. [A] Joe had 1 dime and 7 pennies.
He spent 5 cents.
How much did he have left? 12¢

[B] Jane had 2 dimes and 3 pennies.
She spent 1 dime and 3 cents.
How much did she have left? 10¢

[c] Sue had 6 dimes and 7 pennies.
She spent 5 dimes and 5 cents.
How much did she have left? 12¢

[D] Bill had 8 dimes and 2 pennies.
He spent 40 cents.
How much did he have left? 42¢

[E] Bob had 5 dimes and 9 pennies.
He spent 50 cents.
How much did he have left? 9¢

[F] Ann had 7 dimes and 6 pennies.
She spent 56 cents.
How much did she have left? 20¢

[G] Beth had 4 dimes and 8 pennies.
She spent 25 cents.
How much did she have left? 23¢

[H] Tom had 53 cents.
He spent 50 cents.
How much did he have left? 3¢

[I] Linda had 38 cents.
She spent 18 cents.
How much did she have left? 20¢

[J] Mike had 79 cents.
He spent 43 cents.
How much did he have left? 36¢

Give the students an opportunity to work these exercises on their own. Allow time for a discussion of the exercises when they have finished the page. In this discussion, emphasize that in order to arrive at the total amounts, they should think of putting the dimes together and putting the pennies together. This, of course, leads to a later lesson which involves column addition.

The exercises on these pages are primarily designed to encourage the students to think. You should avoid the usual column notation for finding the total amounts in the given collections.

Study the tables on this page with the students. Give them an opportunity to tell the total amounts of each collection in the table. It may help to provide actual coin collections for them to count during the discussion accompanying this page.

Value of coin collections

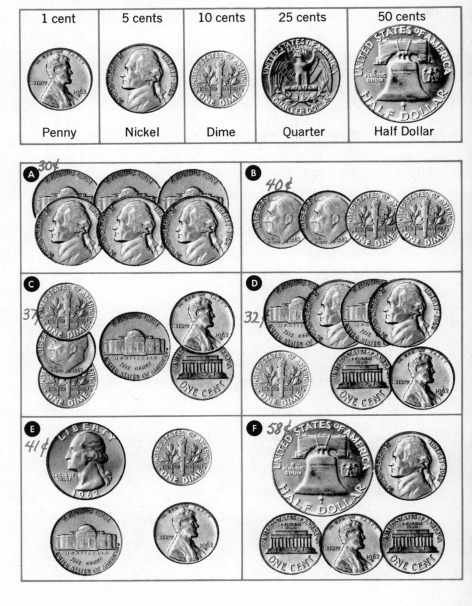

1 cent	5 cents	10 cents	25 cents	50 cents
Penny	Nickel	Dime	Quarter	Half Dollar

A 30¢

B 40¢

C 37¢

D 32¢

E 41¢

F 58¢

Teaching Pages 52 and 53

- **PURPOSE**

    To provide further work with coins

    To provide readiness for two-digit addition and subtraction

EXERCISES

1. Give the value of each coin collection in the table on page 52. *(See table for answers.)*

2. For each part, tell which coin collection has the greater value.

   [A] B or C   [c] A or D   [E] C or D   [G] C or F
   [B] A or B   [d] B or E   [F] C or E   [H] E or F

3. Give the value of each of the two coin collections together.

   [A] A and B 70¢   [D] B and C 77¢   [G] C and D 69¢   [J] E and F 99¢
   [B] B and D 72¢   [E] D and E 73¢   [H] A and E 71¢   [K] D and F 90¢
   [c] A and C 67¢   [F] A and D 62¢   [I] B and F 98¢   [L] C and F 95¢

4. [A] How much more is B than A? 10¢   [G] How much more is F than A? 28¢
   [B] How much more is D than A? 2¢   [H] How much more is F than B? 18¢
   [c] How much more is C than D? 5¢   [I] How much more is E than C? 4¢
   [D] How much more is E than B? 1¢   [J] How much more is F than C? 21¢
   [E] How much more is C than A? 7¢   [K] How much more is F than D? 26¢
   [F] How much more is E than A? 11¢   [L] How much more is E than D? 9¢

5. Which pair of collections has the greater value?

   [A] A and B together, or C and D together
   [B] A and C together or B and D together
   [c] A and B together, or A and C together
   [D] A and B together or A and E together
   [E] C and E together or F and A together
   [F] C and B together, or E and D together

6. Two of the sets on page 52 would look like this if you put them together. Which two sets are they? C and D

PREPARATION

Conduct class activities in which the students find the values of coin collections, compare collections, and put collections together.

Have the students work exercise 1 by writing on their papers the values of the coin collections. Read the correct answers so the students can correct their papers. Instruct them to complete the exercises on the page. Allow time for discussion and checking of papers.

Have the students read the exercise at the top of the page. Give them an opportunity to discuss it, and allow time for all the students to think about the correct answer before anyone is permitted to give the answer. When someone does give the answer, have him explain how he arrived at this answer. Give several students an opportunity to discuss the reasoning behind their answers. Of course, we would like the students to conclude that Lincoln School won the game because the scoreboard showed it had to have at least 48 points, and the team that lost the game had only 47 points at the end of the game. The students will very likely come up with a variety of answers to this problem. The important thing is that they think about the ideas and the logic involved in arriving at the correct answer.

When working through the discussion exercises, be sure the students think about the ideas and arrive at their own answers before you have someone give the answer to the class. Allow the students adequate time to discuss each answer and their methods for arriving at the answer.

Treat exercise 5 as an enrichment activity for the more able students. Depending upon the interest level and abilities of your class, you may or may not choose to treat exercise 5 as a class activity. However, be sure that the more able students are given an opportunity to study the ideas presented in this problem.

Think, Think, Think

With 2 minutes to play, this was the score.

| Lincoln School | 48 |
| Jefferson School | 41 |

At the end of the game, the score was 50 to 47. Who won the game? *Lincoln School*

DISCUSSION EXERCISES

1. Beth was 44 inches tall. Her brother Jim was 47 inches tall. A year later the two children measured 50 inches and 46 inches. How tall was Beth then? *46 inches*

2. Ann had 25 records. She gave some of them to her little brother, and she bought some new records. Then Ann had 26 records. Did she buy more or less than she gave her little brother? *More*

3. Tom had 10 marbles. Bill said, "If you give me 2 of your marbles, then we'll both have the same number." How many marbles did Bill have? *6*

4. If the sum of two numbers is 70, what is the sum of these two numbers and 13? *83*

★5. The sum of two numbers is 20. Their difference is 4. What are the numbers? *12 and 8*

Teaching Pages 54 and 55

● **PURPOSE**

To provide experiences in thinking and drawing conclusions

To provide further readiness for two-digit addition

● **PREPARATION**

The most important preparation you can provide for this lesson is an orientation to the type of thinking required to draw conclusions from the information given in

EXERCISES

1. Find the sums.

[A] Since $20 + 30 = 50$, we know that $20 + 30 + 7 = \blacksquare$. *57*

[B] Since $30 + 40 = 70$, we know that $30 + 5 + 40 = \blacksquare$. *75*

[C] Since $70 + 20 = 90$, we know that $4 + 20 + 70 = \blacksquare$. *94*

[D] Since $40 + 40 = 80$, we know that $40 + 6 + 40 + 2 = \blacksquare$. *88*

[E] Since $30 + 20 = 50$, we know that $2 + 30 + 7 + 20 = \blacksquare$. *59*

[F] Since $40 + 30 = 70$, we know that $4 + 5 + 40 + 30 = \blacksquare$. *79*

[G] Since $20 + 50 = 70$, we know that $20 + 6 + 50 + 3 = \blacksquare$. *79*

[H] Since $40 + 20 = 60$, we know that $4 + 40 + 20 + 4 = \blacksquare$. *68*

[I] Since $30 + 50 = 80$, we know that $50 + 3 + 4 + 30 = \blacksquare$. *87*

2. Find the sums.

[A] Since $40 + 30 = 70$, we know that $43 + 30 = \blacksquare$. *73*

[B] Since $10 + 50 = 60$, we know that $10 + 53 = \blacksquare$. *63*

[C] Since $20 + 60 = 80$, we know that $20 + 66 = \blacksquare$. *86*

[D] Since $40 + 40 = 80$, we know that $45 + 40 = \blacksquare$. *85*

[E] Since $20 + 70 = 90$, we know that $23 + 72 = \blacksquare$. *95*

[F] Since $30 + 50 = 80$, we know that $37 + 51 = \blacksquare$. *88*

[G] Since $40 + 10 = 50$, we know that $44 + 14 = \blacksquare$. *58*

[H] Since $50 + 30 = 80$, we know that $55 + 34 = \blacksquare$. *89*

[I] Since $40 + 30 = 70$, we know that $43 + 36 = \blacksquare$. *79*

3. Find the sums.

[A] Since $30 + 37 = 67$, we know that $29 + 37 = \blacksquare$. *66*

[B] Since $40 + 58 = 98$, we know that $39 + 58 = \blacksquare$. *97*

[C] Since $60 + 17 = 77$, we know that $59 + 17 = \blacksquare$. *76*

[D] Since $50 + 34 = 84$, we know that $49 + 34 = \blacksquare$. *83*

[E] Since $27 + 40 = 67$, we know that $27 + 39 = \blacksquare$. *66*

[F] Since $49 + 30 = 79$, we know that $49 + 29 = \blacksquare$. *78*

[G] Since $50 + 20 = 70$, we know that $50 + 19 = \blacksquare$. *69*

[H] Since $50 + 20 = 70$, we know that $49 + 19 = \blacksquare$. *68*

[I] Since $30 + 60 = 90$, we know that $29 + 59 = \blacksquare$. *88*

Instruct the class to work the first two or three parts of exercise 1 on their own. When they have finished, give several students an opportunity to tell how they arrived at their answers. Have the students complete exercise 1, and when they have finished, discuss the correct answers.

In exercise 2, have the students work the first three or four parts on their own. Discuss these exercises and then direct the students to complete the exercise. Review the exercises with the students when they have finished.

Ask the students to work exercise 3 on their own. Although some of the less able students may have difficulty with the reasoning involved in this exercise, all should be given an opportunity to think about the ideas. Once the students have had an opportunity to examine the ideas, they should be encouraged to discuss the exercise and explain how they arrived at their answers.

the problems. Explain to your class that in this lesson they are going to work problems without using rules; they are going to try to find answers to problems just by reasoning. The students may not understand just what you mean by such a statement, but they will understand that they are to think about the problem and not worry about a rule for working the problem.

In your preparation activities, attempt to instill the spirit of playing a game. Make it clear that you do not expect any great amount of mastery or learning of factual material in this lesson. Do encourage all students to participate.

Have the students read and study the two tables at the top of the page. Treat the questions in the tables as class exercises and give all the students an opportunity to participate in reaching the correct answers. Directly below each table, there is an equation which illustrates the idea shown. Following this discussion, have the students complete the exercises at the bottom of the page.

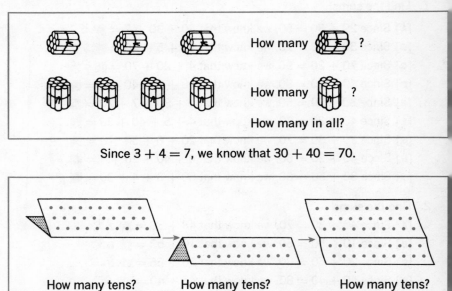

Sums: 10, 20, 30, 40, . . .

How many ?

How many ?

How many in all?

Since $3 + 4 = 7$, we know that $30 + 40 = 70$.

How many tens? How many tens? How many tens?

Since $3 + 2 = 5$, we know that $30 + 20 = 50$.

EXERCISES

1. Find the sums.

[A] Since $5 + 3 = 8$, we know that $50 + 30 = \blacksquare$. *80*

[B] Since $4 + 2 = 6$, we know that $40 + 20 = \blacksquare$. *60*

[C] Since $2 + 3 = 5$, we know that $20 + 30 = \blacksquare$. *50*

[D] Since $7 + 2 = 9$, we know that $70 + 20 = \blacksquare$. *90*

[E] Since $4 + 4 = 8$, we know that $40 + 40 = \blacksquare$. *80*

[F] Since $2 + 5 = 7$, we know that $20 + 50 = \blacksquare$. *70*

[G] Since $6 + 4 = 10$, we know that $60 + 40 = \blacksquare$. *100*

[H] Since $7 + 5 = 12$, we know that $70 + 50 = \blacksquare$. *120*

[I] Since $8 + 7 = 15$, we know that $80 + 70 = \blacksquare$. *150*

[J] Since $7 + 9 = 16$, we know that $70 + 90 = \blacksquare$. *160*

Teaching Pages 56 and 57

- **PURPOSE**

  To develop skill and understanding of sums of multiples of ten

- **MATHEMATICS**

  The following example illustrates the use of the distributive principle in finding a sum such as $30 + 40$.

  $$30 + 40 = (3 \times 10) + (4 \times 10)$$
  $$= (3 + 4) \times 10$$
  $$= 7 \times 10$$
  $$= 70$$

2. Solve the equations.

[A] $60 + 10 = \blacksquare$ _70_   [E] $50 + 60 = \blacksquare$ _110_   [I] $70 + 70 = \blacksquare$ _140_

[B] $50 + 40 = \blacksquare$ _90_   [F] $70 + 60 = \blacksquare$ _130_   [J] $90 + 80 = \blacksquare$ _170_

[C] $40 + 30 = \blacksquare$ _70_   [G] $60 + 30 = \blacksquare$ _90_   [K] $80 + 60 = \blacksquare$ _140_

[D] $30 + 30 = \blacksquare$ _60_   [H] $20 + 40 = \blacksquare$ _60_   [L] $70 + 50 = \blacksquare$ _120_

3. Solve the equations.

[A] $50 + \blacksquare = 70$ _20_   [E] $40 + \blacksquare = 70$ _30_   [I] $60 + \blacksquare = 110$ _50_

[B] $20 + \blacksquare = 50$ _30_   [F] $\blacksquare + 60 = 80$ _20_   [J] $70 + \blacksquare = 120$ _50_

[C] $\blacksquare + 40 = 90$ _50_   [G] $\blacksquare + 50 = 100$ _50_   [K] $\blacksquare + 80 = 140$ _60_

[D] $\blacksquare + 30 = 40$ _10_   [H] $\blacksquare + 40 = 100$ _60_   [L] $90 + \blacksquare = 170$ _80_

4. Find the sums.

[A] $2 + 3 + 4 = \blacksquare$ _9_   [B] $6 + 2 + 7 = \blacksquare$ _15_   [C] $4 + 5 + 3 = \blacksquare$ _12_

[D] $1 + 7 + 2 = \blacksquare$ _10_   [E] $6 + 3 + 4 = \blacksquare$ _13_   [F] $7 + 2 + 5 = \blacksquare$ _14_

[G]	[H]	[I]	[J]	[K]	[L]
2	3	6	6	2	7
7	5	3	2	3	2
+1	+4	+4	+7	+4	+5
_10_	_12_	_13_	_15_	_9_	_14_

5. Find the sums.

[A]	[B]	[C]	[D]	[E]
20	60	40	10	60
30	20	50	70	30
+40	+70	+30	+20	+40
_90_	_150_	_120_	_100_	_130_

[F]	[G]	[H]	[I]	[J]
70	50	60	20	60
20	50	40	70	10
+50	+50	+80	+10	+60
_140_	_150_	_180_	_100_	_130_

[K]	[L]	[M]	[N]	[O]
20	40	60	50	40
30	20	10	20	50
20	10	20	30	10
+10	+50	+70	+40	+30
_80_	_120_	_160_	_140_	_130_

Direct the students to do the exercises. When they have finished, go over the exercises and have the students check their papers. Emphasize in particular the similarity between exercises 4 and 5. The students should see that adding multiples of ten in exercise 5 is much the same as adding the one-digit numbers in exercise 4.

Supplementary exercises, Set 9 (page 332) and Set 10 (page 333) may be assigned as necessary beyond this page.

We do not use this approach since multiplication has not yet been treated in this program. Rather, we use the idea of the union of two sets. By doing this and relating it to the simple one-digit addition combination, we are able to arrive quickly at the correct sum.

PREPARATION

The ability of the students in your class will determine whether you need to provide set demonstrations as preparation for this lesson. If you do choose to provide demonstrations with sets, you can use the set illustrations at the top of page 56 as a guide.

If you choose to approach these exercises in a more abstract manner, a short oral session can be very effective.

Ask a student to give you the sum of 5 and 3. When he responds 8, ask him how much are 5 tens and 3 tens. When he responds 8 tens, ask him how much is 50 and 30. Call on another student and continue this sequence of first adding the one-digit numbers, then finding the number of tens, and then solving the problem involving the multiples of 10. This three-step sequence quickly leads the students to understand addition of multiples of ten.

Have the students work the exercises on their own. When they have finished, allow time for questions and discussion of the exercises. Be sure that the students see that in this lesson they are thinking about putting together groups of ten and groups of ones. This, of course, leads to the exercises on page 59.

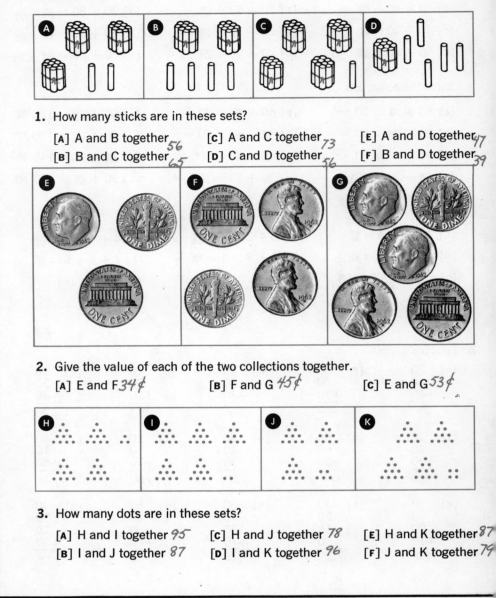

Addition: 2-digit numbers

EXERCISES

1. How many sticks are in these sets?

[A] A and B together _56_ [C] A and C together _73_ [E] A and D together _47_
[B] B and C together _65_ [D] C and D together _56_ [F] B and D together _39_

2. Give the value of each of the two collections together.

[A] E and F _34¢_   [B] F and G _45¢_   [C] E and G _53¢_

3. How many dots are in these sets?

[A] H and I together _95_ [C] H and J together _78_ [E] H and K together _87_
[B] I and J together _87_ [D] I and K together _96_ [F] J and K together _79_

Teaching Pages 58 and 59

- **PURPOSE**

To provide further experiences leading to the processes for two-digit addition

- **PREPARATION**

Provide for the class a short oral review of two-digit place value. Review also the ideas employed in putting together simple coin collections which contain pennies and dimes. It might also be helpful to provide the students with a short oral practice session on basic addition combinations.

EXERCISES

1. Find the sums.

[A] 20 + 30 *50*
20 + 30 + 4 *54*
20 + 30 + 4 + 5 *59*
20 + 4 + 30 + 5 *59*
24 + 30 + 5 *59*
24 + 35 *59*

[B] 40 + 10 *50*
40 + 10 + 2 *52*
40 + 10 + 2 + 6 *58*
40 + 2 + 10 + 6 *58*
40 + 2 + 16 *58*
42 + 16 *58*

[C] 50 + 30 *80*
50 + 30 + 1 *81*
50 + 30 + 1 + 7 *88*
50 + 1 + 30 + 7 *88*
51 + 30 + 7 *88*
51 + 37 *88*

[D] 20 + 60 *80*
20 + 60 + 3 *83*
20 + 60 + 3 + 5 *88*
20 + 3 + 60 + 5 *88*
20 + 3 + 65 *88*
23 + 65 *88*

[E] 10 + 70 *80*
10 + 70 + 2 *82*
10 + 70 + 2 + 2 *84*
10 + 2 + 70 + 2 *84*
12 + 70 + 2 *84*
12 + 72 *84*

[F] 30 + 40 *70*
30 + 40 + 6 *76*
30 + 40 + 6 + 3 *79*
30 + 6 + 40 + 3 *79*
30 + 6 + 43 *79*
36 + 43 *79*

2. Find the sums.

[A]

30 +40	30 6 +40	30 6 40 + 3	36 40 + 3	36 +43
70	*76*	*79*	*79*	*79*

[B]

60 +20	60 5 +20	60 5 20 + 3	60 5 +23	65 +23
80	*85*	*88*	*88*	*88*

[C]

20 +50	20 4 +50	20 4 50 + 3	24 50 + 3	24 +53
70	*74*	*77*	*77*	*77*

[D]

40 +40	40 40 + 5	40 4 40 + 5	40 4 +45	44 +45
80	*85*	*89*	*89*	*89*

[E]

80 +10	80 7 +10	80 7 10 + 2	87 10 + 2	87 +12
90	*97*	*99*	*99*	*99*

[F]

30 +50	30 4 +50	30 4 2 +50	34 2 +50	34 +52
80	*84*	*86*	*86*	*86*

[G]

20 +70	20 1 +70	20 +71	6 20 +71	26 +71
90	*91*	*91*	*97*	*97*

[H]

50 +40	50 +40	2 52 +40	52 7 +40	52 +47
90	*92*	*92*	*99*	*99*

Ask the students to work the exercises on their own. You will notice that these exercises are sequential. Working the exercises in proper order, should help the students understand two-digit addition.

When the students have finished the exercises, have them explain the relationships in the step-by-step pattern. In particular, have the students explain why the last three or four answers in each exercise are the same.

Supplementary exercises, Set 11 (page 333) may be assigned as necessary beyond this page.

Have the students work the exercises. When they have finished, allow time for questions, discussion, and checking answers. In the discussion period take care to see that the students understand that adding hundreds is essentially the same as adding tens in the type of exercises given in exercise 2. It is important that they do not feel that exercise 2 contains anything new or different from what is found in exercise 1.

Supplementary exercises, Set 12 (page 333 and Set 13 (page 334) may be assigned as necessary beyond this page.

Exercises

1. Find the sums.

[A] 15 +42 57	[B] 47 +31 78	[C] 32 +65 97	[D] 41 +23 64	[E] 82 +14 96	[F] 60 +70 130	[G] 62 +73 135	[H] 70 +50 120
[I] 75 +53 128	[J] 84 +72 156	[K] 24 +65 89	[L] 95 +43 138	[M] 72 +72 144	[N] 35 +52 87	[O] 60 +17 77	[P] 60 +7 67
[Q] 50 +30 80	[R] 58 +30 88	[S] 40 +27 67	[T] 60 +78 138	[U] 85 +4 89	[V] 4 +25 29	[W] 43 +36 79	[X] 57 +22 79

2. You add hundreds the same way you add tens. Find the sums.

[A] 236 +541 777	[B] 427 +370 797	[C] 123 +356 479	[D] 208 +710 918	[E] 827 +60 887
[F] 382 +413 795	[G] 600 +400 1000	[H] 623 +456 1079	[I] 735 +542 1277	[J] 834 +652 1486
[K] 428 +910 1338	[L] 506 +973 1479	[M] 614 +614 1228	[N] 837 +242 1079	[O] 657 +741 1398

3. Find the sums.

[A] 23 14 +51 88	[B] 33 22 +11 66	[C] 41 26 +32 99	[D] 30 24 +5 59	[E] 62 15 +21 98
[F] 40 40 +20 100	[G] 70 20 +10 100	[H] 42 43 +24 109	[I] 74 23 +11 108	[J] 62 13 +44 119
[K] 72 24 +41 137	[L] 4 65 +40 109	[M] 23 2 +33 58	[N] 43 43 +43 129	[O] 54 40 +62 156

Teaching Pages 60 and 61

- **PURPOSE**

   To provide practice in two-digit and three-digit addition

   To provide word-problem experiences with two-digit numbers

In the library

After the students have completed the exercises, discuss the various problems and their answers. In connection with exercises 2 and 4, you might choose to provide additional work with the calendar, depending upon the students' needs in this area.

1. The science books were stacked on 3 shelves. Tim counted 31 books on the first shelf, 26 on the second shelf, and 32 on the third shelf. How many science books were there? *89*

2. Jane checked out a book on the thirteenth day of the month. She had to return the book in 14 days. What day was Jane's book due?
   27th day of the month.

3. Sue could read about 132 words each minute. About how many words could Sue read in 3 minutes? *396*

Books	Days
Book **A**	12
Book **B**	14
Book **C**	13

4. Jane kept a record of the number of days it took her to read a book. How many days in all did it take for Jane to read books A, B, and C? *39*

5. Tim started reading a science book on page 62. After he read 25 pages, where was he in the book? *page 87*

PREPARATION

On the chalkboard, provide several exercises similar to those on page 60. Give the students an opportunity to work these exercises on the board. When they have finished, have the students explain the steps in their problems to the class. Follow this by having the student answer any questions that the class may raise about the exercises.

Have the students work the exercises. Observe with them the way each exercise is ordered. That is, in each exercise the students should be able to work each succeeding problem by using facts they have learned in the problem before. Discuss this relationship for each exercise group.

Supplementary exercises, Set 14 (page 334) may be assigned as necessary beyond this page.

Subtracting

1. Find the differences.

[A] 50 − 20 *30*
56 − 20 *36*
56 − 21 *35*

[B] 40 − 10 *30*
45 − 10 *35*
45 − 12 *33*

[C] 70 − 30 *40*
73 − 30 *43*
73 − 33 *40*

[D] 80 − 50 *30*
87 − 50 *37*
87 − 52 *35*

[E] 40 − 10 *30*
45 − 10 *35*
45 − 13 *32*

[F] 50 − 20 *30*
58 − 20 *38*
58 − 22 *36*

[G] 60 − 50 *10*
69 − 50 *19*
69 − 51 *18*

[H] 70 − 50 *20*
76 − 50 *26*
76 − 54 *22*

[I] 120 − 80 *4*
125 − 80 *4*
125 − 84 *4*

[J] 110 − 80 *3*
115 − 80 *3*
115 − 82 *3*

[K] 130 − 70 *6*
136 − 70 *6*
136 − 72 *6*

[L] 150 − 90 *6*
157 − 90 *6*
157 − 93 *6*

2. Find the differences.

[A] 50 −20 = *30*   56 −20 = *36*   56 −21 = *35*   [B] 40 −20 = *20*   48 −20 = *28*   48 −23 = *25*

[C] 60 −30 = *30*   67 −30 = *37*   67 −34 = *33*   [D] 80 −50 = *30*   86 −50 = *36*   86 −55 = *31*

[E] 90 −60 = *30*   97 −60 = *37*   97 −63 = *34*   [F] 70 −20 = *50*   74 −20 = *54*   74 −24 = *50*

[G] 100 −20 = *80*   105 −20 = *85*   105 −21 = *84*   [H] 120 −90 = *30*   126 −90 = *36*   126 −95 = *31*

[I] 160 −80 = *80*   168 −80 = *88*   168 −85 = *83*   [J] 170 −90 = *80*   179 −90 = *89*   179 −95 = *84*

[K] 140 −60 = *80*   147 −60 = *87*   147 −67 = *80*   [L] 130 −70 = *60*   136 −70 = *66*   136 −71 = *65*

Teaching Pages 62 and 63

● **PURPOSE**

To provide experiences leading to an understanding of two-digit subtraction

● **PREPARATION**

If necessary, provide set demonstrations and conduct a short oral practice session on the subtraction combinations.

3. Find the differences.

[A] 78 −32 = *46* [B] 93 −41 = *52* [C] 65 −51 = *14* [D] 49 −32 = *17* [E] 97 −64 = *33* [F] 68 −35 = *33*

[G] 47 −26 = *21* [H] 38 −17 = *21* [I] 59 −19 = *40* [J] 95 −30 = *65* [K] 67 −47 = *20* [L] 84 −64 = *20*

[M] 97 −6 = *91* [N] 76 −50 = *26* [O] 85 −5 = *80* [P] 77 −47 = *30* [Q] 87 −43 = *44* [R] 64 −51 = *13*

[S] 100 −90 = *10* [T] 82 −62 = *20* [U] 126 −74 = *52* [V] 148 −63 = *85* [W] 125 −34 = *91* [X] 178 −92 = *86*

4. Find the differences.

[A] 648 −325 = *323* [B] 739 −516 = *223* [C] 127 −43 = *84* [D] 829 −416 = *413* [E] 264 −124 = *140*

[F] 743 −641 = *102* [G] 928 −528 = *400* [H] 465 −265 = *200* [I] 134 −54 = *80* [J] 847 −325 = *522*

[K] 1000 −700 = *300* [L] 1263 −412 = *851* [M] 1475 −624 = *851* [N] 937 −214 = *723* [O] 657 −642 = *15*

[P] 527 −524 = *3* [Q] 607 −403 = *204* [R] 927 −917 = *10* [S] 1563 −723 = *840* [T] 1738 −935 = *803*

5. In each pair, how much larger is one number than the other? *(See answers at right.)*

[A] 65, 24   [E] 457, 234   [I] 5280, 5395   [M] 9642, 9442
[B] 76, 89   [F] 747, 643   [J] 8027, 8627   [N] 8765, 1234
[C] 324, 374   [G] 1358, 1222   [K] 7288, 7498   [O] 9999, 4444
[D] 267, 246   [H] 6786, 6434   [L] 9000, 8989   [P] 9988, 10,000

DIRECTIONS PAGE 63

Instruct the students to work the exercises. When they have completed them, give each student a chance to check his paper. Discuss any problems that may arise.

Supplementary exercises, Sets 15 and 16 (page 334) may be assigned as necessary beyond this page.

Answers, exercise 3, page 63

[A] 65 is 41 larger
[B] 89 is 13 larger
[C] 374 is 50 larger
[D] 267 is 21 larger
[E] 457 is 223 larger
[F] 747 is 104 larger
[G] 1358 is 136 larger
[H] 6786 is 352 larger
[I] 5395 is 115 larger
[J] 8627 is 600 larger
[K] 7498 is 210 larger
[L] 9000 is 11 larger
[M] 9642 is 200 larger
[N] 8765 is 7531 larger
[O] 9999 is 5555 larger
[P] 10,000 is 12 larger

Have the class read the material at the top of the page and study the portion of the calendar shown. Discuss with them the thermometer and various ideas related to it (e.g., comfortable room temperature is about 70 degrees, the freezing point of water is 32 degrees, sometimes the temperature gets quite low in the winter and quite hot in the summer, the temperature differences for winter and summer and day and night, etc.).

Following this discussion, have the students work the exercises. Conduct a discussion concerning these exercises when they have finished.

Recording temperature

Preparing a five-day mean forecast at the U. S. Weather Bureau's Extended Forecast Section, Suitland, Maryland

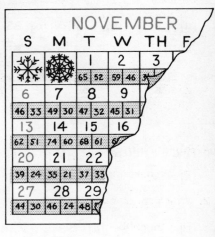

After a field trip to a U.S. Weather Bureau, Joe's class decided to keep a record of high and low temperatures for days in November.

For each day, the students wrote the two temperatures on the school calendar.

EXERCISES

1. What was the difference between the high and the low temperature on each of these days? [A] November 8 *15* [B] November 27 *14* [C] November 1 *13* [D] November 2 *13*

2. How much more was the high temperature on November 15 than the high temperature on November 6? *22 more*

3. November 14 was the warmest day of the month. November 21 was the coldest. What was the difference between the high and the low temperature for November? *53*

4. Water freezes at temperatures of 32 or lower. How many days are shown with freezing temperatures? *7 days*

5. How many days are shown with temperatures above 60? *4 days*

6. Which Sundays had freezing temperatures? *November 20 and 27*

Teaching Pages 64 and 65

- **PURPOSE**

  To provide word-problem experiences in working with two-digit addition and subtraction

- **PREPARATION**

  Give the students an opportunity to work several two-digit addition and subtraction exercises on the chalkboard. Follow this with a discussion of temperatures and the

At the lunch counter

MENU

Sandwiches
Cheese_____25
Ham_____30
Peanut butter___20
Hamburger____30
Hot dog_____20
Tuna_____25
Beef_____35

Soups
Chile_____30
Vegetable___25
Bean_____20

Beverages
Milk_____12
Milk shake___25
Root beer____10
Orange_____10
Coffee_____10
Tea_____10

Desserts
Ice cream___15
Cake_____20
Pie_____20

EXERCISES

1. What costs the most on the menu? *Beef sandwich*

2. Which soup is the least expensive? *Bean soup*

3. How much more is cake than ice cream? *5¢ more*

4. How much less is milk than a milk shake? *13¢ less*

5. How much more is a beef sandwich than a tuna sandwich? *10¢ more*

6. For lunch, Sue had a hot dog, vegetable soup, and a root beer. How much did her lunch cost? *55¢*

7. Bill spent 77 cents for his lunch. What did Bill have to drink? *Milk*

8. Ann had 75 cents to spend for lunch. She spent more than 65 cents. What might Ann have ordered? *Any combination that costs between 67¢ and 75¢.*

9. Tom did not like soup or dessert. He spent 75 cents for lunch. What might Tom have ordered if he had only one beverage? *Any two sandwiches that cost 50¢ together and a milkshake; or Ham,*

10. Jean had one soup, one beverage, and one dessert. *Beef, and a 10¢ drink.* She spent 65 cents. What did she have to drink? *A milkshake.*

Instruct the students to study the illustration at the top of the page and to read the various items and prices on the menu before they begin to work the exercises.

Note that exercises 8, 9, and 10 are starred. These should be reserved primarily for the more able students. If you choose, you might have all the students try them. You are cautioned, however, to use care to see that the less able students are not discouraged by these more difficult exercises.

thermometer. Encourage discussion of such things as normal room temperature, the freezing temperature of water, the boiling point of water, cold temperatures in the winter, hot temperatures in the summer. If necessary, you might also provide the class with some review of work with the calendar.

Have the class study the material at the top of the page. Discuss the figures and the inequality symbols. The statement, "the arrow points to the smaller number," is a simple rule to remind the students how the inequality symbol is used.

Following this introduction to the page, call on the students to take turns reading the inequalities given in the oral exercises. Be sure that they read these from left to right (e.g., in exercise 1, the students should read, "38 is greater than six," rather than, "six is less than 38"). The reason for the convention of left-to-right reading is that one could always read "greater than" depending upon whether he started on the left or on the right.

Inequalities

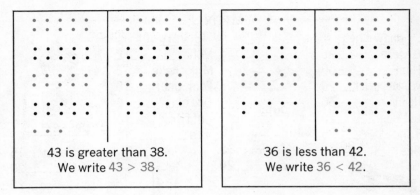

43 is greater than 38.
We write 43 > 38.

36 is less than 42.
We write 36 < 42.

There is an easy way to remember how to use these marks. Think of the mark as an arrow.

The arrow points to the smaller number.

You should learn to read these marks correctly.

ORAL EXERCISES

Read the sentences.

1. 38 > 6	**11.** 69 < 89	**21.** 328 < 338
2. 2 < 19	**12.** 77 > 66	**22.** 956 > 926
3. 5 > 0	**13.** 42 > 39	**23.** 75 < 76
4. 3 < 10	**14.** 23 < 33	**24.** 89 < 90
5. 27 < 100	**15.** 136 < 236	**25.** 70 > 69
6. 3000 > 2	**16.** 419 > 409	**26.** 200 > 199
7. 58 > 28	**17.** 99 < 100	**27.** 6000 > 5999
8. 65 < 95	**18.** 1 > 0	**28.** 318 < 381
9. 27 > 17	**19.** 67 < 670	**29.** 423 < 432
10. 45 > 44	**20.** 100 > 10	**30.** 674 > 647

Teaching Pages 66 and 67

● **PURPOSE**

To focus further attention on the concept of inequalities

To develop skill in working with the inequality symbols

To provide a discovery approach to carrying in addition

● **MATHEMATICS**

In mathematics, we can define the *greater-than* relationship as follows:

To say that $a > b$ means that there is some number c, greater than zero, that adds to b to give a. That is, $a > b$ means $a = b + c$ where c is a number greater than zero.

The students intuitively understand, without a formal

EXERCISES

1. Write each number pair on your paper. Then put the correct mark in place of the ●. Write the two numbers in the order given.

[A] 65 ● 13 >
    (Answer: 65 > 13)
[B] 27 ● 95 <
    (Answer: 27 < 95)
[C] 38 ● 48 <
[D] 29 ● 30 <
[E] 40 ● 10 >
[F] 55 ● 56 <
[G] 97 ● 47 >

[H] 100 ● 99 >
[I] 23 ● 32 <
[J] 124 ● 134 <
[K] 615 ● 605 >
[L] 82 ● 92 <
[M] 75 ● 175 <
[N] 26 ● 20 >
[O] 45 ● 54 <
[P] 69 ● 68 >

[Q] 69 ● 70 <
[R] 743 ● 733 >
[S] 657 ● 756 <
[T] 329 ● 239 >
[U] 102 ● 201 <
[V] 97 ● 970 <
[W] 206 ● 26 >
[X] 307 ● 297 >
[Y] 577 ● 755 <

2. Give the correct mark for each ●.

[A] Since 7 + 5 > 10, we know that 67 + 5 ● 70. >
[B] Since 5 + 4 < 10, we know that 15 + 4 ● 20. <
[C] Since 8 + 6 > 10, we know that 48 + 6 ● 50. >
[D] Since 8 + 4 > 10, we know that 48 + 4 ● 50. >
[E] Since 4 + 5 < 10, we know that 24 + 25 ● 50. <

3. Tell whether each sum is less than 50, more than 50, or equal to 50.

[A] 46 + 3 <, 49   [E] 47 + 1 <, 48
[B] 46 + 4 =, 50   [F] 47 + 2 <, 49
[C] 46 + 5 >, 51   [G] 47 + 3 =, 50
[D] 46 + 6 >, 52   [H] 47 + 4 >, 51

4. Tell whether each sum is less than, more than, or equal to 70.

[A] 68 + 4 >, 72   [E] 67 + 5 >, 72
[B] 62 + 5 <, 67   [F] 63 + 6 <, 69
[C] 69 + 1 =, 70   [G] 64 + 6 =, 70
[D] 68 + 1 <, 69   [H] 64 + 7 >, 71

5. Give the sum for each part of exercises 3 and 4. *(see exercises 3 and 4 for answers.)*

6. Find the sums.

[A] 24
    +4
   ———
    28

[B] 24
    +5
   ———
    29

[C] 24
    +6
   ———
    30

[D] 24
    +7
   ———
    31

[E] 24
    +8
   ———
    32

[F] 24
    +18
   ———
    42

[G] 24
    +28
   ———
    52

[H] 54
    +38
   ———
    92

[I] 54
    +58
   ———
    112

Have the students do the exercises on this page. Some students may need help in working the second exercise. However, be sure that the students are given an opportunity to think about these ideas prior to being given the correct answer. Plan to allow time for a discussion of this set of exercises.

Notice with the students that the problems in exercises 3, 4, 5, and 6 are ordered in a certain way. For example, exercise 3A is less than 50, 3B is equal to 50, and 3C and 3D are both greater than 50. The students should understand how this sequence works. Of course, you will not want to point out at this time that we are progressing to carrying in addition. By adding one more each time, the students see, perhaps by nothing more than counting, the concept associated with carrying in addition.

Be sure to give the students an adequate opportunity to talk about this exercise set.

Supplementary exercises, Sets 17 and 18 (page 335) may be assigned as necessary beyond this page.

definition, what it means for one number to be greater than another. Although students will not express it precisely, their concept of this notion is exactly the same as the mathematical definition above.

PREPARATION

Write several pairs of numbers on the chalkboard. Ask various students to come to the board and draw a ring around the greater number in each pair. Now introduce the symbols for *greater than* and *less than* (shown in the tables at the top of page 66). Have the students place the proper inequality mark between each number pair.

Write three or four more pairs of numbers on the chalkboard. Ask students to come up and, without ringing the larger number, write the proper symbols between the numbers. Now have the students read these inequality expressions.

Study with the students the table labeled Method A. Follow this by discussing the three exercises immediately below the table and showing them on the chalkboard. Call on the students to point out the various steps in these three exercises.

Have the students carefully study Method B. Draw analogies between working exercises using Method B and Method A. Exhibit on the chalkboard the three exercises at the bottom of the page. Have the students find the mistake and then explain the exercises and steps involved.

Sums: 2-digit numbers

Method A

Step 1	Step 2	Step 3
37 +25 12	37 +25 12 50	37 +25 12 50 62
$7 + 5 = 12$	$30 + 20 = 50$	$12 + 50 = 62$

Here are some examples using method A. One example has a mistake. See if you can find it.

$$\begin{array}{r} 47 \\ +34 \\ \hline 11 \\ 70 \\ \hline 81 \end{array} \qquad \begin{array}{r} 65 \\ +28 \\ \hline 13 \\ 80 \\ \hline 93 \end{array} \qquad \begin{array}{r} 6+9=15 \\ 36 \\ +59 \\ \hline 14 \\ 80 \\ \hline 94 \\ 15+80=95 \end{array}$$

Method B

Step 1	Step 2
37 +25 2	37 +25 62
$7 + 5 = 12$	$10 + 30 + 20 = 60$

Here are some examples using method B. One example has a mistake. See if you can find it.

$$\begin{array}{r} 45 \\ +38 \\ \hline 83 \end{array} \qquad \begin{array}{r} 34 \\ +48 \\ \hline 82 \to 72 \end{array} \qquad \begin{array}{r} 29 \\ +16 \\ \hline 45 \end{array}$$

Teaching Pages 68 and 69

- **PURPOSE**

  To introduce two-digit addition with carrying

  To provide an intermediate step for carrying, prior to the use of the usual algorithm

EXERCISES

1. Find these sums, using method A.

[A] 46
+28
74

[B] 37
+44
81

[C] 29
+65
94

[D] 67
+15
82

[E] 48
+6
54

[F] 34
+27
61

[G] 68
+19
87

[H] 17
+35
52

[I] 54
+9
63

[J] 37
+27
64

2. Now do each part of exercise 1 again, using method B.

3. Find the sums.

[A] 57
+85
142

[B] 48
+72
120

[C] 89
+33
122

[D] 58
+77
135

[E] 69
+44
113

[F] 96
+44
140

[G] 85
+77
162

[H] 98
+33
131

[I] 84
+27
111

[J] 75
+58
133

4. Find the sums.

[A] 57
+35
92

[B] 57
+45
102

[C] 67
+45
112

[D] 167
+45
212

[E] 187
+45
232

5. Find the sums.

[A] 68
+7
75

[B] 68
+57
125

[C] 168
+57
225

[D] 368
+57
425

[E] 368
+457
825

6. Find the sums.

[A] 258
+137
395

[B] 258
+167
425

[C] 258
+187
445

[D] 658
+187
845

[E] 658
+787
1445

[F] 546
+125
671

[G] 546
+175
721

[H] 546
+675
1221

[I] 1546
+675
2221

[J] 3546
+675
4221

[K] 804
+307
1111

[L] 906
+218
1124

[M] 937
+105
1042

[N] 839
+965
1804

[O] 315
+685
1000

DIRECTIONS PAGE 69

Direct the students to work these exercises. Plan the lesson to allow time to discuss and display several exercises on the chalkboard after they have finished the page. It may also be helpful to have the students attempt to explain their steps after they have presented an exercise for the class.

Supplementary exercises, Sets 19 and 20 (page 336) may be assigned as necessary beyond this page.

PREPARATION

Conduct a short oral practice session on the basic addition combinations. You may also find it helpful to review two-digit place value. The students should understand thoroughly the ideas of the tens place and the ones place in a two-digit numeral before they attempt problems involving carrying in addition.

Direct the students to study the chart at the top of the page before they begin the exercises. Allow sufficient time to give the students an opportunity to discuss these exercises once they have completed the page.

Getting weighed

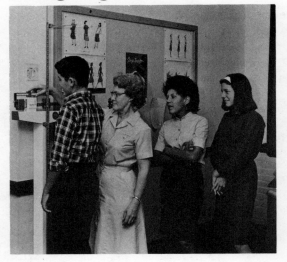

Weight Chart	
Bobby	105
Susan	98
Tom	95
Sara	87
Alan	89
Bill	103
Jane	92
Tony	96
Joan	91
Ann	88
Rick	107

EXERCISES

1. Who weighs most? *Rick*

2. Who weighs least? *Sara*

3. How many students weigh less than 90 pounds? *3*

4. How many students weigh more than 100 pounds? *3*

5. The boys' names are in the blue boxes. Who is the lightest boy? *Alan*

6. Who is the heaviest girl? *Susan*

7. How much do these students weigh together?

[A] Bobby and Alan *194*   [c] Rick and Tony *203*   [E] Sara and Ann

[B] Susan and Sara *185*   [D] Ann and Joan *179*   [F] Bill and Alan

8. Two students got on the scales together. The scales showed 212. Who were the students? *Bobby and Rick*

Teaching Pages 70 and 71

● **PURPOSE**

To provide word-problem experiences involving addition with carrying

To provide readiness for subtraction with borrowing

Reasoning in subtraction

Because we know
$14 - 8 = 6,$ → we see that
$24 - 8 = 16.$

EXERCISES

1. Find the differences.

[A]
12	22	32	42	52
−5	−5	−5	−5	−5
7	17	27	37	47

[C]
13	23	33	43	53
−4	−4	−4	−4	−4
9	19	29	39	49

[B]
14	24	34	44	54
−6	−6	−6	−6	−6
8	18	28	38	48

[D]
15	25	35	45	55
−7	−7	−7	−7	−7
8	18	28	38	48

2. Find the differences.

[A]
12	22	32	32	32
−4	−4	−4	−14	−24
8	18	28	18	8

[C]
14	24	34	34	34
−7	−7	−7	−17	−27
7	17	27	17	7

[B]
13	23	33	33	33
−5	−5	−5	−15	−25
8	18	28	18	8

[D]
15	25	35	35	35
−6	−6	−6	−16	−26
9	19	29	19	9

3. Find the differences.

[A]
25	25	25	25	25
−3	−4	−5	−6	−7
22	21	20	19	18

[B]
34	34	34	34	34
−3	−4	−5	−6	−7
31	30	29	28	27

[C]
53	53	53	53	53
−2	−3	−4	−5	−15
51	50	49	48	38

[D]
72	72	72	72	72
−2	−3	−4	−14	−24
70	69	68	58	48

Exercise for Experts

I can be found
Halfway between
Twenty-seven
And seventeen.   22
_____

Number thirty-one
Is slightly more than me.
I'm that much larger
Than number twenty-three.

WHO AM I?   27

Call attention to the example at the top of the page. Determine with the students that since they know that $14 - 8 = 6$, they can see that $24 - 8$ must be 16 because 24 is ten more than 14, and thus the difference is ten more than 6.

If the students have difficulty understanding this, you can provide a set demonstration to show that putting another 10 with the first number causes the difference to be ten more. You may wish to present additional examples of this type.

Have the students work the exercises on the page. Be sure to observe with them that these exercises are to be worked from left to right. The students should be encouraged and given time to discuss the relationships between the exercises in each part.

Supplementary exercises, Sets 21 and 22 (page 337) may be assigned as necessary beyond this page.

PREPARATION

Before assigning this lesson, provide the students with a review of the material covered so far in the chapter. Take this opportunity to review any ideas with which the students have had particular difficulty.

Follow this review with a short oral practice session on the basic subtraction combinations.

PAGE 72 DIRECTIONS

Study the chart at the top of the page with the students and then go over three different ways to think of 35 (as 30 + 5, 20 + 15, and 10 + 25). Of course, thinking of 35 as 20 + 15 leads to the introduction of borrowing.

Instruct the students to work the exercises on the page.

Place value

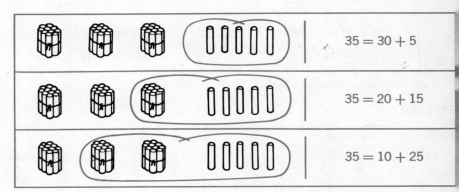

$$35 = 30 + 5$$

$$35 = 20 + 15$$

$$35 = 10 + 25$$

EXERCISES

1. Write the correct numeral for each ▦.

[A] For 6 tens and 2, we write ▦ *62*

[B] For 8 tens and 7, we write ▦ *87*

[C] For 2 tens and 5, we write ▦ *25*

[D] For 5 tens and 2, we write ▦ *52*

[E] For 7 tens and 0, we write ▦ *70*

[F] For 1 ten and 0, we write ▦ *10*

2. Find the missing numbers.

[A] 48 = ▦ + 8 *40*
48 = 30 + ▦ *18*

[B] 72 = 70 + ▦ *2*
72 = ▦ + 12 *60*

[C] 65 = 60 + ▦ *5*
65 = ▦ + 15 *50*

[D] 49 = 40 + ▦ *9*
49 = 30 + ▦ *19*

[E] 37 = ▦ + 7 *30*
37 = 20 + ▦ *17*

[F] 83 = ▦ + 3 *80*
83 = ▦ + 13 *70*

[G] 45 = 40 + ▦ *5*
45 = ▦ + 15 *30*

[H] 54 = 50 + ▦ *4*
54 = 40 + ▦ *14*

[I] 61 = 60 + ▦ *1*
61 = 50 + ▦ *11*

[J] 35 = 30 + ▦ *5*
35 = 20 + ▦ *15*

[K] 56 = 50 + ▦ *6*
56 = 40 + ▦ *16*

[L] 78 = 70 + ▦ *8*
78 = 60 + ▦ *18*

[M] 12 = 10 + ▦ *2*
12 = ▦ + 2 *10*

[N] 99 = 90 + ▦ *9*
99 = ▦ + 19 *80*

[O] 68 = ▦ + 8 *60*
68 = 50 + ▦ *18*

[P] 59 = ▦ + 9 *50*
59 = 40 + ▦ *19*

[Q] 60 = 60 + ▦ *0*
60 = ▦ + 19 *41*

[R] 81 = 80 + ▦ *1*
81 = 70 + ▦ *11*

Teaching Pages 72 and 73

PURPOSE

To review place value

To focus attention on the relation of place value to subtraction with borrowing

To provide a subtraction activity leading to an understanding of the borrowing concept

PREPARATION

Conduct a short session in which you present the class with exercises similar to those on page 72. Follow this by engaging the students in an oral practice of the basic subtraction combinations. It may help during this session if you occasionally slip in an exercise for which there is no whole-number answer. For example, ask one of the more able students to find the difference 5 − 7. When the stu-

Place value and subtraction

To subtract 17 from 52, you use what you have learned about place value.

$$\begin{array}{r} 5\,2 \\ -\ 1\,7 \end{array}$$ ⟵ We cannot subtract 7 from 2.

Here is an example of the way place value is used.

$$\begin{array}{r} 5\,2 \\ -1\,7 \end{array} \longrightarrow \begin{array}{r} 50+2 \\ -(10+7) \end{array} \longrightarrow \begin{array}{r} 40+12 \\ -(10+\ 7) \\ \hline 30+\ 5 \end{array}=35$$

Here is another example.

$$\begin{array}{r} 6\,3 \\ -2\,5 \end{array} \longrightarrow \begin{array}{r} 60+3 \\ -(20+5) \end{array} \longrightarrow \begin{array}{r} 50+13 \\ -(20+\ 5) \\ \hline 30+\ 8 \end{array}=38$$

EXERCISES

1. Find the differences.

[A]
$$\begin{array}{r} 20+5 \\ -(10+2) \\ \hline 10+3 \end{array}$$

[B]
$$\begin{array}{r} 70+8 \\ -(50+6) \\ \hline 20+2 \end{array}$$

[C]
$$\begin{array}{r} 40+13 \\ -(10+\ 6) \\ \hline 30+7 \end{array}$$

[D]
$$\begin{array}{r} 20+17 \\ -(10+\ 8) \\ \hline 10+9 \end{array}$$

[E]
$$\begin{array}{r} 60+14 \\ -(40+\ 7) \\ \hline 20+7 \end{array}$$

[F]
$$\begin{array}{r} 30+13 \\ -(20+\ 5) \\ \hline 10+8 \end{array}$$

[G]
$$\begin{array}{r} 50+11 \\ -(30+\ 5) \\ \hline 20+6 \end{array}$$

[H]
$$\begin{array}{r} 70+10 \\ -(20+\ 8) \\ \hline 50+2 \end{array}$$

[I]
$$\begin{array}{r} 20+12 \\ -\qquad 6 \\ \hline 20+6 \end{array}$$

[J]
$$\begin{array}{r} 50+10 \\ -(10+\ 7) \\ \hline 40+3 \end{array}$$

[K]
$$\begin{array}{r} 30+14 \\ -(20+\ 9) \\ \hline 10+5 \end{array}$$

[L]
$$\begin{array}{r} 80+12 \\ -(60+\ 4) \\ \hline 20+8 \end{array}$$

DISCUSSION EXERCISES

2. Explain why $\begin{array}{r}53\\-16\end{array}$ is like exercise 1c. *Because 53 = 40 + 13 and 16 = 10 + 6.*

3. Explain why $\begin{array}{r}37\\-18\end{array}$ is like exercise 1D. *Because 37 = 20 + 17 and 18 = 10 + 8.*

4. Which part of exercise 1 goes with $\begin{array}{r}43\\-25\end{array}$? [F]

5. Which part of exercise 1 goes with $\begin{array}{r}92\\-64\end{array}$? [L]

---

lent responds, "You can't subtract seven from five," smile and continue on. Doing this from time to time will keep he students on their toes and also help prepare them for he material presented on page 73.

Have the class read and study the material at the top of the page. Discuss these ideas with the students. Show one example on the chalkboard and present, step by step, the ideas involved. That is, notice with the students that in $63-25$, they cannot subtract 5 from 3. Therefore they must think of 63 as $50+13$ rather than as $60+3$. Note with them now that they can subtract 5 from 13 and 20 from 50 and that they get $30+8$ or 38. If the students need additional work with this idea, provide more examples and carefully discuss the ideas again.

Ask the students to work exercise 1. When they have finished, check their papers and allow time for questions.

The discussion exercises at the bottom of the page constitute the key part of this lesson. For example, relating $53-16$ to exercise 1c is the key to the entire lesson. In discussing exercise 2, you should write on the chalkboard

$$\begin{array}{r} 53 \\ -16 \end{array}$$

and then go through the two steps illustrated at the top of the page. First write

$$\begin{array}{r} 50+3 \\ -(10+6), \end{array}$$

then write

$$\begin{array}{r} 40+13 \\ -(10+\ 6). \end{array}$$

Explain to the class that exercise 1c was written as $40+13$ because 6 cannot be subtracted from 3. Have some of the class members attempt to show the steps for $37-18$. Continue focusing attention on the regrouping ideas involved in such an exercise.

Study the example presented at the top of the page with the class. Tell them that the blue shading calls attention to the important points in each step. In the first step the students recognize that they cannot subtract 6 from 4. In step 2, 64 is written as 50 + 14. Note with them the 5 in the tens place and the 14 in the ones place. Note also the equation, 64 = 50 + 14, in the blue box at the bottom. Make sure the students see the relationship between this equation and the method shown in the exercise above it. Now call attention to step 3 in which 6 is subtracted from 14. Note the equation 14 − 6 = 8 and the vertical notation shown in the exercise. Observe with the students that in step 4 they think about 50 − 20. Then call attention to the equation and the step in the problem which is related to this equation. Finally, observe that 64 − 26 = 38.

When going over the discussion exercises, be sure to review each step carefully. Allow time for questions and class participation. If the students are ready, call on them to perform the steps and explain each step as they move along.

Now have all the students do exercise 1. When they have finished, discuss and present on the chalkboard several of these exercises before asking the students to complete the page.

Supplementary exercises, Set 23 (page 338) may be assigned as necessary beyond this page.

Subtraction: 2-digit numbers

Step 1	Step 2	Step 3	Step 4
64 −26	$^{5}_{6}$4 −26	$^{5}_{6}$4 −26 —— 8	$^{5}_{6}$4 −26 —— 38
4 − 6 = !!!	64 = 50 + 14	14 − 6 = 8	50 − 20 = 30

DISCUSSION EXERCISES

Explain the steps for these examples.

$^{6}_{7}$4 $^{5}_{6}$3 $^{4}_{5}$2 $^{7}_{8}$5
−28   −44   −17   −37
——   ——   ——   ——
46   19   35   48

EXERCISES

1. Cover the answers and work the problems, using the short cut.

[A] 74   [B] 52   [C] 92   [D] 83   [E] 61
−26   −35   −64   −27   −25
——   ——   ——   ——   ——
48   17   28   56   36

2. Check each answer in exercise 1 by addition.

3. Find the differences.

[A] 43   [B] 33   [C] 72   [D] 54   [E] 81
−16   −15   −44   −17   −23
——   ——   ——   ——   ——
27   18   28   37   58

[F] 68   [G] 42   [H] 95   [I] 76   [J] 69
−25   −19   −77   −38   −62
——   ——   ——   ——   ——
43   13   18   38   7

[K] 27   [L] 27   [M] 42   [N] 57   [O] 68
−17   −18   −38   −18   −29
——   ——   ——   ——   ——
10   9   4   39   39

[P] 90   [Q] 84   [R] 60   [S] 51   [T] 43
−34   −9   −23   −16   −38
——   ——   ——   ——   ——
56   75   37   35   5

[U] 50   [V] 80   [W] 67   [X] 52   [Y] 63
−16   −47   −30   −8   −36
——   ——   ——   ——   ——
34   33   37   44   27

Teaching Pages 74 and 75

- **PURPOSE**

   To introduce formally the process for subtraction with borrowing

   To provide word-problem experiences involving two-digit subtraction

   To provide experiences in working with charts

   To provide experiences leading to an understanding of graphing concepts

Figuring scores

The numbers given in the chart are the students' scores for each game. For example, Dan scored 47 points in game 3.

	Ann	Bill	Carol	Dan	Ed	Fay
Game 6	31	71	42	54	34	36
Game 5	63	18	43	64	29	67
Game 4	50	76	40	56	67	58
Game 3	39	43	72	47	34	52
Game 2	34	26	58	27	54	23
Game 1	28	27	62	81	60	47

1. [A] What did Bill score in game 5? *18*
   [B] What did Fay score in game 5? *67*
   [C] What did Dan score in game 6? *54*
   [D] What did Carol score in game 1? *62*
   [E] What did Ann score in game 2? *34*
   [F] What did Ed score in game 4? *67*
   [G] What did Ed score in game 3? *34*
   [H] What did Carol score in game 3? *72*

2. [A] Who had the highest score in game 5? *Fay*
   [B] Who had the lowest score in game 1? *Bill*
   [C] Which was Bill's highest score? *Game 4*   [D] Which was Ed's lowest score? *Game 5*

3. [A] Who had a score of 29? *Ed*   [B] In which game was this scored? *Game 5*

4. Give the student's name and the game number for these scores.
   [A] 40 [B] 31 [C] 52 [D] 60 [E] 23 [F] 63
   Carol,4 Ann,6 Fay,3 Ed,1 Fay,2 Ann,5

5. [A] In which game was the lowest score made? *Game 5*   [B] Who had this score? *Bill*

6. [A] Who had the highest score? *Dan*   [B] In which game was this scored? *Game 1*

7. How many points did Fay score in games 2 and 3 together? *75*

8. How many more points did Bill score in game 4 than in game 3? *33*

9. In game 6, whose score was [A] highest? *Ann's* [B] lowest? *Bill's*

10. In game 2, how many points did Carol and Dan score together? *85*

11. In game 5, how much less was Ed's score than Dan's? *35 less*

As you study with the class the material at the top of the page, call particular attention to Dan's score in game 3. Show the students how they trace across from the game-3 row to the column labeled "Dan" to arrive at 47. Explain that reading this table is much like reading a multiplication or addition table.

Following this discussion, give the students an opportunity to work the exercises. Allow time for a question-and-discussion period following completion of the exercises.

MATHEMATICS

The following figure gives an example of the concept of coordinate axes in the plane.

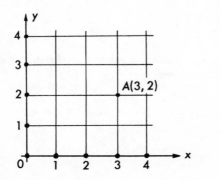

Notice in the figure that we find the coordinates of point *A* by moving vertically down to the reading of 3 on the *x*-axis and horizontally across to the reading of 2 on the *y-axis*. Notice how this idea is similar to the idea shown in the chart on page 75. When the students see that Dan scored 47 points in game 3, they are, in a sense, working with the idea associated with finding the coordinates of a given point in the plane.

PREPARATION

Conduct a short practice session in addition with carrying and subtraction with borrowing.

76 ADDING AND SUBTRACTING

Instruct the class to read the directions and work the exercises. When they have finished, have various students read their answers so that all may check their papers. As the answers are given, again emphasize that the dot, or point, separates the number of dollars from the number of cents.

Supplementary exercises, Set 24 (page 338) and Set 25 (page 339), may be assigned as necessary beyond this page.

Working with dollars and cents

1. Give the missing numbers.

Example: $5.28 means 5 dollars and 28 cents.

[A] $7.16 means ■ dollars and 16 cents. 7
[B] $4.75 means 4 dollars and ■ cents. 75
[C] $2.09 means ■ dollars and 9 cents. 2
[D] $17.34 means ■ dollars and ■ cents. 17, 34
[E] $6.05 means ■ dollars and ■ cents. 6, 5

2. Give the missing numbers.

Example: $4.38 is 438 cents.

[A] $6.52 is ■ cents 652 [D] $1.00 is ■ cents. 100 [G] $.50 is ■ cents.
[B] $1.27 is ■ cents 127 [E] $.76 is ■ cents. 76 [H] $2.86 is ■ cents.
[C] $6.09 is ■ cents 609 [F] $3.98 is ■ cents. 398 [I] $4.75 is ■ cents.

3. Find the total amounts.

Examples: $1.23 and $2.45 is $3.68.
$2.45 and $3.72 is $6.17.

[A] $2.14 and $1.53 is ■ $3.67   [D] $3.60 and $3.60 is ■ $7.2
[B] $5.21 and $2.37 is ■ $7.58   [E] $4.75 and $2.61 is ■ $7.3
[C] $3.50 and $3.50 is ■ $7.00   [F] $1.79 and $3.65 is ■ $5.4

4. Find the total amounts.

Example:	[A] $3.27	[B] $5.38	[C] $7.64
$5.68	4.61	1.25	1.75
2.71	$7.88	$6.63	$9.39
$8.39	[D] $2.76	[E] $3.79	[F] $9.72
	1.85	4.48	8.99
	$4.61	$8.27	$18.71

5. Find the difference in the amounts.

Example:	[A] $6.34	[B] $7.65	[C] $8.32
$5.27	1.52	2.24	4.18
1.43	$4.82	$5.41	$4.14
$3.84	[D] $9.21	[E] $12.72	[F] $10.64
	1.65	5.28	3.95
	$7.56	$7.44	$6.69

Teaching Pages 76 and 77

● **PURPOSE**

To provide experiences in working with dollar and cent notation

To provide a cumulative review of the material presented thus far in the text

Let's Review

- ADDITION
- SUBTRACTION
- MULTIPLICATION
- DIVISION
- MEASUREMENT
- PLACE VALUE
- INEQUALITIES
- PRINCIPLES

1. Four of these exercises are false. Which ones are they?

[A] $15 - 5 = 5$
[B] $26 + 7 > 30$
[C] $34 - 8 > 30$
[D] $39,427 > 38,998$
[E] $48 - 9 < 40$
[F] $48 - 19 > 30$
[G] $67 + 8 = 70 + 5$
[H] $48,265 = 48,165 + 1000$
[I] $528 = 500 + 20 + 8$

2. Find the sums and differences.

| [A] 8 +3 = 11 | [B] 9 −4 = 5 | [C] 7 +6 = 13 | [D] 12 −4 = 8 | [E] 11 −5 = 6 | [F] 4 +5 = 9 | [G] 10 −4 = 6 | [H] 8 +8 = 16 |

| [I] 17 −8 = 9 | [J] 6 +7 = 13 | [K] 10 −8 = 2 | [L] 7 +7 = 14 | [M] 3 +4 = 7 | [N] 13 −5 = 8 | [O] 7 +4 = 11 | [P] 12 −9 = 3 |

| [Q] 5 +8 = 13 | [R] 14 −5 = 9 | [S] 8 +7 = 15 | [T] 16 −9 = 7 | [U] 14 −6 = 8 | [V] 6 +6 = 12 | [W] 18 −9 = 9 | [X] 9 +4 = 13 |

3. Find the sums and differences.

| [A] 23 +65 = 88 | [B] 84 −51 = 33 | [C] 16 +32 = 48 | [D] 27 +62 = 89 | [E] 48 −23 = 25 | [F] 90 −20 = 70 |

| [G] 93 +34 = 127 | [H] 68 +60 = 128 | [I] 135 −82 = 53 | [J] 83 −25 = 58 | [K] 74 +17 = 91 | [L] 92 −27 = 65 |

4. Copy the problems and give the missing digits. *(See answers at right.)*

[A] 1▦ −6 = 11
[B] 26 +▦ = 34
[C] ▦6 +19 = 4▦
[D] 6▦ +▦7 = 91
[E] ▦▦ −47 = 16
[F] 72 −3▦ = ▦8

[G] 43▦ +2▦3 = ▦98
[H] 48▦ +▦54 = 9▦3
[I] 87▦ −▦63 = 6▦5
[J] 663 −▦47 = 4▦▦
[K] 934 −57▦ = ▦▦8
[L] 538 +▦6▦ = 9▦5

Answers, exercise 4, page 77

[A] 17 −6 = 11
[B] 26 +8 = 34
[C] 26 +19 = 45

[D] 64 +27 = 91
[E] 63 −47 = 16
[F] 72 −34 = 38

[G] 435 +263 = 698
[H] 489 +454 = 943
[I] 878 −263 = 615

[J] 663 −247 = 416
[K] 934 −576 = 358
[L] 538 +367 = 905

Instruct the students to work the exercises. When they have finished, allow time for checking papers. Note in particular with the class exercise 4, which requires finding certain missing digits. Give the students an opportunity to discuss these exercises in detail and to discuss how they arrived at their answers for the various digits.

PREPARATION

Select several exercises from page 76 and place them on the chalkboard. Work through these exercises with the class. You will notice that we avoid using plus or minus signs with this type of problem. We prefer to have the students think only of adding and subtracting *numbers* rather than *money*. Encourage the students to think of adding the numbers and then interpreting the answer according to the amount of money.

Do not elaborate on the decimal point in such exercises. You will simply want to indicate that this dot (or period, or point) separates the number of dollars from the number of cents. The student should understand this readily, and it is not likely that it will cause any difficulty. Later in the series, when decimal notation is explored more thoroughly, we point out the relationship between decimals and the symbols used to indicate amounts of money.

If you choose, this page may be used in part as an evaluation of the students' progress in the chapter. Because this chapter review is primarily on the processes of addition and subtraction with carrying and borrowing, it is not a complete instrument of evaluation. Your daily observations of the students' thinking processes and discoveries should be a key part of the total evaluation program.

Supplementary exercises, Sets 26 through 37 (pages 339–344) may be assigned as necessary beyond this page.

Chapter review

1. Find the sums and differences.

[A]
$$23 + 51 = 74$$
[B]
$$78 - 24 = 54$$
[C]
$$56 + 13 = 69$$
[D]
$$60 + 16 = 76$$
[E]
$$57 - 36 = 21$$

[F]
$$42 + 34 = 76$$
[G]
$$95 - 53 = 42$$
[H]
$$36 - 15 = 21$$
[I]
$$17 + 41 = 58$$
[J]
$$92 - 62 = 30$$

2. Find the sums and differences.

[A]
$$27 + 54 = 81$$
[B]
$$62 - 24 = 38$$
[C]
$$48 + 36 = 84$$
[D]
$$75 + 15 = 90$$
[E]
$$43 - 15 = 28$$
[F]
$$51 - 27 = 24$$

[G]
$$67 + 27 = 94$$
[H]
$$86 - 67 = 19$$
[I]
$$70 - 26 = 44$$
[J]
$$38 + 57 = 95$$
[K]
$$79 + 48 = 127$$
[L]
$$123 - 44 = 79$$

[M]
$$46 + 64 = 110$$
[N]
$$156 - 78 = 78$$
[O]
$$92 - 36 = 56$$
[P]
$$83 + 39 = 122$$
[Q]
$$118 - 39 = 79$$
[R]
$$77 + 23 = 100$$

3. Find the sums.

[A]
$$23 + 16 + 50 = 89$$
[B]
$$31 + 26 + 12 = 69$$
[C]
$$42 + 14 + 20 = 76$$
[D]
$$30 + 50 + 20 = 100$$
[E]
$$32 + 50 + 26 = 108$$
[F]
$$32 + 24 + 10 = 66$$

4. Find the differences.

[A]
$$326 - 114 = 212$$
[B]
$$9782 - 1542 = 8240$$
[C]
$$3641 - 1216 = 2425$$
[D]
$$4372 - 144 = 4228$$
[E]
$$6427 - 1309 = 5118$$

5. Find the sums.

[A]
$$36 + 47 + 10 = 93$$
[B]
$$26 + 38 + 12 = 76$$
[C]
$$57 + 33 + 19 = 109$$
[D]
$$28 + 39 + 17 = 84$$
[E]
$$56 + 78 + 89 = 223$$
[F]
$$78 + 25 + 96 = 199$$

★ **6.** Find the differences.

[A]
$$1682 - 427 = 1255$$
[B]
$$4728 - 1452 = 3276$$
[C]
$$3706 - 524 = 3182$$
[D]
$$8002 - 643 = 7359$$
[E]
$$7001 - 28 = 6973$$

Teaching Pages 78 and 79

● **PURPOSE**

To provide more experiences in addition and subtraction word problems

To provide a chapter review

● **PREPARATION**

Review any topics in the chapter with which the students have had particular difficulty.

Add or subtract?

In these exercises no numbers are given. You should decide whether you would add or subtract if numbers were given.

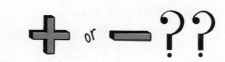

EXERCISES

Answer *A* if you would **add** to answer the question. Answer *S* if you would **subtract.** Think carefully before giving your answer.

1. Joe had ▓ tickets. He gave ▓ to Tom. How many did he have left? *S*

2. Jane counted ▓ cars on one train and ▓ cars on another. How many did she count in all? *A*

3. Sue had ▓ cents. She spent ▓ cents for an apple. How much did she have left? *S*

4. Tom is ▓ years old, and Jim is ▓. How much younger is Jim than Tom? *S*

5. Susan spent ▓ cents for a sandwich and ▓ cents for milk. How much did she spend? *A*

6. In Jane's class there are ▓ students. There are ▓ boys in the class. How many girls are in Jane's class? *S*

7. Tim checked ▓ books out of the library. Later he returned ▓ of the books. How many did he still have? *S*

8. Beth and Sara have ▓ dollars in all. Sara has ▓ dollars. How many dollars does Beth have? *S*

9. Jack read ▓ pages in his book. He has ▓ pages yet to read. How many pages are in the book? *A*

10. Ann said, "▓ years ago, I was ▓ years old." How old is Ann now? *A*

DIRECTIONS **PAGE 79**

Have the students read the material at the top of the page. Emphasize again that the exercises on this page contain no numbers and that the task is not to find a correct number answer but to decide which operation would be performed if the numbers were given. Stress the fact that the students are to use reasoning.

Following this discussion, give the students an opportunity to work the first two exercises. When they have finished, discuss these two exercises and point out the clues which tell whether to add or subtract. Ask the students to complete the page. Allow time at the end for discussion of the exercises.

Teaching
Geometry Lesson 3

- **PURPOSE**

  To provide further experiences in working with circles

  To introduce the concept of diameter

  To show that three points not on one line determine exactly one circle

We begin the lesson by giving the students an opportunity to draw circles with diameters of given sizes. As illustrated on the first page of the lesson, the method for doing this is quite simple.

Following this, the students are given a technique for drawing a circle through three points. Of course, the accuracy with which the students draw the circle through three points depends upon the care taken in the folding of the paper. If some students fold the paper inaccurately and arrive at a circle that does not quite contain the three points, explain that more careful folding would give them better results.

- **MATHEMATICS**

This lesson is merely an extension of the idea presented in Geometry Lesson 2: to draw a circle through two points, we find the line which is the perpendicular bisector of the segment determined by these two points. That is, by using any point on the perpendicular bisector, we can adjust a compass so that the circle contains both points.

When considering three points, we need consider only the three points as two pairs. For example, if we are considering points *A*, *B*, and *C*, we can consider the pair *AB* and the pair *AC*. In doing this, we consider first the perpendicular bisector of *AB* and then the perpendicular bisector of *AC*. Since any point on the respective perpendicular bisectors will contain the two points, we need to look only at the point that is on both perpendicular bisectors. That is, the point on both perpendicular bisectors should be the center point of a circle which will contain all three points.

GEOMETRY - Lesson 3

3 points and a circle

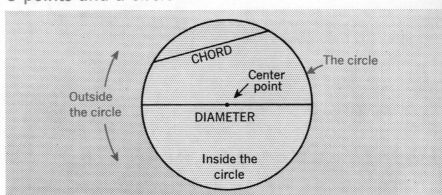

Here is one way to draw a circle with a 2-inch diameter.

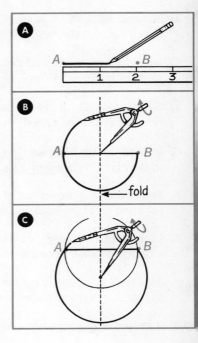

1. [A] Mark points *A* and *B* 2 inches apart. Then draw the segment from *A* to *B*.

   [B] Now use your compass as shown in the picture to draw a circle through points *A* and *B*. Your circle should have a 2-inch **diameter.**

   [C] Put the tip of your compass at a different point on the fold. Now you can draw a circle that has a 2-inch **chord** through points *A* and *B*.

2. Draw a circle with a 3-inch diameter.

3. Draw a circle with a 3-inch chord.

4. Draw a circle with a 10-centimeter diameter.

5. Draw a circle with a 10-centimeter chord.

★ 6. Find a different way to draw a circle with a 2-inch diameter.

   Draw a circle with a 1-inch radius.

80

100

You know how to draw a circle through 2 points. Can you draw a circle that goes through 3 points?

7. Mark 3 points (not lined up) on your paper. Try to draw a circle that goes through all 3 points.

Does your paper look like either of these?

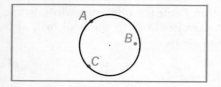

This is not close enough.   This took a lot of guessing.

Here is a way to draw a circle through 3 points **without guessing.**

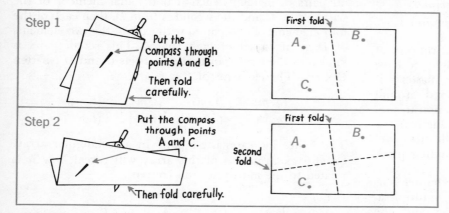

When you place the tip of your compass on the first fold, you can draw a circle through points *A* and *B*. When you place your compass on the second fold, you can draw a circle through points *A* and *C*. Where could you place the tip of your compass to draw a circle through all 3 points? *At the point where the folds intersect.*

8. Mark 3 points on your paper. Use the steps shown above to draw a circle through all 3 points.

9. How many different circles do you think can be drawn through all 3 points?
Only one circle can be drawn.

As in the other geometry lessons, mastery of the concepts of the lesson does not rank as a major objective. Enter into the lesson in the spirit of adventure and discovery. It is most important that these geometry lessons be pleasant experiences for the students.

Observe with the students the circle and the various items labeled in the figure at the top of page 80. Call particular attention to the diameter, which goes through the center point of the circle. Note also the chord. Observe with the class that a diameter can be thought of as a special chord that goes through the center.

Study with the students the method described for drawing a circle with a two-inch diameter and then have them do this on their papers. Following this, direct the students to do exercises 2 through 6.

Have the students follow the instructions given in exercise 7. Direct the students carefully in the four-step method shown for drawing a circle through three points. First, note that they are to mark on their papers three points which are not all in one line. Work carefully through the paper-folding activity with the students. When they have finished, tell them that their papers should look like the paper in the fourth box of the illustration. Point out that the center of the circle containing points *A*, *B*, and *C* should be where the two folds cross. Elicit from the students the reasons why the intersection of the two folds should be the center of the circle. Attempt to get them to state that the first fold should give the center points for circles containing *A* and *B*, and the second fold should give the center points for circles containing *A* and *C*. Therefore, the intersection of the two folds should be the center point of a circle containing all three points.

Have the students complete exercises 8 and 9.

Objectives of Chapter 4

To introduce the concept of multiplication

To associate products with groups of equivalent sets

To associate products with product sets

To associate multiplication with repeated addition

To associate multiplication with the number line and skip counting

To provide word-problems in multiplication

To work toward mastery of multiplication facts

To introduce some basic multiplication principles

To introduce an element of logic in finding products

The main emphasis of Chapter 4 is on the concept of multiplication, but we also expect most students to have attained, by the end of the chapter, a fair mastery of multiplication facts. The content is centered around several different interpretations of multiplication to provide a broad perspective that will help strengthen the students' over-all understanding of multiplication concepts, as well as give them more tools for finding products.

The organization for the early part of the chapter is as follows: multiplication and equivalent sets, multiplication and repeated addition, multiplication and the number line, multiplication and pairing (product sets).

A key feature of this chapter is the utilization of previously developed concepts in building mastery of multiplication facts. The lesson in which students are introduced to all the multiplication facts by means of the multiplication table clearly illustrates this point. By examining the multiplication table and only those facts which are necessary, the students see how an understanding of previously developed concepts can aid in mastery of seemingly routine factual information. Of course, we recognize fully that one cannot escape the necessity for a certain amount of memorization; the students eventually must learn the facts. However, knowledge of certain concepts and basic principles will greatly reduce the number of facts that one must know.

Of course, it may not be reasonable to expect every student to master all the multiplication facts by the end of this chapter. Those who do not will be given additional opportunities throughout the book to increase their skill with multiplication facts. Most students should have an adequate command of multiplication facts by the time they reach Chapter 8, which presents the multiplication algorithm. It is essential that they be familiar with the multiplication facts when they study the division algorithm, Chapter 9. Here, again, we recognize that some of the less able students will not attain these goals, but they will gain a great deal from an exposure to these more advanced ideas which rely on the facts.

You may wish to provide additional drill for those students who do not master the multiplication facts. Perhaps a multiplication table for reference while working the more difficult exercises later in the book will also be necessary for these students.

Mathematics of Chapter 4

We begin the study of multiplication by defining an operation on sets. Consider two sets, $C = \{q, r, s, t\}$ and $D = \{m, n\}$. If you determine from these sets the set of all pairs of elements such that the first member of the pair is from C and the second is from D, then each of the four elements of C is paired with each of the two elements of D giving a set of eight pairs. This set of pairs is known as the *Cartesian product* of sets C and D (written $C \times D$). The elements of $C \times D$ are:

$$(q, m), \quad (r, m), \quad (s, m), \quad (t, m),$$
$$(q, n), \quad (r, n), \quad (s, n), \quad (t, n).$$

The figure indicates these pairs in a rectangular array. Careful examination of this array will reveal how it is related to the multiplication concept.

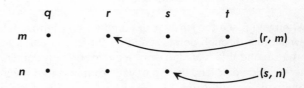

The Cartesian product $C \times D$ has eight elements (pairs); eight is the product of four and two. The numbers four and two are called the *factors* of eight, and eight is a *multiple* of each of these numbers.

The product $D \times C$ is obtained by changing the order of the members in each pair of $C \times D$. Thus $C \times D$ and $D \times C$ have the same number of pairs. This illustrates the order principle for multiplication. We demonstrate this principle for students by having them consider rectangular arrays, first by rows, then by columns.

Teaching Chapter 4

To demonstrate equivalent sets and rectangular arrays, you can use diagrams on the chalkboard as well as set materials. However, you should have suitable set materials available for demonstrating ideas of product sets. An example would be two cups and three saucers (all of different colors). Demonstrating the various color combinations obtained by putting each cup with three saucers illustrates the product 2×3. As you put the cups with the saucers, record the color combinations on the chalkboard to show that there are six different combinations in all and that $2 \times 3 = 6$.

Plan to cover this material in about four weeks. You may need to adjust this time schedule slightly depending upon the background of the students.

To determine whether the students understand how multiplication is related to the various concepts developed in the chapter, you should carefully watch each student's participation in and contribution to the lessons. In evaluating whether the students have mastered the multiplication combinations, you should place a certain premium on the speed with which they arrive at various products. That is, some students may be able to find a product such as 6×7 by using repeated addition. This is fine, but it would not prove mastery of the given combination. Of course, students who can do the repeated addition and have not mastered the combination should not be discouraged; it is important that they have some method for finding products. However, encourage them to master the combinations so that they need not continue to rely on slower methods of addition.

Following the introduction of product sets, a relationship is developed between product sets and rectangular arrays. Do not expect all students to see this relationship. However, do emphasize the fact that they can think about product sets in much the same way as they think about rectangular arrays. As the students become more knowledgeable and are able to handle more and more abstract mathematical concepts, the relationship between product sets and rectangular arrays will become apparent.

Study with the students the material at the top of the page. Give them an opportunity to discuss each statement and its relationship to the set pictures. Have the students work the exercises. When they have finished, again discuss the ideas involved.

Answers, exercises 1 and 2, page 82

1. [A] 3
   [B] 7
   [C] 21
   [D] $7 + 7 + 7 = 21$
   [E] $3 \times 7 = 21$

2. [A] 4
   [B] 3
   [C] 12
   [D] $3 + 3 + 3 + 3 = 12$
   [E] $4 \times 3 = 12$

Chapter **4** **MULTIPLICATION**

The meaning of multiplication

We can think about multiplication like this.

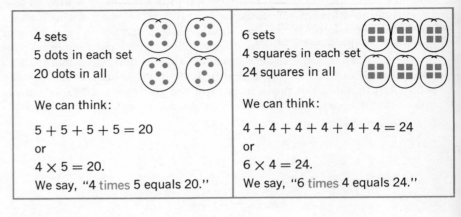

4 sets	6 sets
5 dots in each set	4 squares in each set
20 dots in all	24 squares in all
We can think:	We can think:
$5 + 5 + 5 + 5 = 20$	$4 + 4 + 4 + 4 + 4 + 4 = 24$
or	or
$4 \times 5 = 20.$	$6 \times 4 = 24.$
We say, "4 times 5 equals 20."	We say, "6 times 4 equals 24."

EXERCISES

(See answers at left.)

1. [A] How many sets?
   [B] How many triangles in each set?
   [C] How many triangles in all?
   [D] Write an addition equation about the sets.
   [E] Write a multiplication equation about the sets.

2. [A] How many sets?
   [B] How many squares in each set?
   [C] How many squares in all?
   [D] Write an addition equation about the sets.
   [E] Write a multiplication equation about the sets.

82

Teaching **Pages 82 and 83**

- **PURPOSE**

  To introduce multiplication as it is associated with groups of equivalent sets

  To relate multiplication to repeated addition

- **MATHEMATICS**

  We relate multiplication to groups of equivalent sets and use this relationship as a basic definition of multiplication because it is an extremely simple idea, easily grasped by students. From this basic definition, the students can readily relate multiplication to repeated addition, skip counting, and number-line activities. Later in the chapter, multiplication is related to product sets, and then product sets are related to rectangular arrays.

- **PREPARATION**

  Present some demonstrations of groups of equivalent sets and related multiplication equations. You can do this by drawing groups of equivalent sets on the chalkboard or by exhibiting sets of objects grouped in a special way. Be sure to accompany each set demonstration with the related multiplication equation.

  The phraseology, "three fives are 15" (rather than exclusively saying, "three times five equals 15"), may help some students understand the association of a multiplication

3. Write an addition and a multiplication equation for each exercise.

[A]

[B]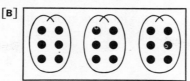

$2+2+2+2+2+2+2=14, 7 \times 2=14$ $6+6+6=18, 3 \times 6=18$

4. Draw the sets. Then write an addition and a multiplication equation for each exercise. *(See answers at right.)*

[A] 2 sets of 8   [D] 3 sets of 3   [G] 3 sets of 7
[B] 4 sets of 2   [E] 5 sets of 4   [H] 4 sets of 6
[C] 6 sets of 3   [F] 2 sets of 5   [I] 2 sets of 6

5. Write a multiplication equation for each exercise.

[A] $4+4+4=12$ $3 \times 4=12$ [F] $6+6=12$ $2 \times 6=12$
[B] $2+2+2+2=8$ $4 \times 2=8$ [G] $8+8+8+8=32$ $4 \times 8=32$
[C] $5+5+5=15$ $3 \times 5=15$ [H] $4+4+4+4+4=20$ $5 \times 4=20$
[D] $3+3+3+3+3+3=18$ [I] $6+6+6+6=24$ $4 \times 6=24$
[E] $7+7+7=21$ $6 \times 3=18$ [J] $1+1+1+1+1=5$ $5 \times 1=5$

$3 \times 7 =21$

6. Write an addition equation for each exercise. *(See answers at right.)*

[A] $6 \times 3=18$ [E] $4 \times 6=24$ [I] $7 \times 2=14$
[B] $2 \times 7=14$ [F] $3 \times 12=36$ [J] $4 \times 8=32$
[C] $3 \times 4=12$ [G] $4 \times 10=40$ [K] $3 \times 6=18$
[D] $3 \times 2=6$ [H] $5 \times 6=30$ [L] $5 \times 4=20$

7. Write an addition equation for these sets. $3+3+3+2=11$

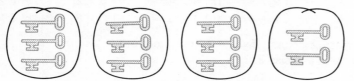

8. Why is it not correct to write the multiplication equation $4 \times 3=12$ for the sets in exercise 7? *Because there are 3 sets of 3 and 1 set of 2, instead of 4 sets of 3.*

★ **9.** Write an equation that is correct for the sets in exercise 7. Use multiplication **and** addition. $(3 \times 3)+2=11$

---

equation with groups of equivalent sets. The phrase "three fives" suggests the idea of three sets of five. Use this language frequently in the beginning. However, make the transition to the language "three times five" as the students become accustomed to the ideas of multiplication.

Instruct the students to work these exercises on their own. Allow time for questions and discussion of the exercises when they have finished.

Exercise 9 is designed primarily for the more able students. Notice that the answer to exercise 9, $(3 \times 3) + 2 = 11$, involves the use of parentheses. To arrive at an answer of 11 using an equation containing both multiplication and addition, one must consider multiplying three times three and then adding two. If the parentheses were around $3 + 2$, we would have $3 \times (3 + 2) = 3 \times 5 = 15$. This, of course, would not be representative of the set picture in exercise 8. If a student writes $3 \times 3 + 2 = 11$, simply point out that we need parentheses to tell which operation to do first.

Answers, exercises 4 and 6, page 83

4. [A] $8 + 8 = 16$
      $2 \times 8 = 16$
   [B] $2 + 2 + 2 + 2 = 8$
      $4 \times 2 = 8$
   [C] $3 + 3 + 3 + 3 + 3 + 3 = 18$
      $6 \times 3 = 18$
   [D] $3 + 3 + 3 = 9$
      $3 \times 3 = 9$
   [E] $4 + 4 + 4 + 4 + 4 = 20$
      $5 \times 4 = 20$
   [F] $5 + 5 = 10$
      $2 \times 5 = 10$
   [G] $7 + 7 + 7 = 21$
      $3 \times 7 = 21$
   [H] $6 + 6 + 6 + 6 = 24$
      $4 \times 6 = 24$
   [I] $6 + 6 = 12$
      $2 \times 6 = 12$

6. [A] $3 + 3 + 3 + 3 + 3 + 3 = 18$
   [B] $7 + 7 = 14$
   [C] $4 + 4 + 4 = 12$
   [D] $2 + 2 + 2 = 6$
   [E] $6 + 6 + 6 + 6 = 24$
   [F] $12 + 12 + 12 = 36$
   [G] $10 + 10 + 10 + 10 = 40$
   [H] $6 + 6 + 6 + 6 + 6 = 30$
   [I] $2 + 2 + 2 + 2 + 2 + 2 + 2 = 14$
   [J] $8 + 8 + 8 + 8 = 32$
   [K] $6 + 6 + 6 = 18$
   [L] $4 + 4 + 4 + 4 + 4 = 20$

Study with the class the material at the top of the page. Emphasize the words *product* and *factor*. Have the students work the first two exercises. When they have finished, allow time for discussion and focus additional attention on the word *product*. Now have the students complete the page. When they have finished, allow time for discussion and questions. During the discussion re-emphasize the word *factor*.

Products and factors

In the multiplication equation $4 \times 7 = 28$, the number 28 is called the product of 4 and 7.

$$4 \times 7 = 28 \leftarrow \text{product}$$

The numbers 4 and 7 are called factors of 28.

$$\underset{\uparrow}{4} \times \underset{\uparrow}{7} = 28$$
$$\text{factor} \quad \text{factor}$$

EXERCISES

1. [A] In $3 \times 5 = 15$, the number 15 is the product of what numbers? *3 and 5*
   [B] In $4 \times 3 = 12$, what is the number 12 called? *the product*
   [C] In $6 \times 7 = 42$, the number 42 is the product of what numbers? *6 and 7*
   [D] In $8 \times 9 = 72$, what is the number 72 called? *the product*
   [E] In $3 \times 5 = 15$, the numbers 3 and 5 are factors of what number? *15*
   [F] In $4 \times 3 = 12$, what are the numbers 4 and 3 called? *factors*
   [G] In $6 \times 7 = 42$, the numbers 6 and 7 are factors of what number? *42*
   [H] In $8 \times 9 = 72$, what are the numbers 8 and 9 called? *factors*

2. Find the product. Then write a multiplication equation.
   [A] $2 \times 3 = 6$ [E] $2 \times 6 = 12$ [I] $3 \times 3 = 9$ [M] $5 \times 3 = 15$ [Q] $3 \times 8 = 2$
   [B] $4 \times 3 = 12$ [F] $2 \times 7 = 14$ [J] $2 \times 2 = 4$ [N] $3 \times 4 = 12$ [R] $4 \times 1 = 4$
   [C] $2 \times 5 = 10$ [G] $3 \times 7 = 21$ [K] $4 \times 4 = 16$ [O] $5 \times 2 = 10$ [S] $2 \times 4 = 8$
   [D] $3 \times 5 = 15$ [H] $3 \times 6 = 18$ [L] $4 \times 5 = 20$ [P] $2 \times 8 = 16$ [T] $1 \times 6 = 6$

3. Find the missing factors. If you need help, look at the factors and products in exercise 2.
   [A] $2 \times \blacksquare = 4$ *2*   [F] $3 \times \blacksquare = 12$ *4*   [K] $4 \times \blacksquare = 4$ *1*
   [B] $3 \times \blacksquare = 6$ *2*   [G] $\blacksquare \times 5 = 15$ *3*   [L] $\blacksquare \times 2 = 8$ *4*
   [C] $2 \times \blacksquare = 10$ *5*   [H] $3 \times \blacksquare = 15$ *5*   [M] $1 \times \blacksquare = 6$ *6*
   [D] $\blacksquare \times 6 = 12$ *2*   [I] $4 \times \blacksquare = 16$ *4*   [N] $4 \times \blacksquare = 12$ *3*
   [E] $\blacksquare \times 3 = 9$ *3*   [J] $\blacksquare \times 8 = 16$ *2*   [O] $\blacksquare \times 2 = 10$ *5*

Teaching Pages 84 and 85

- **PURPOSE**

  To introduce the order principle for multiplication

  To focus further attention on the relationship between rectangular arrays and products

  To introduce the idea of factors

- **MATHEMATICS**

  Rectangular arrays are quite useful for investigating principles of multiplication. As shown in the figure below, each row or each column can be considered as a set.

The order principle for multiplication

We can think about 15 dots in two different ways.

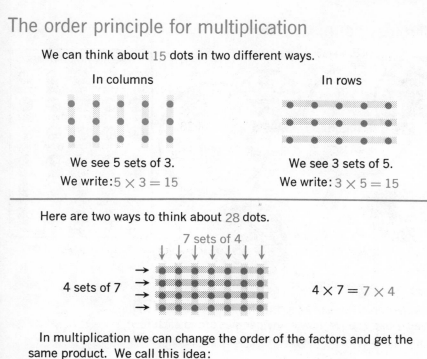

In columns	In rows
We see 5 sets of 3.	We see 3 sets of 5.
We write: $5 \times 3 = 15$	We write: $3 \times 5 = 15$

Here are two ways to think about 28 dots.

7 sets of 4

4 sets of 7

$4 \times 7 = 7 \times 4$

In multiplication we can change the order of the factors and get the same product. We call this idea:

The **ORDER** principle for multiplication.

EXERCISES

1. Write 2 multiplication equations for each set.

[A]   [B]   [C]   [D]

[A] $6 \times 3 = 18, 3 \times 6 = 18$ [B] $5 \times 2 = 10, 2 \times 5 = 10$ [C] $5 \times 4 = 20, 4 \times 5 = 20$ [D] $6 \times 5 = 30, 5 \times 6 = 30$

2. Solve the equations.

[A] $5 \times 4 = 4 \times \blacksquare$ 5   [C] $\blacksquare \times 7 = 7 \times 8$ 8   [E] $853 \times \blacksquare = 324 \times 853$ 324

[B] $9 \times 8 = \blacksquare \times 9$ 8   [D] $6 \times \blacksquare = 9 \times 6$ 9   [F] $976 \times 345 = 976 \times \blacksquare$ 345

3 sets of 4   4 sets of 3

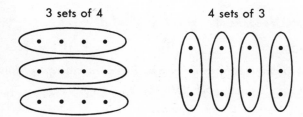

This illustrates the order (commutative) principle for multiplication: if a and b are whole numbers, then

$$a \times b = b \times a.$$

Study and discuss the material at the top of the page with the students. Encourage them to participate actively in the discussion of these ideas. Point out to the students that "the order principle for multiplication" is the name of the idea you have been discussing. The students should be quite familiar with the idea of the order principle, although they have not previously applied it to multiplication. Following this, have the students work the exercises at the bottom of the page.

● **PREPARATION**

Draw on the chalkboard a set of objects arranged in a rectangular array. You might begin by choosing a four-by-three array (four rows with three objects in each row). Call the students' attention to the four rows with three objects in each row. Have one of the students relate this to the idea of four sets of three; then write the multiplication equation $4 \times 3 = 12$. Now call attention to the columns and notice with the students that there are three columns with four objects in each column and that they can think of three sets of four. Exhibit the multiplication equation $3 \times 4 = 12$. Following this, observe with the students that $4 \times 3 = 3 \times 4$.

Ask the students to study the illustrations at the top of the page. Give them an opportunity to discuss the various coins and the markings before directing them to work the exercises. Note that exercise 6 is designed for the more able students. Following the completion of the exercises, allow time for discussion and questions.

Collecting pennies

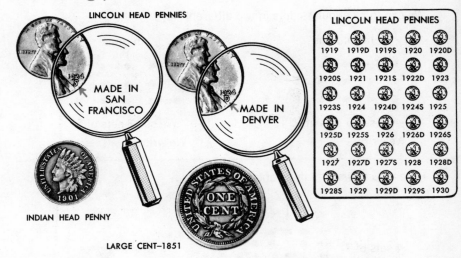

LINCOLN HEAD PENNIES

MADE IN SAN FRANCISCO

MADE IN DENVER

INDIAN HEAD PENNY

LARGE CENT—1851

LINCOLN HEAD PENNIES				
1919	1919D	1919S	1920	1920D
1920S	1921	1921S	1922D	1923
1923S	1924	1924D	1924S	1925
1925D	1925S	1926	1926D	1926S
1927	1927D	1927S	1928	1928D
1928S	1929	1929D	1929S	1930

1. Some coin collectors keep their coins in a folder. In the folder page above, how many pennies are in each row? *5* How many rows are there? How many pennies in all? *6,30*

2. In the folder page above, how many pennies are in each column? How many columns are there? How many *6, 5* pennies in all? *30*

3. Jim collects pennies. He made wrappers for some of his extra pennies. He decided to put 5 pennies in each roll. He put 4 rolls of pennies in a box. How many pennies did he put in the box? *20*

COINS

4. Coin collectors often pay more than 1 cent for certain pennies. Jim's book lists the value of a new 1961**D** penny as 5 cents. Jim has three 1961**D** pennies. How much are they worth? *15¢*

5. Jim had 3 rows of Indian Head pennies with 6 in each row. How many Indian Head pennies did he have? *18*

★6. Suppose a 1962**D** penny is worth 5 cents and a 1959 penny is worth 10 cents. Which is worth more, five 1962**D** pennies or three 1959 pennies?

Teaching Pages 86 and 87

● **PURPOSE**

To provide word-problem experiences in multiplication
To provide more work with coins

● **PREPARATION**

Review with the students the association of multiplication and rectangular arrays. Exhibit several arrays on the chalkboard and have the students write multiplication equations for these arrays.

Collecting dimes

MADE IN SAN FRANCISCO

MADE IN DENVER

ROOSEVELT DIME

LIBERTY DIME

MERCURY HEAD DIMES

1926	1926S	1926D	1927	1927S
1927D	1928	1928S	1928D	1929
1929S	1929D	1930	1930S · 1931	
1931S	1931D	1934	1934D	1935
1935S	1935D	1936	1936S	1936D

1. In the folder page, how many dimes are in each row? *5*
   How many rows are there? How many dimes in all? *5, 25*

2. There are 3 pages in each folder. Bill has 7 folders.
   How many pages does Bill have in his folders? *21*

3. Bill put 10 dimes in a roll.
   How many cents is the roll worth? *100¢*   → 10 dimes ? Cents

4. Bill put 4 rolls in a box. How many dimes did Bill put in the box? *40*

5. Ted had 6 rows of Liberty dimes with 3 dimes in each row.
   How many Liberty dimes did he have? *18*

6. 15,840,000 Mercury dimes were made in San Francisco in 1935.
   159,130,000 Mercury dimes were made in Philadelphia in 1945.
   Which of these dimes do you think Jim is most likely to find?
   The 1945 dimes, because there are about 10 times as many.

★ 7. One page has spaces for 7 rows of Roosevelt dimes with 4 dimes
   in each row. There are only 7 empty spaces. How many Roosevelt
   dimes are on the page? *21*

DIRECTIONS PAGE 87

Study and discuss with the students the illustrations at the top of the page. Allow time to discuss the exercises when the students have completed the page. Note that exercise 7 is designed primarily for the more able students.

Read and study with the students the material at the top of the page. During your discussion, emphasize the relation between the sum of 4 threes and 4×3 and also between the sum of 3 sevens and 3×7. Following this discussion, have the students work the exercises. Allow time for checking papers and answering questions when they have finished.

Answers, exercise 3, page 88

[A] $9 + 9 = 18$
$2 \times 9 = 18$

[B] $2 + 2 + 2 + 2 + 2 + 2 +$
$\qquad 2 + 2 + 2 = 18$
$9 \times 2 = 18$

[C] $7 + 7 + 7 = 21$
$3 \times 7 = 21$

[D] $3 + 3 + 3 + 3 + 3 + 3 + 3 = 21$
$7 \times 3 = 21$

[E] $4 + 4 + 4 + 4 = 16$
$4 \times 4 = 16$

[F] $4 + 4 + 4 + 4 + 4 = 20$
$5 \times 4 = 20$

Multiplication and repeated addition

Addition helps us find products. Look at 4 sets of 3.

$3 + 3 + 3 + 3 = 12$

Since 4 threes are 12, we write: $4 \times 3 = 12$

If we want to find the product of 3×7, we can think: $7 + 7 + 7 = 21$.

Since 3 sevens are 21, we see that $3 \times 7 = 21$.

EXERCISES

1. Find the sums.

[A] $7 + 7 + 7$ 21   [D] $3 + 3 + 3 + 3$ 12   [G] $9 + 9 + 9$ 27
[B] $6 + 6 + 6 + 6$ 24   [E] $4 + 4 + 4 + 4 + 4$ 20   [H] $12 + 12 + 12$ 36
[C] $2 + 2 + 2 + 2 + 2$ 10   [F] $8 + 8$ 16   [I] $23 + 23 + 23$ 69

2. Find the products. (Look at exercise 1.)

[A] 3×7 21   [C] 5×2 10   [E] 5×4 20   [G] 3×9 27   [I] 3×23 69
[B] 4×6 24   [D] 4×3 12   [F] 2×8 16   [H] 3×12 36   [J] 3×10 30

3. Write an addition and a multiplication equation for each exercise. *(see answers at left.)*

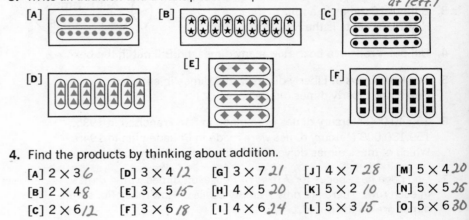

[A]   [B]   [C]   [D]   [E]   [F]

4. Find the products by thinking about addition.

[A] 2×3 6   [D] 3×4 12   [G] 3×7 21   [J] 4×7 28   [M] 5×4 20
[B] 2×4 8   [E] 3×5 15   [H] 4×5 20   [K] 5×2 10   [N] 5×5 25
[C] 2×6 12   [F] 3×6 18   [I] 4×6 24   [L] 5×3 15   [O] 5×6 30

Teaching Pages 88 and 89

- **PURPOSE**

  To focus further attention on repeated addition and its relationship to multiplication

  To provide practice in working with products

  To provide more word-problem experiences

- **MATHEMATICS**

  Relating repeated addition to multiplication is quite simple once we take as our basic working definition the idea of relating multiplication to groups of equivalent sets. In relating multiplication to these sets, we consider

Throwing darts

Ken made a dart board.

1. The first time he threw 6 darts,
the board looked like this.
Nancy was scorekeeper. She wrote
$2 + 2 + 2 + 2 + 2 = 10$.
Ken found his score by multiplication.
Give the multiplication problem Ken worked. *5 × 2 = 10*

2. When Sue's turn came, she threw 3 darts in the blue
center. She missed the board with the other 3 darts.
What was Sue's score? *24*

3. In one game Bob threw all 6 darts in the black ring.
What was his score? *24*

4. Jane threw 3 darts. Her score was 14. Where did the
darts land? *1 dart landed in each ring.*

5. John threw 3 darts. His score was 12. Where could his
darts have landed? *3 darts in black ring. 1 dart in center, 1 in the black
ring, 1 missed board. 2 darts in the white ring, 1 in the center.*

EXERCISES

1. Tell which mark (>, =, or <) should be placed in the ⬤.

[A] 3×4 ⬤ $4 + 4 + 4$ =   [F] 4×3 ⬤ $4 + 4 + 4$ =   [K] 2×5 ⬤ $5 + 5$ =
[B] 3×4 ⬤ 2×4 >   [G] 80 ⬤ 9×10 <   [L] $6 + 6$ ⬤ 3×6 <
[C] 4×7 ⬤ 4×6 >   [H] 6×7 ⬤ 7×6 =   [M] 4×5 ⬤ 5×4 =
[D] 6×7 ⬤ 7×7 <   [I] 4×8 ⬤ 4×7 >   [N] 4×5 ⬤ 10×10 <
[E] 8×9 ⬤ 7×9 >   [J] 700 ⬤ 7×100 =   [O] 3×5 ⬤ 4×5 <

2. Solve the equations.

[A] $8 + 7 = n$ *15*   [D] $14 - 7 = n$ *7*   [G] $3 \times 7 = n$ *21*   [J] $2 \times 9 = n$ *18*
[B] $12 - 5 = n$ *7*   [E] $4 \times 4 = n$ *16*   [H] $87 - 7 = n$ *80*   [K] $17 - 8 = n$ *9*
[C] $6 + 6 = n$ *12*   [F] $12 + 7 = n$ *19*   [I] $4 \times 6 = n$ *24*   [L] $12 + 7 = n$ *19*

★ **3.** Solve the equations.

[A] $(4 \times 6) + (6 \times 6) = n$ *60*   [C] $(2 \times 9) + (8 \times 9) = n$ *90*
[B] $(3 \times 8) + (7 \times 8) = n$ *80*   [D] $(7 \times 7) + (3 \times 7) = n$ *70*

the total number of objects involved, or form the union
of the sets involved.

Of course, the idea of union is related to that of addition, which automatically leads to the interpretation of
multiplication as repeated addition. The chief problem
in such an interpretation comes when one attempts to
work with products involving zero and one. However, at
this stage, the students are working primarily with the
ideas of multiplication that do not involve factors of zero
and one. As it turns out, repeated addition will not be
considered when there is a first factor of zero or one, since
addition is an operation performed on two numbers and
it makes no sense to speak of adding 0 threes or of adding
1 three.

Have the students work the exercises. When they have finished, discuss the word problems and allow
time for checking the other exercises. Note that exercise 3 at the
bottom of the page is designed primarily for the more able students.

● **PREPARATION**

Exhibit some rectangular arrays on the chalkboard and
then show the repeated addition equations associated with
these arrays. (For an example, refer to the top of page 88.)
The students will quickly see that adding 4 threes is the
same as multiplying four times three. Exhibit other arrays
and give the students an opportunity to write the addition
and multiplication equations associated with these arrays.

Read and study the material at the top of the page with the class. Give them a chance to discuss the examples shown. Call attention in particular to the three jumps of six associated with the equations $6 + 6 + 6 = 18$ and $3 \times 6 = 18$. Do this also for the second example. Following this, have the students complete exercise 1.

Multiplication and the number line

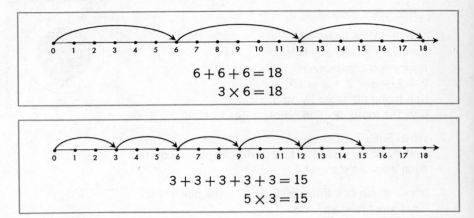

$$6 + 6 + 6 = 18$$
$$3 \times 6 = 18$$

$$3 + 3 + 3 + 3 + 3 = 15$$
$$5 \times 3 = 15$$

EXERCISES

1. Write an addition and a multiplication equation for each number-line picture.

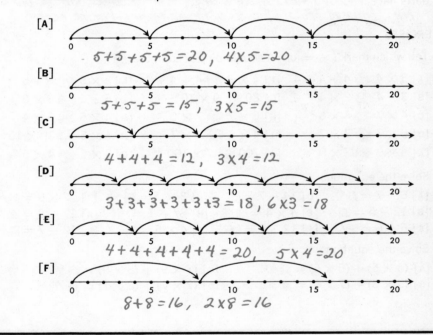

[A] $5+5+5+5=20, \quad 4 \times 5 = 20$

[B] $5+5+5=15, \quad 3 \times 5 = 15$

[C] $4+4+4=12, \quad 3 \times 4 = 12$

[D] $3+3+3+3+3+3=18, \quad 6 \times 3 = 18$

[E] $4+4+4+4+4=20, \quad 5 \times 4 = 20$

[F] $8+8=16, \quad 2 \times 8 = 16$

Teaching Pages 90 and 91

- **PURPOSE**

  To show and interpret the multiplication concept on the number line

  To relate multiplication to skip counting

- **PREPARATION**

  Exhibit on the chalkboard a number line with a sufficient number of points labeled to illustrate several multiplication equations. Show the addition and the multiplication equation related to each number-line picture. Give the students an opportunity to participate in this activity by drawing the skips on the number line and

2. Turn your paper sideways, as shown here. Draw a line 10 inches long and mark every half inch. Now label the points, starting at the left with 0. If you like, you can label every fifth point, as in exercise 1.

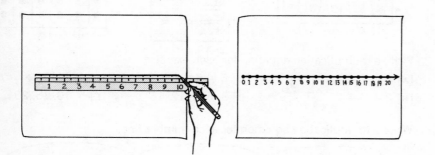

Now show these equations on your number line.

$5 + 5 + 5 = 15$

$3 \times 5 = 15$

3. Draw 3 number lines. For each exercise, show the operations on 1 number line.

[A] $4 + 4 + 4$ [B] $6 + 6$ [C] $2 + 2 + 2 + 2 + 2 + 2$

    3×4 2×6 6×2

4. Give the sums and products in exercise 3.
[A] *12 , 12*   [B] *12, 12*   [C] *12 , 12*

★ 5. Find the missing numbers.

[A] 2, 4, 6, *8* ?__, *10* ?__, *12* ?__, *14* ?__, *16* ?__, 18

[B] 3, 6, 9, *12* ?__, *15* ?__, *18* ?__, *21* ?__, *24* ?__, 27

[C] 4, 8, 12, *16* ?__, *20* ?__, *24* ?__, *28* ?__, *32* ?__, 36

[D] 5, 10, 15, *20* ?__, *25* ?__, *30* ?__, *35* ?__, *40* ?__, 45

[E] 6, 12, 18, *24* ?__, *30* ?__, *36* ?__, *42* ?__, *48* ?__, 54

[F] 7, 14, 21, *28* ?__, *35* ?__, *42* ?__, *49* ?__, *56* ?__, 63

[G] 8, 16, 24, *32* ?__, *40* ?__, *48* ?__, *56* ?__, *64* ?__, 72

[H] 9, 18, 27, *36* ?__, *45* ?__, *54* ?__, *63* ?__, *72* ?__, 81

Work through exercise 2 with the class. This exercise is designed to show the students how to draw their own number lines. When they have finished, write on the chalkboard the correct answer for this exercise. Check to see that each student has correctly drawn the number line and the representation of the equations $5 + 5 + 5 = 15$ and $3 \times 5 = 15$. Have the students complete the page.

Note that exercise 5 is designed primarily for the more able students. Follow up exercise 5, with those students who complete it, by calling attention to the related multiplication facts that one can get from the skip counting. That is, in exercise 5A one can think of $9 \times 2 = 18$. Of course, any other number less than 9, other than zero times two, could also be associated with this skip counting. We can find these other products by counting the number of skips. In exercise 5B one can think of $9 \times 3 = 27$, or possibly $7 \times 3 = 21$.

by writing equations for skips that you draw on the number line. Follow this with a short oral practice on skip counting.

Have the students work the exercises. Allow time for a class discussion when they have finished.

Multiplication review

1. Write a multiplication equation for each exercise.

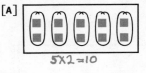 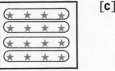

[A] $5 \times 2 = 10$

[B] $4 \times 4 = 16$

[C] $6 \times 3 = 18$

2. Write a multiplication equation for each exercise.

[A] $4 + 4 + 4 + 4 + 4$ $5 \times 4 = 20$

[B] $2 + 2 + 2$ $3 \times 2 = 6$

[C] $6 + 6 + 6 + 6$ $4 \times 6 = 24$

[D] $3, 6, 9, 12, 15$ $5 \times 3 = 15$

[E] $4, 8, 12$ $3 \times 4 = 12$

[F] $5, 10, 15, 20$ $4 \times 5 =$

3. Write a multiplication equation for each number line.

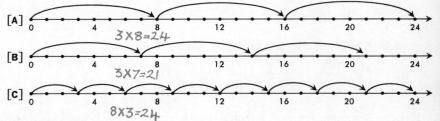

[A] $3 \times 8 = 24$

[B] $3 \times 7 = 21$

[C] $8 \times 3 = 24$

4. Find the products.

[A] 4×4 16 [C] 6×2 12 [E] 2×3 6 [G] 3×6 18 [I] 7×3 21 [K] 5×2 10

[B] 3×5 15 [D] 4×3 12 [F] 8×2 16 [H] 2×7 14 [J] 3×3 9 [L] 3×7 21

5. Find the missing factors.

[A] $4 \times \blacksquare = 16$ 4 [D] $\blacksquare \times 3 = 12$ 4 [G] $3 \times \blacksquare = 18$ 6 [J] $\blacksquare \times 3 = 9$ 3

[B] $\blacksquare \times 5 = 15$ 3 [E] $2 \times \blacksquare = 6$ 3 [H] $\blacksquare \times 7 = 14$ 2 [K] $5 \times \blacksquare = 10$ 2

[C] $6 \times \blacksquare = 12$ 2 [F] $\blacksquare \times 2 = 16$ 8 [I] $7 \times \blacksquare = 21$ 3 [L] $\blacksquare \times 7 = 21$ 3

6. Tell which mark ($>$, $=$, or $<$) should be placed in each ⬤ .

[A] 4×8 ⊛ 3×8

[B] 5×4 ⊜ 4×5

[C] 6×6 ⊛ 6×7

[D] 2×17 ⊜ $17 + 17$

[E] 3×98 ⊛ 4×98

[F] 3×7 ⊜ $7 + 7 + 7$

[G] $6 + 9$ ⊛ 5×9

[H] 8×3 ⊜ 3×8

[I] 9×2 ⊛ 9×3

[J] 7×9 ⊜ 9×7

Teaching Pages 92 and 93

- **PURPOSE**

  To review multiplication concepts presented thus far

  To provide word-problem experiences with product-set ideas

  To provide word-problem experiences with the general concept of multiplication

- **PREPARATION**

  Give the class a short oral review of the various concepts of multiplication presented so far. Have the students discuss the methods that have been used to explain multiplication and tell which method they prefer. Be sure that all

Short stories

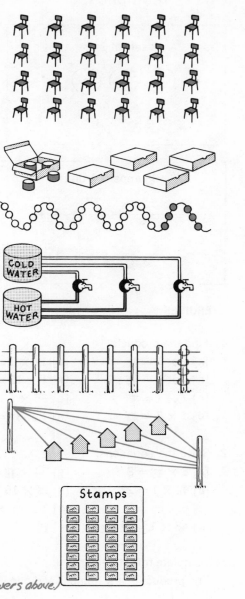

1. 6 chairs in each row.
4 rows.
How many people to fill the
chairs? *24, 4×6 =24*

2. 4 cans in each box.
5 boxes.
How many cans? *20, 5×4=20*

3. How many beads are left
to color? *21, 7×3 =21*

4. How many tanks? *2*
How many faucets? *3*
One pipe goes from each tank
to each faucet.
How many pipes? *6, 2×3=6*

5. How many blue wires for each
post? *4*
How many blue wires are needed
for this fence? *32, 8×4 =32*

6. 2 poles. 5 houses.
One wire from each pole to
each house.
How many wires? *10, 2×5 =10*

7. 4 stamps in each row.
8 rows.
How many stamps? *32, 8×4 =32*

8. Write a multiplication equation
for each exercise above. *(See answers above.)*

DIRECTIONS PAGE 93

Give the students an opportunity to work these exercises on their own. Be sure that they complete exercise 8 by writing the multiplication equations for exercises 1 through 7. Allow time for discussion of the exercises when the students have finished.

methods are brought out and that their relation to multiplication is made clear.

Provide more experiences in working with product sets. If necessary, plan additional demonstrations involving the formation of product sets. Review any of the multiplication concepts with which the students have had difficulty.

Study with the class the material found in the three boxes at the top of the page. Observe with them that in each case one is a factor. Give the students an opportunity to relate the given multiplication equation with the figure. Following this have the students complete the exercises. When they have finished, allow time for checking papers.

One in multiplication

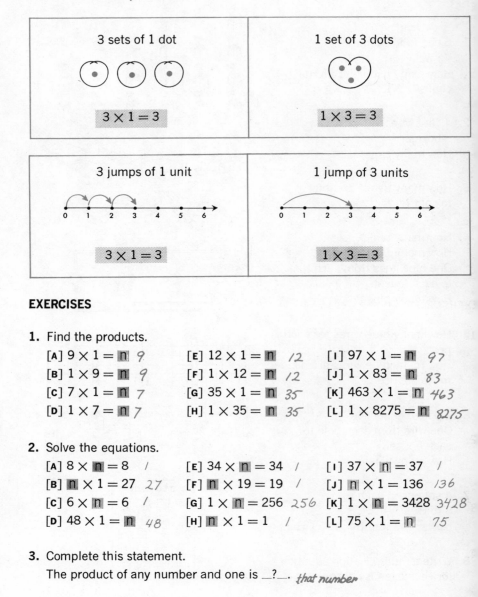

EXERCISES

1. Find the products.

[A] $9 \times 1 = \blacksquare$ 9   [E] $12 \times 1 = \blacksquare$ 12   [I] $97 \times 1 = \blacksquare$ 97

[B] $1 \times 9 = \blacksquare$ 9   [F] $1 \times 12 = \blacksquare$ 12   [J] $1 \times 83 = \blacksquare$ 83

[C] $7 \times 1 = \blacksquare$ 7   [G] $35 \times 1 = \blacksquare$ 35   [K] $463 \times 1 = \blacksquare$ 463

[D] $1 \times 7 = \blacksquare$ 7   [H] $1 \times 35 = \blacksquare$ 35   [L] $1 \times 8275 = \blacksquare$ 8275

2. Solve the equations.

[A] $8 \times \blacksquare = 8$ 1   [E] $34 \times \blacksquare = 34$ 1   [I] $37 \times \blacksquare = 37$ 1

[B] $\blacksquare \times 1 = 27$ 27   [F] $\blacksquare \times 19 = 19$ 1   [J] $\blacksquare \times 1 = 136$ 136

[C] $6 \times \blacksquare = 6$ 1   [G] $1 \times \blacksquare = 256$ 256   [K] $1 \times \blacksquare = 3428$ 3428

[D] $48 \times 1 = \blacksquare$ 48   [H] $\blacksquare \times 1 = 1$ 1   [L] $75 \times 1 = \blacksquare$ 75

3. Complete this statement.

The product of any number and one is __?__. *that number*

Teaching Pages 94 and 95

● **PURPOSE**

To introduce the special multiplicative properties of zero and one

● **MATHEMATICS**

We give here the special multiplicative properties of zero and one. For all whole numbers a,

$$a \times 1 = a.$$

For all whole numbers b,

$$b \times 0 = 0.$$

Zero in multiplication

3 sets of 0 dots	0 sets of 3 dots
◯ ◯ ◯	
$3 \times 0 = 0$	$0 \times 3 = 0$

3 jumps of 0 units	0 jumps of 3 units
0 1 2 3 4 5 6	0 1 2 3 4 5 6
$3 \times 0 = 0$	$0 \times 3 = 0$

EXERCISES

1. Find the products.

[A] $9 \times 0 = \blacksquare$ *0*   [E] $12 \times 0 = \blacksquare$ *0*   [I] $97 \times 0 = \blacksquare$ *0*

[B] $0 \times 9 = \blacksquare$ *0*   [F] $0 \times 12 = \blacksquare$ *0*   [J] $0 \times 83 = \blacksquare$ *0*

[C] $7 \times 0 = \blacksquare$ *0*   [G] $35 \times 0 = \blacksquare$ *0*   [K] $463 \times 0 = \blacksquare$ *0*

[D] $0 \times 7 = \blacksquare$ *0*   [H] $0 \times 35 = \blacksquare$ *0*   [L] $0 \times 8275 = \blacksquare$ *0*

2. Solve the equations.

[A] $8 \times \blacksquare = 0$ *0*   [C] $0 \times 6 = \blacksquare$ *0*   [E] $0 \times 56 = \blacksquare$ *0*

[B] $\blacksquare \times 7 = 0$ *0*   [D] $19 \times \blacksquare = 0$ *0*   [F] $748 \times \blacksquare = 0$ *0*

3. Complete this statement.

The product of any number and zero is __?__. *zero*

4. Can you solve this equation?   *No. The product of any whole*
number and 0 is 0.

$0 \times \blacksquare = 7$

PREPARATION

Provide the class with a short oral practice of simple multiplication combinations.

Study with the class the material found in the three boxes at the top of the page. Again, focus attention on the fact that in each case zero is a factor. Have the students relate the given multiplication equation to the figure. Following this discussion, have the students complete the page. When they have finished, allow time for discussion and checking papers.

Give the students an opportunity to work the exercises on this page. In the discussion which follows the completion of these exercises, elicit from the students the fact that exercise 5 emphasizes the order principle for addition and exercise 6 emphasizes the grouping principle for addition.

Answers, exercise 3, page 96

[A] $4 + 5 = 9$
$9 - 5 = 4$
$5 + 4 = 9$
$9 - 4 = 5$

[B] $6 + 4 = 10$
$10 - 4 = 6$
$4 + 6 = 10$
$10 - 6 = 4$

[C] $8 + 2 = 10$
$10 - 2 = 8$
$2 + 8 = 10$
$10 - 8 = 2$

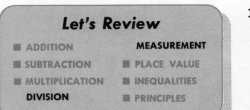

Let's Review

■ ADDITION   MEASUREMENT
■ SUBTRACTION   ■ PLACE VALUE
■ MULTIPLICATION ■ INEQUALITIES
DIVISION   ■ PRINCIPLES

1. For each pair, write the larger number on your paper.
   [A] 3,764,289; 4,764,289
   [B] 4,009,006; 400,006,009
   [C] 3,894,265; 3,943 678
   [D] 67,289; 67,290
   [E] 543,289; 542,290

2. Write numerals for these numbers.
   [A] two hundred sixty-eight thousand four hundred twenty-nine 268,429
   [B] sixty-eight thousand four hundred twenty-nine 68,429
   [C] five million two hundred sixty-eight thousand four hundred twenty-nine 5,268,429
   [D] seventy-five million two hundred sixty-eight thousand four hundred twenty-nine 75,268,429
   [E] seventy-five million two hundred eight thousand four hundred twenty-nine 75,208,429
   [F] seventy-five million two hundred thousand four hundred twenty-nine 75,200,
   [G] seventy-five million eight thousand four hundred twenty-nine 75,800,
   [H] five million eight thousand nine 5,008,009

3. Write 2 addition and 2 subtraction equations for each exercise. *(See answer at left.)*

   [A]  [B] [C]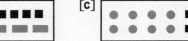

4. Use your ruler to measure the left edge of this page. Give the length to the nearest inch. *9 inches*

5. Solve the equations.
   [A] $6 + 7 = \blacksquare$ 13 [C] $8 + 4 = \blacksquare$ 12 [E] $9 + 3 = \blacksquare$ 12 [G] $5 + 4 = \blacksquare$ 9
   [B] $7 + 6 = \blacksquare$ 13 [D] $4 + 8 = \blacksquare$ 12 [F] $3 + 9 = \blacksquare$ 12 [H] $4 + 5 = \blacksquare$ 9

6. Solve the equations.
   [A] $(4 + 3) + 6 = \blacksquare$ 13
   [B] $4 + (3 + 6) = \blacksquare$ 13
   [C] $(5 + 2) + 4 = \blacksquare$ 11
   [D] $5 + (2 + 4) = \blacksquare$ 11
   [E] $(7 + 3) + 6 = \blacksquare$ 16
   [F] $7 + (3 + 6) = \blacksquare$ 16
   [G] $(8 + 4) + 3 = \blacksquare$ 15
   [H] $8 + (4 + 3) = \blacksquare$ 15

Teaching Pages 96 and 97

● **PURPOSE**

   To review the concepts and skills covered thus far in the text

● **PREPARATION**

   Conduct a short oral practice covering any topics with which the students have had previous difficulty. It may prove most helpful to review the meaning of place value and the meaning of symbols for numbers greater than 1,000,000. This is also an excellent time to provide the students with practice in reading large numbers.

7. Solve the equations.
[A] $7 + 6 = 10 + \blacksquare$ *3*   [C] $8 + 5 = 10 + \blacksquare$ *3*   [E] $8 + 7 = 10 + \blacksquare$ *5*
[B] $9 + 3 = 10 + \blacksquare$ *2*   [D] $7 + 7 = 10 + \blacksquare$ *4*   [F] $9 + 5 = 10 + \blacksquare$ *4*

8. Find the differences.
[A] Since $8 + 9 = 17$, we know that $17 - 9 = \blacksquare$. *8*
[B] Since $13 + 24 = 37$, we know that $37 - 24 = \blacksquare$. *13*
[C] Since $29 + 46 = 75$, we know that $75 - 46 = \blacksquare$. *29*
[D] Since $48 + 26 = 74$, we know that $74 - 26 = \blacksquare$. *48*
[E] Since $95 + 137 = 232$, we know that $232 - 137 = \blacksquare$. *95*

9. Find the sums and differences.

[A]	[B]	[C]	[D]	[E]	[F]
16 −7 *9*	8 +7 *15*	13 −6 *7*	12 −8 *4*	7 +9 *16*	6 +8 *14*

[G]	[H]	[I]	[J]	[K]	[L]
35 −14 *21*	23 +66 *89*	44 −13 *31*	89 −37 *52*	26 +42 *68*	76 −35 *41*

[M]	[N]	[O]	[P]	[Q]	[R]
34 +27 *61*	45 +38 *83*	74 −26 *48*	93 −47 *46*	26 +49 *75*	32 −18 *14*

[S]	[T]	[U]	[V]	[W]	[X]
85 +69 *154*	123 −64 *59*	48 +75 *123*	97 −69 *28*	84 +66 *150*	147 −75 *72*

10. Find the missing numbers.
[A] $\blacksquare + 6 = 14$ *8*   [E] $\blacksquare + 7 = 12$ *5*   [I] $13 + \blacksquare = 18$ *5*
[B] $\blacksquare - 5 = 8$ *13*   [F] $8 + \blacksquare = 16$ *8*   [J] $\blacksquare - 4 = 12$ *16*
[C] $7 + \blacksquare = 17$ *10*   [G] $12 - \blacksquare = 4$ *8*   [K] $15 - \blacksquare = 0$ *15*
[D] $14 - \blacksquare = 8$ *6*   [H] $\blacksquare - 5 = 6$ *11*   [L] $10 + \blacksquare = 20$ *10*

11. Find the products.
[A] 4×3 *12*   [C] 2×6 *12*   [E] 3×6 *18*   [G] 8×0 *0*   [I] 5×4 *20*
[B] 5×3 *15*   [D] 4×4 *16*   [F] 5×5 *25*   [H] 1×9 *9*   [J] 2×7 *14*

12. Find the missing factors.
[A] $\blacksquare \times 3 = 9$ *3*   [E] $\blacksquare \times 9 = 9$ *1*   [I] $\blacksquare \times 7 = 14$ *2*
[B] $\blacksquare \times 3 = 15$ *5*   [F] $5 \times \blacksquare = 25$ *5*   [J] $8 \times \blacksquare = 0$ *0*
[C] $2 \times \blacksquare = 4$ *2*   [G] $4 \times \blacksquare = 12$ *3*   [K] $\blacksquare \times 4 = 16$ *4*
[D] $4 \times \blacksquare = 8$ *2*   [H] $3 \times \blacksquare = 18$ *6*   [L] $4 \times \blacksquare = 20$ *5*

13. Find the missing numbers.
[A] $37{,}286 + \blacksquare = 42{,}286$ *5000*   [C] $\blacksquare - 304{,}060 = 20{,}705$ *324,765*
[B] $531{,}497 + \blacksquare = 634{,}497$ *103,000*   [D] $8{,}763{,}489 - 8{,}060{,}409 = \blacksquare$ *703,080*

Have the students work the exercises. Notice that exercise 13 is designed primarily for the more able students. Allow time at the end for the checking of papers.

In the discussion period, take special care to ensure that the students see the relationship between the first and second equations in each part of exercise 8. The students should see that by knowing the sum of two numbers they can easily find the difference.

In your discussion of exercise 13, avoid any complicated rules. The more able students should observe that they can work this exercise primarily by thinking in terms of place value. If the students need to work these problems by complicated addition and subtraction processes, the exercise should probably be saved until a later time.

Read the first paragraph with the students and then ask them if they know what the product of any number and zero is. When someone responds zero, call attention to the first general principle given at the top of the page. Now observe with the students that because they know this rule, they do not have to memorize the product when zero is a factor. Erase the zero row and the zero column from the table you have drawn on the chalkboard.

Now ask the students if they know what the product is when one is a factor. When someone responds that it is the same as the other factor, point out that since they know this special principle of multiplying by one, they do not have to memorize the one column and the one row. Erase the one column and the one row.

Briefly review the order principle for multiplication. Then, have a student find the product 3×7 on the table. Now ask the students if they can find the product 7×3 on the table. When they have found these two products, point out that if they know one product, they should know the other. Repeat this for several other products. When the students see that knowing one product automatically gives them the other, erase the remainder of the table which corresponds to the shaded portion of the table on this page. Observe again with the students that if they know the products that are left in the table they will know those that are being erased.

Now continue with the remainder of page 98. Emphasize that if the students know the addition facts, they know certain multiplication facts. Call attention to the table containing the doubles and the twos at the bottom of the page. After studying this table, erase the two row on your chalkboard table.

Multiplication facts

There are 100 multiplication facts that you should know. You could try to remember each one, or you could look for ways to make your job easier. Here are some ways to make the job easier.

First, you know special rules for products when 0 and 1 are factors.

1 The product of any number and 0 is 0.

2 The product of any number and 1 is that number.

3 You know that you can change the order of any pair of factors and get the same product. For example, if you know 4×6, you also know 6×4.

The table shows in blue the facts that you already know or can find easily **if** you know others. You started with 100 facts to learn. Now you need to learn only 36 (those in white). Let's try to make the job even easier.

x	0	1	2	3	4	5	6	7	8	9
0	0	0	0	0	0	0	0	0	0	0
1	0	1	2	3	4	5	6	7	8	9
2	0	2	4	6	8	10	12	14	16	18
3	0	3	6	9	12	15	18	21	24	27
4	0	4	8	12	16	20	24	28	32	36
5	0	5	10	15	20	25	30	35	40	45
6	0	6	12	18	24	30	36	42	48	54
7	0	7	14	21	28	35	42	49	56	63
8	0	8	16	24	32	40	48	56	64	72
9	0	9	18	27	36	45	54	63	72	81

You can use addition facts to find the product when 2 is a factor.

Addition Facts	Multiplication Facts
Doubles	Twos
Since $2 + 2 = 4$,	we know that $2 \times 2 = 4$.
Since $3 + 3 = 6$,	we know that $2 \times 3 = 6$.
Since $4 + 4 = 8$,	we know that $2 \times 4 = 8$.
Since $5 + 5 = 10$,	we know that $2 \times 5 = 10$.
Since $6 + 6 = 12$,	we know that $2 \times 6 = 12$.
Since $7 + 7 = 14$,	we know that $2 \times 7 = 14$.
Since $8 + 8 = 16$,	we know that $2 \times 8 = 16$.
Since $9 + 9 = 18$,	we know that $2 \times 9 = 18$.

Teaching Pages 98 and 99

● **PURPOSE**

To focus attention on mastery of multiplication facts
To introduce the multiplication table
To introduce an element of logic in finding products

● **MATHEMATICS**

In this lesson the students are made aware of the usefulness of certain basic principles in arithmetic. Generalization of the special multiplicative properties of zero and one reduces the number of facts the students must learn. The use of the order principle for multiplication further reduces the table; if the students know one product, they

Since you can skip count by fives, you can easily find the product when 5 is a factor.

2 fives		4 fives		6 fives		8 fives	
↓		↓		↓		↓	
5	**10**	**15**	**20**	**25**	**30**	**35**	**40**	**45**
↑		↑		↑		↑		↑
1 five		3 fives		5 fives		7 fives		9 fives

Fives	
Since 2 × 5 = 10, 5 × 2 = 10	Since 6 × 5 = 30, 5 × 6 = 30
Since 3 × 5 = 15, 5 × 3 = 15	Since 7 × 5 = 35, 5 × 7 = 35
Since 4 × 5 = 20, 5 × 4 = 20	Since 8 × 5 = 40, 5 × 8 = 40
Since 5 × 5 = 25, 5 × 5 = 25	Since 9 × 5 = 45, 5 × 9 = 45

Now there are only 21 facts to learn.

If you are good at addition, you might be able to figure out the products in the "3 row" and the "4 row." Then you will have only 10 facts to learn.

Table (A)

x	0	1	2	3	4	5	6	7	8	9
0	0	0	0	0	0	0	0	0	0	0
1	0	1	2	3	4	5	6	7	8	9
2	0	2	4	6	8	10	12	14	16	18
3	0	3	6	9	12	15	18	21	24	27
4	0	4	8	12	16	20	24	28	32	36
5	0	5	10	15	20	25	30	35	40	45
6	0	6	12	18	24	30	36	42	48	54
7	0	7	14	21	28	35	42	49	56	63
8	0	8	16	24	32	40	48	56	64	72
9	0	9	18	27	36	45	54	63	72	81

EXERCISES

Find the products.

1. 1 × 6 = 6
2. 7 × 0 = 0
3. 8 × 1 = 8
4. 0 × 9 = 0
5. 2 × 3 = 6

6. 6 × 2 = 12
7. 2 × 8 = 16
8. 9 × 2 = 18
9. 2 × 7 = 14
10. 5 × 2 = 10

11. Since 6 × 7 = 42, we know that 7 × 6 = ■. 42
12. Since 8 × 9 = 72, we know that 9 × 8 = ■. 72
13. Since 7 × 9 = 63, we know that 9 × 7 = ■. 63
14. Since 6 × 9 = 54, we know that 9 × 6 = ■. 54
15. Since 7 × 8 = 56, we know that 8 × 7 = ■. 56

Have the students do some counting by fives. Discuss the material at the top of the page and remind the students that they have been able to count by fives for some time. Notice with them that if they know how to count by fives very well, they can easily figure out products when five is a factor. Following this, erase the five column and row from your multiplication table.

Observe now that there are only 21 facts left to be memorized in your chalkboard table. You might encourage students to observe that the products 3 × 3, 3 × 4, and 4 × 4 are quite easy and they may already know these products. If the students agree, you can erase this part of the table. This, of course, reduces the table to just 18 entries to be memorized.

At this time, give the students an opportunity to discuss other products that they know or know an easy way to figure. Once your discussion concerning the table has been completed, give the students an opportunity to work the exercises at the bottom of page 99.

Keep in mind that this lesson is designed to make learning multiplication facts more enjoyable. We do not want the students to fear the necessity of remembering multiplication facts. The "discovery" aspects involved here can be exciting for the students.

can conclude the other by simply changing the order (if they know 4 × 6, they also know 6 × 4).

The other reductions in the facts to be memorized are based primarily on intuitive reasoning and the distributive principle, which is intuitively obvious to students in simple situations even though it has not been formally introduced. For example, the fact that $3 + 3 = 2 \times 3$ has already been presented in terms of relating repeated addition to multiplication. The following equation shows the relation to the distributive principle:

$$3 + 3 = (1 \times 3) + (1 \times 3) = 3(1 + 1) = 3 \times 2.$$

● **PREPARATION**

Write on the chalkboard a large multiplication table. Have the students assist you in filling in the entries for this table. Tell the students that they can use repeated addition or any other method for finding the correct products. Once the table has been completed, you are ready to begin the lesson on page 98.

Read and study the material at the top of the page with the students. Observe that in the first box there are two sets of three and then three sets of three and that 3×3 is three more than 2×3. Call attention to the second box and the fact that 4×3 is twice 2×3, or $2 \times (2 \times 3)$.

Following this discussion, give the students an opportunity to work the exercises. When they have finished, allow time for checking the papers and answering questions.

Reasoning to find products

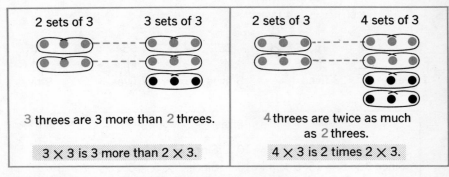

3 threes are 3 more than 2 threes.

3×3 is 3 more than 2×3.

4 threes are twice as much as 2 threes.

4×3 is 2 times 2×3.

Since $2 \times 3 = 6$, we know that $3 \times 3 = 6 + 3$.
Since $2 \times 3 = 6$, we know that $4 \times 3 = 6 + 6$.

EXERCISES

Use reasoning to find the products in the tables.

1.

		Twos	Threes
	[A]	Since $2 \times 3 = 6$,	we know that $3 \times 3 =$ ▩. *9*
	[B]	Since $2 \times 4 = 8$,	we know that $3 \times 4 =$ ▩. *12*
	[C]	Since $2 \times 5 = 10$,	we know that $3 \times 5 =$ ▩. *15*
	[D]	Since $2 \times 6 = 12$,	we know that $3 \times 6 =$ ▩. *18*
	[E]	Since $2 \times 7 = 14$,	we know that $3 \times 7 =$ ▩. *21*
	[F]	Since $2 \times 8 = 16$,	we know that $3 \times 8 =$ ▩. *24*
	[G]	Since $2 \times 9 = 18$,	we know that $3 \times 9 =$ ▩. *27*

2.

		Twos	Fours
	[A]	Since $2 \times 3 = 6$,	we know that $4 \times 3 =$ ▩. *12*
	[B]	Since $2 \times 4 = 8$,	we know that $4 \times 4 =$ ▩. *16*
	[C]	Since $2 \times 5 = 10$,	we know that $4 \times 5 =$ ▩. *20*
	[D]	Since $2 \times 6 = 12$,	we know that $4 \times 6 =$ ▩. *24*
	[E]	Since $2 \times 7 = 14$,	we know that $4 \times 7 =$ ▩. *28*
	[F]	Since $2 \times 8 = 16$,	we know that $4 \times 8 =$ ▩. *32*
	[G]	Since $2 \times 9 = 18$,	we know that $4 \times 9 =$ ▩. *36*

Teaching Pages 100 and 101

● **PURPOSE**

To continue focusing attention on mastery of multiplication facts

● **MATHEMATICS**

Although most of the work in this lesson depends on the distributive property or principle for multiplication over addition, we do not focus attention on this principle at this time. The ideas are presented intuitively to the students in terms of repeated addition. As we pointed out earlier, repeated addition closely parallels the distributive principle.

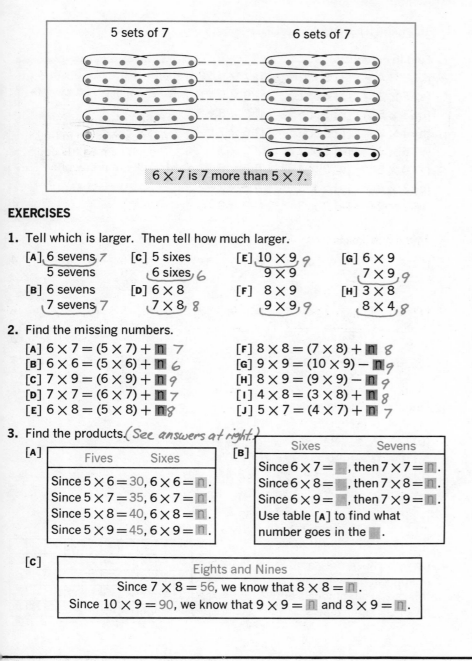

5 sets of 7   6 sets of 7

6 × 7 is 7 more than 5 × 7.

EXERCISES

1. Tell which is larger. Then tell how much larger.

[A] 6 sevens *7*
    5 sevens

[C] 5 sixes
    6 sixes *6*

[E] 10 × 9 *9*
    9 × 9

[G] 6 × 9
    7 × 9 *9*

[B] 6 sevens
    7 sevens *7*

[D] 6 × 8
    7 × 8 *8*

[F] 8 × 9
    9 × 9 *9*

[H] 3 × 8
    8 × 4 *8*

2. Find the missing numbers.

[A] 6 × 7 = (5 × 7) + ▣ *7*

[B] 6 × 6 = (5 × 6) + ▣ *6*

[C] 7 × 9 = (6 × 9) + ▣ *9*

[D] 7 × 7 = (6 × 7) + ▣ *7*

[E] 6 × 8 = (5 × 8) + ▣ *8*

[F] 8 × 8 = (7 × 8) + ▣ *8*

[G] 9 × 9 = (10 × 9) − ▣ *9*

[H] 8 × 9 = (9 × 9) − ▣ *9*

[I] 4 × 8 = (3 × 8) + ▣ *8*

[J] 5 × 7 = (4 × 7) + ▣ *7*

3. Find the products. *(See answers at right.)*

[A]

	Fives	Sixes
	Since 5 × 6 = 30, 6 × 6 = ▣.	
	Since 5 × 7 = 35, 6 × 7 = ▣.	
	Since 5 × 8 = 40, 6 × 8 = ▣.	
	Since 5 × 9 = 45, 6 × 9 = ▣.	

[B]

	Sixes	Sevens
	Since 6 × 7 = ▣, then 7 × 7 = ▣.	
	Since 6 × 8 = ▣, then 7 × 8 = ▣.	
	Since 6 × 9 = ▣, then 7 × 9 = ▣.	
Use table [A] to find what number goes in the ▣.		

[C]

Eights and Nines
Since 7 × 8 = 56, we know that 8 × 8 = ▣.
Since 10 × 9 = 90, we know that 9 × 9 = ▣ and 8 × 9 = ▣.

Read and study the material in the box at the top of the page with the students before directing them to work the exercises on their own. When they have finished, allow time for discussion.

Answers, exercise 3, page 101

[A] 36
  42
  48
  54

[B] 42, 49
  48, 56
  54, 63

[C] 64
  81, 72

The presentation on these pages leads the students through reasoning such as, "If we know 5 × 7, then we know 6 × 7 = (5 × 7) + 7" (that is, 6 × 7 is one more seven than 5 × 7). The following equation illustrates how the distributive principle can be used to demonstrate this idea:

$$6 \times 7 = (5 + 1) \times 7 = (5 \times 7) + 7$$
$$= (5 \times 7) + (1 \times 7).$$

PREPARATION

Conduct a short oral practice session similar to the following. Begin by asking a student how much is 2 sevens or 2 × 7. When he responds 14, ask him if he knows how much 3 × 7 is. Encourage the students to observe that 3 × 7 is one more seven than 2 × 7, or that it is 14 + 7. Continue this type of question for other exercises until the students get the general idea.

Give the students an opportunity to work the exercises on this page. When they have finished, allow time for the checking of papers.

As you discuss the riddle with the students, have them point out the various clues that they used to arrive at the correct answer. Be sure that all the students have an opportunity to think about the riddle before the correct answer is given. Most of the students will understand the riddle whether or not they are able to find the correct number.

Supplementary exercises, Set 38 (page 345) may be assigned as necessary beyond this page.

Practice finding products

1. Find the products.

[A] 3×4 12   [I] 0×7 0   [Q] 7×8 56
[B] 6×2 12   [J] 6×1 6   [R] 9×5 45
[C] 5×5 25   [K] 5×6 30   [S] 8×8 64
[D] 4×2 8   [L] 4×4 16   [T] 6×7 42
[E] 6×3 18   [M] 7×2 14   [U] 8×7 56
[F] 4×5 20   [N] 8×4 32   [V] 6×6 36
[G] 3×8 24   [O] 5×3 15   [W] 9×7 63
[H] 2×9 18   [P] 7×3 21   [X] 9×9 81

> **Exercise for Experts**
>
> Multiply me by myself.
> You're almost up to fifty.
> Though I am a little odd,
> I think I'm pretty nifty.
> *Seven*
> WHO AM I?

2. Find the products.

[A] $6 \times 2 = 12$ [B] $2 \times 7 = 14$ [C] $8 \times 7 = 56$ [D] $4 \times 5 = 20$ [E] $8 \times 4 = 32$ [F] $6 \times 6 = 36$ [G] $4 \times 2 = 8$ [H] $4 \times 4 = 16$

[I] $6 \times 7 = 42$ [J] $3 \times 8 = 24$ [K] $5 \times 3 = 15$ [L] $9 \times 7 = 63$ [M] $5 \times 5 = 25$ [N] $5 \times 6 = 30$ [O] $8 \times 3 = 24$ [P] $6 \times 3 = 18$

[Q] $6 \times 1 = 6$ [R] $9 \times 5 = 45$ [S] $2 \times 9 = 18$ [T] $7 \times 3 = 21$ [U] $9 \times 9 = 81$ [V] $3 \times 4 = 12$ [W] $0 \times 7 = 0$ [X] $7 \times 8 = 56$

3. Find the missing numbers.

[A] 2, 4, 6, _8_, _10_, _12_, 14, _16_, _18_
[B] 5, 10, _15_, _20_, _25_, _30_, 35, _40_, _45_
[C] 3, 6, 9, _12_, _15_, _18_, _21_, _24_, 27
[D] 8, 16, 24, _32_, _40_, _48_, 56, _64_, _72_
[E] 6, 12, _18_, _24_, 30, _36_, _42_, _48_, 54
[F] 9, _18_, 27, _36_, 45, _54_, 63, _72_, 81

4. On your paper, draw a multiplication table like this one. Four products are given. Find the others.

x	0	1	2	3	4	5	6	7	8	9
6	0	6	12	18	24	30	36	42	48	54
7	0	7	14	21	28	35	42	49	56	63
8	0	8	16	24	32	40	48	56	64	72
9	0	9	18	27	36	45	54	63	72	81

Teaching Pages 102 and 103

● **PURPOSE**

To provide more practice in finding products
To provide word-problem experiences with multiplication

● **PREPARATION**

Provide the class with a short oral practice in finding products. After a student has found a given product, query him with regard to the method he used in finding the product. For example, for the product 4×5, one student might think of 5×5 and then 5 less than this product, while another student may think twice 2×5. Of course, some of the students may simply think about adding 4 fives.

The forest ranger

Instruct the students to read and work the word-problem exercises on this page. When they have finished, discuss the exercises and have the students check their papers. Allow the students considerable freedom in discussing some of the ideas. For example, encourage the students to discuss why it can be five times as far by trail as it is straight from the tower to the top of Bald Mountain.

Last summer Frank spent a week with a forest ranger.

1. Frank helped the forest ranger plant some small pine trees. Frank planted 3 rows of trees. He put 8 trees in each row. How many trees did he plant? *24*

2. Frank learned how to build a fire without matches. The ranger let Frank build the fires for 3 meals each day. Frank stayed 7 days. How many fires did he build? *21*

3. One day the ranger showed Frank some fish that were to be put in Blue Lake. The fish were in cans. Frank counted 9 cans. There were 8 fish in each can. How many fish were there in all? *72*

4. On Tuesday, Frank helped put signs on trees. They looked like this. They posted signs on trees along 4 different trails. They put 9 signs on each trail. How many signs did they post? *36*

5. The ranger took Frank to the fire lookout tower. Frank looked through the telescope at the flag on top of Bald Mountain. The ranger said, "It is 4 miles from the tower straight to the top of Bald Mountain. But since you can't fly, it is 5 times as far by the trail." How many miles long is the trail from the tower to the top of the mountain? *20*

Direct the students to work the exercises on this page. Since the riddle on this page is more difficult than some of the others, give some guidance to the less able students so that they do not become discouraged with it. Most of the students will understand the riddle once the correct answer is given. When the students have completed the page, allow time for checking papers.

Supplementary exercises, Set 39 (page 345) may be assigned as necessary beyond this page.

Finding missing factors

1. Find the missing factors.

[A] $3 \times \blacksquare = 9$ 3		[M] $\blacksquare \times 6 = 12$ 2		
[B] $2 \times \blacksquare = 6$ 3		[N] $\blacksquare \times 1 = 1$ 1		
[C] $\blacksquare \times 4 = 16$ 4		[O] $4 \times \blacksquare = 12$ 3		
[D] $\blacksquare \times 1 = 7$ 7		[P] $2 \times \blacksquare = 14$ 7		
[E] $2 \times \blacksquare = 10$ 5		[Q] $\blacksquare \times 5 = 10$ 2		
[F] $\blacksquare \times 5 = 15$ 3		[R] $7 \times \blacksquare = 0$ 0		
[G] $\blacksquare \times 8 = 0$ 0		[S] $3 \times \blacksquare = 15$ 5		
[H] $2 \times \blacksquare = 4$ 2		[T] $\blacksquare \times 2 = 8$ 4		
[I] $3 \times \blacksquare = 6$ 2		[U] $\blacksquare \times 2 = 12$ 6		
[J] $\blacksquare \times 5 = 25$ 5		[V] $9 \times \blacksquare = 9$ 1		
[K] $4 \times \blacksquare = 20$ 5		[W] $\blacksquare \times 9 = 18$ 2		
[L] $\blacksquare \times 3 = 12$ 4		[X] $4 \times \blacksquare = 20$ 5		

Exercise for Experts

When you multiply by me,
I really am quite tame.
No matter what the factor is,
The product stays the same.

WHO AM I? Zero

2. Find the missing factors.

[A] $\begin{array}{r} 3 \\ \times 2 \\ \hline 6 \end{array}$ [B] $\begin{array}{r} 4 \\ \times 3 \\ \hline 12 \end{array}$ [C] $\begin{array}{r} 3 \\ \times 3 \\ \hline 9 \end{array}$ [D] $\begin{array}{r} 2 \\ \times 2 \\ \hline 4 \end{array}$ [E] $\begin{array}{r} 4 \\ \times 2 \\ \hline 8 \end{array}$ [F] $\begin{array}{r} 5 \\ \times 2 \\ \hline 10 \end{array}$ [G] $\begin{array}{r} 4 \\ \times 0 \\ \hline 0 \end{array}$ [H] $\begin{array}{r} 7 \\ \times 1 \\ \hline 7 \end{array}$

[I] $\begin{array}{r} 4 \\ \times 2 \\ \hline 8 \end{array}$ [J] $\begin{array}{r} 4 \\ \times 3 \\ \hline 12 \end{array}$ [K] $\begin{array}{r} 3 \\ \times 5 \\ \hline 15 \end{array}$ [L] $\begin{array}{r} 9 \\ \times 2 \\ \hline 18 \end{array}$ [M] $\begin{array}{r} 1 \\ \times 9 \\ \hline 9 \end{array}$ [N] $\begin{array}{r} 5 \\ \times 5 \\ \hline 25 \end{array}$ [O] $\begin{array}{r} 0 \\ \times 7 \\ \hline 0 \end{array}$ [P] $\begin{array}{r} 4 \\ \times 4 \\ \hline 16 \end{array}$

[Q] $\begin{array}{r} 6 \\ \times 3 \\ \hline 18 \end{array}$ [R] $\begin{array}{r} 8 \\ \times 2 \\ \hline 16 \end{array}$ [S] $\begin{array}{r} 6 \\ \times 2 \\ \hline 12 \end{array}$ [T] $\begin{array}{r} 1 \\ \times 17 \\ \hline 17 \end{array}$ [U] $\begin{array}{r} 5 \\ \times 4 \\ \hline 20 \end{array}$ [V] $\begin{array}{r} 3 \\ \times 5 \\ \hline 15 \end{array}$ [W] $\begin{array}{r} 5 \\ \times 4 \\ \hline 20 \end{array}$ [X] $\begin{array}{r} 6 \\ \times 5 \\ \hline 30 \end{array}$

3. Draw a set of 12 dots on your paper. Ring sets of 3 to find how many threes in 12. Write a multiplication equation about this. $4 \times 3 = 12$

4. Draw a set of 20 dots on your paper. Ring sets of 4 to find how many fours in 20. Write a multiplication equation about this. $5 \times 4 = 20$

5. Find the missing factors.

[A] $6 \times 7 = \blacksquare \times 6$ 7   [D] $9 \times \blacksquare = 6 \times 9$ 6   [G] $7 \times 9 = \blacksquare \times 7$ 9

[B] $8 \times 9 = 9 \times \blacksquare$ 8   [E] $\blacksquare \times 8 = 8 \times 5$ 5   [H] $23 \times 56 = \blacksquare \times 23$ 56

[C] $7 \times 8 = \blacksquare \times 7$ 8   [F] $4 \times \blacksquare = 9 \times 4$ 9   [I] $87 \times 95 = 95 \times \blacksquare$ 87

Teaching Pages 104 and 105

- **PURPOSE**

  To focus attention on finding a missing factor

  To prepare for division

  To provide more word-problem experiences in multiplication

  To continue developing skill in finding products

- **MATHEMATICS**

  Multiplication and division are related just as addition and subtraction are related. Just as finding the missing addend is equivalent to finding the difference, finding the missing factor is equivalent to finding the quotient. For

At the post office

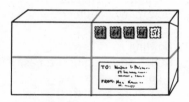

1. Jill bought eight 5-cent stamps. How much did they cost? *40¢*

2. She bought five 8-cent stamps. How much did she spend for them? *40¢*

3. Jill saw some 1-cent stamps. She counted 3 rows and 9 stamps in each row. How many 1-cent stamps did she see? *27*

4. 5-cent stamps come to the post office in sheets with 10 rows and 10 columns. How many stamps are in each sheet? *100*

5. Jill bought 24 airmail stamps. She bought 4 times as many as Kay. How many airmail stamps did Kay buy? *6*

6. Kay pasted 15 stamps in her collection book. She had 5 rows. How many were there in each row? *3*

7. Which costs more, nine 5-cent stamps or seven 6-cent stamps?

8. Jan spent 32 cents for 8-cent stamps. How many stamps did she buy? *4*

9. Bill needed 29 cents worth of stamps to mail his package. He had only 5-cent, 6-cent, 7-cent, and 8-cent stamps. He wanted to use only **2 different kinds** of stamps. One way to stamp the package is given in the picture.

   [A] Find another way, using 7-cent and 8-cent stamps. *three 7¢, one 8¢*
   [B] Find another way, using 5-cent and 8-cent stamps. *three 8¢, one 5¢*
   [C] Find another way. *three 5¢, two 7¢*

Give the students an opportunity to work the exercises. Although exercise 9 is designed for the more able students, all students can gain from participating in a discussion of this exercise. However, caution the less able students against becoming discouraged if they are not successful in attempting this problem on their own.

example, if you know the solution to $4 \times n = 20$, then you know the solution to $20 \div 4 = n$.

PREPARATION

On the chalkboard write several equations similar to those found in exercises 1 and 2 on page 104. Ask the students to find the missing factors in these exercises. Be sure that they check their answers by multiplying to see that they have found the correct missing factor.

Have the students work the story exercises on this page. Notice that exercise 16 is for the more able students. During the discussion period for these exercises, be sure that the students are given an adequate opportunity to discuss any of the exercises which may have caused them difficulty. It may be helpful to have some students write on the board the multiplication equations for certain exercises.

Short sport stories

1. 2 basketball teams.
5 players on each team.
How many players? *10*

2. 2 basketball teams.
4 cheerleaders for each team.
How many cheerleaders? *8*

3. Doubleheader baseball game. Each game 9 innings. How many innings? *18*

4. Baseball game.
6 outs each inning.
9 innings.
How many outs? *54*

5. Red Sox.
3 outs each inning.
9 innings.
How many outs? *27*

6. Basketball game.
4 quarters.
8 minutes each quarter.
How many minutes? *32*

7. Bowling.
Knock down 7 pins 4 times.
1 point for each pin.
How many points? *28*

8. Tennis.
Played 9 games and won 4.
How many games lost? *5*

9. Bowling.
8 balls in each rack.
7 racks.
How many bowling balls? *56*

10. Baseball.
3 strikes, you're out.
8 strikeouts.
How many strikes? *24*

11. Football game.
6 points for a touchdown.
5 touchdowns.
How many points? *30*

12. Football game.
6 points for a touchdown.
7 touchdowns. How many points?

13. Softball.
9 players on each team.
7 teams.
How many players? *63*

14. Basketball.
5 fouls, you're out of the game.
4 players out on fouls.
How many fouls for these players? *20*

15. Baseball game.
4 innings, 0 runs each inning.
How many runs? *0*

★ 16. Football.
6 points for a touchdown.
Bulldogs scored 8 touchdowns and 4 extra points.
What was their score? *52*

Teaching Pages 106 and 107

- **PURPOSE**

  To provide word-problem experiences in multiplication
  To provide a stimulating activity in finding products and missing factors

- **PREPARATION**

  Provide the students with a short oral practice of multiplication facts. If time permits, make up several word problems which use the current multiplication facts.

  Follow this by playing a game similar to the function-machine game. For example, think of a rule, have the

The function game

RULE
Multiply by 3

Input
4

Output
12

The Function Machine

INPUT · FUNCTION RULE · OUTPUT

4 · Multiply by 3 · 12

EXERCISES

Think about the function machine and tell what you think should go in each gray space.

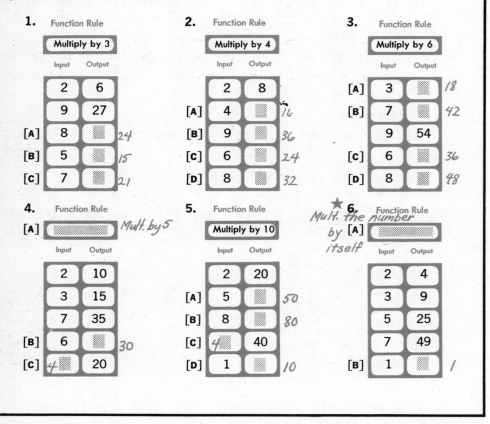

1. Function Rule

Multiply by 3

Input	Output
2	6
9	27
[A] 8	24
[B] 5	15
[C] 7	21

2. Function Rule

Multiply by 4

Input	Output
2	8
[A] 4	16
[B] 9	36
[C] 6	24
[D] 8	32

3. Function Rule

Multiply by 6

Input	Output
[A] 3	18
[B] 7	42
9	54
[C] 6	36
[D] 8	48

4. Function Rule

[A] _Mult. by 5_

Input	Output
2	10
3	15
7	35
[B] 6	30
[C] 4	20

5. Function Rule

Multiply by 10

Input	Output
2	20
[A] 5	50
[B] 8	80
[C] 4	40
[D] 1	10

★**6.** Function Rule

Mult. the number by itself

[A]

Input	Output
2	4
3	9
5	25
7	49
[B] 1	1

As you discuss the material at the top of the page, notice that the illustration shows the boy hearing the number 4, using the rule "multiply by 3," and saying the number 12. Point out how this picture corresponds to the function machine. That is, the input is 4, the rule is "multiply by 3," and the output is 12.

Study the table in exercise 1. Notice with the class that for an input of two and a rule, multiply by three, we get an output of six. Notice next that for an input of nine, using the same rule, we have an output of 27. Now have the students tell the output for the numbers eight, five, and seven and then write these answers on their paper.

Have the students do exercise 2 on their own. When they have completed exercise 2, discuss the four answers and allow each student to check his paper. Now give the students an opportunity to complete the page. Notice that exercise 6 is designed primarily for the more able students.

students give you a number for the input number, you give them the output number, and then have the students guess the rule for the game.

Have the students work the exercises. When they have finished, have several of the exercises exhibited on the chalkboard and have the students explain their work.

Let's Review

■ ADDITION   MEASUREMENT
■ SUBTRACTION   ■ PLACE VALUE
MULTIPLICATION   INEQUALITIES
DIVISION   PRINCIPLES

1. Find the sums.

[A] $\begin{array}{r} 3 \\ +9 \\ \hline 12 \end{array}$ [B] $\begin{array}{r} 8 \\ +3 \\ \hline 11 \end{array}$ [C] $\begin{array}{r} 5 \\ +7 \\ \hline 12 \end{array}$ [D] $\begin{array}{r} 7 \\ +7 \\ \hline 14 \end{array}$

[E] $\begin{array}{r} 8 \\ +5 \\ \hline 13 \end{array}$ [F] $\begin{array}{r} 4 \\ +9 \\ \hline 13 \end{array}$ [G] $\begin{array}{r} 4 \\ +7 \\ \hline 11 \end{array}$ [H] $\begin{array}{r} 9 \\ +6 \\ \hline 15 \end{array}$

[I] $\begin{array}{r} 7 \\ +8 \\ \hline 15 \end{array}$ [J] $\begin{array}{r} 8 \\ +9 \\ \hline 17 \end{array}$ [K] $\begin{array}{r} 6 \\ +8 \\ \hline 14 \end{array}$ [L] $\begin{array}{r} 9 \\ +5 \\ \hline 14 \end{array}$ [M] $\begin{array}{r} 7 \\ +9 \\ \hline 16 \end{array}$ [N] $\begin{array}{r} 9 \\ +9 \\ \hline 18 \end{array}$ [O] $\begin{array}{r} 8 \\ +8 \\ \hline 16 \end{array}$ [P] $\begin{array}{r} 7 \\ +6 \\ \hline 13 \end{array}$

2. Find the differences.

[A] $\begin{array}{r} 11 \\ -9 \\ \hline 2 \end{array}$ [B] $\begin{array}{r} 12 \\ -8 \\ \hline 4 \end{array}$ [C] $\begin{array}{r} 16 \\ -7 \\ \hline 9 \end{array}$ [D] $\begin{array}{r} 11 \\ -8 \\ \hline 3 \end{array}$ [E] $\begin{array}{r} 12 \\ -3 \\ \hline 9 \end{array}$ [F] $\begin{array}{r} 13 \\ -8 \\ \hline 5 \end{array}$ [G] $\begin{array}{r} 14 \\ -9 \\ \hline 5 \end{array}$ [H] $\begin{array}{r} 14 \\ -7 \\ \hline 7 \end{array}$

[I] $\begin{array}{r} 11 \\ -6 \\ \hline 5 \end{array}$ [J] $\begin{array}{r} 17 \\ -8 \\ \hline 9 \end{array}$ [K] $\begin{array}{r} 13 \\ -7 \\ \hline 6 \end{array}$ [L] $\begin{array}{r} 12 \\ -5 \\ \hline 7 \end{array}$ [M] $\begin{array}{r} 15 \\ -7 \\ \hline 8 \end{array}$ [N] $\begin{array}{r} 16 \\ -8 \\ \hline 8 \end{array}$ [O] $\begin{array}{r} 18 \\ -9 \\ \hline 9 \end{array}$ [P] $\begin{array}{r} 15 \\ -9 \\ \hline 6 \end{array}$

3. Find the sums.

[A] $\begin{array}{r} 62 \\ +23 \\ \hline 85 \end{array}$ [B] $\begin{array}{r} 35 \\ +24 \\ \hline 59 \end{array}$ [C] $\begin{array}{r} 16 \\ +51 \\ \hline 67 \end{array}$ [D] $\begin{array}{r} 328 \\ +160 \\ \hline 488 \end{array}$ [E] $\begin{array}{r} 457 \\ +132 \\ \hline 589 \end{array}$ [F] $\begin{array}{r} 615 \\ +204 \\ \hline 819 \end{array}$

4. Find the differences.

[A] $\begin{array}{r} 89 \\ -23 \\ \hline 66 \end{array}$ [B] $\begin{array}{r} 74 \\ -42 \\ \hline 32 \end{array}$ [C] $\begin{array}{r} 68 \\ -51 \\ \hline 17 \end{array}$ [D] $\begin{array}{r} 627 \\ -624 \\ \hline 3 \end{array}$ [E] $\begin{array}{r} 586 \\ -212 \\ \hline 374 \end{array}$ [F] $\begin{array}{r} 858 \\ -331 \\ \hline 527 \end{array}$

5. Find the sums.

[A] $\begin{array}{r} 38 \\ +27 \\ \hline 65 \end{array}$ [B] $\begin{array}{r} 65 \\ +25 \\ \hline 90 \end{array}$ [C] $\begin{array}{r} 73 \\ +18 \\ \hline 91 \end{array}$ [D] $\begin{array}{r} 46 \\ +37 \\ \hline 83 \end{array}$ [E] $\begin{array}{r} 85 \\ +9 \\ \hline 94 \end{array}$ [F] $\begin{array}{r} 16 \\ +39 \\ \hline 55 \end{array}$

[G] $\begin{array}{r} 75 \\ +86 \\ \hline 161 \end{array}$ [H] $\begin{array}{r} 38 \\ +95 \\ \hline 133 \end{array}$ [I] $\begin{array}{r} 67 \\ +67 \\ \hline 134 \end{array}$ [J] $\begin{array}{r} 83 \\ +96 \\ \hline 179 \end{array}$ [K] $\begin{array}{r} 49 \\ +78 \\ \hline 127 \end{array}$ [L] $\begin{array}{r} 36 \\ +95 \\ \hline 131 \end{array}$

Teaching Pages 108 and 109

● **PURPOSE**

To provide review of the material covered thus far in the text

● **PREPARATION**

Give the students a short review covering any topics with which they have had difficulty. It may prove helpful to have the students exhibit addition and subtraction problems on the chalkboard and explain them to members of the class.

6. Find the differences.

[A] 36 −17 *19*	[B] 43 −24 *19*	[C] 52 −17 *35*	[D] 58 −29 *29*	[E] 64 −27 *37*	[F] 80 −68 *12*
[G] 123 −47 *76*	[H] 144 −58 *86*	[I] 163 −76 *87*	[J] 150 −68 *82*	[K] 131 −75 *56*	[L] 155 −67 *88*

7. Find the sums.

[A] 8000 + 700 + 60 + 5 *8765*

[B] 50,000 + 9000 + 700 + 80 + 2 *59,782*

[C] 200,000 + 60,000 + 3000 + 500 + 70 + 1 *263,571*

[D] 9,000,000 + 800,000 + 30,000 + 6000 + 400 + 30 + 6 *9,836,436*

[E] 7000 + 60 + 5 *7065*

[F] 50,000 + 700 + 3 *50,703*

[G] 900,000 + 8000 + 700 *908,700*

[H] 60,000,000 + 700,000 + 900 *60,700,900*

[I] 500,000 + 20,000 + 30 *520,030*

[J] 300,000,000 + 6,000,000 + 9
(See answers below) *306,000,009*

8. Study the example. Then write each number as shown in the example.

Example:

8295 = 8000 + 200 + 90 + 5

[A] 6543 [D] 64,347 [G] 387,265

[B] 8927 [E] 58,126 [H] 3,927,615

[C] 5281 [F] 95,384 [I] 2,834,765

Exercise for Experts

Add the numbers one, two, three.
Now find their product too.
I'm the answer either way,
Whichever one you do. Six

If you add me to myself
Then multiply by two,
It's 12 plus 4 you're sure to get.
You need no other clue.

WHO AM I?

Four

---

9. Find the sums and differences. *(See answers at right.)*

[A] IIII4 +2IIII 97	[B] IIIII −27 12	[C] 36 +IIIII 61	[D] IIII3 −36 5III	[E] 84 −3III III7
[F] IIII4IIII −237 6III2	[G] 885 −III3III 2III2	[H] 63III −207 IIIIII8	[I] 5III7 +III9III 733	[J] 8III6 −339 IIII1III

DIRECTIONS PAGE 109

Have the students work the exercises. Allow time for checking papers when they have finished.

Give all of the students an opportunity to participate in solving the riddles. Most of the students can understand the answers to the riddles once they are given. As you discuss the first riddle, observe that the idea involved is that of a perfect number. That is, if the sum of all the factors of a number except the number itself is that number, then the number is said to be a perfect number. Of course, six is a perfect number. The next perfect number is 28. The faster students may enjoy searching for perfect numbers. On the second riddle, most of the students can understand the correct answer, four, once it has been given. You should, however, give all students an opportunity to seek out the answer before it is given.

Notice that exercise 9 is of the reconstruction type in which the students must search for the missing digits. Give all the students an opportunity to participate in working these problems and in discussing the correct answers. Have the students explain how they found various digits.

Answers, exercises 8 and 9, page 109

8. [A] 6543 = 6000 + 500 + 40 + 3

[B] 8927 = 8000 + 900 + 20 + 7

[C] 5281 = 5000 + 200 + 80 + 1

[D] 64,347 = 60,000 + 4000 + 300 + 40 + 7

[E] 58,126 = 50,000 + 8000 + 100 + 20 + 6

[F] 95,384 = 90,000 + 5000 + 300 + 80 + 4

[G] 387,265 = 300,000 + 80,000 + 7000 + 200 + 60 + 5

[H] 3,927,615 = 3,000,000 + 900,000 + 20,000 + 7000 + 600 + 10 + 5

[I] 2,834,765 = 2,000,000 + 800,000 + 30,000 + 4000 + 700 + 60 + 5

9.

[A] 74 +23 97	[B] 39 −27 12	[C] 36 +25 61
[D] 93 −36 57	[E] 84 −37 47	[F] 849 −237 612
[G] 885 −633 252	[H] 635 −207 428	[I] 537 +196 733
[J] 856 −339 517		

Give the students an opportunity to work the exercises. You may decide to check the papers yourself, depending upon how you choose to use the material on this page and page 111.

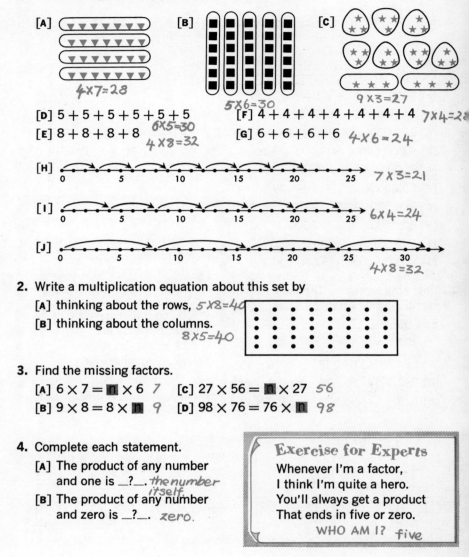

Chapter review

1. Write multiplication equations for each exercise.

[A] 4×7=28 [B] 5×6=30 [C] 9×3=27

[D] 5 + 5 + 5 + 5 + 5 + 5 6×5=30   [F] 4 + 4 + 4 + 4 + 4 + 4 + 4 7×4=28
[E] 8 + 8 + 8 + 8 4×8=32   [G] 6 + 6 + 6 + 6 4×6=24

[H] 7×3=21

[I] 6×4=24

[J] 4×8=32

2. Write a multiplication equation about this set by
[A] thinking about the rows, 5×8=40
[B] thinking about the columns. 8×5=40

3. Find the missing factors.
[A] 6 × 7 = ■ × 6 7   [c] 27 × 56 = ■ × 27 56
[B] 9 × 8 = 8 × ■ 9   [D] 98 × 76 = 76 × ■ 98

4. Complete each statement.
[A] The product of any number and one is _?_. the number itself
[B] The product of any number and zero is _?_. zero.

> **Exercise for Experts**
> Whenever I'm a factor,
> I think I'm quite a hero.
> You'll always get a product
> That ends in five or zero.
> WHO AM I? five

Teaching Pages 110 and 111

● **PURPOSE**

To provide a chapter review

To serve as an evaluation or as a guide for developing your own evaluation

● **PREPARATION**

Provide the students with a short oral practice of the multiplication facts. Now review, step by step, each of the various interpretations which were introduced for multiplication. First review the idea of multiplication associated with sets of sets, then review repeated addition, the number line, skip counting, and finally the idea of product

Have the students work the exercises. You may, if you choose, treat the riddles and exercise 8 as enrichment material for the more able students.

5. Find the products.

[A] 2×4 *8* [I] 2×7 *14* [Q] Since $8 \times 7 = 56$, we know that $7 \times 8 = $ ■. *56*

[B] 6×0 *0* [J] 5×4 *20* [R] Since $9 \times 6 = 54$, we know that $6 \times 9 = $ ■. *54*

[C] 1×8 *8* [K] 2×5 *10* [S] Since $6 \times 7 = 42$, we know that $7 \times 6 = $ ■. *42*

[D] 5×3 *15* [L] 5×6 *30* [T] Since $8 \times 6 = 48$, we know that $6 \times 8 = $ ■. *48*

[E] 2×6 *12* [M] 2×9 *18* [U] Since $9 \times 8 = 72$, we know that $8 \times 9 = $ ■. *72*

[F] 0×9 *0* [N] 5×7 *35* [V] Since $5 \times 5 = 25$, we know that $6 \times 5 = $ ■. *30*

[G] 5×5 *25* [O] 2×8 *16* [W] Since $6 \times 6 = 36$, we know that $7 \times 6 = $ ■. *42*

[H] 7×1 *7* [P] 6×2 *12* [X] Since $7 \times 7 = 49$, we know that $8 \times 7 = $ ■. *56*

[Y] Since $8 \times 8 = 64$, we know that $9 \times 9 = $ ■. *81*

6. Find the products.

[A] 3×3 *9* [E] 4×5 *20* [I] 4×7 *28* [M] 3×8 *24* [Q] 4×6 *24* [U] 6×9 *54*

[B] 7×8 *56* [F] 7×7 *49* [J] 6×8 *48* [N] 4×9 *36* [R] 7×9 *63* [V] 3×7 *21*

[C] 3×4 *12* [G] 3×9 *27* [K] 5×8 *40* [O] 3×6 *18* [S] 3×5 *15* [W] 4×8 *32*

[D] 6×7 *42* [H] 8×8 *64* [L] 4×4 *16* [P] 6×6 *36* [T] 9×9 *81* [X] 8×9 *72*

7. Complete the sentence.
Then find the product.

[A] For 3 sets of 10, we write ■. *30*
$3 \times 10 = $ ■ *30*

[B] For 5 sets of 10, we write ■. *50*
$5 \times 10 = $ ■ *50*

[C] For 8 sets of 10, we write ■. *80*
$8 \times 10 = $ ■ *80*

[D] For 7 sets of 10, we write ■. *70*
$7 \times 10 = $ ■ *70*

[E] For 9 sets of 10, we write ■. *90*
$9 \times 10 = $ ■ *90*

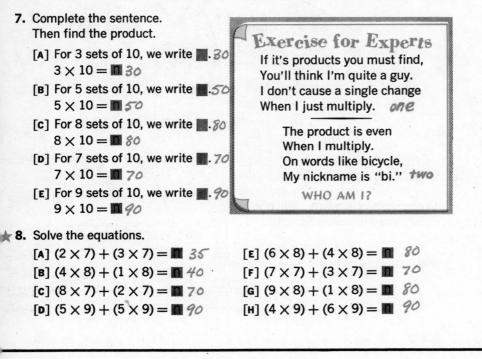

Exercise for Experts

If it's products you must find,
You'll think I'm quite a guy.
I don't cause a single change
When I just multiply. *one*

———

The product is even
When I multiply.
On words like bicycle,
My nickname is "bi." *two*

WHO AM I?

★ **8.** Solve the equations.

[A] $(2 \times 7) + (3 \times 7) = $ ■ *35*

[B] $(4 \times 8) + (1 \times 8) = $ ■ *40*

[C] $(8 \times 7) + (2 \times 7) = $ ■ *70*

[D] $(5 \times 9) + (5 \times 9) = $ ■ *90*

[E] $(6 \times 8) + (4 \times 8) = $ ■ *80*

[F] $(7 \times 7) + (3 \times 7) = $ ■ *70*

[G] $(9 \times 8) + (1 \times 8) = $ ■ *80*

[H] $(4 \times 9) + (6 \times 9) = $ ■ *90*

sets. It is important that the students have all these ideas in mind. Also review the association of multiplication with rectangular arrays of objects. This will be used considerably in future lessons concerning multiplication.

Teaching
Geometry Lesson 4

PURPOSE

To introduce the concept of the angle

To introduce the concept of the triangle

To provide intuitive experience with the sum of the angles of a triangle

To introduce the idea of interior and exterior of angles and triangles

The chief purpose of this lesson is to provide the students with an exciting experience in working with one of the key geometric facts. It is not intended that the students remember all the ideas associated with angles and triangles presented here. The important thing is to give the students an opportunity to discover that placing the three angles of a triangle in the special way suggested will always result in the angles' placement around one point so that two of the sides form a straight line.

MATHEMATICS

The underlying mathematics of this lesson is that the sum of the degree measures of the three angles of any triangle is 180 degrees. The illustration below demonstrates this. You will notice that in explaining the reasoning behind this geometric truth, we utilize the fact that for any pair of parallel lines bisected by a third line, certain pairs of angles have equal degree measures.

The definition of an angle as the two rays (and not the inside portion) may be contrary to previously developed notions. However, this definition is most useful for future work in geometry. It is also compatible with most of the acceptable literature on geometry. Of course, there is no need to discuss this with the students.

Approach this lesson as an exciting adventure in learning something interesting about geometry. So that the students have every opportunity to make the key discovery on their own, you should attempt, so far as possible, to give a minimum exposition with regard to what they are going to find out in this lesson.

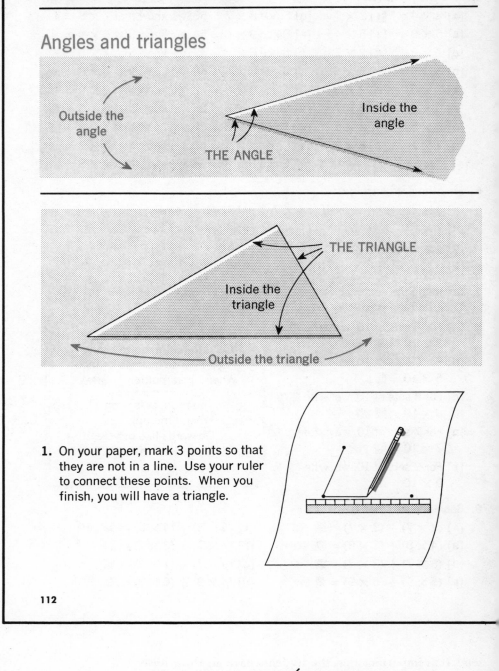

GEOMETRY - Lesson 4

Angles and triangles

Outside the angle

Inside the angle

THE ANGLE

THE TRIANGLE

Inside the triangle

Outside the triangle

1. On your paper, mark 3 points so that they are not in a line. Use your ruler to connect these points. When you finish, you will have a triangle.

112

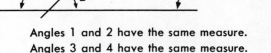

4   1   3   2 — Parallel lines

Angles 1 and 2 have the same measure.
Angles 3 and 4 have the same measure.

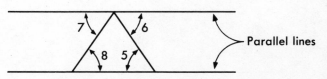

7   6   8   5 — Parallel lines

Angles 5 and 6 have the same measure.
Angles 7 and 8 have the same measure.

2. [A] Color each corner of your triangle a different color.

[B] Now cut out the triangle.

[C] Draw a line on another paper. Mark a point on the line. Tear the corners off your triangle. Then paste the 3 corners around the point like this.

Make the edges touch, but do not let them overlap.

3. [A] Make another triangle and use 3 different colors to color the corners. This time paste your 3 corners around the same point you used before. Put these corners on the other side of the line.

[B] Did the 6 corners go all the way around the point?

[C] Do you think this would happen if you did it again with other triangles of different shapes?

DIRECTIONS
PAGES 112 and 113

Study the material on page 112 with the class. Assist them in marking points on their papers and drawing the triangle as directed at the bottom of the page. Be sure that all the students are able to follow the directions accurately.

Have the students continue reading the directions and looking at the pictures to guide them in their work on page 113. If some students need special help in the passing activity suggested in exercise 2c, demonstrate how to place the pieces so that the edges touch but do not overlap.

When the students have completed exercise 3 and have had adequate time to discover the result, be sure that you emphasize that the six corners of the two different triangles go all the way around the point and that three corners of one triangle go exactly halfway around the point (that is, two of the edges should be on a straight line). If time permits, before you make these observations, you might give the class an opportunity to repeat the experiment with different triangles.

135

Objectives of Chapter 5

To introduce division concepts

To relate division to sets

To relate division to repeated subtraction

To relate division to multiplication

To relate division to the number line

To introduce word problems involving division

To develop skills in finding quotients related to basic multiplication facts

Just as with the other operations, division is introduced first in terms of set concepts. For clarity and to relate division quickly to the idea of repeated subtraction, we use only one set interpretation (the number of equivalent sets) to introduce the concept of division. Later in the chapter, another set interpretation (the number in each set) of division is brought out and emphasized primarily as a key for solving certain types of word problems.

Although the initial introduction to division is in terms of sets, the basic working definition of division is in terms of multiplication. Once a relationship is established between division and multiplication, the set concepts associated with division primarily become aids in relating division to certain physical situations which the students may encounter in various problems. For example, it may well turn out that the student will use more than one concept of division in working a single problem. If a student is working a problem in which he must find the number of sets or the number of objects in each of a given number of equivalent sets, he may decide that division is the correct operation for this particular problem. He then writes a division equation. Once this equation is written, it is not necessary that the student use set ideas to solve the equation. The student may solve the equation either by repeated subtraction or by thinking of the quotient as a missing factor. The important thing is that the student be able to interpret word problems and the set concepts, determine the correct operations, and then consider the problem with an understanding of the operation. The method used to solve the equation need not be the method suggested in the problem.

The relationship between division and repeated subtraction is emphasized for two reasons. First, this provides an excellent opportunity to relate certain ideas of division to those of multiplication (in earlier chapters, multiplication was related to repeated addition, and now division is related to repeated subtraction). Second, and perhaps more important, relating division to repeated subtraction prepares the students for a thorough understanding of the long-division process which will be approached in a later chapter.

Certainly, students must be led to understand why the subtraction process is involved in long division. This careful build-up of the relation between division and repeated subtraction should form the necessary background for such an understanding. Of course, relating division to operations demonstrated on the number line is nothing more than relating division to repeated subtraction or to "backward" skip counting.

Mathematics of Chapter 5

We give here a formal definition of division.

If a, b, and c are whole numbers such that

$$b \neq 0 \quad \text{and} \quad a \times b = c,$$

then

$$a = c \div b.$$

Note in particular that $c \div b$ is the first factor in the equation $a \times b = c$.

$$a \times b = c \qquad (b \neq 0)$$
$$\overbrace{c \div b}$$

An example of this is as follows:

$$2 \times 3 = 6,$$
$$2 = 6 \div 3.$$

The relation between division and multiplication may be brought more clearly into focus by this type of example.

$$n \times 4 = 12 \qquad\qquad 12 \div 4 = n$$

These two numbers are the same.

That is, finding the quotient is equivalent to finding a missing factor. Certainly this idea parallels the addition-subtraction relationship with the single exception that in division one of the factors (the second in our definition) cannot be zero. We rule out division by zero. The reasoning behind this choice is clearly brought out in the students' text, page 124.

Teaching Chapter 5

Plan to cover this material in about three weeks. Set an upper limit of $3\frac{1}{2}$ to four weeks. Here again, you will want to adjust the coverage of this chapter to the abilities and previous achievements of your students.

One of the chief items to consider in evaluating students' progress in this chapter is their ability to find quotients by thinking about missing factors. When the student is asked to find the quotient $48 \div 6$, it is desirable for him to think, "What number times six gives 48? Six eights are 48; therefore, 48 divided by six equals eight." Since we do not emphasize memorization of subtraction or division facts in this series, it is vital that the students become efficient in this method of thinking.

Of course, we also want to have the students understand the various set concepts related to the division concept. Students should be able to relate division to finding both the number of equivalent sets and the number in each of so many equivalent sets.

As we pointed out earlier, set concepts in word problems merely trigger the division operation. Once the student recognizes that he should divide to get the correct answer, then we would hope that he would think about missing factors to find the correct quotient. However, the less able students should not be penalized if they continue to use repeated subtraction for finding quotients.

In conclusion, we would point out that when you design your tests, you should have in mind three main themes. The first, of course, is understanding the general concept of division; the second is skill in finding the quotients related to basic multiplication facts; the third is ability to interpret various kinds of word problems.

Read and work through the discussion exercises at the top of the page with the students. Have the students complete the second exercise set on their own. Allow time for discussion after the students have completed the page.

Chapter **5** **DIVISION**

Division and sets

DISCUSSION EXERCISES

1. [A] How many sets of 6 can we get from a set of 18? 3
   [B] How many sixes are in 18? 3

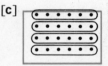

2. [A] How many sets of 4 can we get from a set of 20? 5
   [B] How many fours are in 20? 5

3. [A] How many sets of 3 can we get from a set of 15? 5
   [B] How many threes are in 15? 5

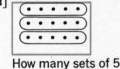

EXERCISES

1. Look at the set. Then answer the question.

[A] 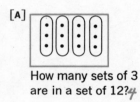 [B] [C]

How many sets of 3 are in a set of 12? 4

How many sets of 5 are in a set of 15? 3

How many sixes are in 24? 4

2. [A] Draw 21 dots. Ring as many sets of 3 as you can. How many sets of 3 did you find? 7

   [B] Draw 24 dots. Ring as many sets of 4 as you can. How many sets of 4 did you find? 6

114

Teaching Pages 114 and 115

- **PURPOSE**

  To introduce the division concept
  To relate division to set concepts

- **MATHEMATICS**

  Once the concept of division is defined in terms of multiplication (the quotient is defined as a missing factor), the relationships between division and sets as well as division and repeated subtraction become quite apparent.

  In this lesson, division is related to finding the number of equivalent sets of a given size. To see how this idea relates to multiplication, we need only to look at our set

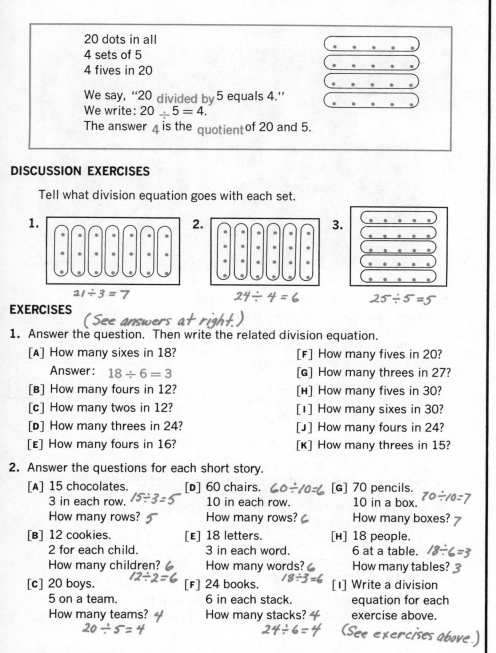

20 dots in all
4 sets of 5
4 fives in 20

We say, "20 divided by 5 equals 4."
We write: 20 ÷ 5 = 4.
The answer 4 is the quotient of 20 and 5.

DISCUSSION EXERCISES

Tell what division equation goes with each set.

1. $21 \div 3 = 7$

2. $24 \div 4 = 6$

3. $25 \div 5 = 5$

EXERCISES

(See answers at right.)

1. Answer the question. Then write the related division equation.

[A] How many sixes in 18?
   Answer: $18 \div 6 = 3$
[B] How many fours in 12?
[C] How many twos in 12?
[D] How many threes in 24?
[E] How many fours in 16?

[F] How many fives in 20?
[G] How many threes in 27?
[H] How many fives in 30?
[I] How many sixes in 30?
[J] How many fours in 24?
[K] How many threes in 15?

2. Answer the questions for each short story.

[A] 15 chocolates. $15 \div 3 = 5$
   3 in each row.
   How many rows? 5

[B] 12 cookies.
   2 for each child.
   How many children? 6
   $12 \div 2 = 6$

[C] 20 boys.
   5 on a team.
   How many teams? 4
   $20 \div 5 = 4$

[D] 60 chairs. $60 \div 10 = 6$
   10 in each row.
   How many rows? 6

[E] 18 letters.
   3 in each word.
   How many words? 6
   $18 \div 3 = 6$

[F] 24 books.
   6 in each stack.
   How many stacks? 4
   $24 \div 6 = 4$

[G] 70 pencils. $70 \div 10 = 7$
   10 in a box.
   How many boxes? 7

[H] 18 people.
   6 at a table. $18 \div 6 = 3$
   How many tables? 3

[I] Write a division
   equation for each
   exercise above.
   (See exercises above.)

As you read and study the material at the top of the page with the students, emphasize the words *divided by, division,* and *quotient.*

Following this preparatory session, use the three discussion exercises to continue emphasizing the ideas presented in the examples at the top of the page.

Have the students complete exercise 1. When they have finished, conduct a discussion similar to that held for the discussion exercises.

Discuss and work through the first one or two problems of exercise 2 with the class. In each case, exhibit a division equation for the exercise once it has been completed. Now give the students an opportunity to complete the page.

Notice that exercise 2I asks the students to write a division equation for each of the previous exercises. If you prefer, you can have them do this after they work *each* exercise rather than after they have worked all the exercises. Allow time at the end for a discussion of the exercises.

Answers, exercise 1, page 115

B. $12 \div 4 = 3$	G. $27 \div 3 = 9$
C. $12 \div 2 = 6$	H. $30 \div 5 = 6$
D. $24 \div 3 = 8$	I. $30 \div 6 = 5$
E. $16 \div 4 = 4$	J. $24 \div 4 = 6$
F. $20 \div 5 = 4$	K. $15 \div 3 = 5$

---

interpretation of multiplication. That is, the equation $3 \times 4 = 12$ is associated with the idea of three sets of four. In division, when we attempt to find the number of sets of four in a set of 12, we actually are finding the factor, three, in the multiplication equation $3 \times 4 = 12$. Note that three is associated with the number of sets and four with the number in each set.

PREPARATION

Exhibit a set and give the students an opportunity to discover, by removing objects from the sets, how many sets of a given size are contained within this set. For example, show a set of 18 and ask the students how many sets of three they can find in a set of 18. Have someone come up

and remove the objects, three at a time, and count the number of threes that he removes. When the class discovers that six sets were removed, write on the chalkboard, "We can get 6 sets of 3 from a set of 18." Continue this type of set demonstration until the students have grasped the idea. Follow this by exhibiting the corresponding division equations for each set demonstration. That is, for the example given above, write on the chalkboard $18 \div 3 = 6$.

Call attention to the new operation, *division;* the phrase, *divided by;* and the fact that in this exercise, six is the *quotient.* Repeat this discussion for the other examples.

Instruct the students to work the exercises. Notice that exercises 6 and 7 are designed primarily for the more able students. Allow time, when the students have finished, for discussion and checking papers.

At the ball game

1. Mr. Smith took Ted and some of his friends to see a baseball game. The children's tickets were $2 each and cost Mr. Smith $10. How many went to the ball game with Mr. Smith? *5*

2. The Blue Sox scored 2 runs in each inning until the scoreboard read How many innings had they played then? *4*

BLUE SOX	8
GREEN SOX	0

3. The final score was 9 to 6. Who won the game? *Blue Sox*

4. During the game, Mr. Smith spent 90 cents for popcorn. The popcorn cost 10 cents a bag. How many bags did he buy? *9*

5. Each team had 6 pitchers. How many pitchers were there in all? *12*

★ 6. Ted lived 15 miles from the ball park. Mr. Smith drove at the rate of 3 miles each 5 minutes. How long did it take to get from the ball park to Ted's house? *25 minutes*

★ 7. Jim lived 6 miles farther from the ball park than Ted. How long would it take Mr. Smith to get from the ball park to Jim's house? *35 minutes*

Teaching Pages 116 and 117

● **PURPOSE**

To continue emphasizing the concept of division

To provide word-problem experiences with the ideas of division

To relate division to repeated subtraction

● **PREPARATION**

If necessary, repeat some set demonstrations similar to those on pages 114 and 115. You will observe that the word problems in this lesson are primarily centered on finding the number of sets of a given size. This, of course, corresponds to the introduction of the division concept. Later,

Division and subtraction

1. Write a subtraction equation for each set.

[A] • • • • • • • • • • • • • • • • (• • • •) *20-4=16*

[B] • • • • • • • • • • • • (• • • •) *16-4=12*

[C] • • • • • • • • (• • • •) *12-4=8*

[D] • • • • (• • • •) *8-4=4*

[E] (• • • •) *4-4=0*

2. [A] Study exercise 1 and tell how many fours are in 20. *5*

[B] Solve this equation. $20 \div 4 = \blacksquare$ *5*

3. Solve the equations.

[A] $15 - 5 = \blacksquare$ *10*   [B] $28 - 7 = \blacksquare$ *21*   [C] $30 - 10 = \blacksquare$ *20*

$10 - 5 = \blacksquare$ *5* $21 - 7 = \blacksquare$ *14* $20 - 10 = \blacksquare$ *10*

$5 - 5 = \blacksquare$ *0* $14 - 7 = \blacksquare$ *7* $10 - 10 = \blacksquare$ *0*

$15 \div 5 = \blacksquare$ *3* $7 - 7 = \blacksquare$ *0* $30 \div 10 = \blacksquare$ *3*

$28 \div 7 = \blacksquare$ *4*

4. [A] Find these differences.

24	20	16	12	8	4
−4	−4	−4	−4	−4	−4
20	*16*	*12*	*8*	*4*	*0*

[B] How many times did you subtract 4? *6*

[C] How many fours are in 24? *6*

[D] Write a division equation about this. *24÷4=6*

5. [A] Find these differences.

21	18	15	12	9	6	3
−3	−3	−3	−3	−3	−3	−3
18	*15*	*12*	*9*	*6*	*3*	*0*

[B] How many times did you subtract 3? *7*

[C] How many threes are in 21? *7*

[D] Write a division equation about this. *21÷3=7*

Give the students an opportunity to work the exercises. Allow time for discussion when they have finished. Call special attention to exercise 1 where the students have an opportunity to observe the idea of repeated subtraction through illustrations with sets. It is an important part of this lesson to associate with each set picture and subtraction equation the one associated division equation.

Observe with the students that in multiplication they can use repeated addition to find the product and that in division they can use subtraction to find the quotient.

Following this discussion, instruct the students to work the exercises. When they have finished, allow time for a discussion of the answers.

we will approach the idea of finding how many in each group of equivalent sets. Subsequently, division will be related to multiplication, and this will become the working definition and chief meaning for the concept of division.

Exhibit a set of 28 objects on a demonstration table. Have the students come to the table and remove the objects seven at a time. Each time a set is removed, write a subtraction equation which illustrates what has happened. For example, the first time a student removes seven objects, write $28 - 7 = 21$. The next time, $21 - 7 = 14$, and so on to $7 - 7 = 0$. Now, count with the students the number of times they were able to remove sets of seven. Observe with them that this shows that there are four sevens in 28 or that $28 \div 7 = 4$. If necessary, repeat this with other examples.

Study the number lines at the top of the page with the students. In each case, relate the operation shown on the number line to the equation below the number line. Following this discussion, give the students an opportunity to work the exercises on this page. Allow time at the end for checking papers.

Answers, exercise 1, page 118

[A] $36 \div 9 = 4$
[B] $40 \div 8 = 5$
[C] $35 \div 5 = 7$
[D] $36 \div 4 = 9$
[E] $36 \div 6 = 6$

Division and the number line

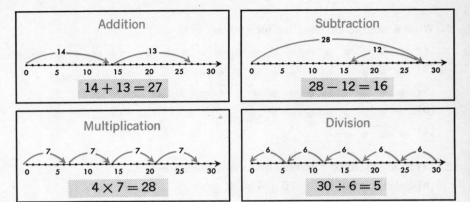

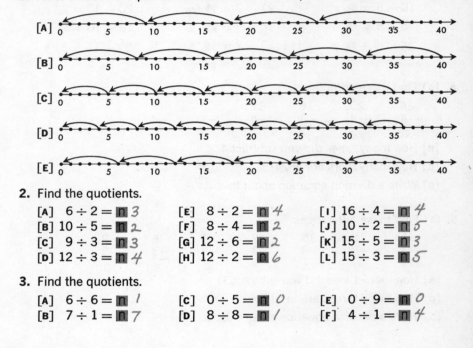

EXERCISES

1. Write a division equation for each number-line picture. *(See answers at left.)*

[A]

[B]

[C]

[D]

[E]

2. Find the quotients.

[A] $6 \div 2 = $ ■ 3   [E] $8 \div 2 = $ ■ 4   [I] $16 \div 4 = $ ■ 4
[B] $10 \div 5 = $ ■ 2   [F] $8 \div 4 = $ ■ 2   [J] $10 \div 2 = $ ■ 5
[C] $9 \div 3 = $ ■ 3   [G] $12 \div 6 = $ ■ 2   [K] $15 \div 5 = $ ■ 3
[D] $12 \div 3 = $ ■ 4   [H] $12 \div 2 = $ ■ 6   [L] $15 \div 3 = $ ■ 5

3. Find the quotients.

[A] $6 \div 6 = $ ■ 1   [C] $0 \div 5 = $ ■ 0   [E] $0 \div 9 = $ ■ 0
[B] $7 \div 1 = $ ■ 7   [D] $8 \div 8 = $ ■ 1   [F] $4 \div 1 = $ ■ 4

Teaching Pages 118 and 119

• **PURPOSE**

To show the division operation, as it is related to the number line

To provide a meaningful activity with division concepts

• **PREPARATION**

Draw on the chalkboard a number line with points labeled to 18. Demonstrate addition, subtraction, and multiplication operations on this number line. Exhibit each time the proper equation for the number-line picture.

Now exhibit on the chalkboard a division combination such as $15 \div 3$. Ask the students if they can guess what the

The function game

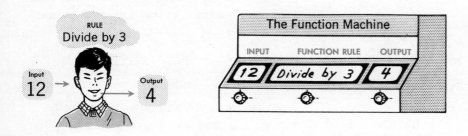

Study with the students the illustration at the top of the page. Note with them that the boy hears the number 12, uses the rule "divide by three," and then says four. Discuss the relationship between the picture of the boy and the function machine. That is, 12 is the input, the machine divides 12 by three, and the output is four.

Now discuss exercise 1 and have the students give the answers for parts A, B, and C. Upon completion of this discussion, instruct the students to finish the page on their own. When they have done this, allow time for discussion and checking papers.

EXERCISES

Think about the function machine and give the missing numbers.

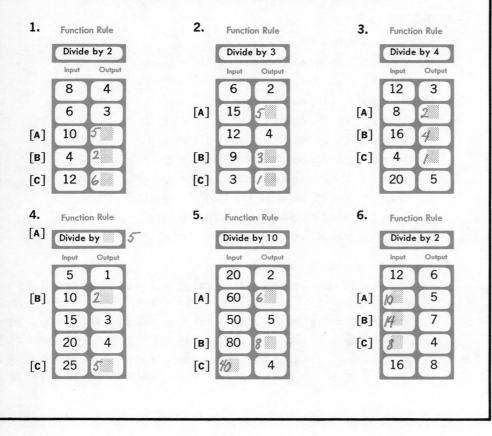

1. Function Rule — Divide by 2

Input	Output
8	4
6	3
[A] 10	5
[B] 4	2
[C] 12	6

2. Function Rule — Divide by 3

Input	Output
6	2
[A] 15	5
12	4
[B] 9	3
[C] 3	1

3. Function Rule — Divide by 4

Input	Output
12	3
[A] 8	2
[B] 16	4
[C] 4	1
20	5

4. Function Rule — [A] Divide by 5

Input	Output
5	1
[B] 10	2
15	3
20	4
[C] 25	5

5. Function Rule — Divide by 10

Input	Output
20	2
[A] 60	6
50	5
[B] 80	8
[C] 40	4

6. Function Rule — Divide by 2

Input	Output
12	6
[A] 10	5
[B] 14	7
[C] 8	4
16	8

jumps on the number line will look like for division. Give them an opportunity to discuss this idea. If the students do not discover the proper procedure for showing division on the number line, it should be demonstrated to them, but it is important that they explore the idea on their own prior to being told.

Once the students discover the proper procedure for exhibiting division on the number line, give them several examples in which they both draw the arrows for a given division and give a division equation for a number-line picture with the arrows drawn.

Study with the students the two boxed examples at the top of the page. Point out in particular that multiplication and division are related to one another in much the same way as addition is related to subtraction.

Following this discussion, have the students work the exercises. When they have finished, allow time for discussion of the exercises and the relationship between division and multiplication.

Division and multiplication

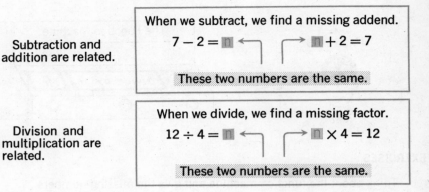

Subtraction and addition are related.

When we subtract, we find a missing addend.

$$7 - 2 = \blacksquare \qquad \blacksquare + 2 = 7$$

These two numbers are the same.

Division and multiplication are related.

When we divide, we find a missing factor.

$$12 \div 4 = \blacksquare \qquad \blacksquare \times 4 = 12$$

These two numbers are the same.

EXERCISES

1. Find the quotients.

   [A] Since $2 \times 4 = 8$, we know that $8 \div 4 = \blacksquare$. 2

   [B] Since $3 \times 3 = 9$, we know that $9 \div 3 = \blacksquare$. 3

   [C] Since $5 \times 2 = 10$, we know that $10 \div 2 = \blacksquare$. 5

   [D] Since $3 \times 5 = 15$, we know that $15 \div 5 = \blacksquare$. 3

   [E] Since $5 \times 3 = 15$, we know that $15 \div 3 = \blacksquare$. 5

   [F] Since $4 \times 5 = 20$, we know that $20 \div 5 = \blacksquare$. 4

   [G] Since $5 \times 4 = 20$, we know that $20 \div 4 = \blacksquare$. 5

   [H] Since $6 \times 3 = 18$, we know that $18 \div 3 = \blacksquare$. 6

   [I] Since $3 \times 6 = 18$, we know that $18 \div 6 = \blacksquare$. 3

   [J] Since $9 \times 8 = 72$, we know that $72 \div 8 = \blacksquare$. 9

2. Find the missing factors and quotients.

   [A] $\blacksquare \times 4 = 12$ 3   [D] $\blacksquare \times 5 = 10$ 2   [G] $\blacksquare \times 5 = 15$ 3   [J] $\blacksquare \times 4 = 16$ 4
   $12 \div 4 = \blacksquare$ 3 $10 \div 5 = \blacksquare$ 2 $15 \div 5 = \blacksquare$ 3 $16 \div 4 = \blacksquare$ 4

   [B] $\blacksquare \times 2 = 6$ 3   [E] $\blacksquare \times 6 = 12$ 2   [H] $\blacksquare \times 2 = 14$ 7   [K] $\blacksquare \times 5 = 20$ 4
   $6 \div 2 = \blacksquare$ 3 $12 \div 6 = \blacksquare$ 2 $14 \div 2 = \blacksquare$ 7 $20 \div 5 = \blacksquare$ 4

   [C] $\blacksquare \times 4 = 8$ 2   [F] $\blacksquare \times 6 = 18$ 3   [I] $\blacksquare \times 3 = 9$ 3   [L] $\blacksquare \times 9 = 18$ 2
   $8 \div 4 = \blacksquare$ 2 $18 \div 6 = \blacksquare$ 3 $9 \div 3 = \blacksquare$ 3 $18 \div 9 = \blacksquare$ 2

Teaching Pages 120 and 121

- **PURPOSE**

  To focus attention on the relation between division and multiplication

  To stress the idea of finding quotients by thinking about missing factors

- **MATHEMATICS**

  This lesson begins the more formal treatment of division, that of relating division to multiplication, and constitutes one of the key lessons of the chapter. As has been discussed previously, the basic working definition for division

Quotients and missing factors

The students checked their papers.
Judy checked Peter's paper.
Under one exercise, she wrote ⟶

$24 \div 4 = 5$ ✗
When 5 and 4 are factors, the product is 20, not 24.

Judy explained, "To find $24 \div 4$, it helps to ask yourself what number multiplied by 4 gives 24."

When Peter found the missing factor 6, he wrote the quotient correctly. $24 \div 4 = 6$

He said, "I know 6 is right because $6 \times 4 = 24$. Then he wrote this rule in his notebook:

We can find **QUOTIENTS** by looking for **MISSING FACTORS.**

EXERCISES

1. Find the missing numbers.

[A] We know that $28 \div 7 = \blacksquare$ because $4 \times 7 = 28$. 4
[B] We know that $42 \div 6 = \blacksquare$ because $7 \times 6 = 42$. 7
[C] We know that $54 \div 9 = 6$ because $\blacksquare \times 9 = 54$. 6
[D] We know that $40 \div 5 = 8$ because $\blacksquare \times 5 = 40$. 8
[E] We know that $63 \div 7 = \blacksquare$ because $9 \times 7 = 63$. 9
[F] We know that $48 \div 6 = \blacksquare$ because $8 \times 6 = 48$. 8
[G] We know that $72 \div 9 = 8$ because $\blacksquare \times 9 = 72$. 8
[H] We know that $36 \div 4 = \blacksquare$ because $9 \times 4 = 36$. 9
[I] We know that $56 \div 8 = 7$ because $\blacksquare \times 8 = 56$. 7
[J] We know that $63 \div 9 = \blacksquare$ because $7 \times 9 = 63$. 7

2. Find each quotient by thinking about a missing factor.

[A] $20 \div 4$ 5	[E] $24 \div 4$ 6	[I] $32 \div 8$ 4	[M] $25 \div 5$ 5	[Q] $56 \div 7$ 8
[B] $18 \div 6$ 3	[F] $27 \div 9$ 3	[J] $35 \div 7$ 5	[N] $36 \div 6$ 6	[R] $63 \div 9$ 7
[C] $12 \div 3$ 4	[G] $10 \div 2$ 5	[K] $48 \div 6$ 8	[O] $21 \div 3$ 7	[S] $81 \div 9$ 9
[D] $15 \div 5$ 3	[H] $30 \div 5$ 6	[L] $42 \div 7$ 6	[P] $16 \div 4$ 4	[T] $72 \div 8$ 9

As you and the students discuss and study the material at the top of the page, stress in particular the statement, "We can find quotients by looking for missing factors." While conducting this discussion, you might point out that this is much the same as finding differences by looking for missing addends.

On completion of this discussion, have the students work the exercises at the bottom of the page. Allow time at the end for the checking of papers.

is in terms of multiplication. That is, if we have three whole numbers a, b, and c, such that $b \neq 0$ and $a \times b = c$, then $a = c \div b$. Of course, in this definition b cannot be zero. In the mathematics section for this chapter, you will find a more complete explanation of the relationship of quotient and missing factor.

PREPARATION

Begin by reviewing for the class the relationship between addition and subtraction. Exhibit on the chalkboard several examples which require the students to find the missing addends. Now have the students consider related subtraction equations. An example of such related equations appears at the top of page 120.

Following this review of the relationship between addition and subtraction, write on the chalkboard a simple multiplication equation which requires finding the missing factor. For example, you might use $n \times 3 = 6$. Once the students find that the missing factor is 2, immediately beside or under this equation write the equation $6 \div 3 = n$. When the students discover that this answer also is 2, point out to them that in each equation the solution is 2. Continue this demonstration with other examples that relate a division equation to a multiplication equation.

Read and study with the class the boxed material at the top of the page. In each case, be sure the students observe how a certain division equation is related either to subtraction, to sets, or to multiplication.

Have the students work the exercises. When they have finished, discuss the exercises and point out that they thought about division and sets in exercise 1 and division and subtraction in exercise 2.

Division review

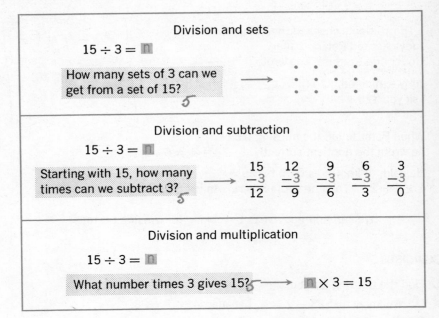

EXERCISES

1. Write a division equation for each exercise.

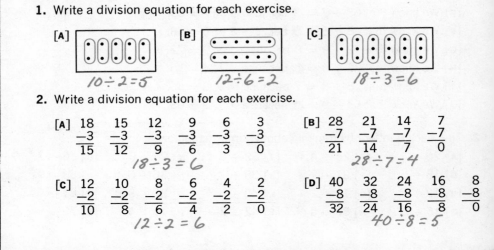

[A] $10 \div 2 = 5$ [B] $12 \div 6 = 2$ [C] $18 \div 3 = 6$

2. Write a division equation for each exercise.

[A]
$$\begin{array}{ccccc} 18 & 15 & 12 & 9 & 6 & 3 \\ -3 & -3 & -3 & -3 & -3 & -3 \\ \hline 15 & 12 & 9 & 6 & 3 & 0 \end{array}$$
$18 \div 3 = 6$

[B]
$$\begin{array}{cccc} 28 & 21 & 14 & 7 \\ -7 & -7 & -7 & -7 \\ \hline 21 & 14 & 7 & 0 \end{array}$$
$28 \div 7 = 4$

[C]
$$\begin{array}{cccccc} 12 & 10 & 8 & 6 & 4 & 2 \\ -2 & -2 & -2 & -2 & -2 & -2 \\ \hline 10 & 8 & 6 & 4 & 2 & 0 \end{array}$$
$12 \div 2 = 6$

[D]
$$\begin{array}{ccccc} 40 & 32 & 24 & 16 & 8 \\ -8 & -8 & -8 & -8 & -8 \\ \hline 32 & 24 & 16 & 8 & 0 \end{array}$$
$40 \div 8 = 5$

Teaching Pages 122 and 123

● **PURPOSE**

To review the various interpretations of division presented thus far

To provide more activity in finding quotients

● **PREPARATION**

Provide for the students an oral review of the various approaches to the division concept presented so far in the chapter. Review division in sets, division in repeated subtraction, and finish by emphasizing the relationship between division and multiplication. One of the most im-

3. Write a division equation for each exercise.

[A]
$$\begin{array}{ccc} 27 & 18 & 9 \\ -9 & -9 & -9 \\ \hline 18 & 9 & 0 \end{array}$$

[B]
$$\begin{array}{ccccc} 35 & 28 & 21 & 14 & 7 \\ -7 & -7 & -7 & -7 & -7 \\ \hline 28 & 21 & 14 & 7 & 0 \end{array}$$

$27 \div 9 = 3$ $35 \div 7 = 5$

4. Solve the equations.   **5.** Now find the quotients.

[A] ▦ $\times 6 = 12$ ⟶ [A] $12 \div 6 =$ ▦ 2, 2

[B] ▦ $\times 3 = 9$ ⟶ [B] $9 \div 3 =$ ▦ 3, 3

[C] ▦ $\times 4 = 8$ ⟶ [C] $8 \div 4 =$ ▦ 2, 2

[D] ▦ $\times 2 = 10$ ⟶ [D] $10 \div 2 =$ ▦ 5, 5

[E] ▦ $\times 3 = 12$ ⟶ [E] $12 \div 3 =$ ▦ 4, 4

[F] ▦ $\times 5 = 25$ ⟶ [F] $25 \div 5 =$ ▦ 5, 5

[G] ▦ $\times 6 = 18$ ⟶ [G] $18 \div 6 =$ ▦ 3, 3

[H] ▦ $\times 5 = 15$ ⟶ [H] $15 \div 5 =$ ▦ 3, 3

[I] ▦ $\times 2 = 14$ ⟶ [I] $14 \div 2 =$ ▦ 7, 7

[J] ▦ $\times 3 = 21$ ⟶ [J] $21 \div 3 =$ ▦ 7, 7

6. In each exercise, tell how many bags of marbles.

[A]	15 marbles 5 bags	③ ③ ... ?
[B]	20 marbles 4 bags	⑤ ⑤ ... ?
[C]	14 marbles 7 bags	② ② ... ?
[D]	18 marbles 3 bags	⑥ ⑥ ... ?
[E]	35 marbles 5 bags	⑦ ⑦ ... ?
[F]	28 marbles 7 bags	④ ④ ... ?

Before the students begin to work the exercises, point out that they will think about division and subtraction in exercise 3 and division and missing factors in exercises 4 and 5.

Some students may need extra help with exercise 6. Note with them that they are to visualize that each bag of marbles in a row contains the same number. That is, the bags of marbles that they can see are clearly labeled with a numeral, and they are to assume that all the other bags of marbles behind the gray tint have that same number. Of course, this exercise gives students an opportunity to think further about division.

When the students have completed this page, allow time for checking the exercises and a discussion of the ideas presented in exercise 6.

portant goals of the chapter is for the students to become adept at finding quotients by thinking about missing factors.

Give the students an opportunity to work and discuss the equations in the discussion exercises. During the discussion, encourage the students to verbalize the ideas being presented. Note in particular that in exercise 1 there is no solution, in exercise 2 any number is a solution, and in exercise 3 zero is the solution.

Discussion of the illustration should provide impetus for some lively and pertinent remarks by the students regarding why they should not divide by zero. Of course, the points to emphasize are that in one case division by zero gives no answer, and in the other case division by zero will give any answer. Proof of this can be made plausible to the students by having them "check" their answers. See the discussion of this in the preceding mathematics section.

Zero in division

DISCUSSION EXERCISES

In these exercises, tell whether each equation has many solutions, one solution, or no solution.

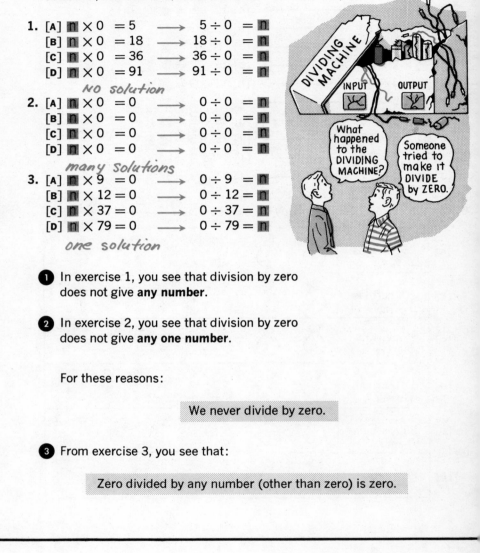

1. [A] ▧ × 0 = 5 ⟶ 5 ÷ 0 = ▧
   [B] ▧ × 0 = 18 ⟶ 18 ÷ 0 = ▧
   [C] ▧ × 0 = 36 ⟶ 36 ÷ 0 = ▧
   [D] ▧ × 0 = 91 ⟶ 91 ÷ 0 = ▧
   No solution

2. [A] ▧ × 0 = 0 ⟶ 0 ÷ 0 = ▧
   [B] ▧ × 0 = 0 ⟶ 0 ÷ 0 = ▧
   [C] ▧ × 0 = 0 ⟶ 0 ÷ 0 = ▧
   [D] ▧ × 0 = 0 ⟶ 0 ÷ 0 = ▧
   many solutions

3. [A] ▧ × 9 = 0 ⟶ 0 ÷ 9 = ▧
   [B] ▧ × 12 = 0 ⟶ 0 ÷ 12 = ▧
   [C] ▧ × 37 = 0 ⟶ 0 ÷ 37 = ▧
   [D] ▧ × 79 = 0 ⟶ 0 ÷ 79 = ▧
   one solution

1 In exercise 1, you see that division by zero does not give **any number**.

2 In exercise 2, you see that division by zero does not give **any one number**.

For these reasons:

We never divide by zero.

3 From exercise 3, you see that:

Zero divided by any number (other than zero) is zero.

Teaching Pages 124 and 125

● **PURPOSE**

To focus attention on zero in division
To focus attention on one in division

● **MATHEMATICS**

Another way to think about the restriction that does not permit division by zero is to consider the method by which we "check" division.

One in division

DISCUSSION EXERCISES

1. Find the missing factors.

   [A] ☐ $\times 6 = 6$ / [B] ☐ $\times 18 = 18$ / [C] ☐ $\times 75 = 75$ /

   Do you see that each factor is 1?

2. Find the quotients.

   [A] Since $1 \times 6 = 6$, we know that $6 \div 6 = $ ☐ . /

   [B] Since $1 \times 18 = 18$, we know that $18 \div 18 = $ ☐ . /

   [C] Since $1 \times 75 = 75$, we know that $75 \div 75 = $ ☐ . /

   Any number (except zero) divided by itself is 1.

3. Find the missing factors.

   [A] ☐ $\times 1 = 9$ *9* [B] ☐ $\times 1 = 23$ *23* [C] ☐ $\times 1 = 86$ *86*

4. Now find these quotients.

   [A] $9 \div 1 = $ ☐ *9* [B] $23 \div 1 = $ ☐ *23* [C] $86 \div 1 = $ ☐ *86*

   Any number divided by 1 is that number.

EXERCISES

1. Find the quotients.

   [A] $7 \div 7 = $ ☐ / [D] $0 \div 18 = $ ☐ *0* [G] $0 \div 1 = $ ☐ *0* [J] $95 \div 95 = $ ☐ /

   [B] $8 \div 1 = $ ☐ *8* [E] $27 \div 27 = $ ☐ / [H] $10 \div 10 = $ ☐ / [K] $95 \div 1 = $ ☐ *95*

   [C] $0 \div 6 = $ ☐ *0* [F] $128 \div 1 = $ ☐ *128* [I] $0 \div 156 = $ ☐ *0* [L] $0 \div 16 = $ ☐ *0*

2. Solve all the equations that you can. Some of them have no solutions.

   (See answers at right.)

   [A] $2 + 3 = $ ☐ [F] ☐ $\div 7 = 1$ [K] $0 \times $ ☐ $= 6$ [P] ☐ $+ 10 = 257$

   [B] $6 - $ ☐ $= 2$ [G] $0 \div 6 = $ ☐ [L] $17 - 9 = $ ☐ [Q] $18 - $ ☐ $= 0$

   [C] $8 \div 2 = $ ☐ [H] $19 \div $ ☐ $= 19$ [M] $0 \times $ ☐ $= 9$ [R] $58 \div $ ☐ $= 1$

   [D] ☐ $\times 4 = 12$ [I] ☐ $\times 0 = 6$ [N] $9 - 9 = $ ☐ [S] ☐ $+ 6 = 196$

   [E] $8 \times $ ☐ $= 0$ [J] $1 \div $ ☐ $= 1$ [O] ☐ $\times 3 = 9$ [T] ☐ $+ 16 = 16$

Division Equation	Check
$12 \div 4 = 3$	$3 \times 4 = 12$
$21 \div 3 = 7$	$7 \times 3 = 21$
$6 \div 0 = ?$	*No* number times zero gives 6.
$0 \div 0 = ?$	*Any* number times zero gives 0.

Since in one case there is no solution because *no* number works and in the other case there are many solutions because *every* number works, we do not divide by zero.

DIRECTIONS PAGE 125

As you read and discuss with the students the material at the top of the page, emphasize particularly that any number, other than zero, divided by itself is one and that any number divided by one is the same as that number. Now direct the students to work the exercises. When they have finished, provide time for discussion and answering questions.

Answers, exercise 2, page 125

[A]	5	[K]	no solution
[B]	4	[L]	8
[C]	4	[M]	no solution
[D]	3	[N]	0
[E]	0	[O]	3
[F]	7	[P]	247
[G]	0	[Q]	18
[H]	1	[R]	58
[I]	no solution	[S]	190
[J]	1	[T]	0

• PREPARATION

Use discussion material similar to that on pages 124 and 125 to prepare for this lesson. If you prefer, you can omit preparation for this lesson and treat the text material as preparation.

Give the students an opportunity to work the exercises. Go over the answers when they have finished so that the students can check their papers.

Let's Review

■ ADDITION   MEASUREMENT
■ SUBTRACTION   PLACE VALUE
MULTIPLICATION   ■ INEQUALITIES
DIVISION   PRINCIPLES

1. Do not try to find the correct answer. Just tell whether each answer is more than 70 or less than 70.

[A] 37 + 38 M   [E] 83 − 8 M
[B] 27 + 38 L   [F] 83 − 18 L
[C] 27 + 48 M   [G] 93 − 28 L
[D] 17 + 58 M   [H] 46 + 27 M

2. Find the sums.

[A] 35
+24
59

[B] 35
+25
60

[C] 48
+26
74

[D] 57
+19
76

[E] 68
+24
92

[F] 73
+14
87

[G] 66
+27
93

[H] 99
+4
103

[I] 88
+7
95

[J] 76
+66
142

[K] 35
+48
83

[L] 87
+32
119

[M] 93
+27
120

[N] 69
+25
94

[O] 46
+58
104

[P] 57
+48
105

[Q] 76
+64
140

[R] 19
+27
46

3. Find the differences.

[A] 83
−22
61

[B] 92
−33
59

[C] 75
−46
29

[D] 57
−34
23

[E] 61
−59
2

[F] 122
−34
88

[G] 74
−68
6

[H] 156
−72
84

[I] 182
−93
89

[J] 65
−37
28

4. Find the sums and differences.

[A] 35
+28
63

[B] 72
−43
29

[C] 68
+78
146

[D] 39
−19
20

[E] 92
−15
77

[F] 67
+67
134

[G] 95
+78
173

[H] 60
−17
43

[I] 34
−19
15

[J] 78
+62
140

[K] 104
−58
46

[L] 69
+76
145

[M] 143
−58
85

[N] 107
−89
18

[O] 36
+99
135

Teaching Pages 126 and 127

● **PURPOSE**

To maintain previously developed concepts and skills
To introduce a second set interpretation for division

● **PREPARATION**

This lesson reviews the processes involved in addition and subtraction exercises. Since this is a cumulative review, you might also include in your preparation activities some work with the multiplication combinations. This would be an excellent time to provide for the class a short oral practice session in the multiplication facts. A multiplication review is of special importance since the students

Division and sets again

In each exercise, the bags all have the same number of marbles.

#	Marbles		Question	Answer
1.	12 marbles	(bags)	How many in each bag?	4
2.	18 marbles	3 3 ?	How many bags?	6
3.	16 marbles	(bags)	How many in each bag?	4
4.	24 marbles	4 4 ?	How many bags?	6
5.	30 marbles	(bags)	How many in each bag?	5
6.	28 marbles	4 4 ?	How many bags?	7
7.	27 marbles	9 9 ?	How many bags?	3
8.	40 marbles	(bags)	How many in each bag?	8
9.	21 marbles	3 3 3 ?	How many bags?	7
10.	35 marbles	5 ? 5	How many bags?	7
11.	42 marbles	(bags)	How many in each bag?	6
12.	40 marbles	(bags)	How many in each bag?	10

After the students have completed the exercises, discuss the answers and the ideas involved. In particular, call attention to the two types of exercises, one where the students are asked to find the number of bags and the other where they are to find the number in each bag. The students should be familiar with the fact that it is helpful to think about the division operation in both cases.

will be working with multiplication and its relation to addition in the remaining part of the chapter.

MATHEMATICS

Since our basic working definition of division is in terms of multiplication we use set interpretations for multiplication to arrive at two different set interpretations for division. Because multiplication is commutative, we can consider division as finding either missing factor in a multiplication equation. For example, if we chose to associate with 4×5 the idea of four sets of five, then we should consider the equation $20 \div 5 = n$ as finding the number of sets and $20 \div 4 = n$ as finding the number in each set.

The set interpretations are used to give the students a meaningful physical activity to explain certain concepts of division and to trigger the division operation in certain types of word problems. That is, if students read a word problem which requires finding the number of equivalent sets of a given size or the number of objects in each of so many equivalent sets, they should again think about division. In each case, however, once the division operation has been triggered, the students should be encouraged to find the quotient by thinking about the missing factor.

If time permits, have the students write a division equation for each exercise. You might also have some of the exercises displayed on the chalkboard during the discussion period. It is often helpful to have students explain various problems to each other since the class often can understand a problem more readily if another classmate explains it.

Short stories

1. Answer the question. Then write a division equation about the story.

[A] 20 marbles.
Same number to
each of 5 boys.
How many marbles
for each boy? $20 \div 5 = 4$

[B] 15 cookies.
3 cookies to each girl.
How many girls
get cookies? $15 \div 3 = 5$

[C] 30 cents.
Apples 6 cents each.
How many apples can we buy? $30 \div 6 = 5$

[D] 24 cents spent for 3 oranges.
How much per orange? $24 \div 3 = 8$

[E] 18 people. 6 in each car.
How many cars are needed? $18 \div 6 = 3$

[F] 24 seats. Same number
in each of 6 rows.
How many seats in each row? $24 \div 6 = 4$

[G] 14 students.
Same number of girls as boys.
How many of each? $14 \div 2 = 7$

[H] 20 players for 4 teams. How
many players for each team? $20 \div 4 = 5$

[I] 18 players. 3 on each team.
How many teams? $18 \div 3 = 6$

[J] 28 days.
7 days per week. $28 \div 7 = 4$
How many weeks?

[K] 16 minutes.
2 minutes per mile.
How many miles? $16 \div 2 = 8$

[L] 24 feet. 3 feet per yard.
How many yards? $24 \div 3 = 8$

[M] 36 feet.
4 per dog.
How many dogs? $36 \div 4 = 9$

2. Answer the question. Then write a division equation about the sets. Remember when you think about division, the sets should have the same number.

[A] 12 dots.
4 in each set.
How many sets? $12 \div 4 = 3$

[B] 12 dots.
2 sets.
How many in each set? $12 \div 2 = 6$

[C] 15 dots.
3 in each set.
How many sets? $15 \div 3 = 5$

[D] 10 dots.
5 sets.
How many in each set? $10 \div 5 = 2$

[E] 15 dots.
3 sets.
How many in each set? $15 \div 3 = 5$

[F] 18 dots.
3 in each set.
How many sets? $18 \div 3 = 6$

[G] 16 dots.
4 sets.
How many in each set? $16 \div 4 = 4$

[H] 24 dots.
6 in each set.
How many sets? $24 \div 6 = 4$

[I] 24 dots. 8 sets.
How many in
each set? $24 \div 8 = 3$

Teaching Pages 128 and 129

● **PURPOSE**

To provide more experiences in working with the idea of the number of sets and the number in each set

To provide practice in finding quotients

To emphasize the importance of thinking about missing factors when finding quotients

● **PREPARATION**

Review for the students the material presented in the last lesson. Give them several exercises in relating two division equations to a given multiplication equation. Provide several equations in which the students are re-

Quotients and missing factors

EXERCISES

1. Find the missing factors.

[A] $\blacksquare \times 6 = 18$ *3* [D] $\blacksquare \times 8 = 24$ *3* [G] $6 \times \blacksquare = 24$ *4* [J] $6 \times \blacksquare = 30$ *5*

[B] $4 \times \blacksquare = 20$ *5* [E] $3 \times \blacksquare = 27$ *9* [H] $\blacksquare \times 8 = 16$ *2* [K] $\blacksquare \times 3 = 21$ *7*

[C] $\blacksquare \times 3 = 12$ *4* [F] $\blacksquare \times 5 = 25$ *5* [I] $9 \times \blacksquare = 27$ *3* [L] $5 \times \blacksquare = 35$ *7*

2. Find the quotients. (If you need help, look at exercise 1.)

[A] $24 \div 8 = \blacksquare$ *3* [D] $12 \div 3 = \blacksquare$ *4* [G] $16 \div 8 = \blacksquare$ *2* [J] $35 \div 5 = \blacksquare$ *7*

[B] $30 \div 6 = \blacksquare$ *5* [E] $27 \div 3 = \blacksquare$ *9* [H] $20 \div 4 = \blacksquare$ *5* [K] $24 \div 6 = \blacksquare$ *4*

[C] $27 \div 9 = \blacksquare$ *3* [F] $21 \div 3 = \blacksquare$ *7* [I] $25 \div 5 = \blacksquare$ *5* [L] $18 \div 6 = \blacksquare$ *3*

3. Find the quotients.

[A] Since $7 \times 8 = 56$, we know that $56 \div 8 = \blacksquare$. *7*

[B] Since $9 \times 7 = 63$, we know that $63 \div 9 = \blacksquare$. *7*

[C] Since $8 \times 6 = 48$, we know that $48 \div 6 = \blacksquare$. *8*

[D] Since $6 \times 7 = 42$, we know that $42 \div 6 = \blacksquare$. *7*

[E] Since $7 \times 5 = 35$, we know that $35 \div 5 = \blacksquare$. *7*

[F] Since $9 \times 8 = 72$, we know that $72 \div 9 = \blacksquare$. *8*

[G] Since $9 \times 6 = 54$, we know that $54 \div 6 = \blacksquare$. *9*

[H] Since $8 \times 8 = 64$, we know that $64 \div 8 = \blacksquare$. *8*

[I] Since $6 \times 10 = 60$, we know that $60 \div 10 = \blacksquare$. *6*

[J] Since $12 \times 3 = 36$, we know that $36 \div 12 = \blacksquare$. *3*

[K] Since $14 \times 3 = 42$, we know that $42 \div 3 = \blacksquare$. *14*

[L] Since $4 \times 15 = 60$, we know that $60 \div 4 = \blacksquare$. *15*

[M] Since $5 \times 19 = 95$, we know that $95 \div 19 = \blacksquare$. *5*

[N] Since $8 \times 12 = 96$, we know that $96 \div 12 = \blacksquare$. *8*

4. Find the quotients.

[A] $18 \div 3$ *6* [E] $27 \div 9$ *3* [I] $30 \div 5$ *6* [M] $0 \div 9$ *0*

[B] $20 \div 5$ *4* [F] $24 \div 4$ *6* [J] $21 \div 7$ *3* [N] $15 \div 3$ *5*

[C] $12 \div 4$ *3* [G] $16 \div 2$ *8* [K] $35 \div 7$ *5* [O] $18 \div 2$ *9*

[D] $24 \div 3$ *8* [H] $27 \div 1$ *27* [L] $14 \div 14$ *1* [P] $28 \div 7$ *4*

DIRECTIONS   PAGE 129

Have the students work the exercises. When they have finished, allow time for checking papers and discussion of the exercises. Focus particular attention on exercise 3 in which the students find quotients by knowing multiplication facts. Take special care to see that the students understand this idea.

quired to find missing factors. Following this, present pairs of division and multiplication equations in which the quotient turns out to be the missing factor.

As you read the material at the top of the page with the class, emphasize that the best way to become skillful at finding quotients is to know the multiplication facts very well. Now give the students an opportunity to do the first set of exercises on finding products. When they have finished, read the correct answers and have each student check his paper.

Instruct the student to do the second set of exercises on quotients as rapidly as possible. Remind them that if they have difficulty finding any quotient, they can find the answer by checking one of the multiplication exercises in the first set of exercises.

Supplementary exercises, Sets 40 and 41 (page 346) may be assigned as necessary beyond this page.

Skills in division

The best way to become skillful at finding quotients is to know multiplication facts very well. In the exercises below, you are first to find products. Then you are to find quotients. Each division exercise is taken from one of the multiplication exercises.

Find the products.

1. 3×4 _12_	11. 9×3 _27_	21. 5×8 _40_	31. 9×6 _54_	41. 5×7 _35_
2. 2×7 _14_	12. 6×6 _36_	22. 3×5 _15_	32. 5×9 _45_	42. 6×5 _30_
3. 9×2 _18_	13. 7×4 _28_	23. 7×6 _42_	33. 7×8 _56_	43. 9×4 _36_
4. 5×4 _20_	14. 1×9 _9_	24. 4×7 _28_	34. 3×9 _27_	44. 7×3 _21_
5. 6×3 _18_	15. 4×6 _24_	25. 2×9 _18_	35. 6×8 _48_	45. 9×8 _72_
6. 8×4 _32_	16. 8×7 _56_	26. 8×3 _24_	36. 9×5 _45_	46. 6×9 _54_
7. 4×4 _16_	17. 4×5 _20_	27. 5×6 _30_	37. 4×8 _32_	47. 9×0 _0_
8. 7×5 _35_	18. 6×4 _24_	28. 4×9 _36_	38. 7×7 _49_	48. 7×9 _63_
9. 3×6 _18_	19. 9×7 _63_	29. 8×9 _72_	39. 3×7 _21_	49. 9×9 _81_
10. 5×5 _25_	20. 3×8 _24_	30. 6×7 _42_	40. 8×5 _40_	50. 8×6

Find the quotients.

1. $16 \div 4$ _4_	11. $36 \div 6$ _6_	21. $24 \div 8$ _3_	31. $54 \div 9$ _6_	41. $54 \div 6$
2. $35 \div 7$ _5_	12. $12 \div 3$ _4_	22. $40 \div 5$ _8_	32. $45 \div 5$ _9_	42. $49 \div 7$
3. $32 \div 8$ _4_	13. $28 \div 7$ _4_	23. $30 \div 5$ _6_	33. $56 \div 7$ _8_	43. $0 \div 9$
4. $18 \div 3$ _6_	14. $9 \div 1$ _9_	24. $24 \div 3$ _8_	34. $30 \div 6$ _5_	44. $32 \div 4$
5. $18 \div 6$ _3_	15. $24 \div 4$ _6_	25. $36 \div 4$ _9_	35. $36 \div 9$ _4_	45. $63 \div 7$
6. $20 \div 5$ _4_	16. $56 \div 8$ _7_	26. $63 \div 9$ _7_	36. $35 \div 5$ _7_	46. $45 \div 9$
7. $25 \div 5$ _5_	17. $28 \div 4$ _7_	27. $72 \div 8$ _9_	37. $21 \div 7$ _3_	47. $81 \div 9$
8. $18 \div 9$ _2_	18. $42 \div 7$ _6_	28. $24 \div 6$ _4_	38. $40 \div 8$ _5_	48. $48 \div 6$
9. $27 \div 9$ _3_	19. $18 \div 2$ _9_	29. $42 \div 6$ _7_	39. $72 \div 9$ _8_	49. $48 \div 8$
10. $14 \div 2$ _7_	20. $15 \div 3$ _5_	30. $20 \div 4$ _5_	40. $21 \div 3$ _7_	50. $27 \div 3$

Teaching Pages 130 and 131

● **PURPOSE**

To develop skill in finding quotients

To re-emphasize the importance of multiplication facts for finding quotients

To provide word-problem experiences in working with division

● **PREPARATION**

Provide the students with a short oral practice session in finding quotients. They should also be given practice with multiplication facts.

At the dairy

1. Cartons of milk are put in boxes, with 6 cartons in each row. If a box holds 24 cartons of milk, how many rows are there? *4*

2. A machine fills 28 half-gallon milk cartons every 4 minutes. How many cartons does it fill in one minute? *7*

3. Cartons of ice cream are placed in large wire racks before they are put in the freezer. Each rack holds 48 cartons in 6 rows. How many cartons are in each row? *8*

4. When Susan's class went to the dairy, they went into the pasteurizing room in groups of 6. There are 30 students in Susan's class. How many groups of 6 did they have? *5*

5. On the way back to school, 5 students rode in each car. How many cars did they need? *6*

6. Miss Smith, the teacher, asked the students to write a paper about their trip to the dairy. Don decided to make up some problems for his paper. See if you can work them.

[A] 20 milk cartons in all MILK How many cartons are in each row? *5*

[B] 42 milk cartons in all MILK How many cartons are in each row? *7*

DIRECTIONS **PAGE 131**

Have the students work the exercises. As you discuss the exercises, it might help to have the students display their work on the chalkboard and attempt to explain the problems to the rest of the class.

Give the students an opportunity to work these exercises. Discuss with them any of the exercises that may have caused particular difficulty.

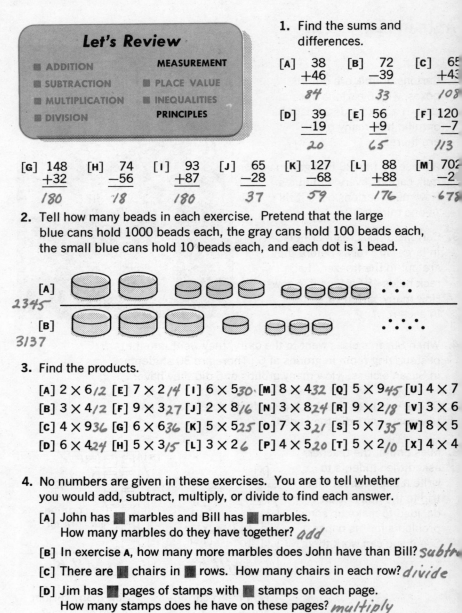

Let's Review

■ ADDITION   MEASUREMENT
■ SUBTRACTION ■ PLACE VALUE
■ MULTIPLICATION ■ INEQUALITIES
■ DIVISION   PRINCIPLES

1. Find the sums and differences.

[A] 38 +46 = 84 [B] 72 −39 = 33 [C] 65 +43 = 108

[D] 39 −19 = 20 [E] 56 +9 = 65 [F] 120 −7 = 113

[G] 148 +32 = 180 [H] 74 −56 = 18 [I] 93 +87 = 180 [J] 65 −28 = 37 [K] 127 −68 = 59 [L] 88 +88 = 176 [M] 702 −2 = 678

2. Tell how many beads in each exercise. Pretend that the large blue cans hold 1000 beads each, the gray cans hold 100 beads each, the small blue cans hold 10 beads each, and each dot is 1 bead.

[A] 2345

[B] 3137

3. Find the products.

[A] 2 × 6 = 12 [E] 7 × 2 = 14 [I] 6 × 5 = 30 [M] 8 × 4 = 32 [Q] 5 × 9 = 45 [U] 4 × 7

[B] 3 × 4 = 12 [F] 9 × 3 = 27 [J] 2 × 8 = 16 [N] 3 × 8 = 24 [R] 9 × 2 = 18 [V] 3 × 6

[C] 4 × 9 = 36 [G] 6 × 6 = 36 [K] 5 × 5 = 25 [O] 7 × 3 = 21 [S] 5 × 7 = 35 [W] 8 × 5

[D] 6 × 4 = 24 [H] 5 × 3 = 15 [L] 3 × 2 = 6 [P] 4 × 5 = 20 [T] 5 × 2 = 10 [X] 4 × 4

4. No numbers are given in these exercises. You are to tell whether you would add, subtract, multiply, or divide to find each answer.

[A] John has ▓ marbles and Bill has ▓ marbles. How many marbles do they have together? *add*

[B] In exercise A, how many more marbles does John have than Bill? *subtract*

[C] There are ▓ chairs in ▓ rows. How many chairs in each row? *divide*

[D] Jim has ▓ pages of stamps with ▓ stamps on each page. How many stamps does he have on these pages? *multiply*

Teaching Pages 132 and 133

● **PURPOSE**

   To provide a cumulative review of the material covered thus far in the text

   To serve as an evaluation, or as a guide for developing your own evaluation

● **PREPARATION**

   Review any of the material in the text with which the students have had difficulty. Conduct a short oral practice session on multiplication and division facts.

Have the students work the exercises. If you choose to treat this set of exercises as a chapter evaluation, you should plan to check the papers yourself.

Chapter review

1. Find the quotients.

[A] Since $4 \times 9 = 36$, we know that

$36 \div 9 = \blacksquare$. *4*

$36 \div 4 = \blacksquare$. *9*

[B] Since $6 \times 8 = 48$, we know that

$48 \div 8 = \blacksquare$. *6*

$48 \div 6 = \blacksquare$. *8*

2. Find the missing factors.

[A] $\blacksquare \times 3 = 12$ *4* [C] $\blacksquare \times 6 = 24$ *4* [E] $\blacksquare \times 3 = 15$ *5* [G] $\blacksquare \times 3 = 27$ *9*

[B] $7 \times \blacksquare = 14$ *2* [D] $3 \times \blacksquare = 24$ *8* [F] $8 \times \blacksquare = 32$ *4* [H] $6 \times \blacksquare = 36$ *6*

3. Find the quotients.

[A] $27 \div 3 = \blacksquare$ *9* [C] $14 \div 7 = \blacksquare$ *2* [E] $12 \div 3 = \blacksquare$ *4* [G] $32 \div 8 = \blacksquare$ *4*

[B] $24 \div 3 = \blacksquare$ *8* [D] $24 \div 6 = \blacksquare$ *4* [F] $36 \div 6 = \blacksquare$ *6* [H] $15 \div 3 = \blacksquare$ *5*

4.

12	9	6	3
-3	-3	-3	-3
9	6	3	0

[A] How many times was 3 subtracted? *4*

[B] How many threes are in 12? *4*

[C] Write a division equation about this.

$12 \div 3 = 4$

5. Write a division equation for the number-line picture.

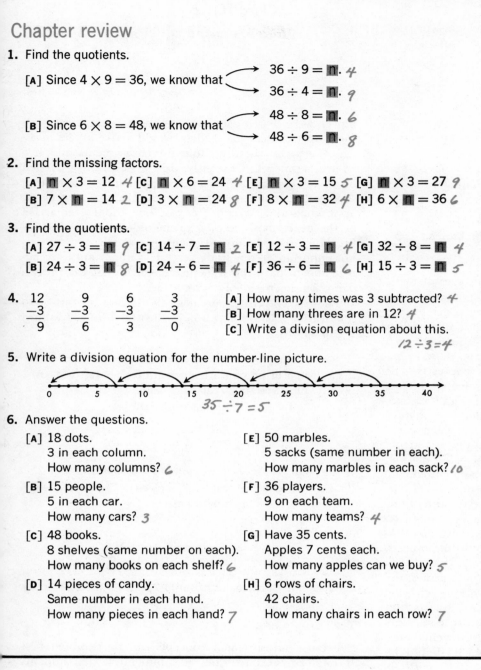

$35 \div 7 = 5$

6. Answer the questions.

[A] 18 dots.
3 in each column.
How many columns? *6*

[B] 15 people.
5 in each car.
How many cars? *3*

[C] 48 books.
8 shelves (same number on each).
How many books on each shelf? *6*

[D] 14 pieces of candy.
Same number in each hand.
How many pieces in each hand? *7*

[E] 50 marbles.
5 sacks (same number in each).
How many marbles in each sack? *10*

[F] 36 players.
9 on each team.
How many teams? *4*

[G] Have 35 cents.
Apples 7 cents each.
How many apples can we buy? *5*

[H] 6 rows of chairs.
42 chairs.
How many chairs in each row? *7*

Objectives of Chapter 6

To introduce length

To provide experiences in estimation

To develop a feeling for selecting appropriate units

To introduce area

To introduce volume

To provide experiences in working with ounces, cups, pints, quarts, and gallons

In this chapter, we explore three basic types of measurement: length, area, and volume. The concepts are introduced simultaneously in the opening pages to give the student a feeling for the different ideas involved in these three types of measurement. Subsequently, each topic is explored individually and in greater depth.

The concept of measurement in this chapter can be divided into two parts: first, that which involves merely the counting of discrete objects within a set and, second, that which, while it involves counting, does not involve the counting of discrete objects. Of course, when measurement can be obtained by merely counting discrete objects, there is no need for approximation or estimation. However, when discrete objects cannot be counted, the concept of approximation or estimation does occur. In this chapter, students are required to make estimates or approximations to determine the length of a given object. However, in most cases the students can arrive at measurements for area or volume merely by counting objects, and no estimation is required.

Following the introduction of volume with arrays, the students are given some experiences in working with the idea of volume involving ounces, cups, pints, quarts, and gallons. Although the concepts involved are essentially the same, the students may find these measurements quite different from those of counting cubes. It should be noted that both ideas involve finding volume with respect to a given unit.

Mathematics of Chapter 6

In measurement, the counting process often is not immediately apparent. Counting to determine length is less obvious than determining volume by counting cubes. However, in every case, even those involving very accurate measurement, it can be demonstrated that the counting process is involved.

In this chapter, the students are not asked to measure more accurately than to the nearest half inch. Of course, when a student arrives at a measure of $4\frac{1}{2}$ inches for a given object, he has counted four 1-inch segments and one $\frac{1}{2}$-inch segment. The fact that the object may not be exactly $4\frac{1}{2}$ inches long does not obviate involvement of the counting process. Suppose, for example, that the object were $4\frac{5}{8}$ inches long to the nearest one-eighth inch. In this case, the student would arrive at the measure of $4\frac{5}{8}$ by counting four 1-inch segments and five $\frac{1}{8}$-inch segments. Obviously, this process can be carried on to any desired degree of accuracy merely by counting smaller and smaller unit segments to arrive at a closer approximation. Whether or not one could ever arrive at the exact measure of a given object by continually breaking apart the unit segment into smaller segments is not important to our study here. It is important to recognize and to have the students recognize that the process of measurement involves counting.

The concept of measurement to the nearest unit or to the nearest fraction of a unit is illustrated in the following diagrams.

If the length of an object is given, to the nearest unit, as 3, the true length is in this range.

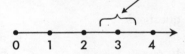

The length is closer (or as close) to 3 than it is to 4 or 2.
If the length, to the nearest $\frac{1}{8}$ unit, is given as $2\frac{5}{8}$, the true length is in this range.

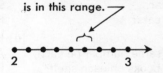

The length is closer (or as close) to $2\frac{5}{8}$ than it is to $2\frac{4}{8}$ or $2\frac{6}{8}$.

Teaching Chapter 6

Because measurement concepts can be explored best through physical activities, it is imperative that students be given an opportunity to make considerable use of various materials in class activities. For example, let the students work with the concept of area by using small squares of cardboard or other materials to measure area. The students should be provided with many opportunities to determine the volume of a given figure by counting the blocks in an array.

Because many varied activities can be conducted in conjunction with this chapter, there is some danger that too much time will be alloted to this work. Therefore, keep in mind that this is an initial introduction to these ideas and that all of the concepts and facts presented need not be completely mastered or memorized by the students. This does not mean that you should place great limitations on the amount of activity for these lessons, but you must be cautious to see that this chapter does not take an undue amount of time.

Plan to spend no more than three weeks on the chapter and attempt to limit it to 2½ weeks.

The chapter review on pages 154 and 155 can be used for evaluating the students' achievement, or you can construct an evaluation test similar to this review. In judging students' achievement in this chapter, keep in mind that complete mastery is not expected but that exploration and recognition of the ideas and concepts is of primary importance.

Since the material does not constitute necessary background material for the remainder of the year's work (although the ideas of the chapter are important to the full development of the student's over-all experiences in mathematics), you should treat the chapter with a light touch. Take special care to see that the students have a successful and enjoyable experience in this chapter.

Have the class read this page and answer the questions in class discussion. During the working of this lesson, the students should view and handle the three types of measuring devices suggested. For example, you can use a wire or a stick, a cardboard square or a floor tile, and some type of block to illustrate these ideas.

Chapter **6** **MEASUREMENT**

Ways of measuring

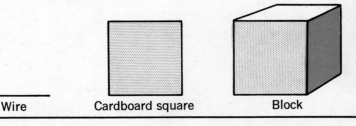

Wire   Cardboard square   Block

You can use a wire, a cardboard square, or a block to **measure** other objects.

Sally wanted to tell the class how large her new bedroom mirror is. She used a cardboard square. What do you think Sally told the class about the size of her mirror? *It takes 4 squares to cover the mirror.*

Tom told the class about the baseball bat he had used all summer. He used a wire to help tell how long it was. What do you think Tom said about the size of his bat? *The bat is as long as 3 of the wires placed end to end.*

Jane had a new aquarium. She used a block to tell the class how much space it had. How many blocks do you think it will take to fill the aquarium? *12*

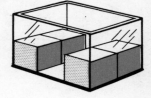

134

Teaching Pages 134 and 135

- **PURPOSE**

    To provide an informal introduction to some concepts basic to the study of length, area, and volume

- **MATHEMATICS**

    The segment, square, and cube are the basic units for finding length, area, and volume, respectively.

    Segments and squares are used almost exclusively as units to find length and area; however, cubes are not exclusive units for volume. At the end of the chapter, the students work with concepts of volume centered around other types of units, such as the ounce, cup, and pint.

EXERCISES

Which object (a wire, a cardboard square, or a block) is best to use if you want to tell:

1. how tall the lamp is? *wire*

2. how much sand the box holds? *block*

3. how much paper we need buy to cover the bulletin board? *cardboard square*

4. how much space is inside the boxcar? *block*

5. how large the garden is? *cardboard square*

6. how far it is from home plate to first base? *wire*

7. how much glass there is in the window? *cardboard square*

8. how much the drawer will hold? *block*

9. how large the desk top is? *cardboard square*

Have the students read the directions. Be sure that they understand how they are to answer these questions. That is, they are to select the most appropriate item for measuring the object mentioned in each exercise. It may prove helpful to have the students use blocks, cardboard squares, or wires to measure some objects in the room.

It may be desirable to work through the first three exercises as a class discussion. Following this, permit the students to complete the page on their own.

Take extra precaution to see that the students do not become concerned with the actual measuring of the objects shown on this page, but rather that they concern themselves with the type of object they would use to answer the questions.

When they have finished the page, discuss each exercise and the correct answer so that the students can check their papers. Encourage free discussion of the ideas involved in the suggested measuring activities.

However, the basic concept of volume can be most easily explored by using the cube, since it is more closely related to the idea of the segment and the square.

PREPARATION

Center your preparation activities around the reading and discussion accompanying pages 134 and 135. During the discussion period, give the students an opportunity to handle and examine various physical objects that could be used as units for measurement, such as a straight piece of wire or a stick for finding length; a cardboard square or tile for finding area; and some kind of a block for finding volume.

After the students have read and studied the page, discuss with them each picture and its relationship to the given idea. Encourage the students to express their views with regard to finding area by using a cardboard square, a stamp, or a floor tile. You can illustrate by calling the students' attention to the fact that they can paste only so many stamps on a given-sized page or that only so many floor tiles are needed to cover a given floor. Similar discussions can be held with regard to length and volume.

Call particular attention to the illustration at the bottom of page 136. Emphasize the words *length* and *segment, area* and *square, volume* and *cube*. Have the class discuss these units, and point out that these words express the ideas we think about when we talk about the physical objects pictured above.

Units for measuring

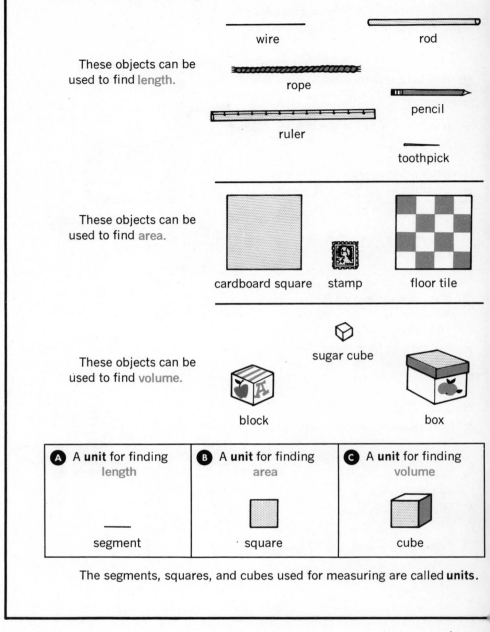

These objects can be used to find length.

wire   rod   rope   ruler   pencil   toothpick

These objects can be used to find area.

cardboard square   stamp   floor tile

These objects can be used to find volume.

sugar cube   block   box

A A **unit** for finding length
segment

B A **unit** for finding area
square

C A **unit** for finding volume
cube

The segments, squares, and cubes used for measuring are called **units.**

Teaching Pages 136 and 137

• **PURPOSE**

To introduce the three common measuring units: segment, square, and cube

To continue to provide experiences which will promote students' understanding of the use of various units for measurement

To introduce formally the words length, area, *and* volume

• **MATHEMATICS**

In this lesson, all the measurement exercises involve only the counting of discrete objects within a given set. For example, the finding of a given segment's length is merely

A We count segment units to find length. The length of the black mark is 6.

UNIT

B We count square units to find area. The area of the big square is 4.

UNIT

C We count cube units to find volume. The volume of the large block is 8.

UNIT

TOP

BOTTOM

EXERCISES

Give the word for each blank.

1. We count squares to find __?__. *area*

2. We count __?__ to find volume. *cubes*

3. We count __?__ to find length. *segments*

4. The segments, squares, and cubes we count when we measure are called __?__. *units*

5. The length of the black mark is __?__. *5*

UNIT

6. The area of this figure is __?__. *5*

UNIT

7. The volume of this figure is __?__. *3*

UNIT

DIRECTIONS PAGE 137

Have the students read the material at the top of the page, and give them an opportunity to discuss the ideas presented. The students should experience little difficulty in recognizing that the length of the black mark is 6 and that the area of the large square is 4. There may be some problem, however, in helping the students to see that the volume of the large block is 8. You can provide a classroom demonstration with blocks if this exercise causes the students any particular difficulty.

Following this discussion, have the students complete the exercises at the bottom of the page. After they have finished, give them an opportunity to participate freely in a discussion of the exercises.

a counting process, since the segment is clearly marked with unit segments. The same is true of the area and volume exercises.

PREPARATION

Provide the students with an opportunity to handle the various devices that might be used for measurement, such as a wire, a cardboard square, or a wooden block.

Arrange various collections of blocks in simple patterns. For example, you might stack a set of eight cubes in such a way as to form one large cube. Give the students an opportunity to find the number of cubes in this one large cube. You can also use small cardboard squares to provide the same kind of activity for area.

This page is primarily an exercise page. After a brief orientation in the units illustrated, the students should be given an opportunity to work most of the exercises on their own. However, you may choose to use a few of the exercises as a class-discussion activity.

After the students have finished, discuss each exercise and the correct answer. Again, you should allow the students considerable freedom in expressing their ideas with respect to these exercises.

Measuring with different unit segments

Here are some units you can use to measure a pencil.

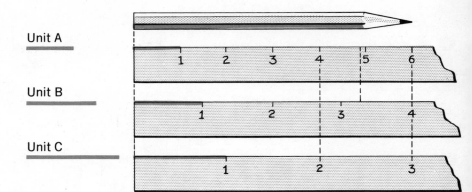

1. Using unit A, how many units long is the pencil? *6*

2. Using unit B, how many units long is the pencil? *4*

3. Using unit C, how many units long is the pencil? *3*

4. Which is the smallest unit? *Unit A*

5. Which unit gives the largest number for the length of the pencil? *Unit A*

6. Which is the largest unit? *Unit C*

7. Which unit gives the smallest number for the length of the pencil? *Unit C*

8. Joe measured his pen using unit A. He found it was 4 units long. What is the length of his pen using unit C? *2*

9. Jane measured her comb using unit B. She found it was a little more than 3 units long. If she had used unit A, what would she have found? *That it was a little less than 5.*

10. Bill and Jane each made a ruler. Jane used a unit as wide as her hand. Bill used a unit as wide as his finger. If they both measure the same thing, who will get the larger number? *Bill*

Teaching Pages 138 and 139

● **PURPOSE**

To introduce formally the idea of finding length

To provide the students with experiences leading to an understanding of the concept of length

To introduce the idea of arbitrarily chosen units of length

● **MATHEMATICS**

This lesson explores two of the most basic ideas in the study of measurement: the choice of a unit and the counting of units. The selection of the unit is usually based on convenience, depending upon the size of the object to be measured. However, it should be recognized that, aside

The unit we choose for measuring should be useful. We would **not** choose this unit ————————————————————
to measure these objects:

We would **not** use an inch unit to answer these questions:

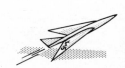 

| How tall is the Washington Monument? | How high does the X-15 airplane fly? | How long is the Mississippi River? |

It helps if we agree to use certain units and give them names. When we do this, other people can understand our measurements because they know the size of the unit we used.

Four units often used are given below. The pictures will help you see **about** how long these units are.

| Inch | Foot | Yard | Mile |
| | 12 inches | 3 foot units | 1760 yards |

A train with 120 boxcars is about 1 mile long.

EXERCISES

Which unit (inch, foot, yard, or mile) would you choose to measure

1. your finger? *inch*
2. a pencil? *inch*
3. the distance from New York to California? *mile*
4. a spoon? *inch*
5. the width of your room? *foot or yard*
6. the distance to the moon? *mile*

Treat the material prior to the exercise set as discussion material. After the students have read and studied this portion of the page, engage them in discussion centered around the selection of a unit and the size of the common units (inch, foot, yard, and mile). The students may become interested in attempting to describe other objects or distances that are about one mile. Keep in mind during this discussion that one of the chief purposes is to give the students a feeling for the sizes of the units and the relationship between the various units.

Following this discussion, have the students complete the exercises. Give them an opportunity to discuss their answers.

from making a convenient choice, the selection of a unit is an arbitrary matter. We can select any unit we please to measure a given object, but if we wish to communicate with others concerning this measurement, they must know the unit that we have used.

In this lesson, the students are given an opportunity to think about the selection of different-sized units to arrive at the measurement of given objects. The idea that the smaller the unit, the larger the number for a given object is explored intuitively.

PREPARATION

Ask two students to select one unit each, and not to allow anyone else to see the size of their units. Suggest

that they keep the units fairly small. Give the two students a ball of string and have them each cut a piece of string that is five units long. Of course, the lengths of the string that they cut will depend upon their choice of units. When they have completed this, have each student hold up his piece of string for the class to see. Now ask the students, "Who chose the larger unit?" Give them an opportunity to discuss the idea that whoever chose the larger unit will have the longer string.

Have the students read and discuss the material above the exercise set. Treat the three questions in this part of the lesson as discussion exercises.

Following this, give the students an opportunity to work the exercises on pages 140 and 141.

Using special units to find length

When we give a measurement, it helps to **name** the unit.

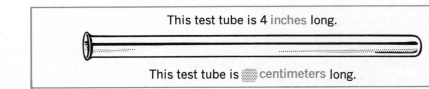

The glass tube is 5 centimeters long.

By heating and pulling, it can be made 5 inches long.

1. Is the unit called a centimeter longer or shorter than an inch? *shorter*

This test tube is 4 inches long.

This test tube is ▓ centimeters long.

2. Do you think the number rubbed out is less than 4? *No*

★ **3.** What is the missing number? *0*

EXERCISES

1. Give the measurement for each object.

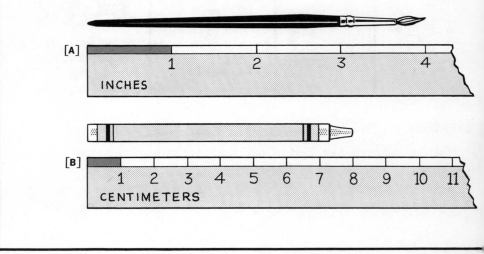

Teaching Pages 140 and 141

- **PURPOSE**

  To introduce inches and centimeters

  To provide measuring experiences, using both inch and centimeter scales

- **PREPARATION**

  Provide the class with several objects which measure very closely to a whole number of inches or centimeters. To avoid the topic of estimation at this point, be sure that the students work only with those objects which measure very closely to a whole number of units.

2. Use your ruler to measure each object in inches.

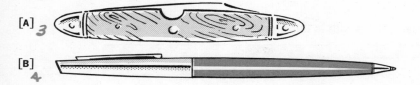

[A] *3*

[B] *4*

You can make a centimeter ruler. Fold a sheet of paper 2 or 3 times. Copy the marks from the ruler below on a folded edge of the paper.

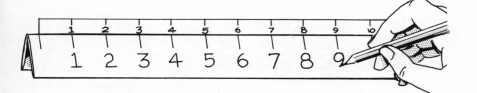

3. Use your centimeter ruler to measure each object.

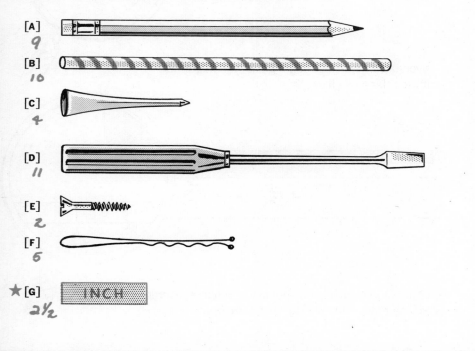

[A] *9*

[B] *10*

[C] *4*

[D] *11*

[E] *2*

[F] *6*

★ [G] INCH

2½

If the students do not have centimeter rulers, you will want to give careful directions for construction of the centimeter ruler, as illustrated on this page. You can treat this as one of the exercises or as an activity which precedes the working of this page. (You might choose to have students construct their own centimeter rulers even though they already have one.) When the students are constructing the centimeter ruler, you will want to move around the class and help those who are less mechanically skilled in this activity. You will need to point out to the students how to make their centimeter rulers longer than the illustration shows. They can do this simply by moving their paper to the left and putting more marks on their paper. Their rulers should be at least 13 centimeters long.

When the students have completed the exercises on this page, provide correct answers and allow time for and encourage the students to ask questions.

Have the students read and study the material on this page. Discuss each of the pictures with them and give them an opportunity to ask questions.

Measurement is not exact

What is the length of this straw?

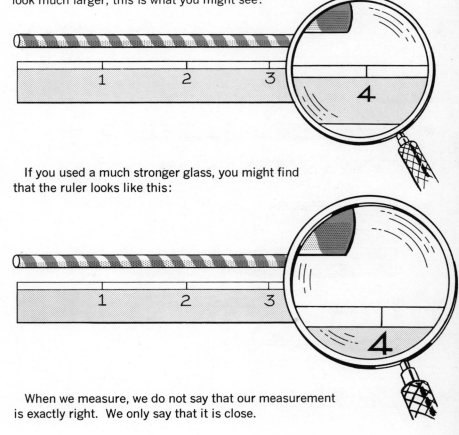

As you can see, the straw is **very close** to 4 inches long. But it is not **exactly** 4 inches. If you held up a glass that made it look much larger, this is what you might see:

If you used a much stronger glass, you might find that the ruler looks like this:

When we measure, we do not say that our measurement is exactly right. We only say that it is close.

Teaching Pages 142 and 143

- **PURPOSE**

  To introduce the idea of approximation or estimation in measurement

- **MATHEMATICS**

  The fact that measurement, as the students think of it, is strictly a physical process and thus exposed to human error is brought out on page 142. This is given as a lead-in to estimation as presented on page 143. Of course, the fact that measurement is subject to error leads us to understand the need for giving measures to the nearest unit or fraction of a unit. For example, if the length of an object

Measuring to the nearest inch

The length of the nail file is **more than** 4 inches, but **less than** 5 inches. Is it closer to 4 or to 5? *It is closer to 5.*

The length of the nail file (to the nearest inch) is 5.

The length of the spring is between 1 and 2 inches. Is it closer to 1 or to 2? *It is closer to 1.*

The length of the spring (to the nearest inch) is 1.

EXERCISES

1. Give the length of each object to the nearest inch.

[A] *2*

[B] *2*

2. Measure each segment to the nearest inch.

[A] *2* ————————— [B] *2* —————

[C] *4* —————————————————

[D] *5* —————————————————

[E] *2* ————————— [F] *1* ——— [G] *2* ————

Have the students read and study the material preceding the exercise set. Give them an opportunity to ask questions and discuss these ideas.

Instruct the students to work all the exercises on their own. After they have finished, give them the correct answers and allow time for discussion.

Some of the students will need extra help with the idea of measuring to the nearest inch. The best time to provide this help is following their completion of this exercise set.

to the nearest unit is 5, this simply means that the true length is between $4\frac{1}{2}$ and $5\frac{1}{2}$ (it is closer to five than it is to either 4 or 6). If the length to the nearest one-sixteenth unit is given as $3\frac{7}{16}$, this means that the true length is closer (or as close) to $3\frac{7}{16}$ than it is to $3\frac{6}{16}$ or $3\frac{8}{16}$.

• PREPARATION

Have the students measure various objects around the classroom. In doing this, the students will quickly become aware that the measuring process does not always end in a whole number of units. When this idea is discovered and explored, explain to the students that for the purposes of this lesson they are to find the measure of an object to

the nearest whole number of units. Of course, there may be some problem if the object appears to fall **exactly** halfway between two units; however, you can make some agreement with the students either to call this the next whole number of units or the previous whole number of units. Give the students some freedom in deciding which they want to call it.

Have the students read and discuss the material preceding the exercise set. Ask them to work the three exercises on their own. Discuss each exercise before having the students read and study the remainder of the page. When they have finished this, conduct a discussion concerning the ideas presented in this portion.

Measuring to the nearest half inch

Bill and Tom were comparing rulers with different units. Bill used an inch ruler. Tom used a ruler that he made using half-inch units. Since Tom's units were a half inch, he decided to call them **hinches**.

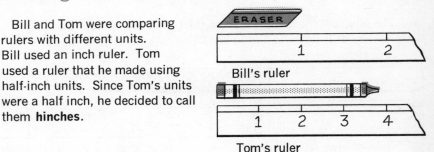

Bill's ruler

Tom's ruler

EXERCISES

1. Bill measured an eraser. It was 1 inch long. How many "hinches" long was the eraser? *2 hinches*

2. Bill measured a pencil and found that it was 6 inches long. How many "hinches" long was the pencil? *12 hinches*

3. Tom found that a crayon was 4 "hinches" long (to the nearest "hinch"). How long was the crayon to the nearest inch? *2 inches*

When Tom measures to the nearest "hinch," he is measuring to the nearest half inch. Here is a ruler (almost like Tom's) with half-inch marks.

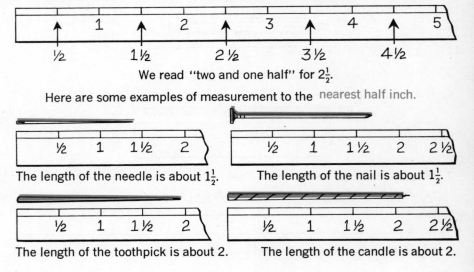

We read "two and one half" for $2\frac{1}{2}$.

Here are some examples of measurement to the nearest half inch.

The length of the needle is about $1\frac{1}{2}$.   The length of the nail is about $1\frac{1}{2}$.

The length of the toothpick is about 2.   The length of the candle is about 2.

Teaching Pages 144 and 145

- **PURPOSE**

  To reinforce the idea of measuring to the nearest unit or one-half unit

- **PREPARATION**

  Draw on the chalkboard a line segment that is about $6\frac{3}{8}$ inches long. Have several students come up and measure this segment to decide whether it measures closer to 6, $6\frac{1}{2}$, or 7. Encourage all students to participate in the discussion. In this way you can lead the students to discover for themselves the extension of the idea of measuring to the

Exercises in measurement

1. Use your inch ruler to measure each object to the nearest half inch.

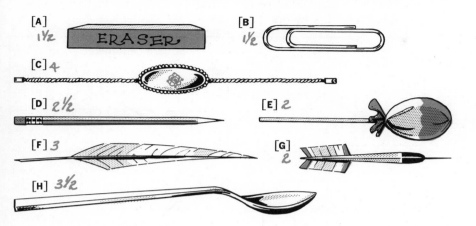

[A] 1½ ERASER

[B] 1½

[C] 4

[D] 2½

[E] 2

[F] 3

[G] 2

[H] 3½

★**2.** Make half-centimeter marks on your centimeter ruler. Measure these segments to the nearest half centimeter:

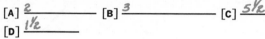

[A] 2 ——— **[B]** 3 ——— **[C]** 5½

[D] 1½ ———

3. Use your centimeter ruler and an inch ruler to find about how many centimeters there are in 2 inches. 5 cm.

4. About how many inches are there in 10 centimeters? 4 in.

5. Bill measured a comb and found it was 4½ inches long. What would Tom find if he measured the comb, using the "hinch" ruler? 9 hinches

6. A pencil is 17 "hinches" long. How many inches long is it? 8½ inches

★**7.** About how many centimeters are there in 1 inch? 2½ (Give your answer to the nearest half centimeter.) How many half inches are in 1 inch? 2 Which is longer, a half inch or a centimeter? half inch

★**8.** There are 12 inches in 1 foot. How many half inches are in 1 foot? 24 There are 3 feet in 1 yard. How many inches are in 1 yard? 36 How many inches are in a half yard? 18 How many half inches are in a half yard? 36

DIRECTIONS PAGE 145

Instruct the students to work the exercises on their own.

Since even your faster pupils may have some difficulty with the starred exercises, you should have the students enter into these exercises in the spirit of adventure. Take care to see that they do not become discouraged. Avoid giving answers to the students having difficulty. Do attempt to ask questions that will encourage them to return to the problem and seek the answer for themselves.

nearest unit. In this case you can point out that they are measuring to the nearest half unit. Provide additional examples to carry on this discussion. Take care to include examples that turn out to be a whole number of units when measured to the nearest half unit so that the students will recognize that their measurement may well turn out to be four inches when they are measuring to the nearest half unit. Obtaining a whole number when measuring to the nearest half unit simply points out that we know that the true measure is within a smaller neighborhood.

After the students have read and studied the page, discuss the two units introduced at the top of the page, the square inch and the square centimeter.

Have the students count the number of squares in the rectangle to see that the area is 12 units. Now ask the students to explain why the area of the triangle is 8 units. Of course, they already have read the explanation, but it is important that they are able to express this in their own words.

Following this, have them count to be sure that the area of the third figure is 12 units.

Finding area

You can find area by counting squares. Some unit squares that are used to find area are the square inch and the square centimeter.

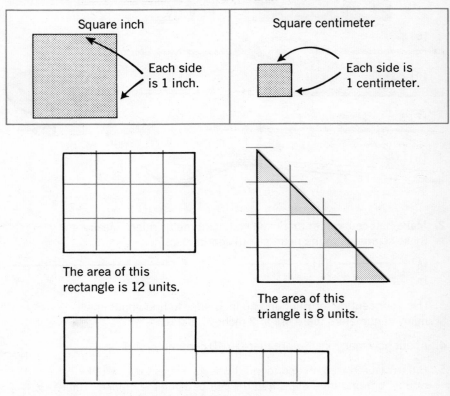

The area of this rectangle is 12 units.

The area of this triangle is 8 units.

The area of this figure is 12 units.

It is easy to count the number of squares in the rectangle. It is harder to count the number of squares in the triangle. If you look carefully, you will see 6 squares and 4 small triangles. Do you see that 2 of the triangles would make 1 square?

In some exercises, squares other than the square inch or the square centimeter will be used for the unit.

Teaching Pages 146 and 147

- **PURPOSE**

  To introduce area
  To introduce units for finding area

- **MATHEMATICS**

  The two concepts basic to the over-all concept of measurement, selection of unit and counting, are the prime ideas of this lesson.

  In this lesson the students will, in each case, be able to count discrete objects in a given set in order to determine area.

EXERCISES

The unit used in these exercises is ▨ . Find the number of square units (area) in each shaded figure.

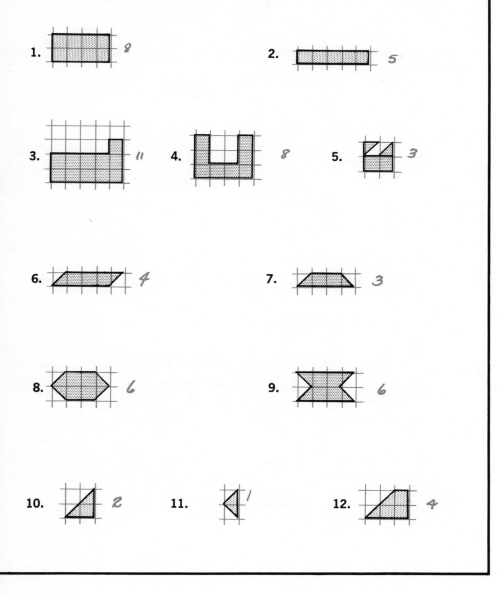

1. *8*

2. *5*

3. *11* 4. *8* 5. *3*

6. *4* 7. *3*

8. *6* 9. *6*

10. *2* 11. *1* 12. *4*

After the students have completed the exercises on their own, give them an opportunity to demonstrate or state how they were able to find the given areas.

• PREPARATION

Provide sets of squares for the students to use in designing various figures and counting the number of squares in each of the figures.

Draw diagrams on the chalkboard similar to those on page 146 and have the students count the number of squares in each diagram.

Have the students work the exercises on their own. You may choose to have only the more able students attempt exericse 5.

In the discussion following completion of the exercises, allow the students considerable freedom in telling how they found a given area.

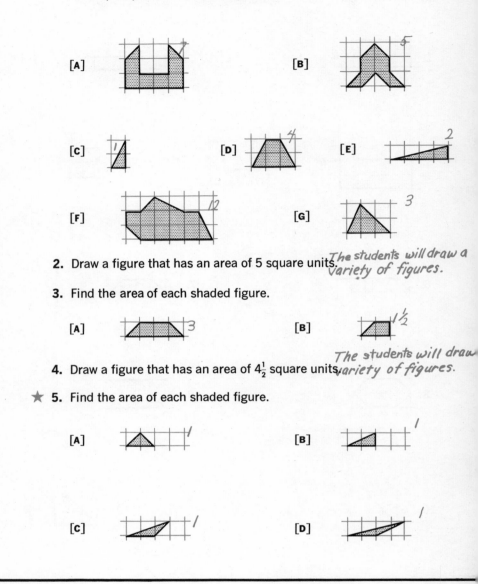

Area exercises

1. The unit used in these exercises is ☐ . Find the number of square units (area) in each shaded figure.

[A] [B]

[C] [D] [E]

[F] [G]

2. Draw a figure that has an area of 5 square units. *The students will draw a variety of figures.*

3. Find the area of each shaded figure.

[A] [B]

The students will draw variety of figures.

4. Draw a figure that has an area of 4½ square units.

★ 5. Find the area of each shaded figure.

[A] [B]

[C] [D]

Teaching Pages 148 and 149

- **PURPOSE**

  To reinforce the concept of area

  To introduce estimation of area

- **PREPARATION**

  Make several drawings on the chalkboard similar to those on page 148 and ask the class to determine the area of each figure.

  Provide the students with sets of cardboard squares and squares cut across one diagonal to form two triangles. Direct them to lay the squares and triangles out in various patterns and then to find the area of the figure they formed.

Estimating area

You will not be able to find the area of these figures **exactly**.
Think carefully and estimate the area of each figure.

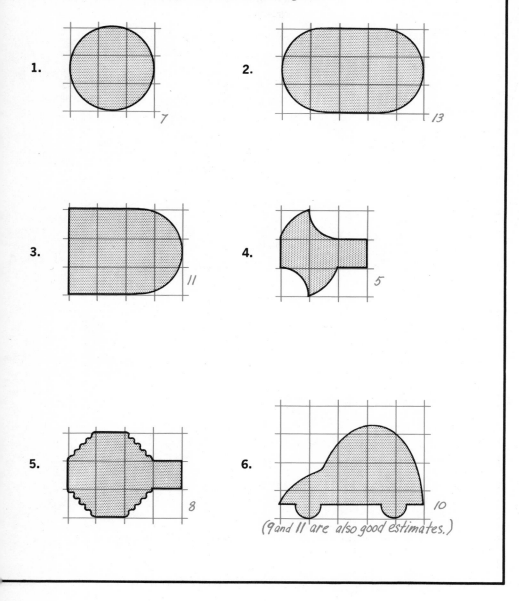

1.

7

2.

13

3.

11

4.

5

5.

8

6.

10

(9 and 11 are also good estimates.)

When the students have finished working the exercises, discuss their answers and elicit from them the methods by which they arrived at their estimations of the areas. Expect, and encourage, a wide variety of responses concerning the various methods used.

It is important that the students enter into this particular activity in the spirit of having fun and attempting to arrive at a very good guess. Do not expect a great degree of accuracy in the students' estimations. Congratulate those students who come fairly close to the area given in the answers.

Following this, put several drawings on the chalkboard similar to those on page 149. Have the students discuss the drawings and estimate the areas. Take care to see that your drawings are relatively simple so that the students can, without too much difficulty, arrive at a good approximation of the area.

After the students have read and studied the page, discuss with them the units shown at the top of the page. Next, give them an opportunity to discuss the three block arrays and to decide how they could arrive at the volumes given below the figures. As these three figures are discussed, it may prove helpful to construct these arrays with your demonstration cubes.

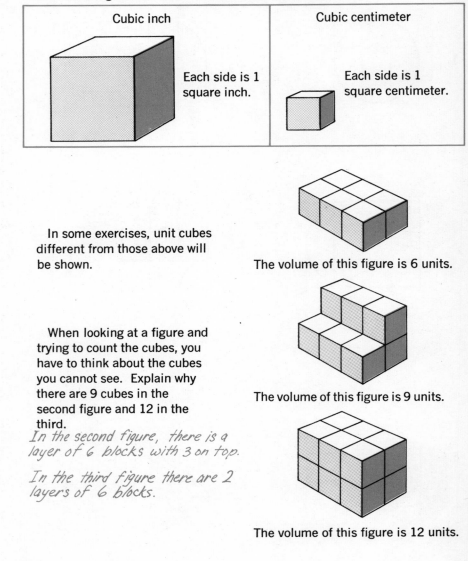

150 MEASUREMENT

Finding volume

You can find volume by counting cubes. Some cubes often used for measuring are the cubic inch and the cubic centimeter.

Cubic inch	Cubic centimeter
Each side is 1 square inch.	Each side is 1 square centimeter.

In some exercises, unit cubes different from those above will be shown.

The volume of this figure is 6 units.

When looking at a figure and trying to count the cubes, you have to think about the cubes you cannot see. Explain why there are 9 cubes in the second figure and 12 in the third.

In the second figure, there is a layer of 6 blocks with 3 on top.

In the third figure there are 2 layers of 6 blocks.

The volume of this figure is 9 units.

The volume of this figure is 12 units.

Teaching Pages 150 and 151

- **PURPOSE**

    To introduce volume
    To introduce the cube as a unit for volume

- **MATHEMATICS**

    As with length and area, the concept of volume involves choosing an appropriate unit and counting.

- **PREPARATION**

    Since many students have difficulty visualizing pictorial representations of three-dimensional objects, your preparation activities for this lesson are very important. Not only

EXERCISES

The unit used in these exercises is 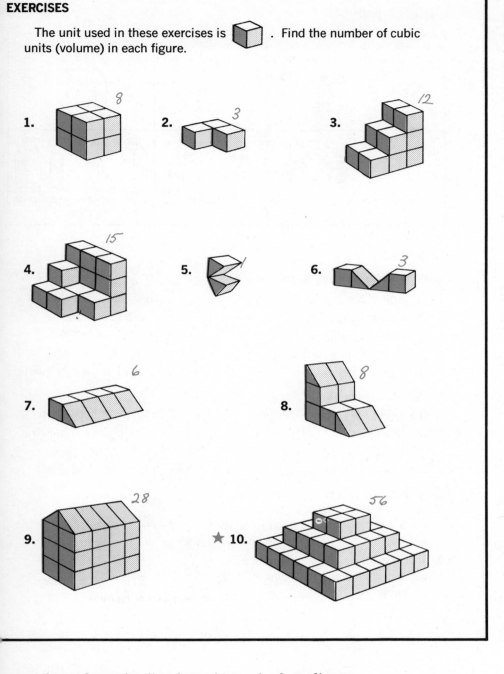. Find the number of cubic units (volume) in each figure.

1. *8*

2. *3*

3. *12*

4. *15*

5. *1*

6. *3*

7. *6*

8. *8*

9. *28*

★ 10. *56*

Give the students sufficient time to work the exercises on their own. When they have finished, discuss each exercise and provide cube demonstrations for some of the exercises.

must the students visualize these pictures in three dimensions, but they must imagine the blocks that are not shown. Your class activities in preparation for this lesson will help the students attain this level of abstraction more easily.

The students should be given many opportunities to discover the number of blocks in a stack. You can effectively lead students to visualize the pictures on the printed page by arranging block arrays similar to those on page 152 and then having the students guess the number of blocks in the stack. When several guesses have been made, ask students to come to the front of the room and take the stack apart to count the blocks.

Give the students an opportunity to work the exercises. When they have finished, discuss the exercises and provide several demonstrations to show why certain answers are correct.

Liquid measure

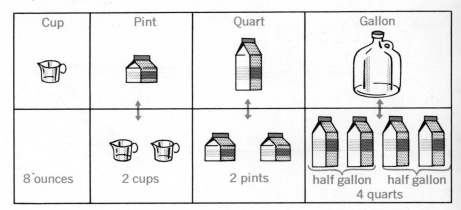

Cup	Pint	Quart	Gallon
8 ounces	2 cups	2 pints	half gallon half gallon 4 quarts

EXERCISES

1. Give the missing numbers.

[A] 2 pints are ▦ cups. *4*

[B] 1 quart is ▦ cups. *4*

[C] 2 quarts are ▦ pints. *4*

[D] 3 quarts are ▦ pints. *6*

[E] 1 gallon is ▦ pints. *8*

[F] $\frac{1}{2}$ cup is ▦ ounces. *4*

[G] 2 cups are ▦ ounces. *16*

[H] 1 pint is ▦ ounces. *16*

[I] $\frac{1}{2}$ gallon is ▦ pints. *4*

[J] 3 gallons 2 pints are ▦ quarts. *13*

2. Tell which is more.

[A] (3 cups) or 1 pint

[B] 12 ounces or (1 pint)

[C] 1 quart or (3 pints)

[D] (3 pints 15 ounces) or 1 quart

[E] (2 quarts) or 3 pints 1 cup

[F] 3 quarts 1 pint or (1 gallon)

[G] 3 pints or (1 half gallon)

[H] (4 quarts 1 pint) or 1 gallon

3. Sometimes milk comes in half-pint cartons. How many cups of milk do you drink when you drink a half pint of milk? *1 cup*

★ **4.** How much more do you need to fill a gallon jug after you have poured in the following? *2 quarts*

Teaching Pages 152 and 153

- **PURPOSE**

  To provide a broader understanding of the volume concept

  To provide experiences in working with ounces, cups, pints, quarts, and gallons

  To provide word-problem experiences

- **PREPARATION**

  Conduct several demonstrations showing the relationships illustrated at the top of page 152. If possible, show an eight-ounce container and illustrate that this is one cup.

Shopping problems

Sally's mother asked her to go to the store. Here is her shopping list: ⟶

SHOPPING LIST
Tomato Juice (small can)
Bread (2 loaves)
Milk (1 gallon)
Eggs (1 carton)
Orange Soda
Grape Drink (enough to fill thermos jug)

1. Sally picked up 3 quarts of milk. How much more should she get? *1 quart*

2. Sally knew that the orange soda was for her little brother's birthday party. If each of the 6 boys at the party drinks a pint of orange soda, how many quart bottles should Sally buy?
3 quarts

3. Sally bought a carton of six 16-ounce bottles. How many pints did she buy? How many quarts did she buy?
6 pints
3 quarts

4. Sally's thermos jug holds 1 gallon. Which should Sally buy to save money— the gallon or the 2 half gallons?
The gallon

GRAPE DRINK 25¢ each half gallon

5. One can held 28 ounces of tomato juice. Another held 1 quart of tomato juice. Which can held more juice? How much more? *The quart.*
It holds 4 ounces more than the 28-ounce can.

Give the students an opportunity to read the material and the shopping list at the top of the page. Now have them work the exercises on their own. When they have finished, read the correct answers and have the students check their papers.

Give them an opportunity to ask questions and discuss each exercise.

Then show two cups filled with water and pour these into a pint container. Follow through using water and suitable containers to demonstrate the relationship between pints and quarts and between quarts and gallons.

You may choose to use this page simply as a review of the chapter or as a test page. You should take the opportunity to follow up the exercises on this page with a carefully planned discussion to strengthen for the students any of the concepts or topics of the chapter which may have caused difficulty.

Chapter review

1. Bob takes steps about this long. ————

   Sue's steps are just half as long. ————

   [A] Who will take the most steps to cross the room? *Sue*

   [B] Who takes the longer step? *Bob*

   [C] If Bob takes 10 steps to cross the room, how many steps will Sue take? *2*

   [D] If Sue takes 12 steps from the door to the teacher's desk, how many steps will Bob take? *6*

2. _____ Twinch _____   _____ Inch _____

   Ted called his unit the twinch. Nancy used the inch. Give the measure of these segments, using the twinch as your unit. You may use your ruler if you like.

   [A] _____ *2 twinches - 4 inches - 10 cm* _____

   [B] _____ *1 twinch - 2 inches - 5 cm* _____

   [C] Give the length of the segments using the inch as your unit.

   [D] Measure the segments to the nearest half centimeter.

3. Does the inch or the centimeter give the larger number when you measure the same object? *the centimeter*

4. [A] Is the inch longer than 2 centimeters? *Yes*

   [B] Is the inch longer than 3 centimeters? *No*

Teaching Pages 154 and 155

- **PURPOSE**

  To provide a review of the ideas presented in this chapter

  To serve as an evaluation instrument or as a guide for constructing such an instrument

- **PREPARATION**

  Review the key topics of the chapter. Give the students an opportunity to discuss the ideas of length, area, and volume. Provide several demonstrations of all three types of measurement.

This page may also be used as an evaluation page. Again, whether you use the page for evaluation or simply as a chapter review, you should follow up with a carefully planned discussion of the exercises. Be sure to give the students an opportunity to ask questions and discuss those problems which caused difficulty.

5. Using the square centimeter as your unit, give the area for each figure.

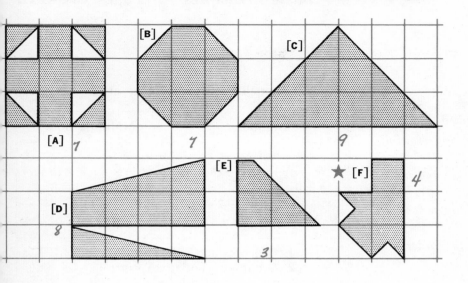

6. Measure to the nearest half centimeter
   [A] the length of each side of the triangle in exercise 5c above. *6, 4, 4*
   [B] the length of each side of the figure in exercise 5E above. *2½, 3, ½, 2*

7. Give the volume of each figure below.

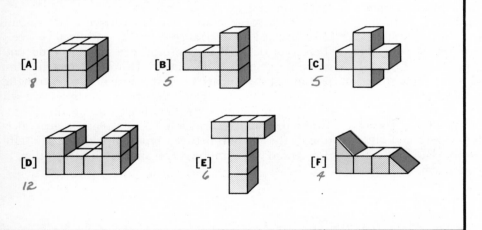

Objectives of Chapter 7

To re-examine all the basic principles studied thus far

To stress the order principle for addition and multiplication

To stress the grouping principle for addition and multiplication

To stress a generalization drawn from the order and grouping principles for addition

To stress a generalization drawn from the order and grouping principles for multiplication

To stress basic principles for zero and one

To introduce the multiplication-addition (distributive) principle

The first four pages of the chapter stress the order and grouping principles for addition and multiplication. Following this introduction, these principles are combined and generalized. That is, by considering both the order and the grouping principles for addition, we can generalize and observe that we can rearrange the addends in any order and still get the same sum. Once this generalization is made, there is little need to continue stressing the principles separately. These principles are also generalized for multiplication.

Next, a brief summary of all the principles is given, with special attention to the principles for zero and one.

The remainder of the chapter is devoted to the distributive principle and receives the main emphasis for this chapter. The distributive principle, which is vital for development of algorithms involving multiplication and division processes, certainly must be considered the most significant principle studied thus far. Since the other principles each have to do with exactly one operation, they are intuitively obvious and quite simple to present to students. The distributive principle, however, concerns both addition and multiplication and requires much more development.

As an aid to understanding, we encourage the use of the words *break apart* with respect to the way in which the students will be using the distributive principle. Of course, the words *break apart* have little meaning with regard to the mathematical concept. However, experience has proved that such descriptive words are meaningful aids to the students' understanding.

Mathematics of Chapter 7

The table below lists the basic principles covered in this chapter.

For all whole numbers a, b, and c:

Addition	Multiplication
1. $a + b = b + a$	$a \times b = b \times a$
2. $(a + b) + c = a + (b + c)$	$(a \times b) \times c = a \times (b \times c)$
3. $a + 0 = a$	$a \times 0 = 0, a \times 1 = a$
4.	$a \times (b + c) = (a \times b + (a \times c)$

1. Order (commutative) principle
2. Grouping (associative) principle
3. Zero and one principle
4. Distributive principle

The most important consequences of the order and grouping principles are the generalizations which arise from them: the order and grouping principles working together allow us to rearrange addends in addition and factors in multiplication.

Once these generalizations are drawn and students have learned to rearrange addends and factors freely, there is little need to continue stressing the order and grouping principles separately. However, since it is important that students understand that the rearranging idea arises from order and grouping principles, we will continue to reinforce this fact from time to time.

The distributive principle is, in a sense, a generalization of the relation between repeated addition and multiplication. The following examples illustrate this.

$$3 \times 4 = (1 + 1 + 1) \times 4 = 4 + 4 + 4$$

$$2 \times 6 = (1 + 1) \times 6 = 6 + 6$$

$$4 \times 5 = (1 + 1 + 1 + 1) \times 5 = 5 + 5 + 5 + 5$$

Teaching Chapter 7

Because of the very nature of this material, your use of set demonstrations in this chapter will be limited. In most instances, when presenting and developing ideas concerning the basic principles, we use small numbers and easy combinations which are familiar to the students. However, we recommend the use of set materials whenever needed, particularly for the less able students.

The distributive principle is the only new principle introduced in this chapter. You will notice that we employ a rather intuitive and descriptive name for this principle to be used with the students. We have called it the multiplication-addition principle to avoid using the word *distributive,* just as we have avoided using the words *commutative* and *associative.* It is not that these words are so difficult for students, but that the more descriptive terms are a greater aid to their comprehension of the ideas and concepts. Certainly, in future work with the basic principles students can easily make the transition to technical names.

Plan to spend about 2½ weeks on this material. Set three weeks as a maximum for covering the chapter.

Since this chapter is concerned primarily with ideas and not with skills, evaluation of students' achievement may be the most difficult of any chapter in the text. Therefore, you should be unusually alert to evaluate students' learning and progress on a day-to-day basis. We have provided a suggested evaluation—a chapter review—but it must be recognized that such an instrument is, at best, only an approximation of the total picture of students' achievement in this chapter.

Since much of this chapter involves review and summary of ideas previously covered, you should be especially alert to see that the lessons move along rapidly. Do not dwell unduly on the lessons in the early part of the chapter. There is some danger that the early pages of the chapter may be somewhat boring for the more able students since they have covered and mastered these ideas previously. Even in the coverage of the distributive principle, you will want to keep things moving at an interesting pace. The introduction of this principle is broken down into such small segments that the fact that the principle is new should not influence you to a slower schedule.

After you have read and studied the material at the top of the page with the students, have them do the exercises. When they finish allow time for discussion.

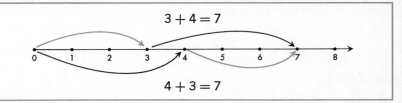

Chapter **7** **BASIC PRINCIPLES**

The order principle for addition

When we change the order of the ADDENDS, we get the same SUM.

$$3 + 4 = 7$$

$$4 + 3 = 7$$

EXERCISES

1. Find the sums.

 [A] $7 + 5$ *2* [B] $6 + 8$ *14* [C] $9 + 7$ *16* [D] $12 + 6$ *18* [E] $12 + 23$ *35* [F] $48 + 35$.
 $5 + 7$ *2* $8 + 6$ *14* $7 + 9$ *16* $6 + 12$ *18* $23 + 12$ *35* $35 + 48$.

 [G] Since $95 + 87 = 182$, we know that $87 + 95 = \blacksquare$. *182*
 [H] Since $792 + 843 = 1635$, we know that $843 + 792 = \blacksquare$. *1635*

2. Use the table on the right to find these sums.

 [A] $6295 + 8934$ *15,229* [E] $6537 + 8756$ *15,293*
 [B] $6276 + 8079$ *14,355* [F] $7354 + 4687$ *12,041*
 [C] $9317 + 7658$ *16,975* [G] $9328 + 8654$ *17,982*
 [D] $6783 + 9265$ *16,048* [H] $8342 + 6875$ *15,217*

$8079 + 6276 = 14{,}355$
$8756 + 6537 = 15{,}293$
$8654 + 9328 = 17{,}982$
$9265 + 6783 = 16{,}048$
$4687 + 7354 = 12{,}041$
$8934 + 6295 = 15{,}229$
$6875 + 8342 = 15{,}217$
$7658 + 9317 = 16{,}975$

3. Solve the equations.

 [A] $\blacksquare + 53 = 53 + 8$ *8* [B] $47 + 95 = \blacksquare + 47$ *95*

Teaching Pages 156 and 157

- **PURPOSE**

  To present the order principles for addition and multiplication

- **MATHEMATICS**

  We present here a formal statement of the order, or commutative, principle for addition and multiplication. For all whole numbers a and b,

  $$a + b = b + a$$

  and

  $$a \times b = b \times a.$$

The order principle for multiplication

When we change the order of the **FACTORS**, we get the same **PRODUCT**.

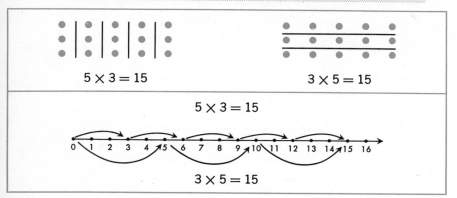

$5 \times 3 = 15$ $3 \times 5 = 15$

$5 \times 3 = 15$

$3 \times 5 = 15$

Read and study the material at the top of the page with the students. Focus particular attention on the first box in which the dots are first considered in columns and then in rows. Notice with the class that in the first case they think of five sets of three and in the second case, three sets of five.

Have the students work the exercises. When they have finished, allow time for discussion.

EXERCISES

1. Find the products.

[A] 2×6 *12* [B] 5×4 *20* [c] 6×3 *18* [D] 5×6 *30* [E] 8×7 *56* [F] 9×8 *72*

    6×2 *12* 4×5 *20* 3×6 *18* 6×5 *30* 7×8 *56* 8×9 *72*

[G] Since $12 \times 3 = 36$, we know that $3 \times 12 = $ ∎. *36*

[H] Since $4 \times 14 = 56$, we know that $14 \times 4 = $ ∎. *56*

[I] Since $16 \times 9 = 144$, we know that $9 \times 16 = $ ∎. *144*

[J] Since $12 \times 16 = 192$, we know that $16 \times 12 = $ ∎. *192*

2. Find the products. Use the table.

80 [A] 92×65 [G] 71×17 *1207*

16 [B] 24×84 [H] 82×34 *2788*

86 [c] 47×38 [I] 27×56 *1512*

20 [D] 15×68 [J] 27×53 *1431*

204 [E] 76×29 [K] 64×25 *1600*

54 [F] 83×38 [L] 65×93 *6045*

$53 \times 27 = 1431$	$65 \times 92 = 5980$
$68 \times 15 = 1020$	$29 \times 76 = 2204$
$25 \times 64 = 1600$	$84 \times 24 = 2016$
$34 \times 82 = 2788$	$93 \times 65 = 6045$
$56 \times 27 = 1512$	$38 \times 83 = 3154$
$38 \times 47 = 1786$	$17 \times 71 = 1207$

3. Solve the equations.

[A] ∎ $\times 3 = 3 \times 4$ *4*   [c] $26 \times 5 = $ ∎ $\times 5$ *26* [E] $17 \times 34 = $ ∎ $\times 17$ *34*

[B] $8 \times $ ∎ $= 4 \times 8$ *4*   [D] $0 \times 3 = 3 \times $ ∎ *0*   [F] $39 \times 44 = 44 \times $ ∎ *39*

PREPARATION

Provide the class with a short, oral practice session in which you cover the basic addition and multiplication combinations. Follow this by asking individual students to solve pairs of exercises such as $8 + 3$, $3 + 8$; 2×7, 7×2; etc.

If necessary, you may choose to provide some set demonstrations for the ideas involved in commutativity of either addition or multiplication. This can be done best for multiplication by showing rectangular arrays and having the students consider them first in columns and then in rows.

Read and study with the class the material at the top of the page. Now have them work the exercises. When they have finished, discuss the exercises and call particular attention to the statement of the grouping principle at the bottom of the page.

The grouping principle for addition

If we do **not** change the order when adding 3 numbers, we have a choice of which addends we can add first.

Addends: 3, 5, 7		
We could add these first. ↓ ↓ 3 + 5 + 7 (3 + 5) + 7 We think: 8 + 7 = 15	or	We could add these first. ↓ ↓ 3 + 5 + 7 3 + (5 + 7) We think: 3 + 12 = 15

EXERCISES

1. Find each sum. Use the grouping shown.
   [A] (3 + 2) + 4 *9*   [B] (5 + 6) + 8 *19*   [c] (3 + 7) + 9 *19*   [D] (4 + 6) + 8
       3 + (2 + 4) *9*   5 + (6 + 8) *19*   3 + (7 + 9) *19*   4 + (6 + 8)

2. Find each sum. Choose the grouping that is most helpful.
   Do not change the order.

   [A] 4 + 6 + 8 *18*   [E] 9 + 13 + 7 *29*   [I] 48 + 52 + 37
   [B] 8 + 9 + 1 *18*   [F] 26 + 4 + 13 *43*   [J] 98 + 55 + 45
   [c] 8 + 6 + 4 *18*   [G] 65 + 5 + 28 *98*   [K] 72 + 63 + 37
   [D] 17 + 3 + 5 *25*   [H] 23 + 6 + 34 *63*   [L] 43 + 27 + 67

3. Find the sums.
   [A] Since (35 + 27) + 68 = 130, we know that 35 + (27 + 68) = ▥. *130*
   [B] Since (56 + 39) + 28 = 123, we know that 56 + (39 + 28) = ▥. *123*
   [c] Since 24 + (43 + 92) = 159, we know that (24 + 43) + 92 = ▥. *159*
   [D] Since 35 + 41 = 76, we know that 41 + 36 = ▥. *77*
   [E] Since (29 + 71) + 43 = 143, we know that 29 + (72 + 43) = ▥. *144*
   [F] Since 48 + 7 = 55, we know that 47 + 8 = ▥. *56*
   [G] Since 96 + 83 = 179, we know that 93 + 86 = ▥. *179*
   [H] Since (86 + 41) + 32 = 159, we know that 86 + (41 + 30) = ▥. *157*
   [I] Since (65 + 83) + 19 = 167, we know that 65 + (83 + 19) = ▥. *167*

When we add, we can change the GROUPING and get the same sum.

Teaching Pages 158 and 159

- PURPOSE

  To present the grouping principles for addition and multiplication

- MATHEMATICS

  Given below is a formal statement of the associative, or grouping, principles for addition and multiplication.
  For all whole numbers a, b, and c,

  $$(a + b) + c = a + (b + c)$$

  and

  $$(a \times b) \times c = a \times (b \times c).$$

The grouping principle for multiplication

If we do **not** change the order when multiplying with 3 factors, we have a choice of which factors we can multiply first.

Factors: 3, 2, 4	
We could multiply these first. $3 \times 2 \times 4$ $(3 \times 2) \times 4$ We think: $6 \times 4 = 24$	We could multiply these first. $3 \times 2 \times 4$ $3 \times (2 \times 4)$ We think: $3 \times 8 = 24$

or

EXERCISES

1. Find each product. Use the groupings shown. In each part, check to see that the two different groupings give the same product.

[A] $(5 \times 1) \times 6$ *30* [B] $(2 \times 2) \times 4$ *16* [C] $(4 \times 2) \times 5$ *40* [D] $(3 \times 2) \times 5$ *30*
$\quad\;\; 5 \times (1 \times 6)$ *30* $\quad 2 \times (2 \times 4)$ *16* $\quad 4 \times (2 \times 5)$ *40* $\quad 3 \times (2 \times 5)$ *30*

2. Find each product. Choose the grouping that is most helpful. Do not change the order.

[A] $(5 \times 2) \times 4$ *40*   [C] $7 \times (5 \times 2)$ *70*   [E] $8 \times (10 \times 10)$ *800*

[B] $9 \times 0 \times 5$ *0*   [D] $593 \times (497 \times 0)$ *0*   [F] $(2 \times 5) \times 3$ *30*
   either grouping

3. Solve the equations.

[A] $(3 \times 7) \times 5 = \blacksquare \times (7 \times 5)$ *3*   [C] $17 \times (4 \times 29) = (\blacksquare \times 4) \times 29$ *6*

[B] $(8 \times 6) \times 10 = 8 \times (\blacksquare \times 10)$ *17*   [D] $(\blacksquare \times 4) \times 7 = 34 \times (4 \times 7)$ *34*

4. Find the products.

[A] Since $(4 \times 6) \times 3 = 72$, we know that $4 \times (6 \times 3) = \blacksquare$. *72*

[B] Since $(5 \times 7) \times 2 = 70$, we know that $5 \times (7 \times 2) = \blacksquare$. *70*

[C] Since $6 \times (8 \times 7) = 336$, we know that $(6 \times 8) \times 7 = \blacksquare$. *336*

[D] Since $(4 \times 9) \times 6 = 216$, we know that $4 \times (9 \times 6) = \blacksquare$. *216*

When we multiply, we can change the **GROUPING** and get the same product.

Read and study the material at the top of the page with the students. After the students complete the exercises, discuss the answers and the statement of the grouping principle at the bottom of the page.

PREPARATION

Review for the class the mathematical meaning of parentheses. You can do this by presenting several addition and multiplication equations which have parentheses to indicate the operations to be performed first.

Following this, give the students an opportunity to work several equation pairs similar to those in exercise 1 on page 158 and in exercise 1 on page 159.

Read and study the material at the top of the page with the class. Particularly emphasize that *both* the order and grouping principles are being used. Using both of these principles, we rearrange the addends in any way that is convenient. Stress this idea and then have the students work the exercises. Allow time for checking papers and discussion.

Rearranging addends

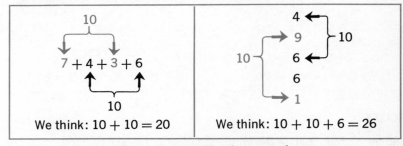

Change the order grouping and the sum is the same.

Because of the order and grouping principles for addition, we can add any two addends first and get the same sum.

We think: 10 + 10 = 20   We think: 10 + 10 + 6 = 26

We can rearrange addends as we please.

EXERCISES

1. Find the sums. Use the grouping given for exercises A and K. You may rearrange the other addends any way you choose.

Add these first

[A] 3 + 9 + 7 /9
[B] 9 + 8 + 1 /8
[C] 6 + 3 + 4 /3
[D] 2 + 8 + 9 /9
[E] 8 + 5 + 5 /8

[F] 8 + 4 + 2 + 6 20
[G] 7 + 1 + 9 + 3 20
[H] 5 + 4 + 6 + 5 20
[I] 8 + 5 + 2 + 5 + 6 26
[J] 9 + 7 + 2 + 1 + 8 27

Add these first

[K] 37 + 40 + 60 /3
[L] 30 + 23 + 70 /2
[M] 23 + 27 + 8 58
[N] 9 + 44 + 26 7
[O] 24 + 35 + 45 /0

2. Find the sums. Use the table on the right.

[A] 48 + 61 + 23 /32
[B] 13 + 18 + 16 47
[C] 59 + 28 + 91 /78
[D] 65 + 44 + 81 /90
[E] 85 + 76 + 28 /89
[F] 73 + 92 + 68 233
[G] 35 + 27 + 19 8/
[H] 65 + 75 + 49 /89

68 + 92 + 73 = 233	16 + 13 + 18 = 47
44 + 65 + 81 = 190	75 + 65 + 49 = 189
19 + 27 + 35 = 81	28 + 85 + 76 = 189
61 + 23 + 48 = 132	91 + 28 + 59 = 178

Teaching Pages 160 and 161

• **PURPOSE**

To arrive at a generalization drawn from the basic order and grouping principles for addition and multiplication

• **MATHEMATICS**

The following list shows all the ways that one can change the order of the grouping of three addends. Notice that each step involves either a change of order or a change of grouping.

In the 12 different ways to consider the sum of the three addends, *a*, *b*, and *c*, we started with $(a + b) + c$ and, by alternating, regrouping steps, and reordering, arrived at

Rearranging factors

Change the → order → and the product is the same.
          → grouping →

Because of the order and grouping principles, we can choose any two factors for our first multiplication and get the same product.

Factors: 2, 3, 4		
We could multiply these first.	We could multiply these first.	We could multiply these first.
↓ ↓ or	↓ ↓ or	↓ ↓
2 × 3 × 4	2 × 3 × 4	2 × 3 × 4
[A] (2 × 3) × 4	[E] (2 × 4) × 3	[I] (3 × 4) × 2
[B] (3 × 2) × 4	[F] (4 × 2) × 3	[J] (4 × 3) × 2
[C] 4 × (3 × 2)	[G] 3 × (4 × 2)	[K] 2 × (4 × 3)
[D] 4 × (2 × 3)	[H] 3 × (2 × 4)	[L] 2 × (3 × 4)

We can rearrange factors as we please.

EXERCISES

1. Find each of the 12 products in parts **A** through **L** in the table above. Are they the same? *All the products are 24.*

2. Find the products. Arrange the factors any way you choose.
   [A] 5 × 8 × 2 *80*   [B] 2 × 9 × 5 *90*   [C] 4 × 2 × 1 *8*   [D] 989 × 7 × 0 *0*

3. Find the products.
   [A] Since 3 × 4 × 5 = 60, we know 5 × 3 × 4 = ▮. *60*
   [B] Since 8 × 7 × 6 = 336, we know 7 × 8 × 6 = ▮. *336*

4. Find the products. Use the table on the right.
   [A] 3 × 27 × 6 *486*   [E] 4 × 27 × 5 *540*
   [B] 5 × 8 × 13 *520*   [F] 65 × 8 × 4 *2080*
   [C] 4 × 65 × 9 *2340*   [G] 3 × 7 × 17 *357*
   [D] 17 × 4 × 6 *408*   [H] 13 × 9 × 8 *936*

```
5 × 27 × 4 = 540
17 × 6 × 4 = 408
8 × 13 × 9 = 936
6 × 3 × 27 = 486
17 × 7 × 3 = 357
8 × 5 × 13 = 520
65 × 9 × 4 = 2340
8 × 4 × 65 = 2080
```

$(a + b) + c$
$a + (b + c)$
$a + (c + b)$
$(a + c) + b$
$(c + a) + b$
$c + (a + b)$
$c + (b + a)$
$(c + b) + a$
$(b + c) + a$
$b + (c + a)$
$b + (a + c)$
$(b + a) + c$
$(a + b) + c$

As you discuss the material at the top of the page, again note that the order and grouping principles for multiplication are used. By using these two principles, we can rearrange the factors in multiplication in any way that is convenient.

Have the students work the exercises. Allow time at the end for discussion and checking papers.

the original form. This clearly shows that we can use the order and grouping principles for addition to arrive at any desired arrangement for three addends. Also we would note that parentheses can be eliminated since we can add any two numbers first.

● **PREPARATION**

Conduct a brief review of the order and grouping principles for addition and multiplication.

Discuss the material at the top of the page with the class. Following this, have them do the exercises. Allow time at the end for the checking of papers.

Review of the principles

When **ADDING** whole numbers:	When **MULTIPLYING** whole numbers:
ORDER PRINCIPLE	
Change the **ORDER** of the addends and the sum is the same.	Change the **ORDER** of the factors and the product is the same.
GROUPING PRINCIPLE	
Change the **GROUPING** of the addends and the sum is the same.	Change the **GROUPING** of the factors and the product is the same.
ZERO AND ONE PRINCIPLES	
The sum of any whole number and 0 is that whole number.	The product of any whole number and 1 is that whole number.

EXERCISES

Give the missing words.

1. In addition, we can change the order and the _?_ *grouping* and the sum is the same.

2. In multiplication, we can change the _?_ *order* and the _?_ *grouping* and the product is the same.

3. In addition, we can rearrange the _?_ *addends* and the sum is the same.

4. In multiplication, we can _?_ *rearrange* the factors and the product is the same.

5. The sum of any whole number and _?_ *zero* is that whole number.

6. The product of any whole number and _?_ *one* is that whole number.

7. The product of any whole number and zero is _?_. *zero*

8. Never _?_ *divide* by zero.

Teaching Pages 162 and 163

● **PURPOSE**

To review the basic principles presented thus far

To provide word-problem experiences leading to the idea of multiplication-addition (distributive) principle

● **PREPARATION**

Review the principles presented thus far in the chapter. Following this, focus attention on the special additive and multiplicative properties of zero and one by giving several exercises which involve adding zero or multiplying by one.

Working in the bookstore

Ned and Ted were helping Mr. Brown
count school supplies in his store. Mr.
Brown called this work "taking inventory."

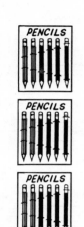

DISCUSSION QUESTION

When they were counting pencils on the cards,

Ted thought: 3 cards, 6 pencils each, $3 \times 6 = 18$.

Ned thought: Blue pencils $\quad 3 \times 2 = 6$ ⟶

Black pencils $3 \times 4 = 12$ ⟶ total: 18.

Were they both correct? Which method would you have used?
yes

EXERCISES

1. [A] How many pens are on these cards? *20*

   [B] Write a multiplication equation that shows how
   Ted would find the number of pens on these cards.
   4×5=20

   [C] Write two multiplication equations that show how
   Ned would find the number of pens on these cards.
   4×3 =12, 4×2=8, total 20

2. Ted sold Nancy 5 pencils and 5 erasers.
   How much did they cost in all? *25¢*

3. Ned sold Jane 4 items that were listed on the
   "Inventory Sale" sign. They cost 15¢.
   What did Jane buy? *2 rulers, 1 eraser, 1 pencil*

4. Ted made a poster as a joke and showed it
   to Ned. The poster reminded Ned of one of the
   principles. Which one? *the order principle
   for multiplication*

5. Ned put a box of 25 yellow rulers and 34 green rulers in
   a drawer. Then he put in a bundle of 41 red rulers. Ted
   put a bundle of 25 yellow rulers in a drawer. Then he put
   a box of 34 green rulers and 41 red rulers in the drawer.
   Find how many rulers each boy put in the drawer.
   Ned : 100 } *100 each*
   Ted : 100

INVENTORY SALE!
Pencils   3¢ each
Erasers   2¢ each
Rulers   5¢ each

Save Money!
Buy **3** of these
blue erasers
for 2¢ each,
instead of **2**
of these gray
erasers
for 3¢ each.

DIRECTIONS PAGE 163

Read and study the material at
the top of the page with the class.
Use the discussion question as
preparation for the first exercise
and to allow the students to become
acquainted with the ideas of this
lesson.

Following this discussion, have
the students work the exercises.
When they have finished, allow
time for questions and general discussion.

Have the students read the directions and work the exercises. When they have finished, discuss the fact that they get the same answer for both equations of each exercise. Notice with the students that the only difference is that in the second part of each exercise they think about breaking apart the set as illustrated by the picture and by the equation.

A new principle

These exercises will help you understand a new principle. Solve the equations.

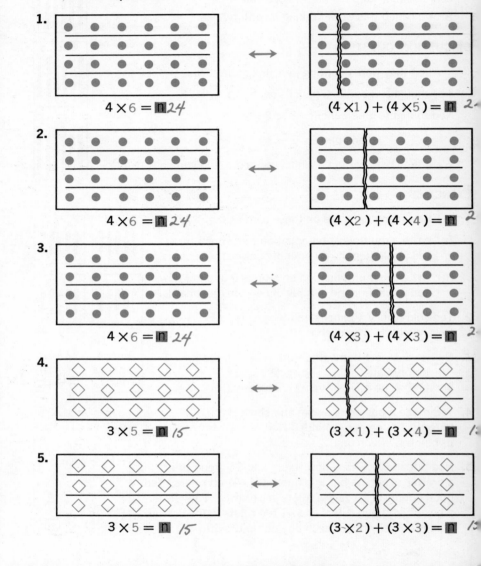

1. $4 \times 6 = \boxed{n}\ 24$ $\longleftrightarrow$ $(4 \times 1) + (4 \times 5) = \boxed{n}\ 2$

2. $4 \times 6 = \boxed{n}\ 24$ $\longleftrightarrow$ $(4 \times 2) + (4 \times 4) = \boxed{n}\ 2$

3. $4 \times 6 = \boxed{n}\ 24$ $\longleftrightarrow$ $(4 \times 3) + (4 \times 3) = \boxed{n}\ 2$

4. $3 \times 5 = \boxed{n}\ 15$ $\longleftrightarrow$ $(3 \times 1) + (3 \times 4) = \boxed{n}\ 15$

5. $3 \times 5 = \boxed{n}\ 15$ $\longleftrightarrow$ $(3 \times 2) + (3 \times 3) = \boxed{n}\ 15$

Teaching Pages 164 and 165

- **PURPOSE**

  To provide an activity leading to the formal introduction of the multiplication-addition principle

- **MATHEMATICS**

  Below is a formal statement of the multiplication-addition principle.

  For all whole numbers a, b, and c,

  $$a \times (b + c) = (a \times b) + (a \times c).$$

  The chief use of this principle comes when the students

6. Solve these equations.

[A] $6 \times 7 = \blacksquare$ 42 $(6 \times 4) + (6 \times 3) = \blacksquare$ 42
[B] $2 \times 9 = \blacksquare$ 18 $(2 \times 5) + (2 \times 4) = \blacksquare$ 18
[C] $6 \times 5 = \blacksquare$ 30 $(6 \times 2) + (6 \times 3) = \blacksquare$ 30
[D] $4 \times 9 = \blacksquare$ 36 $(4 \times 2) + (4 \times 7) = \blacksquare$ 36

7. Find the missing numbers.

[A] [D]

$4 \times 7 = (4 \times 4) + (4 \times \blacksquare)$ 3 $\qquad 3 \times 6 = (3 \times \blacksquare) + (3 \times 2)$ 4

[B] $3 \times 6 = (3 \times \blacksquare) + (3 \times 2)$ 4 [E] $8 \times 7 = (8 \times \blacksquare) + (8 \times 5)$ 2
[C] $7 \times 8 = (7 \times 4) + (7 \times \blacksquare)$ 4 [F] $9 \times 8 = (9 \times 6) + (9 \times \blacksquare)$ 2

8. Find the missing numbers.

[A] [E]

$4 \times \blacksquare = (4 \times 2) + (4 \times 3)$ 5 $\qquad \blacksquare \times 4 = (3 \times 1) + (3 \times 3)$ 3

[B] $\blacksquare \times 9 = (3 \times 5) + (3 \times 4)$ 3 [F] $7 \times \blacksquare = (7 \times 1) + (7 \times 4)$ 5
[C] $8 \times \blacksquare = (8 \times 3) + (8 \times 4)$ 7 [G] $\blacksquare \times 16 = (8 \times 10) + (8 \times 6)$ 8
[D] $\blacksquare \times 8 = (4 \times 5) + (4 \times 3)$ 4 [H] $4 \times \blacksquare = (4 \times 10) + (4 \times 7)$ 17

9. Study the example. Then find the missing numbers.

$(3 \times 10) + (3 \times 4) = 3 \times 14$

[A] $(3 \times 10) + (3 \times 5) = 3 \times \blacksquare$ 15 [C] $(2 \times 10) + (2 \times 6) = 2 \times \blacksquare$ 16
[B] $(4 \times 10) + (4 \times 7) = 4 \times \blacksquare$ 17 [D] $(6 \times 10) + (6 \times 9) = 6 \times \blacksquare$ 19

In this lesson we have been learning a new principle. We call it the multiplication-addition principle. You might think about it like this:

When we multiply, we can "break apart" numbers.

Have the students work the exercises. Discuss the ideas when they have finished. Emphasize the statement at the bottom of the page concerning the breaking apart of numbers.

Be sure that the students understand that in this type of exercise they merely need to think about doing the multiplication in two parts rather than in a single part. For an exercise such as 3×6, they can think of doing $(3 \times 4) + (3 \times 2)$. Upon completion of this lesson, tell the students that we shall call this principle the multiplication-addition principle.

"break apart" numbers for multiplication. Consider this example.

$$a \times (b + c) = (a \times b) + (a \times c)$$
$$2 \times 43 = 2 \times (40 + 3) = (2 \times 40) + (2 \times 3)$$

The descriptive language "break apart" evolves from this type of exercise.

PREPARATION

Provide the students with practice on the following type of equations.

$$(2 \times 5) + (2 \times 6) = n$$
$$(3 \times 4) + (3 \times 2) = n$$
$$(7 \times 2) + (7 \times 3) = n$$

Be sure the students understand that they are to do the two multiplications first and then add the products in order to get the correct answer. The students should be quite adept at this type of exercise before they work pages 164 and 165.

Have the students read the directions and work the exercises. When they have finished, allow time for discussion and checking papers. Again, attempt to get the students to verbalize the idea being presented by these exercises. Help them see how the various sets illustrate the idea of breaking apart numbers in the multiplication-addition principle.

The multiplication–addition principle

These exercises will help you learn more about the multiplication–addition principle.

EXERCISES

Study each picture. Then give the missing numbers.

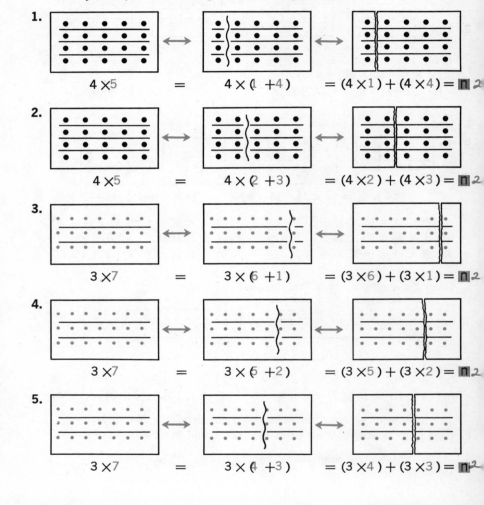

1. $4 \times 5 = 4 \times (1 + 4) = (4 \times 1) + (4 \times 4) = n$

2. $4 \times 5 = 4 \times (2 + 3) = (4 \times 2) + (4 \times 3) = n$

3. $3 \times 7 = 3 \times (6 + 1) = (3 \times 6) + (3 \times 1) = n$

4. $3 \times 7 = 3 \times (5 + 2) = (3 \times 5) + (3 \times 2) = n$

5. $3 \times 7 = 3 \times (4 + 3) = (3 \times 4) + (3 \times 3) = n$

Teaching Pages 166 and 167

● **PURPOSE**

To provide more experiences with the multiplication-addition principle

● **PREPARATION**

Provide review material similar to that on pages 164 and 165. In particular, encourage the students to verbalize on the ideas presented on page 165. If necessary, follow this by giving the students a short oral drill on basic sums and products.

EXERCISES

1. Find the missing numbers.

[A] $3 \times 8 = 3 \times (5 + \blacksquare)$ *3*
[B] $6 \times 7 = 6 \times (\blacksquare + 5)$ *2*
[C] $9 \times 4 = \blacksquare \times (3 + 1)$ *9*
[D] $8 \times \blacksquare = 8 \times (4 + 2)$ *6*
[E] $\blacksquare \times 9 = 6 \times (5 + 4)$ *6*

[F] $\blacksquare \times 3 = 7 \times (1 + 2)$ *7*
[G] $5 \times 7 = \blacksquare \times (3 + 4)$ *5*
[H] $6 \times 10 = 6 \times (\blacksquare + 7)$ *3*
[I] $4 \times 13 = 4 \times (10 + \blacksquare)$ *3*
[J] $7 \times \blacksquare = 7 \times (10 + 2)$ *12*

2. Find the missing numbers.

[A] $3 \times (5 + 3) = (3 \times 5) + (3 \times \blacksquare)$ *3*
[B] $6 \times (2 + 5) = (6 \times \blacksquare) + (6 \times 5)$ *2*
[C] $9 \times (3 + \blacksquare) = (9 \times 3) + (9 \times 1)$ *1*
[D] $8 \times (\blacksquare + 2) = (8 \times 4) + (8 \times 2)$ *4*
[E] $\blacksquare \times (5 + 4) = (6 \times 5) + (6 \times 4)$ *6*

[F] $7 \times (1 + 2) = (7 \times 1) + (7 \times \blacksquare)$ *2*
[G] $5 \times (3 + \blacksquare) = (5 \times 3) + (5 \times 4)$ *4*
[H] $6 \times (\blacksquare + 7) = (6 \times 3) + (6 \times 7)$ *3*
[I] $\blacksquare \times (10 + 3) = (4 \times 10) + (4 \times 3)$ *4*
[J] $7 \times (10 + 2) = (7 \times 10) + (7 \times \blacksquare)$ *2*

3. Solve the equations.

[A] $(3 \times 10) + (3 \times 2) = \blacksquare$ *36*
[B] $(4 \times 10) + (4 \times 1) = \blacksquare$ *44*
[C] $(5 \times 10) + (5 \times 1) = \blacksquare$ *55*
[D] $(2 \times 10) + (2 \times 4) = \blacksquare$ *28*
[E] $(2 \times 10) + (2 \times 3) = \blacksquare$ *26*

[F] $(4 \times 10) + (4 \times 2) = \blacksquare$ *48*
[G] $(5 \times 10) + (5 \times 2) = \blacksquare$ *60*
[H] $(3 \times 10) + (3 \times 4) = \blacksquare$ *42*
[I] $(6 \times 10) + (6 \times 2) = \blacksquare$ *72*
[J] $(7 \times 10) + (7 \times 3) = \blacksquare$ *91*

4. Find the products.

[A] $3 \times (10 + 2) = \blacksquare$ *36*
[B] $4 \times (10 + 1) = \blacksquare$ *44*
[C] $5 \times (10 + 1) = \blacksquare$ *55*
[D] $2 \times (10 + 4) = \blacksquare$ *28*
[E] $2 \times (10 + 3) = \blacksquare$ *26*

[F] $4 \times (10 + 2) = \blacksquare$ *48*
[G] $5 \times (10 + 2) = \blacksquare$ *60*
[H] $3 \times (10 + 4) = \blacksquare$ *42*
[I] $6 \times (10 + 2) = \blacksquare$ *72*
[J] $7 \times (10 + 3) = \blacksquare$ *91*

5. Find the products.

[A] 3×12 *36*   [C] 5×11 *55*   [E] 2×13 *26*   [G] 5×12 *60*   [I] 6×12 *72*
[B] 4×11 *44*   [D] 2×14 *28*   [F] 4×12 *48*   [H] 3×14 *42*   [J] 7×13 *91*

6. Find the products.

[A] 3×11 *33*   [C] 4×13 *52*   [E] 3×15 *45*   [G] 7×12 *84*   [I] 5×16 *80*
[B] 2×15 *30*   [D] 5×13 *65*   [F] 6×11 *66*   [H] 8×11 *88*   [J] 4×17 *68*

DIRECTIONS PAGE 167

Note in particular with the students the sequential organization of exercises 3 through 5. Have the students observe the similarities between exercises 3A, 4A, and 5A. Choose another sequence of exercises, such as exercises 3D, 4D, and 5D, for similar discussion.

Have the students work the exercises. You may choose to provide guidance for the first one or two exercises and then have the students complete the page.

Once the students have finished the page, notice with them that by finding first the area of the gray part and then the blue part of the figure, they can add to get the area of the whole figure; or they could, if they liked, simply find the area of the whole figure at the beginning.

Some of the students will quickly discover the use of multiplication to find area. It will have to be pointed out to others. You should not, however, consider this a key part of the lesson. Some of the students will still rely on the method of counting squares, whether or not they can see the squares (they will imagine the squares in those shaded figures that do not show the grids).

Multiplication–addition exercises

1. [A] What is the area of the gray part of the figure? *25*
   [B] What is the area of the blue part of the figure? *20*
   [C] What is the area of both parts together? *45*

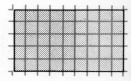

2. [A] What is the area of the gray part? *12*
   [B] What is the area of the blue part? *8*
   [C] What is the area of the figure? *20*

3. [A] What is the area of the figure? *24*
   [B] What is the area of the gray part? *16*
   [C] What is the area of the blue part? *8*

4. [A] What is the area of the gray part? *18*
   [B] What is the area of the blue part? *12*
   [C] What is the area of the figure? *30*

5. [A] What is the area of the blue part? *6*
   [B] What is the area of the gray part? *9*
   [C] What is the area of the figure? *15*

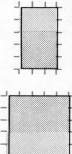

6. [A] What is the area of the figure? *30*
   [B] What is the area of the gray part? *15*
   [C] What is the area of the blue part? *15*

Teaching Pages 168 and 169

- **PURPOSE**

  To focus further attention on the multiplication-addition principle

- **PREPARATION**

  Provide the students with several examples of the following type.

  $$3 \times 7 = (3 \times 4) + (3 \times 3)$$
  $$3 \times 8 = (3 \times 2) + (3 \times 6)$$
  $$3 \times 5 = (3 \times 4) + (3 \times 1)$$

The multiplication–addition principle again

Here is another way to think about the multiplication–addition principle.

Since $4 \times 5 = (4 \times 3) + (4 \times 2)$, we know that $5 \times 4 = (3 \times 4) + (2 \times 4)$.	Since $3 \times 8 = (3 \times 6) + (3 \times 2)$, we know that $8 \times 3 = (6 \times 3) + (2 \times 3)$.

You might think: When we multiply, we can "break apart" the first or second factor.

EXERCISES

1. Give the missing numbers.

[A] Since $3 \times 6 = (3 \times 2) + (3 \times 4)$,
we know that $6 \times 3 = (2 \times 3) + (\blacksquare \times 3)$. *4*

[B] Since $5 \times 7 = (5 \times 4) + (5 \times 3)$,
we know that $7 \times 5 = (\blacksquare \times 5) + (3 \times 5)$. *4*

[C] Since $4 \times 3 = (4 \times 2) + (4 \times 1)$,
we know that $3 \times 4 = (2 \times 4) + (\blacksquare \times 4)$. *1*

[D] Since $7 \times 9 = (7 \times 5) + (7 \times 4)$,
we know that $\blacksquare \times 7 = (5 \times 7) + (4 \times 7)$. *9*

[E] Since $10 \times 5 = (10 \times 4) + (10 \times 1)$,
we know that $5 \times 10 = (\blacksquare \times 10) + (1 \times 10)$. *4*

2. Solve the equations.

[A] $4 \times 5 = \blacksquare$ *20*
$(2 \times 5) + (2 \times 5) = \blacksquare$ *20*

[B] $8 \times 7 = \blacksquare$ *56*
$(5 \times 7) + (3 \times 7) = \blacksquare$ *56*

[C] $9 \times 3 = \blacksquare$ *27*
$(8 \times 3) + (1 \times 3) = \blacksquare$ *27*

[D] $6 \times 8 = \blacksquare$ *48*
$(5 \times 8) + (1 \times 8) = \blacksquare$ *48*

[E] $8 \times 9 = \blacksquare$ *72*
$(4 \times 9) + (4 \times 9) = \blacksquare$ *72*

[F] $12 \times 6 = \blacksquare$ *72*
$(10 \times 6) + (2 \times 6) = \blacksquare$ *72*

3. Solve the equations.

[A] $3 \times 4 = (2 \times 4) + (\blacksquare \times 4)$ *1*

[B] $6 \times 5 = (\blacksquare \times 5) + (1 \times 5)$ *5*

[C] $7 \times 8 = (5 \times 8) + (\blacksquare \times 8)$ *2*

[D] $5 \times 6 = (\blacksquare \times 6) + (3 \times 6)$ *2*

[E] $\blacksquare \times 7 = (4 \times 7) + (3 \times 7)$ *7*

[F] $12 \times 10 = (\blacksquare \times 10) + (2 \times 10)$ *10*

[G] $\blacksquare \times 7 = (10 \times 7) + (3 \times 7)$ *13*

[H] $15 \times 5 = (10 \times 5) + (\blacksquare \times 5)$ *5*

As you discuss the material at the top of the page with the class, observe how, in each equation, one factor is broken apart. Notice with the students that in the first equation the second number is broken apart and that in the second equation this same number is broken apart and now reordered in the first position. Emphasize in this discussion that we can break apart either factor when we multiply.

Following this discussion, have the students work the exercises. Allow time at the end for checking papers and answering any questions the students may have.

Have the students verify the truth of each equation by performing the indicated multiplications and addition. For example, for the first equation, have the students observe that $3 \times 7 = 21$ and that the sum of 3×4 and 3×3 is also 21.

Follow this with a brief review of finding the area of a figure which has each unit clearly marked. Restrict this review to rectangular figures.

Have the students work the exercises. When they have finished, allow time for checking answers and discussion. In particular, discuss the concepts presented in exercises 1 and 2. Give the students an opportunity to verbalize how these set pictures present various concepts of addition, subtraction, multiplication, and division. As another activity, you can have students write two division equations for each multiplication equation in exercise 2.

Answers, exercise 1, page 170

[A] $6 + 3 = 9$
  $9 - 3 = 6$
  $3 + 6 = 9$
  $9 - 6 = 3$

[B] $10 + 5 = 15$
  $15 - 5 = 10$
  $5 + 10 = 15$
  $15 - 10 = 5$

[C] $9 + 1 = 10$
  $10 - 1 = 9$
  $1 + 9 = 10$
  $10 - 9 = 1$

[D] $4 + 5 = 9$
  $9 - 5 = 4$
  $5 + 4 = 9$
  $9 - 4 = 5$

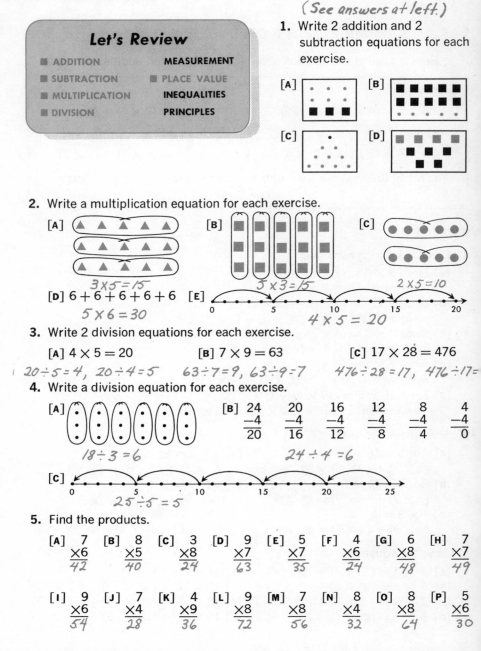

Let's Review

■ ADDITION   MEASUREMENT
■ SUBTRACTION   ■ PLACE VALUE
■ MULTIPLICATION   INEQUALITIES
■ DIVISION   PRINCIPLES

(See answers at left.)

1. Write 2 addition and 2 subtraction equations for each exercise.

[A] [B] [C] [D]

2. Write a multiplication equation for each exercise.

[A] $3 \times 5 = 15$ [B] $5 \times 3 = 15$ [C] $2 \times 5 = 10$

[D] $6 + 6 + 6 + 6 + 6$ $5 \times 6 = 30$ [E] $4 \times 5 = 20$

3. Write 2 division equations for each exercise.

[A] $4 \times 5 = 20$ [B] $7 \times 9 = 63$ [C] $17 \times 28 = 476$

$20 \div 5 = 4, \ 20 \div 4 = 5$ $63 \div 7 = 9, \ 63 \div 9 = 7$ $476 \div 28 = 17, \ 476 \div 17 =$

4. Write a division equation for each exercise.

[A] $18 \div 3 = 6$

[B]
24	20	16	12	8	4
−4	−4	−4	−4	−4	−4
20	16	12	8	4	0

$24 \div 4 = 6$

[C] $25 \div 5 = 5$

5. Find the products.

[A] $\begin{array}{r} 7 \\ \times 6 \\ \hline 42 \end{array}$
[B] $\begin{array}{r} 8 \\ \times 5 \\ \hline 40 \end{array}$
[C] $\begin{array}{r} 3 \\ \times 8 \\ \hline 24 \end{array}$
[D] $\begin{array}{r} 9 \\ \times 7 \\ \hline 63 \end{array}$
[E] $\begin{array}{r} 5 \\ \times 7 \\ \hline 35 \end{array}$
[F] $\begin{array}{r} 4 \\ \times 6 \\ \hline 24 \end{array}$
[G] $\begin{array}{r} 6 \\ \times 8 \\ \hline 48 \end{array}$
[H] $\begin{array}{r} 7 \\ \times 7 \\ \hline 49 \end{array}$

[I] $\begin{array}{r} 9 \\ \times 6 \\ \hline 54 \end{array}$
[J] $\begin{array}{r} 7 \\ \times 4 \\ \hline 28 \end{array}$
[K] $\begin{array}{r} 4 \\ \times 9 \\ \hline 36 \end{array}$
[L] $\begin{array}{r} 9 \\ \times 8 \\ \hline 72 \end{array}$
[M] $\begin{array}{r} 7 \\ \times 8 \\ \hline 56 \end{array}$
[N] $\begin{array}{r} 8 \\ \times 4 \\ \hline 32 \end{array}$
[O] $\begin{array}{r} 8 \\ \times 8 \\ \hline 64 \end{array}$
[P] $\begin{array}{r} 5 \\ \times 6 \\ \hline 30 \end{array}$

Teaching **Pages 170 and 171**

● **PURPOSE**

To provide a review of the material covered thus far in the text

● **PREPARATION**

Review any concepts and skills with which the students have had previous difficulty. If time permits, provide the students with practice in reading large numbers. Follow this by having them explain the place-value meaning of seven-, eight-, and nine-digit numerals.

6. Give a number to complete each sentence.

[A] In 3654, the 6 stands for ▦. *600*   [F] In 9035, the 0 stands for ▦. *0*

[B] In 76,285, the 6 stands for ▦. *6000* [G] In 37,643, the 7 stands for ▦. *7000*

[C] In 327, the 2 stands for ▦. *20*   [H] In 50,123, the 5 stands for ▦. *50,000*

[D] In 8603, the 8 stands for ▦. *8000* [I] In 7052, the 5 stands for ▦. *50*

[E] In 28,650, the 0 stands for ▦. *0*   [J] In 86,347, the 8 stands for ▦. *80,000*

7. Find the sums.

[A] 60,000 + 7000 + 800 + 20 + 3 *67,823*

[B] 20,000 + 3000 + 200 + 60 + 7 *23,267*

[C] 70,000 + 300 + 8 *70,308*

[D] 900,000 + 6000 + 700 + 20 *906,720*

[E] 1,000,000 + 300,000 + 60,000 + 9000 *1,369,000*

8. For these numbers, write sums as in exercise 7. *(See answers at right.)*

[A] 23,475   [C] 90,306   [E] 6,283,000

[B] 6280   [D] 127,000   [F] 7,008,009

9. Find the quotients. (For help, look at exercise 5.)

[A] 56 ÷ 8 *7*   [E] 24 ÷ 8 *3*   [I] 36 ÷ 9 *4*   [M] 28 ÷ 4 *7*

[B] 63 ÷ 7 *9*   [F] 32 ÷ 4 *8*   [J] 24 ÷ 6 *4*   [N] 64 ÷ 8 *8*

[C] 72 ÷ 8 *9*   [G] 40 ÷ 5 *8*   [K] 54 ÷ 6 *9*   [O] 42 ÷ 6 *7*

[D] 49 ÷ 7 *7*   [H] 35 ÷ 7 *5*   [L] 48 ÷ 8 *6*   [P] 30 ÷ 6 *5*

10. Find the sums and differences.

[A] 27 +44 = *71*   [B] 64 −31 = *33*   [C] 24 +65 = *89*   [D] 72 +86 = *158*   [E] 77 +86 = *163*

[F] 64 −34 = *30*   [G] 64 −38 = *26*   [H] 59 +63 = *122*   [I] 92 +88 = *180*   [J] 72 −47 = *25*

[K] 47 +56 = *103*   [L] 93 −26 = *67*   [M] 127 −54 = *73*   [N] 127 −59 = *68*   [O] 136 −48 = *88*

[P] 141 −95 = *46*   [Q] 65 −19 = *46*   [R] 48 +16 = *64*   [S] 78 +69 = *147*   [T] 46 +54 = *100*

DIRECTIONS PAGE 171

Have the students work the exercises. Discuss the answers and have the students check their papers. It may help the less able students to have some of the parts of exercise 10 presented on the chalkboard and explained.

Answers, exercise 8, page 171

[A] 20,000 + 3000 + 400 + 70 + 5

[B] 6000 + 200 + 80

[C] 90,000 + 300 + 6

[D] 100,000 + 20,000 + 7000

[E] 6,000,000 + 200,000 + 80,000 + 3000

[F] 7,000,000 + 8000 + 9

Have the students work the exercises. During your discussion, call particular attention to exercise 3. Help the students see how this illustrates the multiplication-addition principle. Observe with the students that they could think, "Eight sheets of paper, three pictures on each," or they could think of the sheets of paper separately, "Three pictures on each of three red sheets and three pictures on each of five blue sheets." Of course, the point to observe with the students is that the total number of pictures is the same whichever way they think.

---

172   BASIC PRINCIPLES

Chapter review

1. Solve the equation for each set picture.

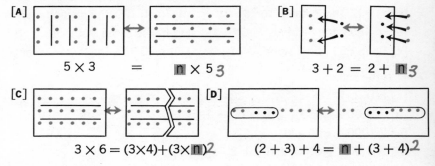

[A] $5 \times 3 = \blacksquare \times 5$ _3_   [B] $3 + 2 = 2 + \blacksquare$ _3_

[C] $3 \times 6 = (3 \times 4) + (3 \times \blacksquare)$ _2_   [D] $(2 + 3) + 4 = \blacksquare + (3 + 4)$ _2_

2. Find the sums and products.

[A] $8 + 10$ _18_   [F] $5 \times 3 \times 2$ _30_   [K] $6 + 7 + 4 + 3 + 5$ _2_

[B] $7 + 3 + 6$ _16_   [G] $3 \times 4 \times 2$ _24_   [L] $6 + 7 + 8 + 9$ _30_

[C] $9 + 4 + 1$ _14_   [H] $3 \times 8 \times 3$ _72_   [M] $98 + 37 + 2$ _137_

[D] $18 + 7 + 2$ _27_   [I] $4 \times 9 \times 2$ _72_   [N] $79 + 6 + 94$ _179_

[E] $1 + 2 + 3 + 4$ _10_   [J] $3 \times 2 \times 1$ _6_   [O] $36 + 29 + 64$ _129_

3. Miss White had 3 sheets of red paper and 5 sheets of blue paper. She pasted 3 pictures on each sheet. How many pictures did she use? _24_

4. [A] Red marbles: 5 sacks. 3 in each sack. Blue marbles: 5 sacks. 4 in each sack. How many marbles in all? _35_

   [B] 5 boys. Each bought 8 marbles. 4 girls. Each bought 8 marbles. How many marbles were bought in all? _72_

   [C] 3 boys. Each bought 5 red marbles and 7 green marbles. How many marbles in all? _36_

   [D] Bob's marbles: 4 bags. Tom's marbles: 5 bags. 7 in each bag. How many more does Tom have than Bob? _7_

5. Solve the equations.

[A] $2 \times 7 = (2 \times 3) + (2 \times \blacksquare)$ _4_

[B] $3 \times 5 = (3 \times 2) + (3 \times \blacksquare)$ _3_

[C] $4 \times 6 = (\blacksquare \times 6) + (2 \times 6)$ _2_

[D] $5 \times 8 = (5 \times \blacksquare) + (5 \times 7)$ _1_

[E] $6 \times 9 = (4 \times 9) + (\blacksquare \times 9)$ _2_

[F] $7 \times 4 = (2 \times 4) + (\blacksquare \times 4)$ _5_

[G] $5 \times 6 = (5 \times 1) + (5 \times \blacksquare)$

[H] $4 \times 7 = (\blacksquare \times 7) + (1 \times 7)$

[I] $3 \times 10 = (3 \times \blacksquare) + (3 \times 6)$

[J] $3 \times 15 = (3 \times 10) + (3 \times \blacksquare)$

[K] $5 \times 17 = (5 \times 10) + (5 \times \blacksquare)$

[L] $7 \times 14 = (7 \times 10) + (7 \times \blacksquare)$

Teaching Pages 172 and 173

- **PURPOSE**

  To provide an evaluation instrument for this chapter
  To provide a chapter review

- **PREPARATION**

  Review any of the concepts and skills with which the students may have had difficulty in this chapter. Focus attention on the two uses of division in solving the word problems: to find the number of sets and to find the number in each set. Help students see that the most efficient way to do the division is to think of the quotient as

6. Solve the equations.

[A] $3 \times (4 + 2) = (3 \times \blacksquare) + (3 \times 2)$ *4*
[B] $4 \times (7 + 2) = (4 \times 7) + (\blacksquare \times 2)$ *4*
[C] $5 \times (3 + 6) = (\blacksquare \times 3) + (5 \times 6)$ *5*
[D] $3 \times (\blacksquare + 4) = (3 \times 2) + (3 \times 4)$ *2*
[E] $5 \times \blacksquare = (5 \times 3) + (5 \times 4)$ *7*
[F] $\blacksquare \times (5 + 4) = (8 \times 5) + (8 \times 4)$ *8*
[G] $(2 + 1) \times 3 = (\blacksquare \times 3) + (1 \times 3)$ *2*
[H] $(5 + 3) \times 4 = (5 \times 4) + (\blacksquare \times 4)$ *3*

7. Solve the equations.

[A] $\blacksquare + 8 = 8 + 9$ *9*
[B] $\blacksquare + (5 + 23) = (41 + 5) + 23$ *41*
[C] $\blacksquare + 29 + 34 = 34 + 17 + 29$ *17*
[D] $9 \times \blacksquare = 7 \times 9$ *7*
[E] $4 \times (2 \times \blacksquare) = (4 \times 2) \times 7$ *7*
[F] $4 \times 2 \times 3 = \blacksquare \times 2 \times 4$ *3*
[G] $8 \times 3 = (8 \times 2) + (8 \times \blacksquare)$ *1*
[H] $95 \times 4 = \blacksquare \times 95$ *4*
[I] $7 \times 5 = (4 \times 5) + (\blacksquare \times 5)$ *3*
[J] $5 + 4 + 3 + 8 = 8 + \blacksquare + 3 + 5$ *4*
[K] $14 \times 3 = (10 \times 3) + (\blacksquare \times 3)$ *4*
[L] $5 \times 16 = (5 \times \blacksquare) + (5 \times 6)$ *10*

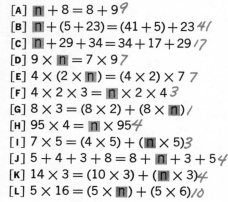

> **Exercise for Experts**
>
> I'm a basic principle.
> On this you can rely,
> Between two operations
> I simply form a tie.
> If it's products you're to find,
> My rule you might apply.
> Just break apart a factor
> Before you multiply.
> WHO AM I?

Multiplication - addition principle

8. Give the missing numbers.

[A] Since $9 + 11 = 20$, we know that $11 + 9 = \blacksquare$. *20*
[B] Since $5 \times 8 = 40$, we know that $8 \times 5 = \blacksquare$. *40*
[C] Since $23 + 35 = 58$, we know that $35 + 25 = \blacksquare$. *60*
[D] Since $(5 \times 10) + (5 \times 2) = 60$, we know that $5 \times (10 + 2) = \blacksquare$ *60*
[E] Since $4 + (17 + 1) = 22$, we know that $(4 + 17) + 1 = \blacksquare$. *22*
[F] Since $6 + 7 + 8 + 9 = 30$, we know that $4 + (9 + 6 + 8 + 7) = \blacksquare$. *34*
[G] Since $(4 \times 10) + (4 \times 3) = 52$, we know that $4 \times 13 = \blacksquare$ *52*
[H] Since $1 + 2 + 3 + 4 = 10$,
we know that $(1 + 1) + (2 + 2) + (3 + 3) + (4 + 4) = \blacksquare$. *20*
[I] Since $8 \times 7 = (8 \times 5) + (8 \times 2)$,
we know that $7 \times 8 = (\blacksquare \times 8) + (2 \times 8)$ *5*
[J] Since $3 \times 2 \times 1 = 6$, we know that $(1 \times 2 \times 3) \times 2 = \blacksquare$. *12*
[K] Since $(7 \times 10) + (7 \times 8) = 126$, we know that $7 \times 18 = \blacksquare$ *126*
[L] Since $4 \times 25 = 100$, we know that $8 \times 25 = \blacksquare$ *200*
[M] Since $8 \times 37 = 296$, we know that $9 \times 37 = 296 + \blacksquare$ *37*

Have the students work the exercises. Again, you may choose to check the papers yourself.

Note that the riddle might be difficult for some of the students. However, you should include all students in a discussion of the riddle and the correct answer. Be sure that the students who attempt the riddle are given adequate time to think about the ideas before they hear the correct answer.

Once the correct answer to a riddle is given, you can point out various clues in it which would help the students see the correct answer. For example, the first clue is the first line, "I'm a basic principle." To explain the second clue, "Between two operations I simply form a tie," point out that there is only one basic principle that involves two operations. Notice with the class the last clue which discusses breaking apart a factor before multiplying.

a missing factor. It may be helpful during this preparation period to invent some exercises similar to those in exercise 4 on page 170.

Teaching
Geometry Lesson 5

- **PURPOSE**

To introduce right angles

To provide simple methods for constructing right angles

Since we are interested primarily in building a specific concept in this lesson, the discovery element does not receive as much emphasis as it did in previous geometry lessons. This lesson is designed to give the students a feeling for the idea of a right angle. The idea is first introduced by a diagram, and then students are given some rather primitive methods for constructing right angles.

As the students investigate these methods, some rather important mathematical concepts arise. The basis for the method presented in exercise 3 is the fact that the set of all points which are equidistant from two given points forms the perpendicular bisector of the segment containing these points. Of course, perpendicular lines form right angles.

Exercise 4 presents another key idea with regard to right angles. Here, the students discover that any angle inscribed in a semicircle is a right angle. The students are asked to draw a circle and a diameter of the circle, mark a point on the circle, and then connect this point to the ends of the diameter.

Of course, at this stage, the students do not have any accurate measuring devices and must test the accuracy of their right angles simply by using the corner of a book or some other previously established right angle. Although these methods are elementary, they do constitute an important experience in working with and gaining a feeling for right angles.

- **MATHEMATICS**

The following illustrations show pairs of supplementary

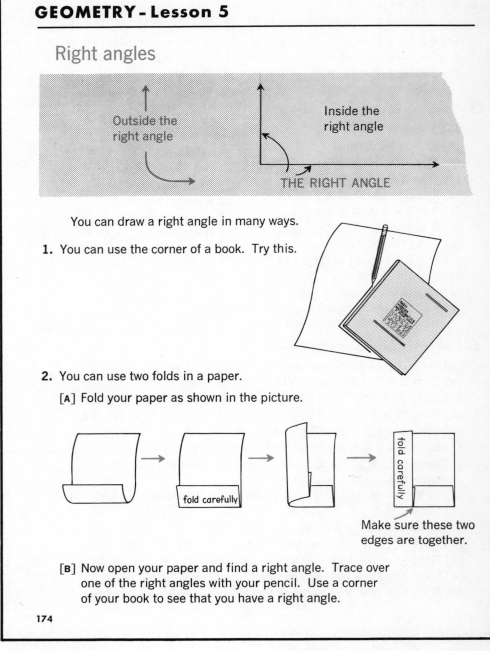

Angles 1 and 2 are supplementary to each other.
Angles 3 and 4 are supplementary to each other.
Angles 5 and 6 are supplementary to each other.

angles. Note that the angles in the illustrations which are supplementary to each other have sides which lie on one line.

Now consider this pair of supplementary angles.

Angles 7 and 8 are supplementary to each other *and* have the same size or same degree measure.

A *right angle* is an angle that is the same size (or has the same degree measure) as its supplement.

Even though the activities in this lesson are more direct and involve less in the way of discovery, you should approach this material in the spirit of adventure and dis-

---

GEOMETRY - Lesson 5

Right angles

Outside the right angle

Inside the right angle

THE RIGHT ANGLE

You can draw a right angle in many ways.

1. You can use the corner of a book. Try this.

2. You can use two folds in a paper.

   [A] Fold your paper as shown in the picture.

   fold carefully

   fold carefully

   Make sure these two edges are together.

   [B] Now open your paper and find a right angle. Trace over one of the right angles with your pencil. Use a corner of your book to see that you have a right angle.

174

---

3. You can use 2 points and 1 fold of the paper.

[A] Mark 2 points on your paper.
Use your ruler to connect the points.

[B] Put the point of your compass through the 2 dots. Fold the paper carefully.

[C] Now open the paper and find a right angle. Trace over the right angle with your pencil. Use a corner of your book to see that you have a right angle.

4. You can use a circle.

[A] Draw a large circle on your paper.
Draw a diameter of the circle.

[B] Mark a point on the circle.
Use your ruler to connect it to the ends of the diameter.

[C] Find the right angle. Use a corner of your book to see that it is a right angle.

[D] Try this again by marking a different point on the circle. Will this always give you a right angle?
You will get a right angle for any point on the circle you choose, except the endpoints of the diameter.

Study the illustration of the right angle at the top of page 174. If you choose, you can have the class read the instructions for exercises 1 and 2 and proceed on their own, or you can guide the class in completing these activities one at a time.

Be sure that in exercise 4 the students draw their circles large enough to get a right angle with sufficiently long sides so that they can test it with the corner of a book or some other previously established right angle. Encourage the students to practice this activity with several points on the circle so that they will discover that any point they choose (other than the ends of the diameter) will produce a right angle.

covery. The students will be excited about performing these various activities and will be given the opportunity to discover that the method involving the circle produces a right angle regardless of what point is chosen.

Objectives of Chapter 8

To introduce the multiplication algorithm
To provide appropriate word-problem experiences
To maintain understanding of multiplication concepts

To fulfill the first objective of this chapter, understanding of the multiplication algorithm, it is necessary to develop understanding of multiplication by ten and 100, multiplication by multiples of ten, utilization of the distributive principle, and work with estimation.

Of course, the use of the distributive principle to arrive at the multiplication algorithm is of the greatest significance. The steps needed to arrive at the algorithm by using only one-digit multipliers are shown below. We do not emphasize the use of the distributive principle here. Rather, we show only that which must be developed with regard to multiplication involving factors which are multiples of ten.

Consider the steps involved in working the following exercise.

$$\begin{array}{r} 463 \\ \times 5 \\ \hline \end{array}$$

Step 1: $5 \times 3 = 15$ (This the students should be able to do.)

Step 2a: $5 \times 60 = ?$ (This must be developed.)
$5 \times 60 = 5 \times (6 \times 10) = (5 \times 6) \times 10$
$= 30 \times 10$

Step 2b: $30 \times 10 = ?$ (This must be developed.)
$30 \times 10 = (3 \times 10) \times 10 = 3 \times (10 \times 10)$
$= 3 \times 100$
$= 300$

Step 3: $5 \times 400 = ?$ (This must be developed as in step 2.)

Step 4: $15 + 300 + 2000 = 2315$ (This the students should be able to do.)

Much of the early part of the chapter is concerned with developing steps 2 and 3. Once the students understand these ideas, the short cuts are presented and adequate practice is provided.

Toward the end of the chapter many experiences are provided in practicing the algorithm and in working with word problems.

Mathematics of Chapter 8

The chief mathematical concept involved in the work in this chapter is the utilization of the distributive principle to find products such as 4×23. The example below illustrates this.

$$4 \times 23 = 4 \times (20 + 3) = (4 \times 20) + 4 \times 3$$
$$= 80 + 12$$
$$= 92$$

Examination of the use of the distributive principle in this example illustrates why we chose to use the descriptive words *break apart* in the last chapter. The students must recognize that when they do a multiplication such as 4×23, they break apart the 23 into 20 and 3 and do the multiplication in parts, 4×20 and 4×3, and then add the two products to get the final answer.

Teaching Chapter 8

There are no new mathematical concepts in this chapter. Rather, this chapter brings together many previously developed ideas in order to attain a specific goal—ability to multiply, using the standard multiplication algorithm.

You should plan to spend from four to $4\frac{1}{2}$ weeks on this chapter. Again, this time schedule will vary with the interests and abilities of your class.

Evaluation in a chapter that has as its chief objective the development of an algorithm is, for the most part, quite simple. There should be no problem in determining whether or not the students have mastered the algorithm. However, the fact that students can *use* the algorithm successfully does not guarantee that they *understand* it. As we have recommended before, evaluation of students' understanding should be based on day-to-day observation.

If most of the students have not mastered the multiplication facts by the time this chapter is reached, you should allow some time at the beginning to review and work toward better mastery of these facts. Lack of proficiency in multiplication facts could hinder understanding of the algorithm. It is undesirable for the students to be worrying about the multiplication facts when they should be concentrating on the more important purpose of coordinating ideas previously covered to attain a new goal.

Read and study the boxed material at the top of the page with the class. Following this, have the students complete the exercises on the page. Allow time at the end for checking papers.

Answers, exercise 2, page 176

[A]	80	[K]	160
[B]	130	[L]	150
[C]	190	[M]	170
[D]	120	[N]	60
[E]	10	[O]	90
[F]	600	[P]	120
[G]	160	[Q]	140
[H]	100	[R]	70
[I]	30	[S]	180
[J]	170	[T]	20

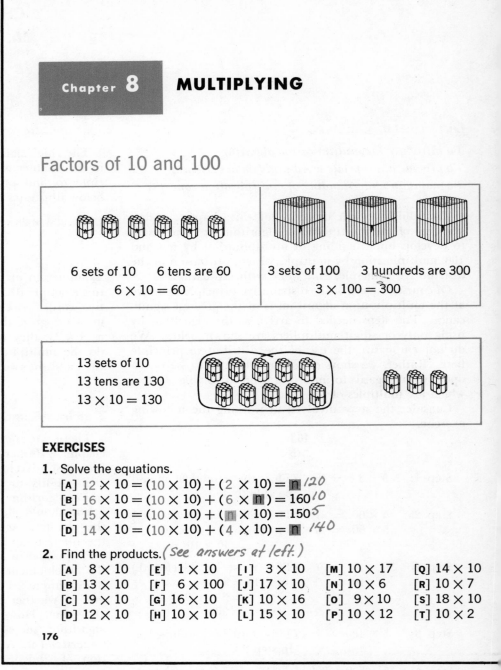

Chapter **8** **MULTIPLYING**

Factors of 10 and 100

6 sets of 10   6 tens are 60
$6 \times 10 = 60$

3 sets of 100   3 hundreds are 300
$3 \times 100 = 300$

13 sets of 10
13 tens are 130
$13 \times 10 = 130$

EXERCISES

1. Solve the equations.
[A] $12 \times 10 = (10 \times 10) + (2 \times 10) = $ ■ *120*
[B] $16 \times 10 = (10 \times 10) + (6 \times $ ■ $) = 160$ *10*
[C] $15 \times 10 = (10 \times 10) + ($ ■ $ \times 10) = 150$ *5*
[D] $14 \times 10 = (10 \times 10) + (4 \times 10) = $ ■ *140*

2. Find the products. *(see answers at left.)*

[A] 8×10	[E] 1×10	[I] 3×10	[M] 10×17	[Q] 14×10
[B] 13×10	[F] 6×100	[J] 17×10	[N] 10×6	[R] 10×7
[C] 19×10	[G] 16×10	[K] 10×16	[O] 9×10	[S] 18×10
[D] 12×10	[H] 10×10	[L] 15×10	[P] 10×12	[T] 10×2

176

Teaching Pages 176 and 177

● **PURPOSE**

To provide practice in multiplying by ten and 100

● **MATHEMATICS**

In this lesson, you will notice the use of the associative and distributive principles in arriving at products involving factors of ten and 100. For example, the associative principle is employed to find a product such as 30×10.

$$30 \times 10 = (3 \times 10) \times 10$$
$$= 3 \times (10 \times 10)$$
$$= 3 \times 100$$
$$= 300$$

You will notice that similar examples given at the top of page 177 do not employ parentheses. The parentheses are omitted because through careful development of the idea of rearranging factors we lead the students to see that we do not actually need the parentheses in this type of problem.

The following example employs the distributive principle.

$$72 \times 10 = (70 + 2) \times 10 = (70 \times 10) + (2 \times 10)$$
$$= 700 + 20$$
$$= 720$$

● **PREPARATION**

If your class is unusually good at working with abstractions, you can prepare for this lesson simply by offering examples of multiplying by ten and by 100. Follow this

206

Study these examples.

$$30 \times 10 = 3 \times 10 \times 10 = 3 \times 100 = 300$$
$$50 \times 10 = 5 \times 10 \times 10 = 5 \times 100 = 500$$

ORAL EXERCISES

Find the products. *(see answers at right.)*

1. 20×10 4. 60×10 7. 90×10 10. 10×40 13. 10×90
2. 40×10 5. 10×10 8. 30×10 11. 10×60 14. 10×30
3. 80×10 6. 50×10 9. 70×10 12. 10×50 15. 10×70

Study these examples.

$$72 \times 10 = (70 \times 10) + (2 \times 10) = 720$$
$$38 \times 10 = (30 \times 10) + (8 \times 10) = 380$$

EXERCISES

1. Solve the equations.
   [A] $24 \times 10 = (20 \times 10) + (4 \times 10) = \blacksquare$ *240*
   [B] $56 \times 10 = (50 \times 10) + (6 \times \blacksquare) = 560$ *10*
   [C] $37 \times 10 = (30 \times 10) + (\blacksquare \times 10) = 370$ *7*
   [D] $95 \times 10 = (90 \times 10) + (5 \times 10) = \blacksquare$ *950*
   [E] $81 \times 10 = (80 \times 10) + (\blacksquare \times 10) = 810$ *1*
   [F] $39 \times 10 = (30 \times 10) + (9 \times 10) = \blacksquare$ *390*

2. Solve the equations.
   [A] $(40 \times 10) + (3 \times 10) = \blacksquare$ *430*
       $(40 + 3) \times 10 = \blacksquare$ *430*
       $43 \times 10 = \blacksquare$ *430*
   [B] $(70 \times 10) + (2 \times 10) = \blacksquare$ *720*
       $(70 + 2) \times 10 = \blacksquare$ *720*
       $72 \times 10 = \blacksquare$ *720*
   [C] $(30 \times 10) + (1 \times 10) = \blacksquare$ *310*
       $(30 + 1) \times 10 = \blacksquare$ *310*
       $31 \times 10 = \blacksquare$ *310*
   [D] $(60 \times 10) + (5 \times 10) = \blacksquare$ *650*
       $(60 + 5) \times 10 = \blacksquare$ *650*
       $65 \times 10 = \blacksquare$ *650*
   [E] $(20 \times 10) + (9 \times 10) = \blacksquare$ *290*
       $(20 + 9) \times 10 = \blacksquare$ *290*
       $29 \times 10 = \blacksquare$ *290*
   [F] $(50 \times 10) + (6 \times 10) = \blacksquare$ *560*
       $(50 + 6) \times 10 = \blacksquare$ *560*
       $56 \times 10 = \blacksquare$ *560*

3. Find the products. *(see answers at right.)*
   [A] 24×10 [E] 75×10 [I] 10×68 [M] 10×81 [Q] 70×10
   [B] 36×10 [F] 37×10 [J] 24×10 [N] 58×10 [R] 10×30
   [C] 10×24 [G] 10×83 [K] 92×10 [O] 39×10 [S] 66×10
   [D] 10×36 [H] 10×50 [L] 10×95 [P] 10×33 [T] 10×14

DIRECTIONS PAGE 177

Read and study the material at the top of the page with the class. Give all the students an opportunity to participate in working the oral exercises.

As you discuss the boxed examples beneath the oral exercises, you might, if necessary, write these equations on the chalkboard. Discuss how the multiplication-addition principle is used to find these products. That is, we break the 72 into 70 and 2, multiply each number by ten, and then add the products.

Have the students work the exercises. Allow time at the end for discussion and checking papers. During the discussion try to get the students to generalize what they have learned in this lesson. You might motivate them by asking for a rule when ten is a factor.

Answers, oral exercises and exercise 3, page 177

1. 200	9. 700
2. 400	10. 400
3. 800	11. 600
4. 600	12. 500
5. 100	13. 900
6. 500	14. 300
7. 900	15. 700
8. 300	

3.
[A] 240	[K] 920
[B] 360	[L] 950
[C] 240	[M] 810
[D] 360	[N] 580
[E] 750	[O] 390
[F] 370	[P] 330
[G] 830	[Q] 700
[H] 500	[R] 300
[I] 680	[S] 660
[J] 240	[T] 140

by giving the students a short oral practice session in finding such products.

If you feel it is necessary, you can provide set demonstrations involving a given number of tens and of hundreds. For example, you can exhibit six bundles of ten and remark to students that you have six sets of ten: Write 6×10 on the chalkboard. Now ask the students how many in all. When they respond 60, complete the equation $6 \times 10 = 60$.

If you do not have enough objects to give a demonstration of multiplication by 100, you can use empty paper bags and ask the students to pretend that each bag contains 100 objects. Again, during this demonstration, exhibit the equation which corresponds to the set demonstration.

Have the students work these exercises. Allow time for checking papers when they have finished.

Most of the students should be able to do the riddle because of the nature of the previous exercises and study concerning the factor of ten. Certainly all students should understand the riddle once the correct answer is given.

Supplementary exercises, Set 42 (page 347) may be assigned as necessary beyond this page.

Answers, exercise 2, page 178

[A] 50¢	[F] 400¢
[B] 100¢	[G] 520¢
[C] 200¢	[H] 910¢
[D] 150¢	[I] 560¢
[E] 270¢	[J] 480¢

Multiplying by 10

EXERCISES

1. Give the value in cents for each set of dimes.

[A] *80¢*

[B] *100¢*

[C] *140¢*

[D] *230¢*

2. Give the value in cents for each coin collection. *(See answers at left.)*

[A] 5 dimes [C] 20 dimes [E] 27 dimes [G] 52 dimes [I] 56 dimes
[B] 10 dimes [D] 15 dimes [F] 40 dimes [H] 91 dimes [J] 48 dimes

3. Find the products.

[A] 27×10 *270* [F] 65×10 *650* [K] 10×14 *140* [P] 8×100 *800* [U] 10×96 *960*
[B] 10×38 *380* [G] 91×10 *910* [L] 10×80 *800* [Q] 10×21 *210* [V] 87×10 *870*
[C] 43×10 *430* [H] 10×10 *100* [M] 19×10 *190* [R] 86×10 *860* [W] 60×10 *600*
[D] 11×10 *110* [I] 10×82 *820* [N] 76×10 *760* [S] 52×10 *520* [X] 10×48 *480*
[E] 10×34 *340* [J] 73×10 *730* [O] 10×50 *500* [T] 10×7 *70* [Y] 28×10 *280*

4. Find the products.

[A] $(3 \times 2) \times 10$ *60*   [D] $(5 \times 7) \times 10$ *350*
 $3 \times (2 \times 10)$ *60* $5 \times (7 \times 10)$ *350*
 3×20 *60* 5×70 *350*

[B] $(3 \times 4) \times 10$ *120*   [E] $(7 \times 4) \times 10$ *280*
 $3 \times (4 \times 10)$ *120* $7 \times (4 \times 10)$ *280*
 3×40 *120* 7×40 *280*

[C] $(9 \times 3) \times 10$ *270*   [F] $(7 \times 8) \times 10$ *560*
 $9 \times (3 \times 10)$ *270* $7 \times (8 \times 10)$ *560*
 9×30 *270* 7×80 *560*

> **Exercise for Experts**
> Now I am a number
> You rarely can beat.
> When I am a factor
> I surely am neat.
> Use the other factor.
> Make zero the tail.
> You'll see the product.
> You really can't fail.
> WHO AM I? *10*

Teaching Pages 178 and 179

• **PURPOSE**

To continue stressing multiplication by ten

To provide experiences in multiplying by multiples of ten

• **MATHEMATICS**

In this lesson, the associative principle is used for finding products such as 3×40. The following example illustrates this.

$$3 \times 40 = 3 \times (4 \times 10)$$
$$= (3 \times 4) \times 10$$
$$= 12 \times 10$$
$$= 120$$

Factors 10, 20, 30, . . .

Study these examples.

$$3 \times 40 = 3 \times 4 \times 10 = 12 \times 10 = 120$$
$$5 \times 70 = 5 \times 7 \times 10 = 35 \times 10 = 350$$

EXERCISES

1. Solve the equations.

[A] $2 \times 60 = 12 \times 10 = $ ▥ *120*
[B] $4 \times 60 = 24 \times $ ▥ $= 240$ *10*
[C] $7 \times 40 = $ ▥ $\times 10 = 280$ *28*
[D] $8 \times 20 = 16 \times 10 = $ ▥ *160*

[E] $6 \times 50 = $ ▥ $\times 10 = 300$ *30*
[F] $5 \times 40 = 20 \times $ ▥ $= 200$ *10*
[G] $7 \times 70 = $ ▥ $\times 10 = 490$ *49*
[H] $6 \times 80 = $ ▥ $\times 10 = 480$ *48*

2. Find the missing numbers.

[A] $4 \times 60 = $ ▥ $\times 10$ *24* [D] $5 \times 50 = $ ▥ $\times 10$ *25* [G] $6 \times 70 = $ ▥ $\times 10$ *42*
[B] $3 \times 50 = $ ▥ $\times 10$ *15* [E] $6 \times 30 = $ ▥ $\times 10$ *18* [H] $5 \times 80 = $ ▥ $\times 10$ *40*
[C] $7 \times 20 = $ ▥ $\times 10$ *14* [F] $4 \times 30 = $ ▥ $\times 10$ *12* [I] $3 \times 90 = $ ▥ $\times 10$ *27*

3. Find the products.

[A] 4×60 *240* [F] 4×30 *120* [K] 60×5 *300* [P] 4×80 *320* [U] 2×50 *100*
[B] 3×50 *150* [G] 70×6 *420* [L] 9×20 *180* [Q] 60×8 *480* [V] 4×90 *360*
[C] 20×7 *140* [H] 5×80 *400* [M] 40×4 *160* [R] 7×60 *420* [W] 90×7 *630*
[D] 5×50 *250* [I] 90×3 *270* [N] 7×80 *560* [S] 5×20 *100* [X] 9×90 *810*
[E] 30×6 *180* [J] 70×2 *140* [O] 6×50 *300* [T] 70×3 *210* [Y] 2×60 *120*

4. If you think you have found a rule for multiplying by 10, try these exercises. Find the products. *(See answers at right.)*

[A] 275×10
[B] 10×654
[C] 789×10
[D] 695×10
[E] 10×790
[F] 7285×10

[G] 7006×10
[H] 10×8307
[I] 6520×10
[J] 10×8300
[K] $68,293 \times 10$
[L] $10 \times 74,657$

[M] $90,000 \times 10$
[N] $35,000 \times 10$
[O] $10 \times 60,200$
[P] $10 \times 100,000$
[Q] $756,298 \times 10$
[R] $10 \times 654,200$

5. Find the products. *(See answers at right.)*

[A] $(3 \times 6) \times 100 = $ ▥ [C] $(4 \times 7) \times 100 = $ ▥ [E] $(5 \times 6) \times 100 = $ ▥
[B] $(5 \times 3) \times 100 = $ ▥ [D] $(6 \times 3) \times 100 = $ ▥ [F] $(6 \times 8) \times 100 = $ ▥

Discuss the boxed example at the top of the page and then direct the students to do the exercises.

Although exercise 5 is designed as enrichment for the more able students, many of the students will be able to complete this exercise.

Supplementary exercises, Set 43 (page 347) may be assigned as necessary beyond this page.

Answers, exercise 4 and 5, page 179

4.			
[A] 2750		[J]	83,000
[B] 6540		[K]	682,930
[C] 7890		[L]	746,570
[D] 6950		[M]	900,000
[E] 7900		[N]	350,000
[F] 72,850		[O]	602,000
[G] 70,060		[P]	1,000,000
[H] 83,070		[Q]	7,562,980
[I] 65,200		[R]	6,542,000

5.			
[A] 1800		[D]	1800
[B] 1500		[E]	3000
[C] 2800		[F]	4800

PREPARATION

Provide the class with additional practice in finding products with a factor of ten or 100.

Provide a demonstration (see examples at the top of page 179) for products involving one of the multiples of ten.

Study and discuss with the class the set pictures and related equations at the top of the page. Instruct the students to do exercise 1.

You should guide the students in working exercise 2. Although this exercise is not starred, it is of a slightly unusual nature and involves considerable thought on the part of the students. For example, in exercise 2B the students must recognize that 4×62 is eight more than 240. Avoid giving the students a rule for finding these products. Use these exercises in the spirit of playing a game and encourage the students to think through the answers for themselves.

Related products

3 sets of 4 $3 \times 4 = 12$

3 sets of 40 $3 \times 40 = 120$

3 sets of 400 $3 \times 400 = 1200$

EXERCISES

1. Find the products.

[A] 4×6 *24*　　[D] 6×5 *30*　　[G] 8×6 *48*　　[J] 7×4 *28*
4×60 *240*　　6×50 *300*　　8×60 *480*　　7×40 *280*
4×600 *2400*　　6×500 *3000*　　8×600 *4800*　　7×400 *2800*

[B] 6×3 *18*　　[E] 5×7 *35*　　[H] 3×9 *27*　　[K] 5×8 *40*
6×30 *180*　　5×70 *350*　　3×90 *270*　　5×80 *400*
6×300 *1800*　　5×700 *3500*　　3×900 *2700*　　5×800 *4000*

[C] 3×7 *21*　　[F] 9×4 *36*　　[I] 6×6 *36*　　[L] 6×9 *54*
3×70 *210*　　9×40 *360*　　6×60 *360*　　6×90 *540*
3×700 *2100*　　3×400 *3600*　　6×600 *3600*　　6×900 *5400*

2. Find the products.

[A] Since $5 \times 70 = 350$, we know that $5 \times 71 = $ ■ . *355*
[B] Since $4 \times 60 = 240$, we know that $4 \times 62 = $ ■ . *248*
[C] Since $3 \times 80 = 240$, we know that $3 \times 83 = $ ■ . *249*
[D] Since $6 \times 50 = 300$, we know that $6 \times 53 = $ ■ . *318*
[E] Since $4 \times 30 = 120$, we know that $4 \times 33 = $ ■ . *132*
[F] Since $5 \times 50 = 250$, we know that $5 \times 52 = $ ■ . *260*
[G] Since $7 \times 40 = 280$, we know that $7 \times 42 = $ ■ . *294*
[H] Since $6 \times 90 = 540$, we know that $6 \times 94 = $ ■ . *564*

Teaching Pages 180 and 181

● **PURPOSE**

To introduce an element of logic in finding products that are multiples of ten or 100

To provide more practice in the chapter material covered so far

● **MATHEMATICS**

In this lesson we introduce products that are multiples of 100 by relating them to the corresponding one-digit and two-digit multiples. For example, the product 3×400 is related to the products 3×4 and 3×40. We could, however, have used the same idea as we used for 3×40. The

Practice finding products

1. Find the products.

[A] 3 × 7 *21* [F] 3 × 8 *24* [K] 7 × 9 *63* [P] 4 × 7 *28* [U] 3 × 9 *27*
[B] 7 × 8 *56* [G] 5 × 9 *45* [L] 9 × 9 *81* [Q] 5 × 5 *25* [V] 5 × 7 *35*
[C] 4 × 6 *24* [H] 4 × 4 *16* [M] 5 × 8 *40* [R] 7 × 7 *49* [W] 6 × 8 *48*
[D] 5 × 4 *20* [I] 5 × 6 *30* [N] 8 × 8 *64* [S] 4 × 9 *36* [X] 8 × 9 *72*
[E] 6 × 6 *36* [J] 3 × 6 *18* [O] 6 × 9 *54* [T] 6 × 7 *42* [Y] 7 × 5 *35*

2. Find the products.

[A] 4 × 10 *40* [F] 9 × 10 *90* [K] 10 × 5 *50* [P] 11 × 10 *110* [U] 10 × 88 *880*
[B] 12 × 10 *120* [G] 18 × 10 *180* [L] 61 × 10 *610* [Q] 10 × 19 *190* [V] 66 × 10 *660*
[C] 10 × 8 *80* [H] 10 × 83 *830* [M] 79 × 10 *790* [R] 35 × 10 *350* [W] 10 × 64 *640*
[D] 10 × 75 *750* [I] 49 × 10 *490* [N] 10 × 48 *480* [S] 56 × 10 *560* [X] 26 × 10 *260*
[E] 26 × 10 *260* [J] 15 × 10 *150* [O] 7 × 10 *70* [T] 10 × 10 *100* [Y] 10 × 74 *740*

3. Find the products.

[A] 3 × 70 *210* [F] 3 × 80 *240* [K] 7 × 90 *630* [P] 40 × 7 *280* [U] 30 × 9 *270*
[B] 70 × 8 *560* [G] 50 × 9 *450* [L] 90 × 9 *810* [Q] 50 × 5 *250* [V] 5 × 7 *35*
[C] 4 × 60 *240* [H] 4 × 40 *160* [M] 5 × 80 *400* [R] 7 × 70 *490* [W] 60 × 8 *480*
[D] 5 × 40 *200* [I] 50 × 6 *300* [N] 8 × 80 *640* [S] 4 × 90 *360* [X] 8 × 90 *720*
[E] 60 × 6 *360* [J] 30 × 6 *180* [O] 60 × 9 *540* [T] 60 × 7 *420* [Y] 3 × 50 *150*

4. Find the products.

[A] 49 ×10 *490*	[B] 50 ×6 *300*	[C] 60 ×9 *540*
[D] 50 ×4 *200*	[E] 70 ×3 *210*	[F] 80 ×6 *480*
[G] 67 ×10 *670*	[H] 20 ×8 *160*	[I] 43 ×10 *430*
[J] 90 ×5 *450*	[K] 70 ×5 *350*	[L] 70 ×7 *490*

> ## Exercise for Experts
>
> If it's products you are after,
> I will lend a helping hand.
> Just use me over and over,
> On the answer you will land.
>
> WHO AM I?
> *Addition*

Have the students work the exercises. If you choose, you may use the riddle for enrichment. Even though all students may not be able to solve the riddle, most will understand the answer once it is presented. It is not important that a large or small number of students are able to solve a given riddle. What is important is that the students enjoy working with the riddles and understand the ideas once the correct answer is given.

following example illustrates this idea by showing the use of the associative principle for a product such as 3×400.

$$3 \times 400 = 3 \times (4 \times 100)$$
$$= (3 \times 4) \times 100$$
$$= 12 \times 100$$
$$= 1200$$

PREPARATION

Provide the students with a brief review of the material covered thus far in the chapter. Focus particular attention on products that are multiples of ten, such as 3×40.

You might also provide a demonstration of products that are multiples of 100 by using the associative principle as illustrated in the mathematics section for this lesson.

Study the material at the top of the page with the students. Notice with them that in the top set diagram they think merely of three sets of seven or 3×7. Observe that this product is 21. Notice with them that the second set diagram is just like the first except that the set is broken into three sets of four and three sets of three. Observe with them the related symbols, 3×4 and 3×3.

Have the students work the exercises. Allow time for the checking of papers when they have finished.

The multiplication–addition principle

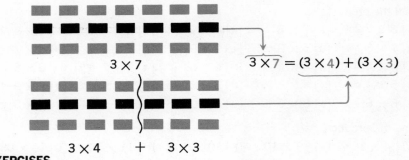

3×7

$\overline{3 \times 7} = \underbrace{(3 \times 4) + (3 \times 3)}$

3×4 + 3×3

EXERCISES

1. Find the missing numbers.

[A] $3 \times 6 = (3 \times 2) + (3 \times \blacksquare)$ *4*

[B] $5 \times 8 = (5 \times \blacksquare) + (5 \times 5)$ *3*

[C] $7 \times 4 = (7 \times 2) + (7 \times \blacksquare)$ *2*

[D] $8 \times 10 = (8 \times 5) + (8 \times \blacksquare)$ *5*

[E] $2 \times 10 = (2 \times \blacksquare) + (2 \times 8)$ *2*

[F] $5 \times 10 = (5 \times 7) + (5 \times \blacksquare)$ *3*

2. Find the missing numbers.

[A] $3 \times 12 = (3 \times 10) + (3 \times \blacksquare)$ *2*

[B] $4 \times 26 = (4 \times 20) + (4 \times \blacksquare)$ *6*

[C] $5 \times 18 = (5 \times \blacksquare) + (5 \times 8)$ *10*

[D] $4 \times 63 = (4 \times 60) + (4 \times \blacksquare)$ *3*

[E] $7 \times 52 = (7 \times \blacksquare) + (7 \times 2)$ *50*

[F] $6 \times 18 = (6 \times 10) + (6 \times \blacksquare)$ *8*

3. Solve the equations.

[A] $(3 \times 10) + (3 \times 2) = \blacksquare$ *36*

[B] $(4 \times 10) + (4 \times 1) = \blacksquare$ *44*

[C] $(2 \times 10) + (2 \times 4) = \blacksquare$ *28*

[D] $(3 \times 10) + (3 \times 3) = \blacksquare$ *39*

[E] $(4 \times 10) + (4 \times 2) = \blacksquare$ *48*

[F] $(5 \times 10) + (5 \times 1) = \blacksquare$ *55*

[G] $(2 \times 10) + (2 \times 3) = \blacksquare$ *26*

[H] $(3 \times 10) + (3 \times 1) = \blacksquare$ *33*

[I] $(2 \times 10) + (2 \times 2) = \blacksquare$ *24*

[J] $(6 \times 10) + (6 \times 1) = \blacksquare$ *66*

[K] $(6 \times 10) + (6 \times 2) = \blacksquare$ *72*

[L] $(6 \times 10) + (6 \times 3) = \blacksquare$ *78*

4. Solve the equations.

[A] $3 \times 12 = \blacksquare$ *36*

[B] $4 \times 11 = \blacksquare$ *44*

[C] $2 \times 14 = \blacksquare$ *28*

[D] $3 \times 13 = \blacksquare$ *39*

[E] $4 \times 12 = \blacksquare$ *48*

[F] $5 \times 11 = \blacksquare$ *55*

[G] $2 \times 13 = \blacksquare$ *26*

[H] $3 \times 11 = \blacksquare$ *33*

[I] $2 \times 12 = \blacksquare$ *24*

[J] $6 \times 11 = \blacksquare$ *66*

[K] $6 \times 12 = \blacksquare$ *72*

[L] $6 \times 13 = \blacksquare$ *78*

Teaching Pages 182 and 183

- **PURPOSE**

  To review the multiplication-addition principle

- **MATHEMATICS**

  We give below a formal statement of the distributive principle.

  $$a \times (b + c) = (a \times b) + (a \times c)$$

  The chief use the students will make of this principle (in this chapter) is illustrated by the following example.

  $$4 \times 37 = (4 \times 30) + (4 \times 7)$$

Multiplication–addition problems

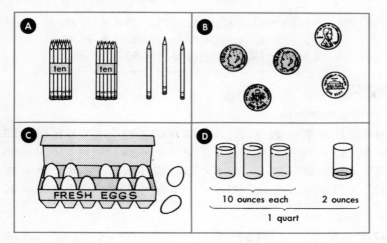

1. [A] How many pencils do you see in box A? *23*

   [B] If you had 2 times that many pencils, how many would you have? *46*

   [C] Suppose a box has 3 times as many pencils as box A.
   How many pencils are there in the box? *69*

2. [A] What is the value in cents of the money pictured in box B? *32¢*

   [B] If you had twice that much money, how much would you have? *64¢*

   [C] Suppose a ticket cost 3 times as much as the amount
   pictured in box B. How much does the ticket cost? *96¢*

3. [A] One dozen is 10 and 2. (See box C.) How many are in a dozen? *12*

   [B] How many are in 3 dozen? *36*

   [C] How many are in 4 dozen? *48*

   ★ [D] How many are in 5 dozen? *60*

4. [A] Look at box D and tell how many ounces are in a quart. *32*

   [B] How many ounces are in 2 quarts? *64*

   [C] How many ounces are in 3 quarts? *96*

   ★ [D] How many ounces are in 5 quarts? *160*

If you choose, you can have the students study, on their own, the material in the boxes at the top of the page and then attempt to work the exercises. You may, however, choose to provide additional guidance in working exercise 1 and then have the students proceed on their own.

Exercises 3D and 4D are starred, but many students may be able to do these without too much difficulty.

PREPARATION

Review for the students the ideas of the multiplication-addition principle. For example, exhibit on the chalkboard an equation such as

$$3 \times 8 = (3 \times 3) + (3 \times 5).$$

Have the students verify the validity of this statement by finding the product of 3×8 and then the products 3×3 and 3×5 and adding the last two together to see that they get 24.

Discuss the equations at the top of the page before instructing the students to do the exercises. Allow time at the end for discussion and checking papers. In particular, emphasize for the students the relationship between exercises 1, 2, and 3. For example, notice with them that in exercise 1E they are breaking apart the 34 into 30 and 4 and multiplying each part by two. Observe with them that in exercise 2E they are adding the two products, 60 and 8; then in exercise 3E they are simply finding the product 2 × 34. Give the students an opportunity to observe that having worked exercises 1 and 2, they have already found the product 2 × 34.

Using the multiplication–addition principle

$$3 \times 12 = (3 \times 10) + (3 \times 2) = 30 + 6 = 36$$
$$2 \times 24 = (2 \times 20) + (2 \times 4) = 40 + 8 = 48$$
$$4 \times 23 = (4 \times 20) + (4 \times 3) = 80 + 12 = 92$$

EXERCISES

1. Solve the equations.

[A] $4 \times 12 = 40 + \blacksquare$ *8*   [E] $2 \times 34 = 60 + \blacksquare$ *8*   [I] $5 \times 14 = 50 + \blacksquare$

[B] $3 \times 11 = \blacksquare + 3$ *30*   [F] $2 \times 23 = 40 + \blacksquare$ *6*   [J] $6 \times 13 = 60 + \blacksquare$

[C] $2 \times 13 = 20 + \blacksquare$ *6*   [G] $3 \times 23 = \blacksquare + 9$ *60*   [K] $4 \times 24 = \blacksquare + 16$ *8*

[D] $5 \times 11 = \blacksquare + 5$ *50*   [H] $4 \times 13 = \blacksquare + 12$ *40*   [L] $3 \times 27 = 60 + \blacksquare$

2. Find the sums.

[A] $40 + 8$ *48*   [D] $50 + 5$ *55*   [G] $60 + 9$ *69*   [J] $60 + 18$

[B] $30 + 3$ *33*   [E] $60 + 8$ *68*   [H] $40 + 12$ *52*   [K] $80 + 16$

[C] $20 + 6$ *26*   [F] $40 + 6$ *46*   [I] $50 + 20$ *70*   [L] $60 + 21$

3. Find the products.

[A] 4×12 *48*   [D] 5×11 *55*   [G] 3×23 *69*   [J] 6×13 *78*

[B] 3×11 *33*   [E] 2×34 *68*   [H] 4×13 *52*   [K] 4×24 *96*

[C] 2×13 *26*   [F] 2×23 *46*   [I] 5×14 *70*   [L] 3×27 *81*

4. Find the missing numbers.

[A] $3 \times 12 = (3 \times 10) + (3 \times 2) = 30 + 6 = \blacksquare$ *36*

[B] $2 \times 24 = (2 \times 20) + (2 \times 4) = 40 + \blacksquare = 48$ *8*

[C] $4 \times 23 = (4 \times 20) + (4 \times 3) = \blacksquare + 12 = 92$ *80*

[D] $4 \times 12 = (4 \times 10) + (4 \times \blacksquare) = 40 + 8 = 48$ *2*

[E] $3 \times 11 = (3 \times \blacksquare) + (3 \times 1) = 30 + 3 = 33$ *10*

[F] $2 \times 13 = (2 \times 10) + (2 \times 3) = 20 + 6 = \blacksquare$ *26*

[G] $5 \times 11 = (5 \times 10) + (5 \times 1) = 50 + \blacksquare = 55$ *5*

[H] $2 \times 34 = (2 \times 30) + (2 \times 4) = \blacksquare + 8 = 68$ *60*

[I] $2 \times 23 = (2 \times 20) + (2 \times \blacksquare) = 40 + 6 = 46$ *3*

[J] $3 \times 23 = (3 \times \blacksquare) + (3 \times 3) = 60 + 9 = 69$ *20*

Teaching Pages 184 and 185

● **PURPOSE**

To show how the multiplication-addition principle is used for finding products involving two-digit numbers

To provide word-problem experiences in working with the ideas of this lesson

● **PREPARATION**

Review the multiplication-addition principle by presenting equations similar to those found at the top of page 184. Observe that, for a product such as 4 × 23, they consider the two products 4 × 20 and 4 × 3 and then add the products.

Multiplication—addition problems

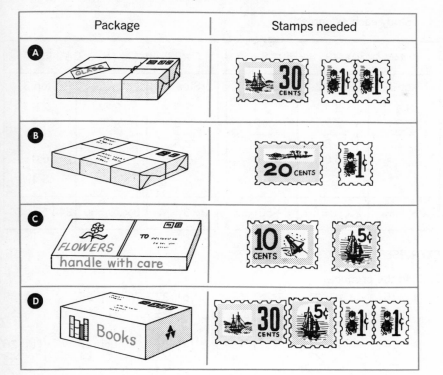

Have the students do the exercises. Discuss the answers and ideas when they have finished. During the discussion of the exercises, select two or three of the exercises and exhibit for these exercises equations similar to those on page 184. Help the students to see how they break apart numbers in multiplication of this type.

1. [A] How much did it cost to mail package A? 32 ¢
   [B] How much would it cost to mail 3 packages like this one? 96 ¢

2. [A] How much did it cost to mail package B? 21 ¢
   [B] How much would it cost to mail 4 packages like this one? 84 ¢

3. [A] How much did it cost to mail package C? 15 ¢
   [B] How much would it cost to mail 2 packages like this? 30 ¢
   [C] How much would it cost for 3 such packages? 45 ¢

4. [A] How much did it cost to mail package D? 37 ¢
   [B] How much would it cost to mail 2 packages like this? 74 ¢
   [C] How much would it cost to mail 5 such packages? 185 ¢

Study the material at the top of the page with the class. Explain to the class that the blue shading behind the numerals and the equations helps them see exactly what is happening in each step. You should call the students' attention to this as you explain the ideas in each step. You might give several students the opportunity to explain these ideas to the class.

Following this discussion, have the students do the exercises.

Exercise 2 is starred only because some products are numbers greater than 100. This idea may not trouble any students; however, it does involve one more step in their thinking. Since many students will be able to work the exercises without recognizing that anything new is happening, you should encourage all the students to try exercise 2. Some of the less able students will gain a considerable feeling of accomplishment from having worked starred exercises.

2-digit factors

Study each example.

2×34=(2×30)+(2×4)=60+8=68		
Step 1	Step 2	Step 3
3 4 ×2 — 8	3 4 ×2 — 8 6 0	3 4 ×2 — 8 6 0 — 6 8
2×4=8	2×30=60	8+60=68

3×28=3×(20+8)=60+24=84		
Step 1	Step 2	Step 3
2 8 ×3 — 2 4	2 8 ×3 — 2 4 6 0	2 8 ×3 — 2 4 6 0 — 8 4
3×8=24	3×20=60	24+60=84

EXERCISES

1. Find the products.

[A] 15 ×3 = 45 [B] 21 ×4 = 84 [C] 16 ×2 = 32 [D] 37 ×2 = 74 [E] 25 ×3 = 75 [F] 38 ×2 = 76

[G] 14 ×5 = 70 [H] 24 ×3 = 72 [I] 19 ×4 = 76 [J] 34 ×2 = 68 [K] 17 ×4 = 68 [L] 26 ×3 = 78

[M] 22 ×4 = 88 [N] 18 ×3 = 54 [O] 35 ×2 = 70 [P] 19 ×3 = 57 [Q] 27 ×3 = 81 [R] 18 ×2 = 36

★ 2. Find the products.

[A] 63 ×2 = 126 [B] 36 ×2 = 72 [C] 57 ×2 = 114 [D] 48 ×3 = 144 [E] 67 ×4 = 268 [F] 93 ×3 = 279

[G] 38 ×6 = 228 [H] 47 ×4 = 188 [I] 67 ×7 = 469 [J] 86 ×5 = 430 [K] 58 ×6 = 348 [L] 75 ×8 = 600

[M] 94 ×3 = 282 [N] 29 ×5 = 145 [O] 65 ×8 = 520 [P] 73 ×4 = 292 [Q] 69 ×7 = 483 [R] 47 ×8 = 376

Teaching Pages 186 and 187

- **PURPOSE**

  To introduce multiplication involving two-digit products in the familiar vertical notation

- **MATHEMATICS**

  It should be pointed out to the students during this lesson that although the notation is different, the ideas are the same. They are simply learning a different and more convenient way to write their work on paper.

  Notice that the distributive principle is being used in exactly the same way as it is in working problems in the horizontal notation. The fact that the only difference here

A short cut

Study each example.

```
 25     25
 ×3     ×3
⑴⑸     75
 60
 7⑸
```

In these short cuts, you think about the same things. You just write less on your paper.

```
 17     ¹⁷
 ×4     ×4
⑵⑻     6 8
 40
 6⑻
```

Explain how you think for each of these examples.

```
¹24      ²18      ³19
 ×3       ×3       ×4
 72       54       76
```

EXERCISES

1. Find the products.

[A] 24 ×4 96	[B] 15 ×3 45	[C] 38 ×2 76	[D] 14 ×6 84	[E] 19 ×3 57	[F] 27 ×3 81
[G] 39 ×2 78	[H] 31 ×3 93	[I] 21 ×4 84	[J] 30 ×2 60	[K] 13 ×4 52	[L] 37 ×2 74
[M] 16 ×5 80	[N] 29 ×3 87	[O] 19 ×5 95	[P] 42 ×4 168	[Q] 22 ×3 66	[R] 32 ×2 64
[S] 34 ×2 68	[T] 23 ×4 92	[U] 35 ×2 70	[V] 25 ×3 75	[W] 26 ×3 78	[X] 17 ×4 68

★ **2.** Find the products.

[A] 37 ×3 111	[B] 46 ×3 138	[C] 54 ×5 270	[D] 67 ×5 335	[E] 83 ×3 249	[F] 75 ×6 450
[G] 37 ×6 222	[H] 54 ×4 216	[I] 68 ×4 272	[J] 57 ×3 171	[K] 44 ×4 176	[L] 76 ×3 228

Read and study the material at the top of the page with the class. Pay particular attention to the three examples that the students are asked to explain. Exhibit these on the chalkboard and have the students explain each step. Following this discussion, have the students do the exercises.

Again, exercise 2 involves no new ideas; in most cases all that is new is the fact that the product is a number greater than 100. Since most students will be able to do these exercises without recognizing any additional difficulty, you should encourage all students to attempt them.

---

is in the organization of the work on the paper is emphasized in the presentation at the top of page 186 by showing the related equation for each step.

PREPARATION

Provide for your class a demonstration similar to those at the top of page 186. For example, exhibit on the chalkboard an equation such as $2 \times 34 = (2 \times 30) + (2 \times 4) = 60 + 8 = 68$ and present the three-step procedure used on page 186. Show the students that the first step is to multiply two and 30, the second step is to multiply two and four, and the third step is to add these products. Relate these three steps to the original equation.

Following this, introduce some problems involving carrying and the short-cut notation involved in such an exercise. Provide several exercises similar to the second example on page 186 and the examples at the top of page 187.

During this presentation emphasize that all of the ideas are the same as those the students have been using throughout this chapter and that the only difference is in the way they write their work on the paper.

As you discuss the boxed material at the top of the page, demonstrate, by using an example on the chalkboard, the type of thinking that is illustrated. Write on the chalkboard the three exercises given below the box and give the students an opportunity to explain the steps in these exercises.

Following this discussion, have the students work the exercises.

The short cut again

$\begin{array}{r}{}^{\prime}25\\\times 3\\\hline 75\end{array}$

We think

1 $3 \times 5 = 15$. Write 5 and "carry" the 10.

2 $3 \times 20 = 60$. $60 + 10 = 70$. Write the 7 to the left of the 5.

$\begin{array}{r}{}^{\prime}25\\\times 3\\\hline 75\end{array}$

We could think

1 $3 \times 5 = 15$. Write 5 and "carry" 1.

2 $3 \times 2 = 6$. $6 + 1 = 7$. Write the 7 to the left of the 5.

Here are some more examples.

$\begin{array}{r}{}^{2}17\\\times 4\\\hline 68\end{array}$

1 $4 \times 7 = 28$. Write 8 and "carry" 2.

2 $4 \times 1 = 4$. $4 + 2 = 6$. Write 6 to the left of 8.

$\begin{array}{r}{}^{2}28\\\times 3\\\hline 84\end{array}$

1 $3 \times 8 = 24$. Write 4 and "carry" 2.

2 $3 \times 2 = 6$. $6 + 2 = 8$. Write 8 to the left of 4.

$\begin{array}{r}{}^{4}19\\\times 5\\\hline 95\end{array}$

1 $5 \times 9 = 45$. Write 5 and "carry" 4.

2 $5 \times 1 = 5$. $5 + 4 = 9$. Write 9 to the left of 5.

EXERCISES

Find the products.

1. $\begin{array}{r}16\\\times 2\\\hline 32\end{array}$	2. $\begin{array}{r}19\\\times 4\\\hline 76\end{array}$	3. $\begin{array}{r}35\\\times 2\\\hline 70\end{array}$	4. $\begin{array}{r}28\\\times 3\\\hline 84\end{array}$	5. $\begin{array}{r}24\\\times 3\\\hline 72\end{array}$	6. $\begin{array}{r}18\\\times 2\\\hline 36\end{array}$
7. $\begin{array}{r}37\\\times 2\\\hline 74\end{array}$	8. $\begin{array}{r}34\\\times 2\\\hline 68\end{array}$	9. $\begin{array}{r}18\\\times 3\\\hline 54\end{array}$	10. $\begin{array}{r}19\\\times 3\\\hline 57\end{array}$	11. $\begin{array}{r}16\\\times 3\\\hline 48\end{array}$	12. $\begin{array}{r}17\\\times 5\\\hline 85\end{array}$
13. $\begin{array}{r}22\\\times 4\\\hline 88\end{array}$	14. $\begin{array}{r}14\\\times 5\\\hline 70\end{array}$	15. $\begin{array}{r}15\\\times 3\\\hline 45\end{array}$	16. $\begin{array}{r}25\\\times 3\\\hline 75\end{array}$	17. $\begin{array}{r}17\\\times 4\\\hline 68\end{array}$	18. $\begin{array}{r}27\\\times 3\\\hline 81\end{array}$
19. $\begin{array}{r}29\\\times 3\\\hline 87\end{array}$	20. $\begin{array}{r}38\\\times 2\\\hline 76\end{array}$	21. $\begin{array}{r}26\\\times 3\\\hline 78\end{array}$	22. $\begin{array}{r}18\\\times 4\\\hline 72\end{array}$	23. $\begin{array}{r}15\\\times 4\\\hline 60\end{array}$	24. $\begin{array}{r}43\\\times 2\\\hline 86\end{array}$

Teaching Pages 188 and 189

- **PURPOSE**

  To introduce further refinement of the multiplication short cut

  To provide word-problem experiences in working with products

- **PREPARATION**

  Provide the students with several exercises in working with the algorithm learned in the last lesson. Display exercises on the chalkboard and give individual students an opportunity to explain to the class the steps for working the problems.

Miles per gallon

Have the students work the exercises. Notice that exercise 5 is primarily for more able students. Allow time when the students have finished for discussion of the exercises. During this discussion period, it may be helpful to review the various steps involved in the multiplication algorithm.

1. Mr. White can drive his car about 17 miles on one gallon of gas. How far can he drive on 5 gallons of gas? *85 miles*

2. Mr. Brown's car goes only 14 miles on each gallon of gas. How far can he drive on 7 gallons of gas? *98 miles*

3. Mr. Grey has a small car and can drive 24 miles on a gallon of gas. How far can he drive on 4 gallons of gas? *96 miles*

4. Mr. Jones can drive 33 miles on 2 gallons of gas.
Mr. Smith can drive 16 miles on 1 gallon of gas.

[A] Who can drive farther on 4 gallons of gas? *Mr. Jones*

[B] Who can drive farther on 2 gallons of gas? *Mr. Jones*

[C] Who can drive farther on 1 gallon of gas? *Mr. Jones*

[D] Who can drive farther on 1 quart of gas? *Mr. Jones*

5. Mr. Black can drive his car 20 miles on a gallon of gas.

[A] How far can he drive on $2\frac{1}{2}$ gallons of gas? *50 miles*

[B] How far can he drive on 1 gallon and 1 quart of gas? *25 miles*

[C] How much gas would he use in driving 70 miles? *3½ gallons*

Although we introduce the short cut in this lesson and we want students to become proficient in working with the multiplication process, we do not want the students to abandon completely the method of thinking of 3×20 rather than 3×2. Therefore, from time to time, you will want to review the ideas involved in such an exercise.

Discuss the examples at the top of the page. If necessary, exhibit these on the chalkboard and have the students explain them.

Have the students work the exercises. Note that the six exercises at the bottom of the page are primarily for the more able students. These involve two or more carryings, but for students who really understand the ideas so far presented, these will be easily worked.

Supplementary exercises, Set 44 (page 348) may be assigned as necessary beyond this page.

The short cut again

Study these examples.

45	'45		68	³68
×3	×3		×4	×4
15	135		32	272
120			240	
135			272	

EXERCISES

Find the products.

1. 37 ×4 = 148	**2.** 56 ×2 = 112	**3.** 95 ×3 = 285	**4.** 43 ×4 = 172	**5.** 82 ×5 = 410	**6.** 96 ×6 = 576
7. 54 ×9 = 486	**8.** 38 ×6 = 228	**9.** 69 ×5 = 345	**10.** 57 ×7 = 399	**11.** 70 ×3 = 210	**12.** 58 ×2 = 116
13. 49 ×5 = 245	**14.** 68 ×4 = 272	**15.** 65 ×4 = 260	**16.** 85 ×7 = 595	**17.** 66 ×9 = 594	**18.** 77 ×8 = 616
19. 72 ×6 = 432	**20.** 48 ×5 = 240	**21.** 75 ×8 = 600	**22.** 57 ×6 = 342	**23.** 79 ×7 = 553	**24.** 59 ×3 = 177
25. 67 ×4 = 268	**26.** 58 ×6 = 348	**27.** 88 ×4 = 352	**28.** 64 ×3 = 192	**29.** 98 ×3 = 294	**30.** 63 ×8 = 504
31. 76 ×5 = 380	**32.** 75 ×7 = 525	**33.** 74 ×9 = 666	**34.** 59 ×8 = 472	**35.** 47 ×8 = 376	**36.** 78 ×2 = 156
37. 99 ×6 = 594	**38.** 87 ×6 = 522	**39.** 97 ×5 = 485	**40.** 86 ×9 = 774	**41.** 94 ×4 = 376	**42.** 89 ×7 = 623

★ Find the products.

1. 386 ×2 = 772	**2.** 386 ×3 = 1158	**3.** 386 ×4 = 1544	**4.** 386 ×8 = 3088	**5.** 578 ×7 = 4046	**6.** 6874 ×5 = 34,370

Teaching Pages 190 and 191

● PURPOSE

To continue developing skills with the multiplication algorithm

To introduce exercises with larger products than previously encountered

To provide word-problem experiences in working with products

● PREPARATION

Provide the class with several exercises similar to those given at the top of page 190. Many of the students will notice little difference between this type of exercise and

Time

National Bureau of Standards' "Atomic Clock" which provides the national standard for measurement of time. A clock kept in continuous operation by this instrument might vary no more than a second, loss or gain, in 3000 years.

1. There are 60 seconds in 1 minute. How many seconds are in 5 minutes? *300*

2. There are 60 minutes in 1 hour. How many minutes are in 9 hours? *540*

3. There are 24 hours in 1 day and 7 days in a week.
How many hours are in a week? *168*

4. There are 12 months in 1 year. How many months are in 8 years? *96*

5. There are about 52 weeks in 1 year. About how many
weeks are in 6 years? *312*

6. In each year, there are 7 months that have 31 days each.
How many days in all are in these 7 months? *217*

7. In each year, there are 4 months that have 30 days each.
How many days in all are in these 4 months? *120*

8. How many days are in a year when February has 28 days?
(Use your answers to exercises 6 and 7.) *365*

9. How many days are in a year when February has 29 days? *366*

10. How many seconds are in one hour? *3600*

11. How many seconds are in one day? *86,400*

Give the students an opportunity to work the exercises. Exercises 8 through 11 are primarily for the more able students. Allow time when the students have finished to check papers and discuss the exercises.

An interesting type of enrichment exercise could be used to follow this lesson. For example, you might ask what day is 20 days from May 17 or 25 days from August 16, etc.

those they have had before. Of course, the only difference is that in most exercises the second product is greater than 100. This should cause no additional difficulty for the students.

Have the students work the exercises. When they have finished, allow time for checking papers and a discussion of the various ideas and skills presented on this page.

---

192 MULTIPLYING

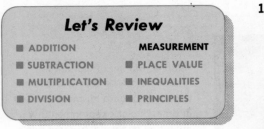

Let's Review

■ ADDITION   **MEASUREMENT**

■ SUBTRACTION   ■ PLACE VALUE

■ MULTIPLICATION   ■ INEQUALITIES

■ DIVISION   ■ PRINCIPLES

1. Find the missing numbers.

[A] $67 = 60 + \blacksquare$ *7*

[B] $58 = \blacksquare + 8$ *50*

[C] $235 = 200 + \blacksquare + 5$ *30*

[D] $762 = \blacksquare + 60 + 2$ *700*

[E] $348 = 300 + 40 + \blacksquare$ *8*

[F] $658 + 10 = \blacksquare$ *668*

[G] $7285 + \blacksquare = 7385$ *100*

2. Jack started with a number and multiplied it by 7. Then he added 75, subtracted 75, and divided by 7. Jack's answer was 19. With what number did he start? *19*

3. Find the sums, differences, and products.

[A]	[B]	[C]	[D]	[E]	[F]
63 +18 = *81*	95 +7 = *102*	68 +25 = *93*	83 +72 = *155*	69 +54 = *123*	93 +67 = *160*

[G]	[H]	[I]	[J]	[K]	[L]
64 −27 = *37*	75 −46 = *29*	36 −17 = *19*	127 −54 = *73*	146 −67 = *79*	152 −74 = *78*

[M]	[N]	[O]	[P]	[Q]	[R]
45 ×3 = *135*	67 ×2 = *134*	58 ×4 = *232*	83 ×3 = *249*	58 ×6 = *348*	71 ×7 = *497*

4. Think carefully to decide how to find the answer.

[A] How much for 5 apples? *40¢*

[B] How much in all for 1 pound of grapes and 1 pound of bananas? *23¢*

[C] 3 pears cost how much more than 4 lemons? *5¢*

[D] How much does 1 lemon cost? *5¢*

[E] How much is 1 dozen oranges? *84¢*

[F] How much is 1 orange? *7¢*

[G] How much in all for 3 pears, 1 pound of grapes, and ½ dozen oranges? *81¢*

[H] Which costs more, 1 apple or 1 pear? *1 pear*

Oranges.....42¢ for ½ dozen
Apples............8¢ each
Bananas........9¢ a pound
Grapes.........14¢ a pound
Pears..........3 for 25¢
Lemons........4 for 20¢

Teaching Pages 192 and 193

● **PURPOSE**

To review the material covered thus far in the text

To provide additional practice in working with products

● **PREPARATION**

Review those topics with which the students may have had particular difficulty in earlier parts of the book. Provide exercises in which the students must decide on a particular operation according to the language of the problem. You might also give the students an opportunity to make up some word problems of their own involving any

Finding products

1. Find the products.

[A] 3 × 6 *18*   [G] 3 × 7 *21*   [M] 6 × 4 *24*   [S] 5 × 6 *30*
[B] 7 × 4 *28*   [H] 8 × 3 *24*   [N] 4 × 8 *32*   [T] 5 × 5 *25*
[C] 3 × 9 *27*   [I] 4 × 9 *36*   [O] 9 × 5 *45*   [U] 9 × 6 *54*
[D] 5 × 8 *40*   [J] 6 × 8 *48*   [P] 5 × 7 *35*   [V] 6 × 7 *42*
[E] 9 × 8 *72*   [K] 9 × 9 *81*   [Q] 7 × 9 *63*   [W] 5 × 4 *20*
[F] 7 × 7 *49*   [L] 8 × 7 *56*   [R] 6 × 6 *36*   [X] 8 × 8 *64*

2. Find the products.

[A] 6 × 10 *60*   [G] 6 × 50 *300*   [M] 9 × 50 *450*   [S] 70 × 4 *280*
[B] 20 × 3 *60*   [H] 10 × 34 *340*   [N] 9 × 90 *810*   [T] 3 × 90 *270*
[C] 10 × 9 *90*   [I] 80 × 10 *800*   [O] 10 × 84 *840*   [U] 2 × 60 *120*
[D] 40 × 4 *160*   [J] 7 × 20 *140*   [P] 7 × 30 *210*   [V] 70 × 10 *700*
[E] 15 × 10 *150*   [K] 10 × 68 *680*   [Q] 80 × 6 *480*   [W] 85 × 10 *850*
[F] 5 × 30 *150*   [L] 7 × 40 *280*   [R] 5 × 90 *450*   [X] 60 × 7 *420*

3. Find the products.

[A] 32 ×3 *96*	[B] 43 ×2 *86*	[C] 44 ×2 *88*	[D] 24 ×2 *48*	[E] 23 ×3 *69*	[F] 46 ×2 *92*
[G] 17 ×2 *34*	[H] 28 ×3 *84*	[I] 19 ×4 *76*	[J] 26 ×3 *78*	[K] 37 ×2 *74*	[L] 45 ×2 *90*

4. Find the products.

[A] 47 ×4 *188*	[B] 56 ×5 *280*	[C] 87 ×2 *174*	[D] 63 ×8 *504*	[E] 24 ×9 *216*	[F] 36 ×8 *288*
[G] 27 ×7 *189*	[H] 56 ×6 *336*	[I] 65 ×6 *390*	[J] 71 ×7 *497*	[K] 85 ×8 *680*	[L] 64 ×6 *384*
[M] 73 ×8 *584*	[N] 65 ×5 *325*	[O] 76 ×3 *228*	[P] 57 ×4 *228*	[Q] 87 ×5 *435*	[R] 59 ×6 *354*
[S] 74 ×8 *592*	[T] 67 ×7 *469*	[U] 89 ×4 *356*	[V] 65 ×8 *520*	[W] 76 ×7 *532*	[X] 83 ×9 *747*

DIRECTIONS PAGE 193

Have the students work the exercises. Allow time for checking papers when they have finished. Have several students present some of the more difficult exercises on the chalkboard and explain these to the class.

one of the four operations. Emphasize how different problems trigger various operations.

Write on the chalkboard several exercises similar to those on page 193. Call on two or three students to explain to the class the steps for working the problems. It may be helpful during this preparation period to have a number of students go to the chalkboard and work exercises similar to exercises 3 and 4 on page 193.

Ask the students to study the illustrations and the moon facts. Give them an opportunity to discuss the ideas and work the exercises when they have finished the page. The discussion period accompanying this lesson is a vital part of the arithmetic program. That is, lessons such as this are provided not only for their own value in improving students' skill in working with word problems and arithmetic concepts, but also to provide scientific information and stimulation as a part of the arithmetic program. For this reason, you should give the students considerable freedom in discussing the various aspects of this page of problems.

A moon trip

Peter thinks he would like to be an astronaut and go to the the moon. He read some books to learn more about the moon. Peter wrote this paper to show his teacher.

1. Peter figured he would weigh only 12 pounds on the moon. How much does Peter weigh on earth? *72 pounds*

2. Peter's father would weigh 27 pounds on the moon. How much does he weigh on earth? *162 pounds*

3. About how long does it take the moon to go around the earth 4 times? *112 days*

4. Suppose you could fly straight to the moon and back. How far would you travel? *480,000 miles*

5. Peter drinks 4 cups of water each day.

   [A] How much water would he have to take for a 36-day moon trip? *144 cups*

   [B] How many quarts would this be? *36 quarts*

   [C] How many gallons? *9 gallons*

Moon Facts

1. The moon is much smaller than the earth.
2. People weigh 6 times as much on earth as they would on the moon.
3. The moon goes around the earth once in about 28 days.
4. The moon is about 240,000 miles from earth.
5. Scientists believe there is no air or water on the moon.

Peter L.

Teaching Pages 194 and 195

● **PURPOSE**

To provide word-problem experiences concerning products

To provide more practice in working with the multiplication algorithm

To provide an interesting and unusual exercise which requires finding products

● **PREPARATION**

Review for the class the ideas involved in finding the area of rectangular figures. Attempt to get the students to express the relationship between multiplication and finding area. Elicit from the students the fact that if they

How many . . .

1. Give the number of squares for each strip of paper.

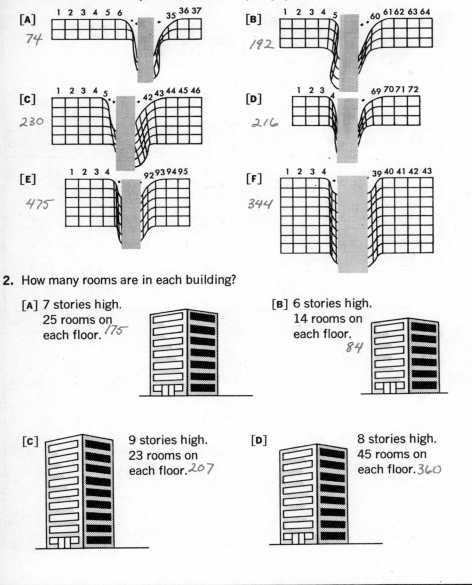

[A] 74

[B] 192

[C] 230

[D] 216

[E] 475

[F] 344

2. How many rooms are in each building?

[A] 7 stories high.
25 rooms on
each floor. 175

[B] 6 stories high.
14 rooms on
each floor. 84

[C] 9 stories high.
23 rooms on
each floor. 207

[D] 8 stories high.
45 rooms on
each floor. 360

Discuss exercise 1A with the class. Notice with them that they cannot see all the squares on this strip of paper, but they can imagine the square that they cannot see. Elicit from the students the fact that since they know there are two rows with 37 squares in each row, they can find the number of squares by multiplication.

Check the students' answers to this exercise before directing them to complete the page.

know the number of rows and the number of columns, they can multiply to find the number of squares in a rectangular figure. Encourage the students to multiply to find the area of various rectangles rather than to count the number of squares.

As the students study the boxed material at the top of the page, point out that the blue shading shows the relationship between the steps in horizontal and vertical notation. Have the students follow through these steps one at a time. If you choose, you may exhibit these steps one at a time with the corresponding equations.

Now exhibit on the chalkboard the two examples of the short cut given under the first table. Have the students work carefully through these examples, explaining each step of the operation.

Following this, exhibit the last example on the chalkboard and have the students work through it step by step. If necessary, you may also choose to show the long form for this exercise to highlight for the students the ideas involved in the carrying process. Provide one or two more examples of this type.

Have the students work the exercises. Allow time at the end for presentation of some of the problems on the chalkboard and a discussion of the processes.

Supplementary exercises, Set 45 (page 348) may be assigned as necessary beyond this page.

3-digit factors

Study the examples.

Step 1	Step 2	Step 3	Step 4
237 ×4 28	237 ×4 28 120	237 ×4 28 120 800	237 ×4 28 120 800 948
$4 \times 7 = 28$	$4 \times 30 = 120$	$4 \times 200 = 800$	$28 + 120 + 800 = 948$

Study these 2 short cuts.

```
  237      237        347      347
  ×4       ×4         ×6       ×6
  28       948        42       2082
  120                 40
  800                 1800
  948                 2082
```

Explain each step in this example.

```
 746        746        746
 ×4    →    ×4    →    ×4
 4          84         2984
```

EXERCISES

Find the products.

1. 289
   ×3
   867

2. 357
   ×4
   1428

3. 621
   ×5
   3105

4. 324
   ×2
   648

5. 607
   ×6
   3642

6. 528
   ×4
   2112

7. 982
   ×7
   6874

8. 671
   ×3
   2013

9. 743
   ×6
   4458

10. 862
    ×5
    4310

11. 511
    ×9
    4599

12. 764
    ×8
    6112

13. 925
    ×7
    6475

14. 278
    ×6
    1668

15. 179
    ×5
    895

16. 826
    ×6
    4956

17. 534
    ×7
    3738

18. 921
    ×8
    7368

19. 807
    ×9
    7263

20. 680
    ×6
    4080

Teaching Pages 196 and 197

• PURPOSE

To introduce products involving three-digit factors

To provide word-problem experiences in working with products

• PREPARATION

Give the class several review exercises in finding products such as 4×30 and 3×300. If necessary, follow this with a brief review of multiplication involving a two-digit factor and a one-digit factor. It is important that the

At the airport

1. Joe visited the airport. While he was there, he saw 3 jet planes take off for Europe. Each plane carried 97 people. How many people in all left on the 3 planes? *291*

2. Each large jet airliner has 4 engines. If each engine gives about 16,000 pounds of thrust (push) during takeoff, what is the total thrust during takeoff? *64,000 pounds*

3. During most of the trip each engine gives about 6000 pounds of thrust. What is the total thrust then? *24,000 pounds*

4. Suppose a large jet plane flies at the rate of 583 miles each hour. How far would it fly in 6 hours? *3498 miles*

5. A pilot told Joe that in a few years jet airliners would fly 3 times as fast as they do now. If they fly about 575 miles an hour now, about how fast will they fly in a few years? *1725 Mph*

Have the class work the exercises. Allow time when they have finished for discussion of these exercises. Again, the discussion period is one of the important parts of this lesson. That is, we expect lessons of this type to stimulate students not only to greater interest in arithmetic, but also to a greater interest in science and some of the uses of arithmetic.

students be familiar with the steps for finding this type of product since this lesson involves exactly the same ideas with larger numbers.

Discuss the examples at the top of the page. Exhibit these examples on the chalkboard and have the students explain the steps as they are worked.

Ask the students to do the exercises.

Notice that the five exercises at the bottom of the page are starred. When the students have finished the page, exhibit several exercises on the chalkboard, and give them an opportunity to explain the steps necessary to find the answers.

Supplementary exercises, Set 46 (page 349) may be assigned as necessary beyond this page.

Factors with 4 or more digits

Study these examples. Try to explain each step.

$$\begin{array}{r} 3\,6^{3}4\,7 \\ \times\,5 \\ \hline 5 \end{array} \qquad \begin{array}{r} 3^{2}6^{3}4\,7 \\ \times\,5 \\ \hline 3\,5 \end{array} \qquad \begin{array}{r} {}^{3}3^{2}6^{3}4\,7 \\ \times\,5 \\ \hline 2\,3\,5 \end{array} \qquad \begin{array}{r} {}^{3}3^{2}6^{3}4\,7 \\ \times\,5 \\ \hline 1\,8\,2\,3\,5 \end{array}$$

$$\begin{array}{r} 7\,6^{3}8\,9 \\ \times\,4 \\ \hline 6 \end{array} \qquad \begin{array}{r} 7^{3}6^{3}8\,9 \\ \times\,4 \\ \hline 5\,6 \end{array} \qquad \begin{array}{r} {}^{2}7^{3}6^{3}8\,9 \\ \times\,4 \\ \hline 7\,5\,6 \end{array} \qquad \begin{array}{r} {}^{2}7^{3}6^{3}8\,9 \\ \times\,4 \\ \hline 3\,0\,7\,5\,6 \end{array}$$

EXERCISES

Find the products.

1. 924 ×8	2. 913 ×6	3. 480 ×4	4. 693 ×2	5. 554 ×4
7392	5478	1920	1386	2216
6. 271 ×9	**7.** 185 ×3	**8.** 303 ×7	**9.** 244 ×6	**10.** 908 ×2
2439	555	2121	1464	1816
11. 817 ×5	**12.** 905 ×5	**13.** 272 ×3	**14.** 708 ×9	**15.** 894 ×7
4085	4525	816	6372	6258
16. 9142 ×4	**17.** 5068 ×2	**18.** 7625 ×3	**19.** 6369 ×7	**20.** 4179 ×6
36,568	10,136	22,875	44,583	25,074
21. 8346 ×6	**22.** 7037 ×8	**23.** 6305 ×8	**24.** 3648 ×9	**25.** 7296 ×8
50,076	56,296	50,440	32,832	58,368
26. 7514 ×5	**27.** 5007 ×9	**28.** 5230 ×7	**29.** 7626 ×4	**30.** 7809 ×7
37,570	45,063	36,610	30,504	54,663

★ Find the products.

1. 86,194 ×2	2. 96,824 ×4	3. 48,057 ×6	4. 60,795 ×8	5. 35,678 ×5
172,388	387,296	288,342	486,360	178,390

Teaching Pages 198 and 199

● **PURPOSE**

To provide experiences in finding products with factors of four or more digits

To provide more word-problem experiences in working with products

● **PREPARATION**

Review the algorithm from the last lesson involving a three-digit factor. Following this, present on the chalkboard an exercise with a four-digit factor and a one-digit

Short stories

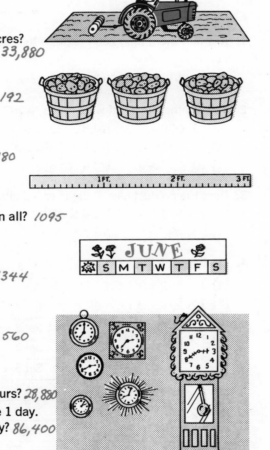

1. 4 rolls of tickets.
   375 tickets on each roll.
   How many tickets? *1500*

2. 4840 square yards in an acre.
   How many square yards in 7 acres?
   33,880

3. 64 pints in 1 bushel.
   How many pints in 3 bushels? *192*

4. 36 inches in 1 yard.
   How many inches in 5 yards? *180*

5. If 3 years had 365 days each,
   how many days would this be in all? *1095*

6. 168 hours in 1 week.
   How many hours in 8 weeks? *1344*

7. 5280 feet in 1 mile.
   How many feet in 2 miles? *10,560*

8. [A] 3600 seconds in 1 hour.
   How many seconds in 8 hours? *28,880*

   [B] Three 8-hour periods make 1 day.
   How many seconds in a day? *86,400*

   [C] 7 days in 1 week.
   How many seconds in 1 week?
   604,800

Have the students work the exercises. Discuss each exercise after the students have completed the page. Notice that exercise 8 is designed primarily for more able students. You will find, however, that a discussion of exercise 8 will prove of high interest to the entire class. For this reason, you may choose to have all the students attempt exercise 8, with the warning that they should not become discouraged if they are not able to get the correct answers.

factor. Give the students an opportunity to work through this as a class activity. Present several more similar exercises and have the students work and explain them.

Discuss the illustration at the top of the page and then have the students do the exercises. When the students get to exercise 4, point out that the sets are numbered according to the left-hand digit. That is, set 1 is the one hundreds, set 2 is the two hundreds, and so on. Encourage the students to attempt to find the correct set without actually computing the product.

Discuss the page when the students have finished the exercises. Elicit from the students their reasons for making certain decisions. The students should be able to explain just how they arrived at their various estimations.

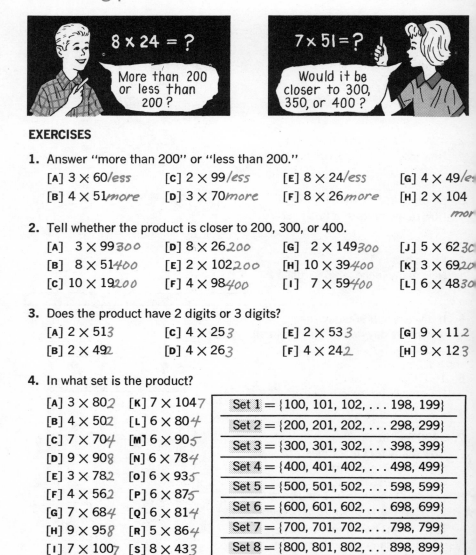

Estimating products

EXERCISES

1. Answer "more than 200" or "less than 200."

[A] 3 × 60 *less*   [C] 2 × 99 *less*   [E] 8 × 24 *less*   [G] 4 × 49 *less*

[B] 4 × 51 *more*   [D] 3 × 70 *more*   [F] 8 × 26 *more*   [H] 2 × 104 *more*

2. Tell whether the product is closer to 200, 300, or 400.

[A] 3 × 99 *300*   [D] 8 × 26 *200*   [G] 2 × 149 *300*   [J] 5 × 62 *300*

[B] 8 × 51 *400*   [E] 2 × 102 *200*   [H] 10 × 39 *400*   [K] 3 × 69 *200*

[C] 10 × 19 *200*   [F] 4 × 98 *400*   [I] 7 × 59 *400*   [L] 6 × 48 *300*

3. Does the product have 2 digits or 3 digits?

[A] 2 × 51 *3*   [C] 4 × 25 *3*   [E] 2 × 53 *3*   [G] 9 × 11 *2*

[B] 2 × 49 *2*   [D] 4 × 26 *3*   [F] 4 × 24 *2*   [H] 9 × 12 *3*

4. In what set is the product?

[A] 3 × 80 *2*	[K] 7 × 104 *7*	Set 1 = {100, 101, 102, . . . 198, 199}
[B] 4 × 50 *2*	[L] 6 × 80 *4*	Set 2 = {200, 201, 202, . . . 298, 299}
[C] 7 × 70 *4*	[M] 6 × 90 *5*	Set 3 = {300, 301, 302, . . . 398, 399}
[D] 9 × 90 *8*	[N] 6 × 78 *4*	Set 4 = {400, 401, 402, . . . 498, 499}
[E] 3 × 78 *2*	[O] 6 × 93 *5*	Set 5 = {500, 501, 502, . . . 598, 599}
[F] 4 × 56 *2*	[P] 6 × 87 *5*	Set 6 = {600, 601, 602, . . . 698, 699}
[G] 7 × 68 *4*	[Q] 6 × 81 *4*	Set 7 = {700, 701, 702, . . . 798, 799}
[H] 9 × 95 *8*	[R] 5 × 86 *4*	Set 8 = {800, 801, 802, . . . 898, 899}
[I] 7 × 100 *7*	[S] 8 × 43 *3*	Set 9 = {900, 901, 902, . . . 998, 999}
[J] 7 × 98 *6*	[T] 9 × 101 *9*	

Teaching Pages 200 and 201

- **PURPOSE**

  To provide experiences in estimating products
  To provide word-problem experiences involving estimation

- **PREPARATION**

  Play the following game with the class. Write some number, such as 37, on the chalkboard. Give the students several combinations whose products are close to 37 (e.g., 6 × 6, 5 × 6, 5 × 8, 2 × 13, 2 × 14, etc.) and have them tell whether the products are more than 37 or less than 37. Tell the students that during this activity there are times when they need not find the exact answer to decide

Making the best guess

There are 3 answers after each question.
One of them is very close to the right answer.
You are to decide which answer is best.

1. An airplane flew 502 miles each hour for 4 hours. About how many miles did it fly? [A] 100 [B] 2000 [C] 750

2. An orchard has 8 rows of trees with 49 trees in each row. About how many trees are in this orchard?
[A] 100 [B] 500 [C] 400

3. Each of 6 books has 312 pages. About how many pages are there in all? [A] 2000 [B] 600 [C] 3000

4. If there are 365 days in each of 3 years, about how many days is this in all? [A] 100 [B] 1000 [C] 10,000

5. There are 5280 feet in 1 mile. About how many feet are in 2 miles? [A] 1000 [B] 100,000 [C] 10,000

6. There are 36 inches in a yard. About how many inches are in 9 yards? [A] 100 [B] 350 [C] 1000

7. There are 8 pints in 1 gallon. About how many pints are in 98 gallons? [A] 100 [B] 8000 [C] 800

★ 8. There are 52 weeks in a year. About how many weeks are in $2\frac{1}{2}$ years? [A] 100 [B] 200 [C] 125

★ 9. There are 60 minutes in an hour. About how many minutes are in $8\frac{1}{4}$ hours? [A] 450 [B] 500 [C] 550

★10. There are 1760 yards in a mile. About how many yards are in $2\frac{1}{2}$ miles? [A] 4500 [B] 3500 [C] 5000

Read the directions with the students and have them do the exercises. Exercises 8, 9, and 10 are starred. When they have finished, encourage the students to explain their reasoning in arriving at certain answers. Having the students verbalize their reasons for arriving at certain estimations is one of the most important parts of this lesson.

Supplementary exercises, Set 47 (page 349) may be assigned as necessary beyond this page.

whether it is more or less than the number you write on the chalkboard.

Now try this game with a larger number, such as 80. Again, give the students products which are close to 80 but not exactly 80.

Repeat this game using the number 100. Notice with the students that all they have to decide is whether the product you give them contains two digits or three digits to decide whether it is more than 100 or less than 100; they need not find the actual product. Of course, you will not want to give a product that is exactly 100. Repeat this until the students have grasped the idea of deciding, without actual computation, whether the product is more or less than the number you exhibit.

Have the students work the exercises. Notice that exercise 2 is the reconstruction type in which the students must find missing digits. As you discuss these answers, have the students explain how they found the various digits.

When the students have finished, allow time to check exercises and discuss any questions they may have.

Answers, exercise 2, page 202

[A]
$$89 \\ -34 \\ \hline 55$$
[F]
$$23 \\ \times 2 \\ \hline 46$$

[B]
$$59 \\ -31 \\ \hline 28$$
[G]
$$31 \\ \times 7 \\ \hline 217$$

[C]
$$39 \\ +67 \\ \hline 106$$
[H]
$$492 \\ +368 \\ \hline 860$$

[D]
$$83 \\ -37 \\ \hline 46$$
[I]
$$921 \\ -356 \\ \hline 565$$

[E]
$$972 \\ -236 \\ \hline 736$$
[J]
$$42 \\ \times 6 \\ \hline 252$$

---

1. Find the sums and differences.

Let's Review

■ ADDITION   MEASUREMENT
■ SUBTRACTION   PLACE VALUE
■ MULTIPLICATION   INEQUALITIES
■ DIVISION   PRINCIPLES

[A]
$$34 \\ +51 \\ \hline 85$$
[B]
$$76 \\ -24 \\ \hline 52$$
[C]
$$67 \\ +12 \\ \hline 79$$

[D]
$$87 \\ -32 \\ \hline 55$$
[E]
$$15 \\ +84 \\ \hline 99$$
[F]
$$95 \\ -13 \\ \hline 82$$

[G]
$$67 \\ +89 \\ \hline 156$$
[H]
$$132 \\ -57 \\ \hline 75$$
[I]
$$76 \\ +98 \\ \hline 174$$
[J]
$$161 \\ -82 \\ \hline 79$$
[K]
$$85 \\ +67 \\ \hline 152$$
[L]
$$153 \\ -95 \\ \hline 58$$

2. Copy the problems and give the missing digits. *(See answers at left.)*

[A]
$$\blacksquare 9 \\ -3\blacksquare \\ \hline 55$$
[B]
$$59 \\ -\blacksquare\blacksquare \\ \hline 28$$
[C]
$$39 \\ +6\blacksquare \\ \hline \blacksquare\blacksquare 6$$
[D]
$$83 \\ -3\blacksquare \\ \hline \blacksquare 6$$
[E]
$$97\blacksquare \\ -2\blacksquare 6 \\ \hline \blacksquare 36$$

[F]
$$23 \\ \times \blacksquare\blacksquare \\ \hline 46$$
[G]
$$3\blacksquare \\ \times 7 \\ \hline \blacksquare\blacksquare 7$$
[H]
$$\blacksquare 9\blacksquare \\ +3\blacksquare 8 \\ \hline 860$$
[I]
$$921 \\ -3\blacksquare 6 \\ \hline \blacksquare 6\blacksquare$$
[J]
$$\blacksquare\blacksquare \\ \times 6 \\ \hline 252$$

3. Find the missing factors.

[A] $6 \times \blacksquare = 42$ 7   [G] $6 \times \blacksquare = 48$ 8   [M] $3 \times \blacksquare = 27$ 9   [S] $9 \times \blacksquare = 0$ 0

[B] $\blacksquare \times 5 = 15$ 3   [H] $\blacksquare \times 4 = 36$ 9   [N] $6 \times \blacksquare = 36$ 6   [T] $7 \times \blacksquare = 49$ 7

[C] $8 \times \blacksquare = 32$ 4   [I] $\blacksquare \times 5 = 35$ 7   [O] $\blacksquare \times 7 = 42$ 6   [U] $\blacksquare \times 3 = 9$ 3

[D] $6 \times \blacksquare = 30$ 5   [J] $9 \times \blacksquare = 18$ 2   [P] $\blacksquare \times 9 = 81$ 9   [V] $\blacksquare \times 1 = 0$ 0

[E] $\blacksquare \times 3 = 21$ 7   [K] $\blacksquare \times 5 = 25$ 5   [Q] $6 \times \blacksquare = 24$ 4   [W] $8 \times \blacksquare = 64$ 8

[F] $\blacksquare \times 2 = 8$ 4   [L] $\blacksquare \times 8 = 40$ 5   [R] $\blacksquare \times 7 = 28$ 4   [X] $\blacksquare \times 9 = 54$ 6

4. Find the quotients as quickly as you can.

[A] $42 \div 6$ 7   [F] $63 \div 9$ 7   [K] $50 \div 5$ 10   [P] $81 \div 9$ 9   [U] $45 \div 5$

[B] $35 \div 5$ 7   [G] $49 \div 7$ 7   [L] $72 \div 9$ 8   [Q] $56 \div 8$ 7   [V] $35 \div 7$ 5

[C] $45 \div 9$ 5   [H] $20 \div 10$ 2   [M] $63 \div 7$ 9   [R] $40 \div 5$ 8   [W] $40 \div 8$ 5

[D] $56 \div 7$ 8   [I] $72 \div 8$ 9   [N] $42 \div 7$ 6   [S] $48 \div 6$ 8   [X] $48 \div 8$ 6

[E] $54 \div 6$ 9   [J] $64 \div 8$ 8   [O] $80 \div 10$ 8   [T] $54 \div 9$ 6   [Y] $24 \div 6$ 4

Teaching **Pages 202 and 203**

● **PURPOSE**

To provide a review of the text material covered thus far

To provide experiences in working with maps

To provide additional word-problem experiences

To provide an enrichment activity involving two 2-digit factors

● **PREPARATION**

Review for the students the topics covered thus far with which they may have had difficulty. Since considerable time has been spent with the processes of multiplication in this chapter, it might be helpful to concentrate most of

Map problems

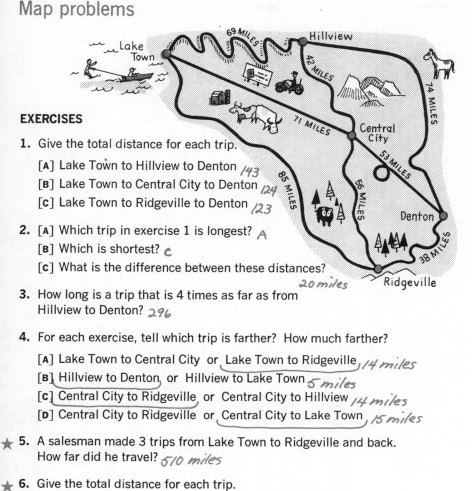

EXERCISES

1. Give the total distance for each trip.

[A] Lake Town to Hillview to Denton *143*

[B] Lake Town to Central City to Denton *124*

[C] Lake Town to Ridgeville to Denton *123*

2. [A] Which trip in exercise 1 is longest? *A*

[B] Which is shortest? *C*

[C] What is the difference between these distances? *20 miles*

3. How long is a trip that is 4 times as far as from Hillview to Denton? *296*

4. For each exercise, tell which trip is farther? How much farther?

[A] Lake Town to Central City or Lake Town to Ridgeville *14 miles*

[B] Hillview to Denton or Hillview to Lake Town *5 miles*

[C] Central City to Ridgeville or Central City to Hillview *14 miles*

[D] Central City to Ridgeville or Central City to Lake Town *15 miles*

★ **5.** A salesman made 3 trips from Lake Town to Ridgeville and back. How far did he travel? *510 miles*

★ **6.** Give the total distance for each trip.

[A] Central City to Ridgeville to Denton to Hillview *168*

[B] Lake Town to Ridgeville to Central City to Hillview *183*

[C] Denton to Ridgeville to Lake Town to Hillview *192*

[D] Hillview to Lake Town to Ridgeville to Denton *192*

[E] Central City to Denton to Ridgeville to Central City to Hillview to Lake Town *258*

As you study the map with the students, have them give various distances between pairs of cities that you might name. Begin by naming city pairs that will not require computation to find the distance (e.g., Lake Town and Hillview, Hillview and Central City, Central City and Denton). Once the students have an understanding of map reading, you might present several city pairs which involve computation to find the distances (e.g., Lake Town to Denton).

Have the students do the exercises. When they have finished, allow time for discussion.

Notice that exercises 5 and 6 are designed primarily for the more able students.

---

your efforts in this review lesson on the processes for adding and subtracting two- and three-digit numbers.

One of the purposes of this lesson is to present problems involving the reading of a map. In preparation for this, you might find it helpful to display a map of a local territory and have the students read various distances from this map. Also, it will be helpful to have them locate various cities according to directions found on the map.

Do not attempt to prepare for page 203 unless you intend to assign this page to the entire class. If the page is to be used for the entire class, you will want to prepare carefully, going over exercises similar to exercises 1 through 6 at the top of the page. Then, during the presentation of the page, you can study the boxed example with the students.

Have the students work the exercises. If this page is to be used for evaluation, you may choose to check the papers yourself. However this lesson is used, you will want to give the students an opportunity to present and discuss the exercises on this page.

Chapter review

1. Find the missing numbers.
   [A] $2 \times 34 = (2 \times 30) + (2 \times \blacksquare) = 60 + 8 = 68$ *4*
   [B] $4 \times 70 = 4 \times (7 \times 10) = (4 \times 7) \times 10 = \blacksquare \times 10 = 280$ *28*
   [C] $3 \times 231 = (3 \times \blacksquare) + (3 \times 30) + (3 \times 1) = 693$ *200*
   [D] $4 \times 57 = (4 \times 50) + (4 \times 7) = 200 + \blacksquare = 228$ *28*
   [E] $6 \times 78 = (6 \times 70) + (\blacksquare \times 8) = 420 + 48 = 468$ *6*
   [F] $6 \times 374 = (6 \times 300) + (6 \times 70) + (6 \times 4) = 1800 + \blacksquare + 24 = 2244$ *420*
   [G] $8 \times 709 = (8 \times 700) + (8 \times 9) = \blacksquare + 72 = 5672$ *5600*
   [H] $9 \times 80 = 9 \times (8 \times 10) = (9 \times 8) \times 10 = 72 \times \blacksquare = 720$ *10*
   [I] $10 \times 23 = (10 \times 20) + (10 \times 3) = \blacksquare + 30 = 230$ *200*
   [J] $10 \times 70 = 10 \times (7 \times 10) = 10 \times (10 \times 7) = (10 \times 10) \times \blacksquare = 100 \times 7 = 700$ *7*
   [K] $7 \times 356 = 7 \times (300 + 50 + 6) = 2100 + 350 + 42 = \blacksquare$ *2492*
   [L] $9 \times 47 = 9 \times (40 + 7) = (9 \times 40) + (9 \times 7) = \blacksquare + 63 = 423$ *360*

2. Find the products.
   [A] 100×18 *1800*   [D] 2×10 *20*   [G] 100×24 *2400*   [J] 75×10 *750*
   [B] 78×10 *780*   [E] 10×136 *1360*   [H] 75×100 *7500*   [K] 10×23 *230*
   [C] 6×100 *600*   [F] 37×10 *370*   [I] 20×10 *200*   [L] 4×100 *400*

3. Find the products.

[A] 23 ×2	[B] 14 ×2	[C] 32 ×3	[D] 12 ×4	[E] 11 ×5	[F] 43 ×2
46	*28*	*96*	*48*	*55*	*86*

[G] 13 ×3	[H] 22 ×4	[I] 33 ×2	[J] 24 ×2	[K] 11 ×6	[L] 12 ×3
39	*88*	*66*	*48*	*66*	*36*

4. Find the products.

[A] 37 ×4	[B] 46 ×6	[C] 25 ×7	[D] 39 ×9	[E] 43 ×6	[F] 62 ×8
148	*276*	*175*	*351*	*258*	*496*

[G] 923 ×3	[H] 849 ×4	[I] 965 ×7	[J] 438 ×6	[K] 4092 ×4	[L] 2958 ×5
2769	*3396*	*6755*	*2628*	*16,368*	*14,790*

Teaching Pages 204 and 205

- **PURPOSE**

  To provide a suggested evaluation instrument for this chapter

  To provide a chapter review

- **PREPARATION**

  Review those topics from the chapter with which the students have had most difficulty. If the students seem to need very little in the way of review, you might focus attention on the relationship between multiplication and division in preparation for the next chapter.

5. Complete each sentence.

[A] Since 4 × 27 = 108, we know that 5 × 27 = 108 + ▥. *27*

[B] Since 6 × 78 = 468, we know that 7 × 78 = 468 + ▥. *78*

[C] Since 6 × 78 = 468, we know that 5 × 78 = 468 − ▥. *78*

[D] Since 9 × 57 = 513, we know that 8 × 57 = 513 − ▥. *57*

[E] Since 7 × 83 = 581, we know that 8 × 83 = 581 + ▥. *83*

[F] Since 8 × 47 = 376, we know that 7 × 47 = 376 − ▥. *47*

[G] Since 4 × 348 = 1392, we know that 5 × 348 = 1392 + ▥. *348*

[H] Since 9 × 176 = 1584, we know that 8 × 176 = 1584 − ▥. *176*

[I] Since 27 × 38 = 1026, we know that 28 × 38 = 1026 + ▥. *38*

[J] Since 85 × 67 = 5695, we know that 84 × 67 = 5695 − ▥. *67*

Short stories

1. 13 rows of chairs. 6 chairs in each row. How many chairs? *78*

2. 3 classes of children. 34 children in each class. How many children? *102*

3. 427 pages in each book. 7 books. How many pages? *2989*

4. 36 rooms on each floor. 9 floors. How many rooms? *324*

5. 10 pencils in each bundle. 68 bundles. How many pencils? *680*

6. 7 dozen eggs. How many eggs. *84*

7. 4 cups in a quart. 83 quarts. How many cups? *332*

8. 12 inches in a foot. 7 feet. How many inches? *84*

9. 36 inches in a yard. How many inches in 10 yards? *360*

10. 100 yard dash. 3 feet per yard. How many feet in the dash? *300*

Have the students work the exercises. You may choose to check the papers yourself depending upon how you intend to use this page.

Again, an important part of this lesson is the discussion which accompanies the working of the problems on this page. In particular, the short stories on this page merit considerable attention in class discussion.

Teaching
Geometry Lesson 6

• PURPOSE

To introduce right triangles

To introduce rectangles

The students already have encountered in Chapter 6 the idea of the square. A more formal introduction to the properties of squares and rectangles is given in this lesson.

The fact that a right triangle is a triangle that has exactly one right angle is introduced intuitively at the beginning of the lesson. The students are then given several other facts about right triangles. The Pythagorean Theorem is presented intuitively by having the students draw a right triangle which has legs of three and four inches; then the students observe that this right triangle has a third side of five inches. The other fact which is explored is that the sum of the two acute triangles of a right triangle is the same as a right angle. The students explore this by tearing the corners off a right triangle and pasting them in the interior of the right angle.

• MATHEMATICS

We give here some formal definitions.

A *right triangle* is a triangle that has one right angle.

A *rectangle* is a parallelogram (opposite sides parallel) that has one right angle. (Note: if a parallelogram has one right angle, then it has four right angles.)

A *square* is a rectangle with two adjacent sides of the same length. (Note: If a rectangle has two adjacent sides of the same length, then all of its sides have the same length.)

The following is a statement of the Pythagorean Theorem of geometry.

In any right triangle, the square of the length of the hypotenuse is equal to the sum of the squares of the length of the other two sides.

GEOMETRY – Lesson 6

Right triangles and rectangles

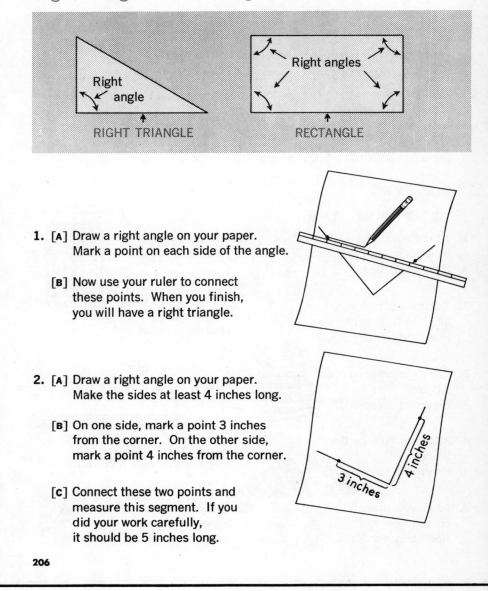

1. [A] Draw a right angle on your paper. Mark a point on each side of the angle.

   [B] Now use your ruler to connect these points. When you finish, you will have a right triangle.

2. [A] Draw a right angle on your paper. Make the sides at least 4 inches long.

   [B] On one side, mark a point 3 inches from the corner. On the other side, mark a point 4 inches from the corner.

   [C] Connect these two points and measure this segment. If you did your work carefully, it should be 5 inches long.

206

Consider now a right triangle with legs of 3 and 4. Note that $(3 \times 3) + (4 \times 4) = 25$. Therefore, 25 is the square of the hypotenuse, and we conclude that the hypotenuse is 5.

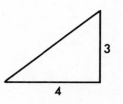

3. [A] Draw a right angle on your paper. Use a wide ruler or a carefully folded paper to draw lines like this.

[B] When you finish, you should have a square. A square is a special kind of rectangle. Trace over the square with a red pencil or crayon. Use your ruler to see if all the sides have the same length. Use a corner of your book to see if all the angles are right angles.

4. [A] Draw a right triangle. Color inside the two angles that are not right angles. Use a different color for each.

[B] Cut out the triangle and tear off the two corners you colored.

[C] Paste the corners over the right angle like this. Do your work carefully, and you will discover something interesting.

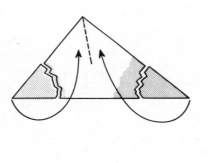

Study with the students the two figures at the top of page 206. Observe with them that a right triangle is a triangle that has one right angle and that a rectangle has four right angles and four sides.

Now, begin the exercises and follow along with the students carefully. You may choose to treat these exercises more as a class activity in which all the students work simultaneously on a given exercise, or you may permit the students to go ahead on their own as rapidly as they can.

In exercise 2c, note that we demonstrate the Pythagorean Theorem by showing that a right triangle with legs of three and four will have a hypotenuse of five. Of course, it need not be pointed out to the students that they are working with this theorem. If you choose to pursue this idea further, you might have the students draw a right angle on a very large sheet of paper and measure legs of 5 and 12 inches to find that they will have the third side of 13 inches.

Notice in exercise 3 that we refer to the use of a wide ruler or carefully folded paper for drawing a square. If the students use a standard ruler, they can still get a square, but it will perhaps be too small for easy recognition. For this reason, you might direct the students to take an 8½-by-11-inch piece of paper and fold it twice very carefully to get a wide marking object with parallel sides. If some other wide object which has parallel sides is available to the students, it would be preferable to have them use this since it is not easy for the students to draw a line along the side of folded paper.

In exercise 4, the students are given further opportunity to discover some of the relationships between angles of a triangle.

Objectives of Chapter 9

To maintain understanding of division concepts
To develop the division algorithm for one-digit divisors
To provide a variety of word-problem experiences
To provide experiences in estimation

The chief objective of this chapter is to present with complete understanding the long-division algorithm. The students are not given meaningless rules for division procedures; rather, they are led through a carefully planned, step-by-step procedure to the final algorithm. At each stage, the meaning of division is maintained for the students through sets of word problems which are designed to focus attention on the current phase of the procedure and to elucidate the ideas of division.

Multiples of ten and 100 are reviewed, and then the students are given experiences in working with various types of repeated subtraction to lead to the idea of subtraction in the division algorithm. Much emphasis again is placed on quotients associated with multiples of ten and 100.

Next the students are given an opportunity to work with inequalities. A large amount of material is devoted to inequalities and estimates in order to prepare students for making accurate estimates in the division algorithm.

With this background, the ideas associated with the division algorithm are then developed in a step-by-step procedure which leads students to the final algorithm for one-digit divisors. Once this has been accomplished, the idea of remainders is introduced at the end of the chapter.

Mathematics of Chapter 9

The only new mathematical concept introduced is that of remainders in division. The mathematical background developed in previous chapters makes it possible to approach the division algorithm by utilizing previously developed concepts.

We give below a brief discussion of remainders in division. Our basic definition for division (if $a \times b = c$ and $b \neq 0$, then $a = c \div b$) must be extended to allow for remainders in division. When considering remainders, one must recognize that the numbers a, b, and c may not be whole numbers; thus, the definition of division must now be considered in terms of rational numbers. However, at this stage of development only whole numbers will be considered for a, b, and c, and so we must extend our definition of division to include the idea of a remainder. We give the following definition of division which allows for remainders.

If a, b, c, and d are whole numbers such that $(a \times b) + d = c$ and $b \neq 0$ and $d < b$, we say that for $c \div b$, a is the quotient and d is the remainder.

Notice that in this definition if $d = 0$, we have the original definition. That is, we would have simply $a \times b = c$ or $c \div b = a$.

Of course, if we wanted to make a statement of equality with regard to $c \div b$, we would be involved with rational numbers. That is, we would have $c \div b = a + d/b$. An example of this would be $14 \div 3$.

$$\begin{array}{r} 4 \\ 3\overline{)14} \\ 12 \\ \hline 2 \end{array} \quad \longrightarrow \quad 14 \div 3 = 4 + \tfrac{2}{3} \text{ or } 4\tfrac{2}{3}$$

When we develop rational numbers in future work, we can return to this idea of remainders in division and show exactly how non-zero remainders give a quotient which is not a rational number.

You will note that we are considering two different ways of thinking about quotients. That is, sometimes we think of quotients only as whole numbers with a number called the remainder related to this quotient. At other times, we choose to think of the quotient as a rational number such that the quotient times the divisor equals the dividend in every case.

Teaching Chapter 9

Plan to cover this material in about six weeks. This chapter is quite long, and you are cautioned to maintain a fairly rapid pace in order that the students do not become bored. You will notice, from time to time, that several exciting activities have been incorporated to keep the students alert and thinking.

The gradual development and introduction of the division algorithm allows for a rather rapid coverage of this material.

In evaluating students' progress for this chapter, keep in mind that the over-all objective of the chapter is to teach the division algorithm with understanding. Your evaluation will involve two phases: determining whether the students can work with the division algorithm and determining whether they understand the concepts involved. Of course, as with other evaluations, your best means for determining the extent of students' comprehension is to make daily observations of their participation in and contribution to class discussions.

We do not expect all students to completely master the concepts of the division algorithm in this chapter. However, most of the students should gain some understanding of the processes involved and also remember some of the ideas involved in the division algorithm. Keep in mind that a more important objective than mastery of the algorithm is to develop in the students a good over-all understanding of the estimation and subtraction ideas associated with division.

Read and study the material at the top of the page. If the students need additional preparation activities, exhibit more examples on the chalkboard and discuss them one at a time. You may choose to show other similar multiplication equations and have the students write related division equations.

Following this discussion, have the students do the exercises. When they have finished, allow time for checking papers.

Chapter **9** **DIVIDING**

Quotients with zero endings

$7 \times 4 = 28$ $\longrightarrow$	$28 \div 4 = 7$
$70 \times 4 = 280$ $\longrightarrow$	$280 \div 4 = 70$
$700 \times 4 = 2800$ $\longrightarrow$	$2800 \div 4 = 700$

$6 \times 9 = 54$ $\longrightarrow$	$54 \div 6 = 9$
$6 \times 90 = 540$ $\longrightarrow$	$540 \div 6 = 90$
$6 \times 900 = 5400$ $\longrightarrow$	$5400 \div 6 = 900$

EXERCISES

1. Find the products.

[A] 5×9 *45* [F] 9×9 *81* [K] 5×7 *35* [P] 7×4 *28* [U] 9×7 *63*

[B] 6×3 *18* [G] 3×8 *24* [L] 6×8 *48* [Q] 8×5 *40* [V] 7×7 *49*

[C] 4×5 *20* [H] 8×8 *64* [M] 9×4 *36* [R] 6×6 *36* [W] 5×3 *15*

[D] 4×8 *32* [I] 4×6 *24* [N] 6×5 *30* [S] 5×5 *25* [X] 9×8 *72*

[E] 3×7 *21* [J] 3×9 *27* [O] 7×8 *56* [T] 7×6 *42* [Y] 7×9 *63*

2. Find the quotients.

[A] $49 \div 7$ *7* [F] $24 \div 6$ *4* [K] $35 \div 7$ *5* [P] $42 \div 6$ *7* [U] $45 \div 9$ *5*

[B] $28 \div 4$ *7* [G] $56 \div 8$ *7* [L] $21 \div 7$ *3* [Q] $63 \div 7$ *9* [V] $24 \div 8$ *3*

[C] $27 \div 9$ *3* [H] $72 \div 8$ *9* [M] $18 \div 3$ *6* [R] $36 \div 6$ *6* [W] $36 \div 4$ *9*

[D] $32 \div 8$ *4* [I] $15 \div 3$ *5* [N] $64 \div 8$ *8* [S] $48 \div 8$ *6* [X] $25 \div 5$ *5*

[E] $20 \div 5$ *4* [J] $40 \div 5$ *8* [O] $30 \div 5$ *6* [T] $81 \div 9$ *9* [Y] $63 \div 9$ *7*

208

Teaching Pages 208 and 209

● **PURPOSE**

To develop skill in finding quotients with zero endings

● **PREPARATION**

Exhibit on the chalkboard several multiplication equations that have factors with zero endings (30, 40, 80, 600, 900, etc). Now, associate a related division equation with each of these multiplication equations. For example, with $70 \times 4 = 280$, associate the division equation $280 \div 4 = 70$. Have the students make these associations.

As further preparation, review the meaning of division and provide the class with some oral drill on the basic division facts.

3. Find the products.

[A] 5 × 90 *450* [F] 70 × 6 *420* [K] 30 × 5 *150* [P] 50 × 7 *350* [U] 40 × 5 *200*
[B] 80 × 8 *640* [G] 6 × 50 *300* [L] 9 × 70 *630* [Q] 6 × 80 *480* [V] 4 × 80 *320*
[C] 7 × 80 *560* [H] 5 × 50 *250* [M] 60 × 6 *360* [R] 30 × 2 *60* [W] 30 × 7 *210*
[D] 70 × 7 *490* [I] 90 × 4 *360* [N] 8 × 50 *400* [S] 60 × 3 *180* [X] 6 × 40 *240*
[E] 3 × 30 *90* [J] 3 × 80 *240* [O] 30 × 9 *270* [T] 8 × 80 *640* [Y] 5 × 60 *300*

4. Find the quotients.

[A] 210 ÷ 7 *30*   [G] 360 ÷ 4 *90*   [M] 200 ÷ 5 *40*   [S] 630 ÷ 9 *70*
[B] 450 ÷ 5 *90*   [H] 360 ÷ 6 *60*   [N] 490 ÷ 7 *70*   [T] 350 ÷ 7 *50*
[C] 640 ÷ 8 *80*   [I] 400 ÷ 8 *50*   [O] 900 ÷ 3 *300*   [U] 480 ÷ 6 *80*
[D] 560 ÷ 7 *80*   [J] 270 ÷ 9 *30*   [P] 420 ÷ 6 *70*   [V] 60 ÷ 2 *30*
[E] 300 ÷ 6 *50*   [K] 180 ÷ 3 *60*   [Q] 240 ÷ 8 *30*   [W] 320 ÷ 4 *80*
[F] 250 ÷ 5 *50*   [L] 720 ÷ 9 *80*   [R] 150 ÷ 5 *30*   [X] 240 ÷ 6 *40*

5. Find the products. *(See answers at right.)*

[A] 9 × 400   [E] 8 × 800   [I] 3 × 700
[B] 300 × 8   [F] 700 × 8   [J] 400 × 8
[C] 5 × 700   [G] 7 × 700   [K] 4 × 500
[D] 3 × 900   [H] 300 × 3   [L] 800 × 8

> **Exercise for Experts**
> Now here's a simple rule
> That should prove quite
>   a friend.
> When you multiply by me,
> Put two zeros on the end.
> WHO AM I? *100*

6. Find the missing factors.

[A] 5 × ▦ = 350 *70*   [G] ▦ × 8 = 2400 *300*   [M] 9 × ▦ = 450 *50*
[B] ▦ × 7 = 490 *70*   [H] 7 × ▦ = 5600 *800*   [N] ▦ × 8 = 6400 *800*
[C] 4 × ▦ = 200 *50*   [I] ▦ × 8 = 3200 *400*   [O] 3 × ▦ = 2100 *700*
[D] ▦ × 6 = 420 *70*   [J] 5 × ▦ = 4500 *900*   [P] ▦ × 5 = 300 *60*
[E] 9 × ▦ = 630 *70*   [K] ▦ × 2 = 600 *300*   [Q] 6 × ▦ = 2400 *400*
[F] ▦ × 8 = 640 *80*   [L] 6 × ▦ = 1800 *300*   [R] ▦ × 6 = 360 *60*

7. Find the quotients.

[A] 400 ÷ 8 = ▦ *50*   [F] 3500 ÷ 5 = ▦ *700*   [K] 2500 ÷ 5 = ▦ *500*
[B] 180 ÷ 6 = ▦ *30*   [G] 2000 ÷ 4 = ▦ *500*   [L] 3600 ÷ 6 = ▦ *600*
[C] 450 ÷ 5 = ▦ *90*   [H] 6300 ÷ 9 = ▦ *700*   [M] 3000 ÷ 5 = ▦ *600*
[D] 560 ÷ 7 = ▦ *80*   [I] 900 ÷ 3 = ▦ *300*   [N] 640 ÷ 8 = ▦ *80*
[E] 630 ÷ 7 = ▦ *90*   [J] 1800 ÷ 3 = ▦ *600*   [O] 4800 ÷ 8 = ▦ *600*

DIRECTIONS PAGE 209

Have the students do the exercises. The riddle may be used as enrichment for more able students or for all the students. Some of the students may have difficulty in arriving at the correct answer. However, most will understand the riddle when the correct answer is discussed. Be sure that all students who attempt the riddle have time to think about it before the correct answer is given.

Supplementary exercises, Set 48 (page 349) may be assigned as necessary beyond this page.

Answers, exercise 5, page 209

[A] 3600	[E] 6400	[I] 2100
[B] 2400	[F] 5600	[J] 3200
[C] 3500	[G] 4900	[K] 2000
[D] 2700	[H] 900	[L] 6400

Explain to the students that this table gives the approximate top speed for each item listed. Give the students an opportunity to discuss the table and talk about the various items with regard to the speed at which they travel.

About how fast they can go

Pike	Runner	Sailboat
10 miles per hour	20 miles per hour	30 miles per hour

Race horse	Deer	Homing pigeon	Cheetah
40 miles per hour	50 miles per hour	60 miles per hour	70 miles per hour

Monorail train	Vulture	Pitched baseball	Arrow
80 miles per hour	90 miles per hour	100 miles per hour	200 miles per hour

Racing car	Jet plane	Bullet	Satellite
400 miles per hour	600 miles per hour	1400 miles per hour	17,000 miles per hour

Teaching Pages 210 and 211

- **PURPOSE**

To provide word-problem experiences with products having a zero ending

- **PREPARATION**

Conduct a short oral practice session involving the basic multiplication facts. Follow this by providing the class with additional practice experiences involving finding products with factors such as 30, 70, 90, 400, and 600. If necessary, point out, or have the students point out, the relationship between products such as 30×6 and 3×6.

EXERCISES

1. A helicopter can fly about 3 times as fast as a homing pigeon. How fast can the helicopter fly? *180 mph*

2. Racing bikes can be made to go 2 times as fast as a deer. How fast can racing bikes go? *100 mph*

3. A jet speed boat goes 9 times as fast as a sailboat. How fast does a jet speed boat go? *270 mph*

4. What object can go 10 times as fast as a pike can swim? *pitched baseball*

5. A racing car runs for 9 hours. A jet flies for 7 hours. Which goes farther? How much farther? *a jet 600 miles*

6. A propeller plane can fly 5 times as fast as a vulture. How fast can a propeller plane fly? *450 mph*

7. A golden eagle can fly about 4 times as fast as a sailboat can sail. How fast can the golden eagle fly? *120 mph*

8. A bullet goes how many times as fast as an arrow? *7 times*

9. If a cheetah could run 6 times as fast as usual, could it catch a racing car? How fast would the cheetah be running? *420 mph*

10. A man flies in a jet from Coast City to East City. It takes him 5 hours for the trip. About how far is it from Coast City to East City? *3000 miles*

11. A boy rode for 7 hours on a monorail train. How far did he ride? *560 miles*

12. A homing pigeon was taken 300 miles from home. About how many hours would it take the pigeon to fly back home? *5 hours*

13. A racing car can go how many times as fast as a deer? *8 times*

14. How much faster than its usual rate would a vulture have to fly to pass a jet plane? *7 times as fast*

15. A satellite circles the earth for 5 hours. How far does it travel? *85,000 miles*

16. A turtle would have to go 10 times faster than usual to go 1 mile in an hour. How many hours would it take a turtle to go 10 miles? *100 hours*

Have the students work the exercises. Notice that exercises 14 through 16 are designed primarily for the more able students. When the students have finished, discuss each exercise. Keep in mind that such lessons can often be used to generate interest in topics other than those specifically of an arithmetic nature.

The following explanations should help the students understand the answer to exercise 16.

[A] Since the turtle would have to go 10 times faster than usual to go one mile per hour, the turtle really goes *one mile* in 10 hours. Therefore, it takes the turtle 10 × 10, or 100 hours to go 10 miles.

[B] *If* the turtle *could* go 10 times as fast, it could go 10 miles in 10 hours. Since it cannot go 10 times as fast, the fact is that it must take it 10 times as long, or 10 × 10 hours to go 10 miles.

Instruct the students to work the exercises. When they have finished, discuss each exercise and encourage the students to verbalize on the ideas involved. If time permits, give the students an opportunity to make up some word problems of their own in which division is involved.

At camp

1. 8 girls slept in each cabin. How many cabins were used by the 56 girls from Pine City? *7*

2. 54 boys went to Camp Eagle in 6 station wagons. There were the same number of boys in each station wagon. How many went in each station wagon? *9*

3. There were 270 girls at Camp Sunrise. There were 9 groups of the same size. How many were in each group? *30*

4. One week 280 boys came to Camp Eagle. They lived in tents. 4 boys slept in each tent. How many tents were used? *70*

5. 320 girls ate meals in a large cabin. 8 girls sat at each table. How many tables were there? *40*

6. 48 campers planned to take a boating trip from Camp Eagle to Camp Sunrise. If each boat could hold 6, how many boats were needed? *8*

7. On July 4, a group leader at Camp Eagle bought a bottle of soda for each camper. There were 540 at the campfire party. How many cartons of 6 bottles did he buy? *90*

8. During the summer 810 campers visited an Indian museum. The guide took them through the museum in groups of 9. How many trips did he make in all? *90*

Teaching Pages 212 and 213

● **PURPOSE**

To provide word problems for division

● **PREPARATION**

Review with the students the material covered thus far in the chapter. Stress in the review the meaning of division and exercises involving estimation. Following this, make up several word problems involving division concepts. Then have the students make up some word problems which involve division.

Short stories

1. 300 baseball cards.
5 on each page.
How many pages? *60*

2. 320 airplane cards.
4 cards on each page.
How many pages? *80*

3. 160 marching-band players.
8 rows. Same number in each
row. How many in each row? *20*

4. To the zoo in buses.
210 students.
7 buses.
Same number on each bus.
How many students on each bus? *30*

5. 480 bottles of soda.
6 in each carton.
How many cartons? *80*

6. 360 boys.
9 boys on each team.
How many teams? *40*

7. Square dancing. 160 girls.
8 girls make a square.
How many squares? *20*

8. 400 trading stamps.
8 pages.
Pasted same number on each
page. How many stamps
on each page? *50*

9. 240 photographs.
6 on each page.
How many pages? *40*

10. 480 tickets. 8 bundles
of the same size.
How many in each bundle? *60*

11. 560 trading stamps.
8 stamps in a row.
How many rows? *70*

12. 630 miles in 9 hours. Same
number of miles each hour.
How many miles each hour? *70*

13. 540 pieces of candy.
6 pieces in each bag.
How many bags? *90*

14. Use 8 gallons of gasoline
to go 320 miles.
How many miles traveled
on each gallon? *40*

15. 720 pennies.
Same number in each of 8 cans.
How many in each can? *90*

★16. Light bulb.
Blinks 9 times each minute.
729 blinks. How many
minutes have passed? *81*

Have the students work the exercises. When they have finished, allow time for discussion. Although exercise 16 is designed primarily for the more able students, you may choose to use exercise 16 as a class-discussion exercise rather than an enrichment exercise. If you do, begin by having the students attempt to estimate the number of minutes that have passed while the light blinks 729 times. Following these estimations, have some of the students attempt to find exactly how many minutes this number of blinks would take.

Discuss the illustration at the top of the page. Point out that the boy pictured hears 350, uses the rule "divide by 7," and says 50. Relate this to the function-machine picture which has an input of 350, a rule of divide by 7, and an output of 50.

Following this discussion, have the students work the exercises. If more instruction is needed, work through exercise 1 with the class.

Notice that exercise 6 is designed primarily for the more able students.

Discuss each exercise when the students have completed the page. Give the students every opportunity possible to verbalize their reasoning in arriving at certain answers.

The function game

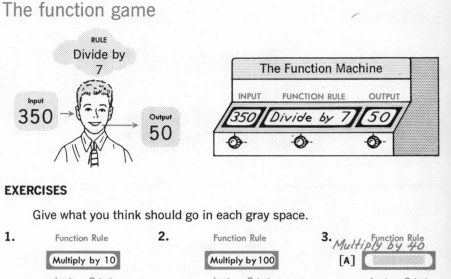

RULE
Divide by 7

Input 350

Output 50

The Function Machine

INPUT	FUNCTION RULE	OUTPUT
350	Divide by 7	50

EXERCISES

Give what you think should go in each gray space.

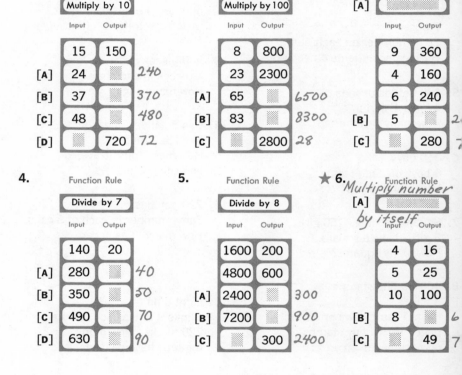

1. Function Rule — Multiply by 10

	Input	Output	
	15	150	
[A]	24	▦	240
[B]	37	▦	370
[C]	48	▦	480
[D]	▦	720	72

2. Function Rule — Multiply by 100

	Input	Output	
	8	800	
	23	2300	
[A]	65	▦	6500
[B]	83	▦	8300
[C]	▦	2800	28

3. Function Rule — *Multiply by 40* [A]

	Input	Output	
	9	360	
	4	160	
	6	240	
[B]	5	▦	2
[C]	▦	280	7

4. Function Rule — Divide by 7

	Input	Output	
	140	20	
[A]	280	▦	40
[B]	350	▦	50
[C]	490	▦	70
[D]	630	▦	90

5. Function Rule — Divide by 8

	Input	Output	
	1600	200	
	4800	600	
[A]	2400	▦	300
[B]	7200	▦	900
[C]	▦	300	2400

★ 6. Function Rule — *Multiply number by itself* [A]

	Input	Output	
	4	16	
	5	25	
	10	100	
[B]	8	▦	6
[C]	▦	49	7

Teaching Pages 214 and 215

- **PURPOSE**

  To provide a stimulating activity involving some concepts of division

  To provide more practice in working with quotients which have zero endings

- **PREPARATION**

  Review the idea of the function machine by playing the function game with the class. Think of a rule, have the students give you a number, and then you give them a number according to the rule that you are using. For example, you might use the rule "multiply by three." If a

This function machine uses the output number as a new input number and keeps operating. A counter tells how many times the rule is used.

Here is a record of the machine's operations.

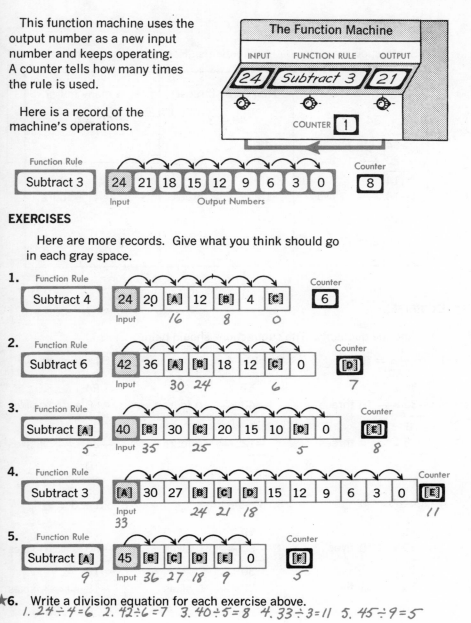

EXERCISES

Here are more records. Give what you think should go in each gray space.

6. Write a division equation for each exercise above.
1. $24 \div 4 = 6$ 2. $42 \div 6 = 7$ 3. $40 \div 5 = 8$ 4. $33 \div 3 = 11$ 5. $45 \div 9 = 5$

As you discuss the function machine at the top of the page, call attention to the new feature on the machine, the counter. Explain to the students that, as before, they are to think about putting the number 24 into the machine, applying the rule "subtract 3," and getting an output of 21. However, this time they are going to take the number 21 and put it back into the machine on the input side, as indicated by the arrow at the bottom of the machine. Tell the students that the counter tells them how many times the rule is used. In this way we get the students to think about the number of times that three must be subtracted to get from 24 to zero.

Observe now the example under the machine with the rule "subtract 3." Notice with the students that the counter registers eight subtractions. That is, to get from 24 to zero, they must subtract three 8 times. This tells, of course, that there are 8 threes in 24 or that $24 \div 3 = 8$.

Now have the students work the first exercise by giving the correct numbers for boxes A, B, and C. Notice with them that the number four was subtracted 6 times to get from 24 to zero; therefore, they see that there are 6 fours in 24 or that $24 \div 4 = 6$.

Have the students complete the exercises. Allow time for the checking of papers.

student gives you the number six, you give the number 18. Play this game using addition, subtraction, or multiplication, and then a rule involving division. You are cautioned to see that the rule will work for all input numbers.

Read and study the material at the top of the page with the class. Give them an opportunity to discuss each division shown in the boxes. Following this discussion, have the students work the exercises.

Reasoning in division

Subtraction can help you find quotients. Here are some examples.

How many twos?	How many threes?	How many fours?
$34 \div 2$	$48 \div 3$	$60 \div 4$
34	48	60
$-20 \leftarrow$ 10 twos	$-30 \leftarrow$ 10 threes	$-40 \leftarrow$ 10 fours
14	18	20
$-14 \leftarrow$ 7 twos	$-18 \leftarrow$ 6 threes	$-20 \leftarrow$ 5 fours
0	0	0
$34 \div 2 = 17$	$48 \div 3 = 16$	$60 \div 4 = 15$

EXERCISES

Find the quotients. The subtractions should help.

1. $36 \div 3 = $ ▥ *12*

36
$-30 \leftarrow$ 10 threes
6
$-6 \leftarrow$ 2 threes
0

2. $52 \div 4 = $ ▥ *13*

52
$-40 \leftarrow$ 10 fours
12
$-12 \leftarrow$ 3 fours
0

3. $84 \div 6 = $ ▥ *14*

84
$-60 \leftarrow$ 10 sixes
24
$-24 \leftarrow$ 4 sixes
0

4. $65 \div 5 = $ ▥ *13*

65
$-50 \leftarrow$ 10 fives
15
$-15 \leftarrow$ 3 fives
0

5. $90 \div 6 = $ ▥ *15*

90
$-60 \leftarrow$ 10 sixes
30
$-30 \leftarrow$ 5 sixes
0

6. $78 \div 6 = $ ▥ *13*

78
$-60 \leftarrow$ 10 sixes
18
$-18 \leftarrow$ 3 sixes
0

Teaching Pages 216 and 217

● **PURPOSE**

To continue stressing the subtraction of a multiple of one given number from another

To provide activities which lead toward the ideas embodied in the division algorithm

● **PREPARATION**

Provide preparation exercises similar to those in the boxes on pages 216 and 217. Give the students an opportunity to participate in the discussion of each exercise. Begin the lesson by showing the students how many of a given number have been subtracted (as is done in the

Study these examples.

How many threes?	How many fours?	How many sixes?
78 ÷ 3	**136 ÷ 4**	**390 ÷ 6**
78	**136**	**390**
−60 ⟵ 20 threes	−120 ⟵ 30 fours	−360 ⟵ 60 sixes
18	16	30
−18 ⟵ 6 threes	−16 ⟵ 4 fours	−30 ⟵ 5 sixes
0	0	0
78 ÷ 3 = 26	136 ÷ 4 = 34	390 ÷ 6 = 65

EXERCISES

1. Find the quotients. The subtractions should help.

[A] 92 ÷ 4 = ▥ *23*   [B] 68 ÷ 2 = ▥ *34*   [C] 75 ÷ 3 = ▥ *25*

92	68	75
−80 ⟵ 20 fours	−60 ⟵ 30 twos	−60 ⟵ 20 threes
12	8	15
−12 ⟵ 3 fours	−8 ⟵ 4 twos	−15 ⟵ 5 threes
0	0	0

2. Find the quotients. The subtractions should help.

[A] 78 ÷ 2 *39*   [B] 93 ÷ 3 *31*   [C] 115 ÷ 5 *23*   [D] 132 ÷ 6 *22*   [E] 154 ÷ 7 *22*

78	93	115	132	154
−60	−90	−100	−120	−140
18	3	15	12	14
−18	−3	−15	−12	−14
0	0	0	0	0

[F] 184 ÷ 8 *23*   [G] 182 ÷ 7 *26*   [H] 148 ÷ 4 *37*   [I] 185 ÷ 5 *37*   [J] 177 ÷ 3 *59*

184	182	148	185	177
−160	−140	−120	−150	−150
24	42	28	35	27
−24	−42	−28	−35	−27
0	0	0	0	0

Again have the class study the boxed material at the top of the page and participate in a discussion of the way the quotient is found once they see how many of a given number have been subtracted. Following this, have the students do exercise 1.

Although it is starred, you may choose to have all of the students try parts of exercise 2.

When the students have completed the assigned exercises, allow time for discussion. You may also choose to treat exercise 2 as a class discussion and follow-up to this lesson. Certainly the entire class can benefit from a discussion of exercise 2.

boxed examples) so that they can easily solve the division equation. Continue this until the students reach the stage where they will be able to do problems such as those in exercise 2 on page 217.

Following this, you can, if you choose, exhibit several problems similar to exercise 2 and give the students an opportunity to decide how many of a given number have been subtracted in order to find the quotient.

PAGE 218 DIRECTIONS

Have the class do the exercises. Note that exercise 4 is designed primarily for the more able students. Allow time for checking papers and a discussion of any exercises which may have caused difficulty.

During the discussion period for this page, focus particular attention on exercise 2. Giving students a thorough review in this type of exercise will further enhance their chances for success in working with the division algorithm.

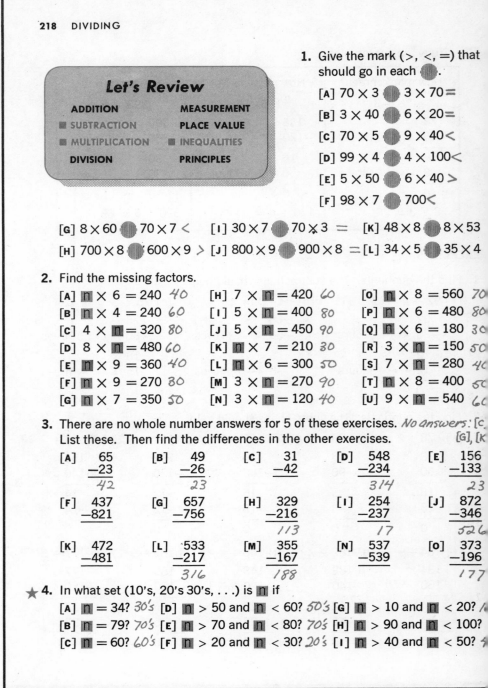

218 DIVIDING

Let's Review

ADDITION   MEASUREMENT
■ SUBTRACTION   PLACE VALUE
■ MULTIPLICATION   ■ INEQUALITIES
DIVISION   PRINCIPLES

1. Give the mark (>, <, =) that should go in each ⬤.
   [A] 70 × 3 ⬤ 3 × 70 =
   [B] 3 × 40 ⬤ 6 × 20 =
   [C] 70 × 5 ⬤ 9 × 40 <
   [D] 99 × 4 ⬤ 4 × 100 <
   [E] 5 × 50 ⬤ 6 × 40 >
   [F] 98 × 7 ⬤ 700 <

   [G] 8 × 60 ⬤ 70 × 7 <   [I] 30 × 7 ⬤ 70 × 3 =   [K] 48 × 8 ⬤ 8 × 53
   [H] 700 × 8 ⬤ 600 × 9 > [J] 800 × 9 ⬤ 900 × 8 = [L] 34 × 5 ⬤ 35 × 4

2. Find the missing factors.
   [A] ⬛ × 6 = 240 40   [H] 7 × ⬛ = 420 60   [O] ⬛ × 8 = 560 70
   [B] ⬛ × 4 = 240 60   [I] 5 × ⬛ = 400 80   [P] ⬛ × 6 = 480 80
   [C] 4 × ⬛ = 320 80   [J] 5 × ⬛ = 450 90   [Q] ⬛ × 6 = 180 30
   [D] 8 × ⬛ = 480 60   [K] ⬛ × 7 = 210 30   [R] 3 × ⬛ = 150 50
   [E] ⬛ × 9 = 360 40   [L] ⬛ × 6 = 300 50   [S] 7 × ⬛ = 280 40
   [F] ⬛ × 9 = 270 30   [M] 3 × ⬛ = 270 90   [T] ⬛ × 8 = 400 50
   [G] ⬛ × 7 = 350 50   [N] 3 × ⬛ = 120 40   [U] 9 × ⬛ = 540 60

3. There are no whole number answers for 5 of these exercises. *No answers:* [C,
   List these. Then find the differences in the other exercises. [G], [k

   [A] 65   [B] 49   [C] 31   [D] 548   [E] 156
       −23   −26   −42   −234   −133
        42   23   314   23
   [F] 437   [G] 657   [H] 329   [I] 254   [J] 872
       −821   −756   −216   −237   −346
                                 113   17   526
   [K] 472   [L] 533   [M] 355   [N] 537   [O] 373
       −481   −217   −167   −539   −196
                     316   188   177

★ 4. In what set (10's, 20's 30's, . . .) is ⬛ if
   [A] ⬛ = 34? 30's [D] ⬛ > 50 and ⬛ < 60? 50's [G] ⬛ > 10 and ⬛ < 20?
   [B] ⬛ = 79? 70's [E] ⬛ > 70 and ⬛ < 80? 70's [H] ⬛ > 90 and ⬛ < 100?
   [C] ⬛ = 60? 60's [F] ⬛ > 20 and ⬛ < 30? 20's [I] ⬛ > 40 and ⬛ < 50?

Teaching Pages 218 and 219

● **PURPOSE**

To provide a review of the material covered thus far in the text

To provide review material which is directly related to ideas to be developed in the remainder of the chapter

● **PREPARATION**

Review any topics with which the students have had difficulty in previous parts of the text. If time permits, use the remaining part of the preparation period to give students an opportunity to create word problems of their own. Allow them to use any operations they please in

Checkers

1.	Black box: 34 Blue box: 34		How many checkers? 68	
2.	Checkerboard: 8 rows 8 squares in each		How many squares? 64	
3.	32 checkers	8 8 ?	How many boxes? 4	
4.	36 checkers	? ? ? ?	How many in each box? 9	
5.	63 checkers	? ? ? ? ? ? ? ? ?	How many in each box? 7	
6.	63 checkers	7 7 ?	How many boxes? 9	
7.	56 checkers	? ? ? ? ? ? ?	How many in each box? 8	
8.	72 checkers	9 9 ?	How many boxes? 8	
9.	10 blue checkers 6 black checkers		How many checkers must you move from the blue pile to the black pile to make the piles even? 2	
10.	To start the game: 12 blue checkers 12 black checkers		How many empty squares? 40	
11.	32 blue squares. 32 black squares. 2 checkers on the blue squares and 3 on the black.		How many checkers in all? 160	

creating these problems. Give other students the chance to try to decide what operation is involved in a given student's word problem. Focus more attention upon the operation involved in a given word problem than upon the actual computation.

Enter into a discussion of this page in the spirit of playing a game to find out various things about the checkers. Of course, no rules are given, and the students should be encouraged to think about the ideas in each problem for themselves. Some of the less able students may need your guidance as they work this page.

Notice that exercises 10 and 11 are designed primarily for the more able students. However, once these students have had an opportunity to work on them, you may decide to discuss the exercises with the entire class.

Study the material in the first box with the students. Observe with them that this set presentation asks for the number of fours in 48. This can be broken into $(40 \div 4) + (8 \div 4)$; that is, we can think of division in parts in much the same way as we thought of multiplication in parts.

Do not discuss with the students the fact that only the number that is being divided can be broken; the divisor cannot be broken. This should cause no particular problem with the students at this time.

Observe the relationship shown in the second box between the repeated subtraction and the horizontal notation. Have the students work the exercises. Allow time for more discussion when they have completed the page.

Division and addition

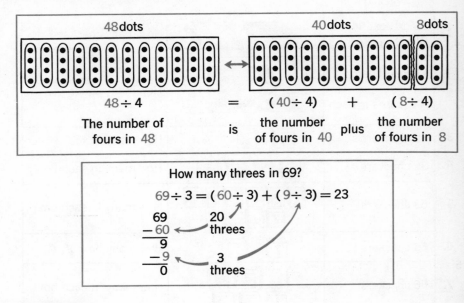

EXERCISES

1. Give the missing numbers.

[A] $126 \div 3 = (120 \div 3) + (\blacksquare \div 3)$ 6   [c] $84 \div 3 = (\blacksquare \div 3) + (24 \div 3)$ 6

[B] $155 \div 5 = (\blacksquare \div 5) + (5 \div 5)$ 150   [D] $\blacksquare \div 5 = (100 \div 5) + (25 \div 5)$ 12

2. Give the missing numbers.

[A] $(160 + 8) \div 4 = (160 \div 4) + (\blacksquare \div 4)$ 8

[B] $(210 + 9) \div 3 = (210 \div 3) + (\blacksquare \div 3)$ 9

[c] $(250 + 15) \div 5 = (\blacksquare \div 5) + (15 \div 5)$ 250

[D] $(180 + 12) \div 6 = (\blacksquare \div 6) + (12 \div 6)$ 180

[E] $(280 + 21) \div 7 = (280 \div 7) + (\blacksquare \div 7)$ 21

[F] $(320 + 16) \div 8 = (\blacksquare \div 8) + (16 \div 8)$ 320

[G] $(450 + 27) \div 9 = (450 \div 9) + (\blacksquare \div 9)$ 27

[H] $(\blacksquare + 50) \div 10 = (400 \div 10) + (50 \div 10)$ 400

3. Find the quotients. Exercise 2 should help.

[A] $168 \div 4$ 42   [c] $265 \div 5$ 53   [E] $301 \div 7$ 43   [G] $477 \div 9$ 53

[B] $219 \div 3$ 73   [D] $192 \div 6$ 32   [F] $336 \div 8$ 42   [H] $450 \div 10$ 45

Teaching Pages 220 and 221

- **PURPOSE**

  To provide another element of reasoning in finding quotients

  To focus attention on the relation of the multiplication-addition principle to division

  To introduce a short cut for estimating quotients

  To introduce a new notation for division

- **PREPARATION**

  Present several exercises similar to those found in exercise 4 on page 221. Ask the students to find the correct quotients, and when they have finished, have them discuss how they found these quotients. Keep in mind that an important part of this activity is to have students verbalize their reasoning in arriving at certain answers.

  Exhibit the following on the chalkboard.

  $$60 \div 6 =$$
  $$120 \div 6 =$$
  $$180 \div 6 =$$
  $$240 \div 6 =$$
  $$300 \div 6 =$$
  $$360 \div 6 =$$
  $$420 \div 6 =$$
  $$480 \div 6 =$$
  $$540 \div 6 =$$

Study this example. $(160 + 12) \div 4 = 40 + 3$ $4\overline{)160 + 12} \rightarrow 40 + 3$

4. Find the quotients. Work from left to right.

[A] $3\overline{)30}$ = 10 $3\overline{)6}$ = 2 $3\overline{)30 + 6}$ = 10+2 $3\overline{)36}$ = 12

[B] $3\overline{)60}$ = 20 $3\overline{)9}$ = 3 $3\overline{)60 + 9}$ = 20+3 $3\overline{)69}$ = 23

[C] $3\overline{)120}$ = 40 $3\overline{)9}$ = 3 $3\overline{)120 + 9}$ = 40+3 $3\overline{)129}$ = 43

[D] $4\overline{)200}$ = 50 $4\overline{)8}$ = 2 $4\overline{)200 + 8}$ = 50+2 $4\overline{)208}$ = 52

Study this example.

Since $4\overline{)240 + 12}$ = 60 + 3, we know that $4\overline{)252}$ = 63.

5. Find the quotients. The table on the right should help you.

[A] $6\overline{)324}$ = 54   [B] $6\overline{)198}$ = 33   [C] $4\overline{)188}$ = 47

[D] $6\overline{)468}$ = 78   [E] $4\overline{)92}$ = 23   [F] $4\overline{)288}$ = 72

6. Check each quotient in exercise 5 by multiplying.

7. Find the quotients.

[A] Since $120 \div 4 = 30$, we know that $124 \div 4 = \blacksquare$. 31
[B] Since $60 \div 6 = 10$, we know that $66 \div 6 = \blacksquare$. 11
[C] Since $100 \div 5 = 20$, we know that $110 \div 5 = \blacksquare$. 22
[D] Since $160 \div 4 = 40$, we know that $168 \div 4 = \blacksquare$. 42
[E] Since $140 \div 7 = 20$, we know that $161 \div 7 = \blacksquare$. 23
[F] Since $240 \div 8 = 30$, we know that $264 \div 8 = \blacksquare$. 33
[G] Since $300 \div 6 = 50$, we know that $336 \div 6 = \blacksquare$. 56
[H] Since $250 \div 5 = 50$, we know that $265 \div 5 = \blacksquare$. 53
[I] Since $180 \div 3 = 60$, we know that $192 \div 3 = \blacksquare$. 64
[J] Since $360 \div 4 = 90$, we know that $376 \div 4 = \blacksquare$. 94

Table on the right:

[E] $4\overline{)80 + 12}$ = 20 + 3

[C] $4\overline{)160 + 28}$ = 40 + 7

[F] $4\overline{)280 + 8}$ = 70 + 2

[B] $6\overline{)180 + 18}$ = 30 + 3

[A] $6\overline{)300 + 24}$ = 50 + 4

[D] $6\overline{)420 + 48}$ = 70 + 8

Notice in particular that exercise 4 is designed sequentially. For example, in exercise 4A, the students first find the quotient $30 \div 3$, then $6 \div 3$, then $(30 + 6) \div 3$, and finally $36 \div 3$.

Before having the students begin exercise 5, discuss the example with the class. Now have the students relate exercise 5A to some example in the table in order to find the solution. When they have done this, be sure that everyone sees that the example,

$$6\overline{)300 + 24} = 50 + 4$$

gives them the clue for the answer to exercise 5A.

Have the students try exercise 5B. Discuss the relationship between the example in the table and the exercise. Instruct the students to complete the exercises on the page.

Discuss the answers when the students have completed the exercises.

Have the students assist you in finding these quotients. Following this, select several other division exercises involving a divisor of six (for example, $252 \div 6$, $426 \div 6$, $144 \div 6$). Have the students decide between what two multiples of ten the quotient lies. For example, they should find that the quotient of $252 \div 6$ is between 40 and 50 because they know that $240 \div 6 = 40$ and $300 \div 6 = 50$ and that 252 is between 240 and 300.

After the students thoroughly understand this, exhibit on the chalkboard a division equation such as $24 \div 6 = 4$. Show the corresponding form using the notation indicated.

Use arrows to establish the relationship between the equation and the new notation. Give the students an opportunity to practice writing this new notation for several other division equations.

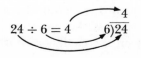

$$24 \div 6 = 4 \qquad 6\overline{)24} = 4$$

Observe with the students the pairs at the top of the page. If your preparation activities covered exercises of this type, you should have the students proceed immediately to the exercises.

When the students have finished, put several problems from each exercise on the chalkboard and discuss them with regard to the reasons for choosing a certain pair.

Estimating the quotient

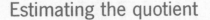

Pairs:	1	2	3	4	5	6	7	8	9
	10	20	30	40	50	60	70	80	90
	20	30	40	50	60	70	80	90	100

EXERCISES

1. Give the pair that should go in each gray space.

[A] ▨×3=30
▨×3=60
(Answer: Pair 1)

[C] ▨×7=280
▨×7=350
pair 4

[E] ▨×8=400
▨×8=480
pair 5

[G] ▨×9=720
▨×9=810
pair 8

[B] ▨×6=180
▨×6=240
pair 3

[D] ▨×9=540
▨×9=630
pair 6

[F] ▨×5=450
▨×5=500
pair 9

[H] ▨×8=560
▨×8=640
pair 7

2. Give the pair that should go in each gray space.

[A] ▨×4<116
▨×4>116
pair 2

[D] ▨×4<192
▨×4>192
pair 4

[G] ▨×6<504
▨×6>504
pair 8

[J] ▨×5<475
▨×5>475
pair 9

[B] ▨×3<36
▨×3>36
pair 1

[E] ▨×7<343
▨×7>343
pair 4

[H] ▨×9<801
▨×9>801
pair 8

[K] ▨×8<609
▨×8>609
pair 7

[C] ▨×5<360
▨×5>360
pair 7

[F] ▨×6<210
▨×6>210
pair 3

[I] ▨×8<416
▨×8>416
pair 5

[L] ▨×9<547
▨×9>547
pair 6

3. Give the pair that should go in each gray space.

[A] 116÷4 > ▨
116÷4 < ▨
pair 2

[D] 192÷4 > ▨
192÷4 < ▨
pair 4

[G] 547÷9 > ▨
547÷9 < ▨
pair 6

[J] 423÷9 > ▨
423÷9 < ▨
pair 4

[B] 36÷3 > ▨
36÷3 < ▨
pair 1

[E] 360÷5 > ▨
360÷5 < ▨
pair 7

[H] 801÷9 > ▨
801÷9 < ▨
pair 8

[K] 474÷6 > ▨
474÷6 < ▨
pair 7

[C] 210÷6 > ▨
210÷6 < ▨
pair 3

[F] 416÷8 > ▨
416÷8 < ▨
pair 5

[I] 632÷8 > ▨
632÷8 < ▨
pair 7

[L] 855÷9 > ▨
855÷9 < ▨
pair 9

4. Study the example. Then find the missing numbers.
Example: 116 ÷ 4 is between 20 and 30.

[A] 210 ÷ 6 is between ▨ and ▨.
30 40

[C] 663 ÷ 7 is between ▨ and ▨.
90 100

[B] 162 ÷ 3 is between ▨ and ▨.
50 60

[D] 474 ÷ 6 is between ▨ and ▨.
70 80

Teaching Pages 222 and 223

● **PURPOSE**

To provide more experiences leading toward accurate estimation of quotients

● **PREPARATION**

Exhibit on the chalkboard ordered pairs like those at the top of page 222. Select problems from exercises 1, 2, and 3 and exhibit them on the chalkboard. Ask the students to decide which pair goes in the space. Discuss each answer with the students. For example, if you select exercise 1F to exhibit on the chalkboard, the students should

DISCUSSION EXERCISES
(See answers at right.)

1. $30 \times 4 = 120$

$132 \div 4 = $ ▥

$40 \times 4 = 160$

The quotient is in
the 30's set.
Explain why.

2. $50 \times 7 = 350$

$371 \div 7 = $ ▥

$60 \times 7 = 420$

The quotient is in
the 50's set.
Explain why.

10's set =	{10, 11, 12, 13, 14, 15, 16, 17, 18, 19}
20's set =	{20, 21, 22, 23, 24, 25, 26, 27, 28, 29}
30's set =	{30, 31, 32, 33, 34, 35, 36, 37, 38, 39}
40's set =	{40, 41, 42, 43, 44, 45, 46, 47, 48, 49}
50's set =	{50, 51, 52, 53, 54, 55, 56, 57, 58, 59}
60's set =	{60, 61, 62, 63, 64, 65, 66, 67, 68, 69}
70's set =	{70, 71, 72, 73, 74, 75, 76, 77, 78, 79}
80's set =	{80, 81, 82, 83, 84, 85, 86, 87, 88, 89}
90's set =	{90, 91, 92, 93, 94, 95, 96, 97, 98, 99}

EXERCISES

1. Complete each sentence.

[A] Since $\begin{array}{l} 30 \times 4 = 120 \\ 40 \times 4 = 160 \end{array}$ we know that $128 \div 4$ is in the ▥ set.

(Answer: 30's)

[B] Since $\begin{array}{l} 40 \times 3 = 120 \\ 50 \times 3 = 150 \end{array}$ we know that $129 \div 3$ is in the ▥ set.

40's

[C] Since $\begin{array}{l} 60 \times 2 = 120 \\ 70 \times 2 = 140 \end{array}$ we know that $134 \div 2$ is in the ▥ set.

60's

[D] Since $\begin{array}{l} 20 \times 5 = 100 \\ 30 \times 5 = 150 \end{array}$ we know that $120 \div 5$ is in the ▥ set.

20's

2. In what set (10's, 20's, . . . 90's) is the quotient?

[A] $124 \div 4 = $ ▥ *30's*	[F] $180 \div 5 = $ ▥ *30's*	[K] $432 \div 6 = $ ▥ *70's*
[B] $132 \div 2 = $ ▥ *60's*	[G] $192 \div 3 = $ ▥ *60's*	[L] $76 \div 4 = $ ▥ *10's*
[C] $126 \div 3 = $ ▥ *40's*	[H] $94 \div 2 = $ ▥ *40's*	[M] $119 \div 7 = $ ▥ *10's*
[D] $348 \div 4 = $ ▥ *80's*	[I] $192 \div 8 = $ ▥ *20's*	[N] $891 \div 9 = $ ▥ *90's*
[E] $132 \div 3 = $ ▥ *40's*	[J] $285 \div 3 = $ ▥ *90's*	[O] $184 \div 8 = $ ▥ *20's*

Point out to the class that in the table at the top of the page the numbers from ten to 99 have been divided into nine sets. Have the students read the names of these sets. Exhibit the discussion exercises on the chalkboard, and have the students explain why the quotient is in the thirties set for exercise 1 and in the fifties set for exercise 2.

Following this, have the students explain why the quotient in exercise 1A is in the thirties set. Now have the students do exercises 1B and C and then discuss the selections made by the students. Instruct the students to complete the page. When they have finished, discuss several exercises so the students can verbalize their thinking on each exercise.

Answers, discussion exercises, page 223

1. Since $30 \times 4 < 132$ and $40 \times 4 > 132$, the quotient (33) is between 30 and 40, or in the 30's set.
2. Since $50 \times 7 < 371$ and $60 \times 7 > 371$, the quotient (53) is between 50 and 60, or in the 50's set.

observe that they selected pair 9 because 5×90 is 450 and 5×100 is 500. For exercise 2C the students should observe that the correct answer is pair 7 because $70 \times 5 = 350$, which is less than 360, and 80×5 is 400, which is greater than 360.

Conduct similar discussions for the problems that you select from exercise 3.

Study with the class the material at the top of the page. Have the students do the exercises. When they have finished, present several exercises on the chalkboard and discuss each.

Finding the tens digit for quotients

Think about this exercise.

We want to find the tens digit.

$$6\overline{)192}$$

Since $30 \times 6 = 180$, let's try 3.

Now check by multiplication.

$$\begin{array}{r} 32 \\ \times 6 \\ \hline 192 \end{array} \longrightarrow 6\overline{)192}$$

EXERCISES

Find the quotients. Check your answers by multiplication.

1. 4)84

2. 3)96

3. 5)105

4. 6)126

5. 2)128

6. 7)154

7. 4)136

8. 5)165

9. 3)102

10. 6)138

11. 8)344

12. 2)156

13. 7)308

14. 5)375

15. 4)384

16. 6)450

17. 3)207

18. 5)435

19. 7)378

20. 9)306

21. 6)222

22. 4)148

23. 8)704

24. 9)504

25. 5)135

26. 7)469

27. 4)248

28. 8)240

29. 7)490

30. 9)891

31. 6)174

32. 6)348

33. 4)300

34. 7)581

35. 2)134

Teaching Pages 224 and 225

● **PURPOSE**

To provide another step leading toward the division algorithm

To provide more experiences in estimating quotients

● **PREPARATION**

Provide the class with several review exercises in determining the set (tens, twenties, thirties, forties, etc.) for given quotients. You can select exercises from page 223. Follow this by choosing two or three exercises from page 224 and having the students guess the tens digit. Relate

More on finding the tens digit

Suppose we do not know the ones digit. ⌐
Can we find the tens digit? ⟶ ▦ ◄┘
4)212

Answer these questions.

? × 4 < 212	**1.** Are there as many as 30 fours in 212?
	2. Are there as many as 40 fours in 212?
? × 4 > 212	**3.** Are there as many as 50 fours in 212?
	4. Are there as many as 60 fours in 212?

Since ⟶ 50 × 4 < 212 ⟶
⟶ 60 × 4 > 212 ⟶ we see that 5 is the tens digit of the quotient.

EXERCISES

Copy each exercise. Then find the tens digit
and write it in the proper place.

1. 21
4)84

2. 21
6)126

3. 64
2)128

4. 22
7)154

5. 34
4)136

6. 33
5)165

7. 34
3)102

8. 23
6)138

9. 27
5)135

10. 37
4)148

11. 37
6)222

12. 62
4)248

13. 87
5)435

14. 69
3)207

15. 75
6)450

16. 78
2)156

17. 44
7)308

18. 75
5)375

19. 34
9)306

20. 54
7)378

21. 67
7)469

22. 30
8)240

23. 56
9)504

24. 43
8)344

25. 88
8)704

26. 39
8)312

27. 61
7)427

28. 93
4)372

29. 88
6)528

30. 29
9)261

Study the material at the top of the page with the class. If necessary, relate this to the idea of estimating in what set the quotient lies.

Have the students do the exercises. When they have finished, allow time for the presentation of several exercises and a discussion of each.

this to the previous activity of deciding what set contains the quotient. In each case, have the students check the quotient by multiplication.

Read through and discuss the material on this page with the students. Exhibit the examples at the bottom of the page on the chalkboard and have the students explain them. For example, in the first exercise, be sure the students understand the reason why we add 30 fives and 2 fives in order to arrive at the correct quotient, 32.

Finding the ones digit in quotients

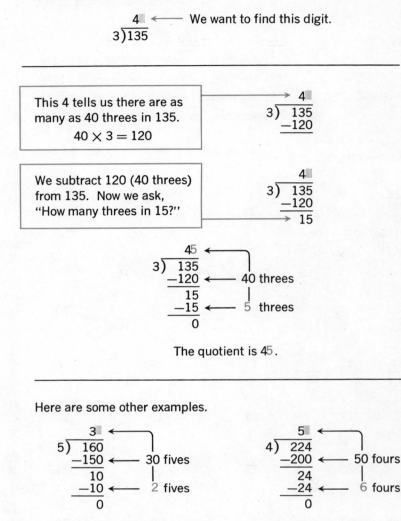

Think about this exercise.

$$4\overline{} \leftarrow \text{ We want to find this digit.}$$
$$3\overline{)135}$$

This 4 tells us there are as many as 40 threes in 135.
$$40 \times 3 = 120$$

$$\begin{array}{r} 4 \\ 3\overline{)135} \\ -120 \end{array}$$

We subtract 120 (40 threes) from 135. Now we ask, "How many threes in 15?"

$$\begin{array}{r} 4 \\ 3\overline{)135} \\ -120 \\ \hline 15 \end{array}$$

$$\begin{array}{r} 45 \\ 3\overline{)135} \\ -120 \leftarrow \text{ 40 threes} \\ \hline 15 \\ -15 \leftarrow \text{ 5 threes} \\ \hline 0 \end{array}$$

The quotient is 45.

Here are some other examples.

$$\begin{array}{r} 3 \\ 5\overline{)160} \\ -150 \leftarrow \text{ 30 fives} \\ \hline 10 \\ -10 \leftarrow \text{ 2 fives} \\ \hline 0 \end{array} \qquad \begin{array}{r} 5 \\ 4\overline{)224} \\ -200 \leftarrow \text{ 50 fours} \\ \hline 24 \\ -24 \leftarrow \text{ 6 fours} \\ \hline 0 \end{array}$$

The quotient is 32. The quotient is 56.

Teaching Pages 226 and 227

● **PURPOSE**

To provide another step leading to the development of the division algorithm

To provide practice in finding the ones digit once the tens digit has been found

● **PREPARATION**

Review several exercises from the lesson on pages 216 and 217. Exhibit these on the chalkboard and discuss them in much the same way as you did for that lesson.

EXERCISES

1. Find the quotients.

[A]	[B]	[C]	[D]	[E]
3‖3	8‖3	3‖5	3‖3	2‖4
4) 132	3) 249	5) 175	6) 258	7) 168
−120	−240	−150	−240	−140
12	9	25	18	28

[F]	[G]	[H]	[I]	[J]
8‖3	5‖6	5‖4	4‖2	3‖3
4) 332	3) 168	6) 324	8) 336	9) 297
−320	−150	−300	−320	−270

2. Find the quotients.

[A]	[B]	[C]	[D]	[E]
2‖1	3‖4	3‖3	3‖4	2‖2
6)126	3)102	5)165	4)136	7)154

[F]	[G]	[H]	[I]	[J]
9‖6	7‖5	4‖4	7‖8	4‖3
4)384	5)375	7)308	2)156	8)344

[K]	[L]	[M]	[N]	[O]
3‖4	5‖4	8‖7	6‖9	7‖5
9)306	7)378	5)435	3)207	6)450

[P]	[Q]	[R]	[S]	[T]
2‖7	8‖8	3‖7	3‖0	6‖2
5)135	8)704	6)222	8)240	4)248

3. Find the quotients.

```
          65              73              69
[A] 5) 325      [B] 4) 292      [C] 3) 207
   −300 ← 60 fives  −280 ← 70 fours   −180 ← 60 threes
     25              12              27
    −25 ←  5 fives  −12 ←  3 fours  −27 ←  9 threes
      0               0               0
```

```
         62          78          93          73          83
[D] 4) 248  [E] 2) 156  [F] 5) 465  [G] 6) 438  [H] 7) 581
   −240      −140      −450      −420      −560
      8        16        15        18        21
     −8       −16       −15       −18       −21
      0         0         0         0         0
```

Have the students work exercises 1A and B. Discuss these exercises before having the students complete exercise 1. When they have finished exercise 1, check their answers and discuss two or three more of the exercises.

Now have the students do exercises 2 and 3. When they have completed the page, again allow time for the presentation of several exercises and related discussion.

Have the students work exercises 1 through 5. Follow this by having one or two of these problems presented on the chalkboard and explained. Now have the students do exercises 6 through 10. Again, have some of these put on the chalkboard and explained.

Have the students complete the exercises. Have some of these exercises placed on the chalkboard and explained.

Can you find the missing digits?

Copy and complete each exercise.

Exercises 1–25 — long division problems with missing digits to be filled in.

1. 5)135 quotient 27 ...
2. 3)204 quotient 68 ...
3. 4)252 ...
4. 6)216 ...
5. 7)308 ...
6. 5)160 ...
7. 3)171 ...
8. 6)372 ...
9. 8)496 ...
10. 9)387 ...
11. 4)216 ...
12. 6)282 ...
13. 5)465 ...
14. 8)664 ...
15. 7)448 ...
16. 3)198 ...
17. 5)415 ...
18. 6)588 ...
19. 8)200 ...
20. 7)378 ...
21. 4)328 ...
22. 5)215 ...
23. 6)378 ...
24. 7)518 ...
25. 8)440 ...

Teaching Pages 228 and 229

- **PURPOSE**

  To introduce the division algorithm

  To provide practice in finding two-digit quotients

  To provide a short cut for working with the division algorithm

- **PREPARATION**

  Provide the students with a review of any material covered thus far in the chapter with which they have had difficulty. In particular, review the lesson on pages 226 and 227. Review of this lesson is of utmost importance since it leads to the development of the algorithm found on page 228.

Finding 2-digit quotients

We can find the quotients as follows:

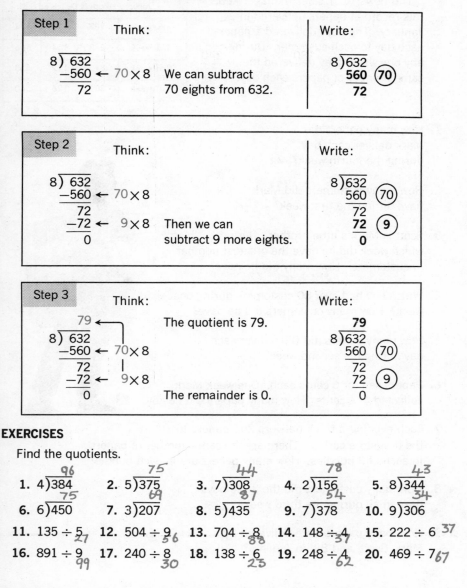

Step 1

Think:

$8 \overline{)632}$
$-560 \leftarrow 70 \times 8$ We can subtract
$\overline{72}$ 70 eights from 632.

Write:

$8 \overline{)632}$
560 (70)
72

Step 2

Think:

$8 \overline{)632}$
$-560 \leftarrow 70 \times 8$
$\overline{72}$
$-72 \leftarrow 9 \times 8$ Then we can
$\overline{0}$ subtract 9 more eights.

Write:

$8 \overline{)632}$
560 (70)
72
72 (9)
0

Step 3

Think:

    79 ←
$8 \overline{)632}$
$-560 \leftarrow 70 \times 8$ The quotient is 79.
$\overline{72}$
$-72 \leftarrow 9 \times 8$
$\overline{0}$ The remainder is 0.

Write:

79
$8 \overline{)632}$
560 (70)
72
72 (9)
0

EXERCISES

Find the quotients.

1. $4\overline{)384}$ 2. $5\overline{)375}$ 3. $7\overline{)308}$ 4. $2\overline{)156}$ 5. $8\overline{)344}$
   96   *75*   *44*   *78*   *43*

6. $6\overline{)450}$ 7. $3\overline{)207}$ 8. $5\overline{)435}$ 9. $7\overline{)378}$ 10. $9\overline{)306}$
   75   *69*   *87*   *54*   *34*

11. $135 \div 5$ 12. $504 \div 9$ 13. $704 \div 8$ 14. $148 \div 4$ 15. $222 \div 6$ *37*
     27   *56*   *88*   *37*

16. $891 \div 9$ 17. $240 \div 8$ 18. $138 \div 6$ 19. $248 \div 4$ 20. $469 \div 7$ *67*
     99   *30*   *25*   *62*

Study the three steps with the class. Note that on the right side of each box we show in bold-face type what is to be written for each step. Observe with the students that we begin by subtracting 70 eights. Since the difference is 72, we can subtract 9 more eights and arrive at a quotient of 79.

If the students do not readily understand the first example you may choose to present on the chalkboard some of the exercises at the bottom of the page before having the students proceed on their own. Once they have completed these exercises, it will be beneficial to have various students write exercises on the chalkboard and explain their thinking and how they found their estimates for each step.

At this time it is important that the students learn the procedure for writing down their quotient estimates as they go along. Also, keep in mind that the students should be encouraged to make the most accurate estimate possible, but if they do not succeed, they should be allowed to make successive guesses. Some of the students will never become very efficient at working with the long-division algorithm. The important objective, then, is to lead these students to understand the division algorithm so that even though they must use a much longer process, they can at least find the quotient correctly.

Supplementary exercises, Set 49 (page 350) may be assigned as necessary beyond this page.

Discuss the introductory paragraph and the chart at the top of the page before directing the students to work the exercises. Exercises 8 and 9 are primarily for the more capable students. When the students have completed these exercises, allow time for a discussion.

Delivering newspapers

The newspaper sales manager kept this record of papers delivered in January. The boys delivered 1 paper each day to each customer. During any one week, they delivered the same number of papers each day.

January—Papers Delivered			
	Mark Jones	Scott Jones	Bill Cook
4th week	287	98	574
3rd week	273	154	546
2nd week	315	112	553
1st week	301	126	560

1. How many papers did Mark deliver each day during the fourth week? *41*

2. How many customers did Mark have during the first week? *43*

3. Scott is Mark's little brother. During which week did he have the greatest number of customers? How many did he have? *3rd week; 22*

4. Which boy had over 80 customers during one week? How many customers did he have? *Bill; 82*

5. How many papers did Bill deliver each day during the second week? *79*

6. Papers sell for 6 cents each. One week Mark collected 498 cents. How many papers did he sell? *83*

7. Each evening a truck delivers 252 papers to the drugstore corner. There are the same number of papers in each of 3 bundles. How many papers are in each bundle? *84*

★ 8. How many customers did the three boys have in all during the third week? *139*

★ 9. How many papers were delivered by Mark, Scott, and Bill in January? *3899*

Teaching Pages 230 and 231

● **PURPOSE**

To provide word-problem experiences with division concepts

To provide more practice with the division algorithm

To provide word-problem experiences with all operations

● **PREPARATION**

Review any topics concerning the division algorithm with which the students have had particular difficulty. Have several students write long-division exercises on the chalkboard and explain the solutions.

Short stories

1. 78 students.
9 more came later.
How many students in all? **87**

2. 162 students.
Same number of students
in each of 6 groups.
How many in each group? **27**

3. 82 pupils.
37 boys.
How many girls? **45**

4. 62 girls.
54 boys.
How many more girls than boys?
8

5. 315 chairs.
7 rows.
Same number in each row.
How many in each row? **45**

6. 6 bushels.
48 pounds per bushel.
How many pounds in all? **288**

7. Satellite makes 558 orbits.
9 orbits each day.
How many days? **62**

8. 184 chairs.
8 in each row.
How many rows? **23**

9. 108 eggs. 9 cartons.
Same number in each carton.
How many in each carton? **12**

10. 7 days in a week.
364 days.
How many weeks? **52**

11. 112 ounces are 7 pounds.
How many ounces in 1 pound?
16

12. 5280 feet in a mile.
How many feet in 2 miles? **10,560**

13. 87 cents for 3 pints
of ice cream.
How much per pint? **29**

14. 4 quarts in a gallon.
96 cents per gallon.
How much per quart? **24¢**

★ 15. 2 pints in a quart.
4 quarts in a gallon.
$1.92 (192 cents) per gallon.
How much per pint? **24¢**

DIRECTIONS **PAGE 231**

Have the students work these
exercises. Discuss and answer any
questions when they have finished.
If time permits during this discussion period, have the students make
up some word problems which involve any of the four operations.
So that division with remainders
will not come up at this time, concentrate your activity with the students' word problems only upon
the operation involved rather than
upon any particular computing.

Discuss the exercises after the students have completed the page. As an additional activity for this page, you might have the students make up other problems concerning the prices given for the various items. For example, some student might ask the question, "How much would a seven-pound ham cost?" or "How much would two pounds of white grapes cost?" The important thing in a discussion of this type is to get the students to think about ways of using arithmetic in word-problem situations.

Comparing prices

1. A small box of Brand X holds 3 ounces and sells for 48 cents. A large box of Brand X holds 5 ounces and sells for 75 cents.

   [A] What is the cost per ounce in the small box? *16¢*
   [B] What is the cost per ounce in the large box? *15¢*
   [C] Which is the better buy? *large box*

2. A 4-pound beef roast costs $3.56 (356 cents). A 5-pound ham costs $3.95 (395 cents).

   [A] How much is the beef per pound? *89¢*
   [B] How much is the ham per pound? *79¢*
   [C] Which meat is more expensive? *beef*

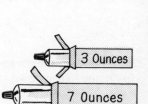

3. White grapes are 3 pounds for 84 cents and blue grapes are 5 pounds for 95 cents.

   [A] How much are the white grapes per pound? *28¢*
   [B] How much are the blue grapes per pound? *19¢*
   [C] Which grapes are less expensive? *blue*

4. A 7-ounce tube of tooth paste costs 84 cents. A 3-ounce tube of tooth paste costs 54 cents.

   [A] In the large tube, how much is the tooth paste per ounce? *12¢*
   [B] In the small tube, how much is the tooth paste per ounce? *18¢*
   [C] Which is the better buy? *large*

5. A 6-ounce can of tea costs $2.16 (216 cents). An 8-ounce can of tea costs $2.96 (296 cents).

   [A] How much per ounce is the tea in the small can? *36¢*
   [B] How much per ounce is the tea in the large can? *37¢*
   [C] Which is more expensive? *large*

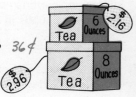

Teaching Pages 232 and 233

- **PURPOSE**

  To provide word-problem experiences

  To provide an interesting activity leading toward the concept of remainders in division

- **PREPARATION**

  During this preparation period, have the students make up several word problems of their own. Give other students in the class an opportunity to tell what operation is involved in each word problem. Avoid actual computation during this lesson in order to concentrate on the operation involved in a given word problem.

Short stories: time

1. 4 o'clock now. Sleep for 7 hours. What time will it be? *11 O'clock*

2. Walk a mile in 23 minutes. Run a mile in 9 minutes. How much quicker to run? *14 minutes*

3. 60 minutes in 1 hour. 8 hours. How many minutes? *480*

4. Machine runs 424 minutes a day. Makes one thing each 8 minutes. How many things? *53*

5. 1 day has 24 hours. 9 days. How many hours? *216*

6. 126 days make 9 fortnights. 1 fortnight is how many days? *14*

7. Total sleep, 736 hours. 8 hours each day. How many days? *92*

8. 658 days. How many weeks? *94*

9. Turbojet goes 577 mph (miles per hour). Gas-engine plane goes 334 mph. How much faster is the turbojet? *243 mph.*

10. 420 seconds. Same as 7 minutes. How many seconds in a minute? *60*

Animals, trees, birds, and insects grow old. These exercises tell how old they sometimes grow.

11. An old cat: 15 years old. An old turtle: 10 times as old. How old is an old turtle? *150 years*

12. An old rabbit: 6 years old. An old goose: 11 times as old. How old is an old goose? *66 years*

13. An old bear: 35 years old. An old camel: 28 years old. How much older is an old bear than an old camel? *7 years*

14. An old reindeer: 12 years old. An old whale: 6 times as old. How old is an old whale? *72 years*

15. Spruce tree: 243 years old. Lives 339 more years. How old? *582 years*

16. An old eagle: 46 years old. An old elm tree: 7 times as old. How old is an old elm tree? *322 years*

17. An old elephant: 61 years old. An old cow: 24 years old. How much older is an old elephant than an old cow? *37 years*

18. An old butterfly: 8 weeks old. An old housefly: 6 weeks old. How many **days** older is the old butterfly? *14 days*

Have the students work the exercises. Allow time for a discussion when they have finished the page. Keep in mind that the discussion which accompanies a page of problems such as these is an important phase of the lesson since such exercises are designed to stimulate students' interest in arithmetic and its applications.

Have the students work the exercises. Allow time at the end for checking papers. The students may enjoy a discussion centered around exercise 4, in which they are to find the missing digits. This type of exercise is particularly stimulating if the students treat it in the spirit of playing a game to find the missing digits.

Answers, exercise 4, page 234

[A]	35 +46 81	[F]	67 −28 39	[K]	46 ×2 92
[B]	78 +34 112	[G]	54 −16 38	[L]	37 ×4 148
[C]	65 +73 138	[H]	183 −64 119	[M]	56 ×3 168
[D]	92 +69 161	[I]	127 −56 71	[N]	43 ×5 215
[E]	56 +37 93	[J]	134 −57 77	[O]	64 ×3 192

Let's Review

- ADDITION
- SUBTRACTION
- MULTIPLICATION
- DIVISION
- MEASUREMENT
- PLACE VALUE
- INEQUALITIES
- PRINCIPLES

1. Find the sums and differences.

[A] 124 −67 = 57 [B] 103 +45 = 148
[C] 111 −64 = 47 [D] 158 +78 = 236
[E] 170 −83 = 87 [F] 104 −66 = 38

[G] 100 −72 = 28 [H] 162 +45 = 207 [I] 156 −56 = 100 [J] 163 −74 = 89 [K] 784 −90 = 694

2. Find the products.

[A] 34 ×2 = 68 [B] 26 ×3 = 78 [C] 42 ×4 = 168 [D] 37 ×5 = 185 [E] 73 ×6 = 438
[F] 68 ×5 = 340 [G] 59 ×6 = 354 [H] 74 ×7 = 518 [I] 83 ×8 = 664 [J] 92 ×9 = 828

3. Find the sums.

[A] 15 32 40 = 87 [B] 62 24 41 = 127 [C] 74 30 53 = 157 [D] 26 17 33 = 76 [E] 56 72 48 = 176

4. Find the missing digits. *(See answers at left.)*

[A] ▓5 +4▓ = 81 [B] ▓8 +3▓ = 112 [C] 6▓ +▓3 = 138 [D] 9▓ +▓9 = 161 [E] ▓6 +3▓ = 93

[F] 6▓ −▓8 = 39 [G] ▓4 −1▓ = 38 [H] 18▓ −▓4 = 119 [I] 1▓7 −5▓ = 71 [J] 13▓ −▓7 = 77

[K] ▓6 ×2 = 92 [L] 3▓ ×4 = 148 [M] ▓6 ×3 = 168 [N] 4▓ ×5 = 215 [O] ▓4 ×3 = 192

5. Answer "more than 100" or "less than 100" for each product.

[A] 3 × 33 *less*   [D] 4 × 33 *more*   [G] 6 × 20 *more*   [J] 11 × 11 *more*
[B] 3 × 34 *more*   [E] 5 × 21 *more*   [H] 10 × 9 *less*   [K] 9 × 11 *les*
[C] 4 × 22 *less*   [F] 5 × 19 *less*   [I] 10 × 11 *more*   [L] 9 × 12 *more*

Teaching Pages 234 and 235

● **PURPOSE**

To review the material covered thus far in the text

To provide work involving the usual decimal notation for dollars and cents

● **PREPARATION**

Review any topic from previous work in the text with which the students have had difficulty. In particular, it will be helpful if you will review the meaning of the decimal point in work with the usual notation for money.

Money problems

1. Give the missing numbers.

Examples:

$3.47 means **3** dollars and **47** cents.
$3.47 means **347** cents.

1 dollar

is worth

100 pennies

[A] $5.39 means ▮ dollars and ▮ cents. *5; 39*
[B] $3.86 means ▮ dollars and ▮ cents. *3; 86*
[C] $4.23 means 3 dollars and ▮ cents. *123*
[D] $7.33 means ▮ cents. *733*
[E] $5.37 means 4 dollars and ▮ cents. *137*

2. Find the total amounts.

Example: **$1.34** and **$3.23** is **$4.57**

[A] $3.32 and $2.45 *$5.77*   [C] $3.64 and $4.58 *$8.22*   [E] $ 7.32
[B] $12.57 and $8.32 *$20.89*   [D] $8.64 and $1.36 *$10.00*   12.68
                                                            $20.00

3. Find the difference in the amounts.

Example:

	[A]	[B]	[C]	[D]
$4.65	$5.86	$9.47	$8.52	$4.38
3.13	2.42	2.13	3.36	2.53
$1.52	*$3.44*	*$7.34*	*$5.16*	*$1.85*

4. [A] Susan bought a record and a book. The clerk wrote the costs down like this. Find the total amount. *$5.84*

Record.... *3.49*
Book..... *2.35*

Total _____

[B] Susan gave the clerk 6 dollars. How much change did she get? *16¢*

[C] Susan had $8.67 when she left home. She spent $6.34. How much did she have left? *$2.33*

5. Ken bought a baseball and a bat. Find the total cost. *$5.25*

$3.36 $1.89

6. Bob went to a store where the same ball and bat cost a total of $4.89. How much more did Ken's ball and bat cost than Bob's? *36¢*

Have the students work the exercises. Allow time for the checking of papers. If time permits, give the students an opportunity to create word problems involving work with money. To accompany this lesson, it might be helpful to have the students write the usual dollar notation on the chalkboard when someone else says the amount.

Study with the students the three examples at the top of the page. If necessary, use concrete objects in a demonstration situation to illustrate these examples.

Have the students complete the exercises. Allow time for discussion when they have finished.

Remainders in division

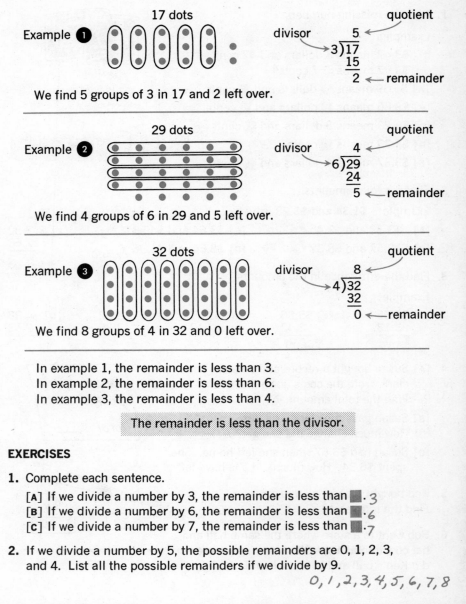

We find 5 groups of 3 in 17 and 2 left over.

We find 4 groups of 6 in 29 and 5 left over.

We find 8 groups of 4 in 32 and 0 left over.

In example 1, the remainder is less than 3.
In example 2, the remainder is less than 6.
In example 3, the remainder is less than 4.

The remainder is less than the divisor.

EXERCISES

1. Complete each sentence.

   [A] If we divide a number by 3, the remainder is less than ▮. 3
   [B] If we divide a number by 6, the remainder is less than ▮. 6
   [C] If we divide a number by 7, the remainder is less than ▮. 7

2. If we divide a number by 5, the possible remainders are 0, 1, 2, 3, and 4. List all the possible remainders if we divide by 9.

   0, 1, 2, 3, 4, 5, 6, 7, 8

Teaching Pages 236 and 237

● **PURPOSE**

To introduce remainders in division

● **PREPARATION**

Exhibit for the class a set containing 19 objects. Ask the students to remove the objects three at a time to find out how many sets of three they can get from a set of 19. When the students have done this, observe with them that they were able to remove six sets of three with one left.

EXERCISES

1. Study the examples. Complete the sentences.

1
$$
\begin{array}{r}
6 \\
4\overline{)26} \\
24 \\
\hline
2
\end{array}
$$

2
$$
\begin{array}{r}
3 \\
7\overline{)25} \\
21 \\
\hline
4
\end{array}
$$

3
$$
\begin{array}{r}
27 \\
5\overline{)136} \\
100 \\
\hline
36 \\
35 \\
\hline
1
\end{array}
$$

4
$$
\begin{array}{r}
45 \\
3\overline{)135} \\
120 \\
\hline
15 \\
15 \\
\hline
0
\end{array}
$$

[A] In example 1, the quotient is ▓ and the remainder is ▓. *6; 2*

[B] In example 2, the __?__ is 3 and the __?__ is 4. *quotient; remainder*

[C] In example 3, the __?__ is 5 and the __?__ is 27. *divisor; quotient*

[D] In example 4, the remainder is ▓ and the quotient is ▓. *0; 45*

[E] In each example, the __?__ is less than the __?__. *remainder; divisor*

[F] In any division, the __?__ is less than the __?__. *remainder; divisor*

2. Find the quotients and remainders.

[A] *9 R1* $3\overline{)28}$ [B] *9 R3* $4\overline{)39}$ [C] *8 R2* $5\overline{)42}$ [D] *7 R3* $6\overline{)45}$ [E] *8 R3* $7\overline{)59}$

[F] *9 R6* $8\overline{)78}$ [G] *7 R8* $9\overline{)71}$ [H] *11 R2* $4\overline{)46}$ [I] *32 R2* $3\overline{)98}$ [J] *23 R5* $7\overline{)166}$

[K] *59 R1* $4\overline{)237}$ [L] *42 R1* $8\overline{)337}$ [M] *60 R1* $3\overline{)181}$ [N] *41 R7* $9\overline{)376}$ [O] *72 R4* $5\overline{)364}$

3. Susan had 57 pictures for her new album. She put 6 pictures on each page.

[A] How many full pages could she get? *9*

[B] How many pictures would be left over for the last page? *3*

4. Jim has 221 Indian-head pennies. His coin book has room for 9 pennies on each page.

[A] How many full pages could he get? *24*

[B] How many pennies would be left over for the last page? *5*

Now, exhibit the corresponding vertical division notation:

$$
\begin{array}{r}
6 \\
3\overline{)19} \\
18 \\
\hline
1
\end{array}
$$

Point out to the students that the "one" is called the remainder and that "six" is called the quotient and that the number three, by which they divide, is called the divisor. Emphasize these words for the students and point out that the remainder is less than the divisor.

Have the students work the exercises. When they have finished, allow time for discussion.

Supplementary exercises, Set 50 (page 350) may be assigned as necessary beyond this page.

Repeat this demonstration for other sets for which a non-zero remainder is obtained. In each case, write the usual vertical notation for this type of exercise. Again, emphasize *quotient, remainder,* and *divisor,* and the fact that the remainder is less than the divisor. You should elicit from the students the explanation that the remainder is always less than the divisor because if the remainder were greater than the divisor, there would be at least one more of the divisor in the number. Therefore, we see that the remainder must always be less than the divisor.

When you instruct the students to work the exercises, remind them that they have worked similar exercises several times previously. You might notice with the students before they begin the page that in some exercises there are marbles left over. These are pictured with the small dots.

When the students have finished, discuss each exercise and point out to them the ideas concerning the left-over marbles. You should not mention remainders in division at this time; however, some of the students may express some ideas which are very close to those which will be pursued in the next lesson.

Notice that exercise 11 is designed for the more able students.

Division and sets

1.	28 marbles	[7] [7] [?]	How many bags? *4*
2.	42 marbles	[?] [?] [?] [?] [?] [?]	How many in each bag? *7*
3.	57 marbles	[?] [?] [?]	How many in each bag? *19*
4.	132 marbles	[6] [6] [?]	How many bags? *22*
5.	161 marbles	[?] [?] [?] [?] [?] [?] [?]	How many in each bag? *23*
6.	43 marbles	[?] [?] [?] [?] • • •	3 left over. How many in each bag? *10*
7.	35 marbles	[8] [8] [8] [8] [?]	How many left over? *3*
8.	39 marbles	[7] [7] [?] • • • •	4 left over. How many bags? *5*
9.	27 marbles	[?] [?] [?] [?] • • •	3 left over. How many in each bag? *6*
10.	44 marbles	[?] [5] • • • •	4 left over. How many bags? *8*
★11.	60 marbles	[9] [9] [?]	Less than 9 left over. How many bags? *6* How many left over? *6*

Teaching Pages 238 and 239

• **PURPOSE**

To provide an interesting activity leading toward the concept of remainders in division

To provide more experiences with the division algorithm and non-zero remainders

• **PREPARATION**

Provide the class with several exercises similar to those introduced at the top of page 239. As you present the method for checking, point out in particular that the remainder must be added to the product of the divisor and the quotient in order to get the number into which we are dividing.

Checking division

When the remainder is zero, we check by multiplication.

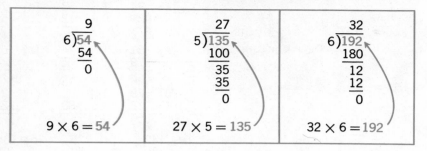

See if you can find how to check when the remainder is not zero.

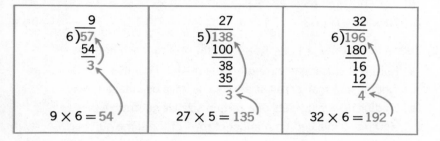

Study with the students the material in the two boxes at the top of the page. Direct the students to work the exercises. Allow time for discussion when they have finished.

EXERCISES

Find the quotients and remainders. Then check your answers.

6 R1 1. 4)25	5 R2 2. 5)27	3 R1 3. 3)10	6 R3 4. 6)39	9 R1 5. 2)19
7 R2 6. 5)37	4 R5 7. 6)29	9 R2 8. 7)65	7 R2 9. 4)30	9 R2 10. 3)29
25 R6 11. 8)206	25 R4 12. 6)154	55 R1 13. 5)276	26 R3 14. 7)185	22 R2 15. 6)134
60 R2 16. 3)182	58 R4 17. 9)526	69 R3 18. 5)348	60 R2 19. 4)242	26 R6 20. 7)188
51 R2 21. 6)308	15 R4 22. 5)79	28 R0 23. 3)84	30 R8 24. 9)278	85 R2 25. 4)342

Have the students work the exercises. Allow time for a discussion and checking papers. During the discussion focus particular attention on exercise 2. Give the students an opportunity, if time permits, to create other problems similar to the various parts of exercise 2.

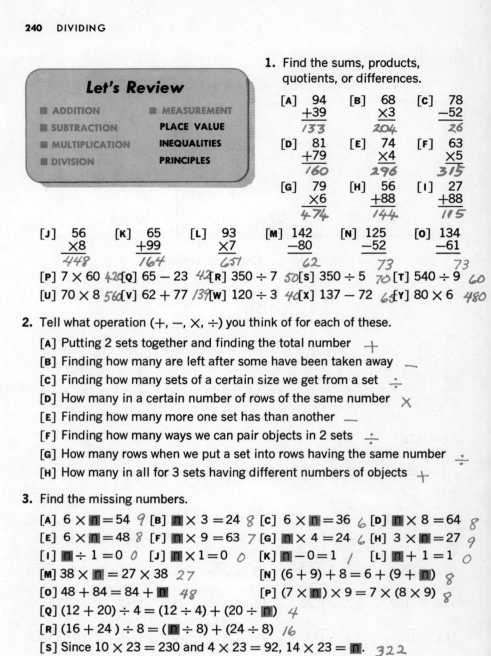

240 DIVIDING

Let's Review

- ADDITION
- SUBTRACTION
- MULTIPLICATION
- DIVISION
- MEASUREMENT
- PLACE VALUE
- INEQUALITIES
- PRINCIPLES

1. Find the sums, products, quotients, or differences.

[A] 94
    +39
    133

[B] 68
    ×3
    204

[C] 78
    −52
    26

[D] 81
    +79
    160

[E] 74
    ×4
    296

[F] 63
    ×5
    315

[G] 79
    ×6
    474

[H] 56
    +88
    144

[I] 27
    +88
    115

[J] 56
    ×8
    448

[K] 65
    +99
    164

[L] 93
    ×7
    651

[M] 142
    −80
    62

[N] 125
    −52
    73

[O] 134
    −61
    73

[P] 7 × 60 420   [Q] 65 − 23 42   [R] 350 ÷ 7 50   [S] 350 ÷ 5 70   [T] 540 ÷ 9 60
[U] 70 × 8 560   [V] 62 + 77 139   [W] 120 ÷ 3 40   [X] 137 − 72 65   [Y] 80 × 6 480

2. Tell what operation (+, −, ×, ÷) you think of for each of these.

[A] Putting 2 sets together and finding the total number +

[B] Finding how many are left after some have been taken away −

[C] Finding how many sets of a certain size we get from a set ÷

[D] How many in a certain number of rows of the same number ×

[E] Finding how many more one set has than another −

[F] Finding how many ways we can pair objects in 2 sets ÷

[G] How many rows when we put a set into rows having the same number ÷

[H] How many in all for 3 sets having different numbers of objects +

3. Find the missing numbers.

[A] 6 × ■ = 54 9   [B] ■ × 3 = 24 8   [C] 6 × ■ = 36 6   [D] ■ × 8 = 64 8

[E] 6 × ■ = 48 8   [F] ■ × 9 = 63 7   [G] ■ × 4 = 24 6   [H] 3 × ■ = 27 9

[I] ■ ÷ 1 = 0 0   [J] ■ × 1 = 0 0   [K] ■ − 0 = 1 1   [L] ■ + 1 = 1 0

[M] 38 × ■ = 27 × 38 27   [N] (6 + 9) + 8 = 6 + (9 + ■) 8

[O] 48 + 84 = 84 + ■ 48   [P] (7 × ■) × 9 = 7 × (8 × 9) 8

[Q] (12 + 20) ÷ 4 = (12 ÷ 4) + (20 ÷ ■) 4

[R] (16 + 24) ÷ 8 = (■ ÷ 8) + (24 ÷ 8) 16

[S] Since 10 × 23 = 230 and 4 × 23 = 92, 14 × 23 = ■. 322

Teaching Pages 240 and 241

- **PURPOSE**

To review the material covered in the text

- **PREPARATION**

Review any of the material from the text with which the students have had particular difficulty. You might use the remaining part of this preparation period to strengthen the students' ability to work word problems. You can do this by either making up some word problems and having the students discuss and work them or by having the students make their own word problems.

Eating at the restaurant

Kay and her mother went to a large restaurant. This is the menu they used to order their lunch.

Menu

Lamb chops......	$ 2.25
¼ Chicken	$ 1.39
Meat loaf	$ .89
Children's plate	$ .55

Dessert and Beverage included Thank you

1. There were 36 tables in the restaurant. There were 4 chairs at each table. How many chairs were there? *144*

2. There were 9 waiters. How many tables might be assigned to each waiter? *4*

3. The waiters filled 1 pitcher of water for each 4 people. Kay counted 56 people. How many pitchers of water did they need? *14*

4. Kay had meat loaf. Her mother had lamb chops. What was the total cost of their lunches? *$3.14*

5. Kay's mother gave the waiter $3.50. How much change did she get back? *$.36*

6. Their lunch cost about $3.00. Kay's mother decided to "tip" the waiter 15 cents for each dollar that the lunch cost. How much extra did she give the waiter for his good service? *$.45*

7. If Kay and her mother had both bought chicken, what would the total cost have been? *$2.78*

8. There was a party room at the restaurant. There were 360 people at a special lunch in this room. 8 people sat at each table. How many tables did they need? *45*

9. Kay saw this sign in the window.

Open **7** days each week
24 hours a day
We've been open for [168] days without closing Manager

[A] How many weeks has the restaurant been open without closing? *24*

★ [B] How many hours has it been open without closing? *4032*

DIRECTIONS PAGE 241

Have the students work the exercises. Allow time at the end for discussion. Notice that exercise 9B is starred and should be reserved primarily for the more able students. If time permits, have the students create a menu on the chalkboard and then invent several problems for this menu.

Have the students work the exercises. If you use this lesson as chapter evaluation, you will want to correct the papers yourself. Notice that most of the material on this page is of a fairly simple nature and that a lengthy discussion should not be necessary. Actually, the material on this page deals more with the concepts of division and division facts than it does with any particular preparation for the division algorithm.

Chapter review

1. Write a division equation to answer each question.

[A]

How many sets of 3 are in a set of 21?

$21 \div 3 = 7$

[B]

If we put 24 dots into 4 sets of the same number, how many dots are in each set? $24 \div 4 = 6$

[C]

Starting at 40, how many jumps of 5 does it take to get to 0? $40 \div 5 = 8$

[D]
$$\begin{array}{ccc} 42 & 35 & 28 \\ -7 & -7 & -7 \cdots \\ \hline 35 & 28 & \end{array}$$

Starting with 42, how many times do we subtract 7 to get 0?

$42 \div 7 = 6$

[E] 56, 48, 40, . . .

Starting at 56, how many times do we subtract 8 to get to 0? $56 \div 8 = 7$

[F] $\blacksquare \times 9 = 54$ What number times 9 gives 54? $54 \div 9 = 6$

2. Find the quotients.

[A] Since $8 \times 9 = 72$, we know that
$72 \div 9 = \blacksquare. 8$
$72 \div 8 = \blacksquare. 9$

[B] Since $11 \times 23 = 253$, we know that
$253 \div 23 = \blacksquare. 11$
$253 \div 11 = \blacksquare. 23$

[C] Since $7 \times 58 = 406$, we know that
$406 \div 7 = \blacksquare. 58$
$406 \div 58 = \blacksquare. 7$

3. Find the quotients.

[A] $64 \div 8$ 8	[F] $45 \div 5$ 9	[K] $48 \div 6$ 8	[P] $72 \div 9$ 8	[U] $36 \div 9$ 4
[B] $28 \div 4$ 7	[G] $42 \div 7$ 6	[L] $54 \div 6$ 9	[Q] $81 \div 9$ 9	[V] $16 \div 4$ 4
[C] $20 \div 5$ 4	[H] $36 \div 6$ 6	[M] $24 \div 6$ 4	[R] $18 \div 2$ 9	[W] $35 \div 7$ 5
[D] $18 \div 6$ 3	[I] $49 \div 7$ 7	[N] $32 \div 8$ 4	[S] $25 \div 5$ 5	[X] $30 \div 5$ 6
[E] $27 \div 9$ 3	[J] $40 \div 8$ 5	[O] $56 \div 8$ 7	[T] $45 \div 5$ 9	[Y] $54 \div 9$ 6

Teaching Pages 242 and 243

- **PURPOSE**

  To review material covered in this chapter

  To serve as a possible evaluation instrument for achievement in this chapter

- **PREPARATION**

  Review any topics in the chapter with which the students have had difficulty. Of course, since the chief goal of this chapter was to develop with complete understanding the division algorithm, you will want to have the division algorithm presented and explained on the chalkboard.

4. Find the quotients.

[A] 5)315 $\overset{63}{}$ [B] 6)264 $\overset{44}{}$ [C] 3)228 $\overset{76}{}$ [D] 4)372 $\overset{93}{}$ [E] 2)168 $\overset{84}{}$

[F] 4)300 $\overset{75}{}$ [G] 7)700 $\overset{100}{}$ [H] 6)420 $\overset{70}{}$ [I] 8)272 $\overset{34}{}$ [J] 9)558 $\overset{62}{}$

5. Find the quotients and the remainders.

[A] 3)128 $\overset{42R2}{}$ [B] 5)342 $\overset{68R2}{}$ [C] 7)618 $\overset{88R2}{}$ [D] 6)415 $\overset{69R1}{}$ [E] 4)321 $\overset{80R1}{}$

[F] 2)101 $\overset{50R1}{}$ [G] 8)327 $\overset{40R7}{}$ [H] 6)243 $\overset{40R3}{}$ [I] 4)219 $\overset{54R3}{}$ [J] 9)576 $\overset{64R0}{}$

[K] 5)314 $\overset{62R4}{}$ [L] 3)194 $\overset{64R2}{}$ [M] 7)627 $\overset{89R4}{}$ [N] 6)245 $\overset{40R5}{}$ [O] 9)706 $\overset{78R4}{}$

6.	258 marbles	(6 bags)	How many in each bag? 43
7.	175 marbles	(bags of 7) ?	How many bags? 25
8.	7 bags	(bags of 9) ?	How many marbles? 63

9. Jan had 35 favors for her party. There were 8 guests at the party. Each guest got the same number of favors, and there were 3 left over. How many favors did each guest get? 4

10. Jim had 50 cents. Table tennis balls cost 9 cents each.
[A] How many could he buy? 5
[B] If he bought only 3 balls, how much money would he have left? 23¢
[C] If he bought as many as he could, how much money would he have left? 5¢

11. Sara had 75 cents when she went shopping.
[A] How many pencils could she buy if they were 6 cents each? 12
[B] How much would she have left if she bought as many pencils as she could? 3¢
[C] If pencils were 9 cents each, how many could she buy? 8 How much money would she have left? 3¢

Have the students work the exercises. You may choose to correct these papers yourself. Following completion of the page, discuss and explain any exercises with which the students have had particular difficulty.

Supplementary exercises, Sets 51 and 52 (page 351), may be assigned as necessary beyond this page.

Teaching
Geometry Lesson 7

- **PURPOSE**

  To introduce quadrilaterals

  To introduce the concept of the sum of the angles of a quadrilateral

  Quadrilaterals are introduced intuitively through the use of pictures. Again, we emphasize the idea that these geometric figures have an interior and an exterior by using the blue shading for the interior and the gray shading for the exterior of the figure.

  Following this introduction, the students are given an opportunity to draw a rectangle and experiment with the sum of the angles for a rectangle. Of course, since the angles are all right angles, the students can quickly see, or perhaps even predict, that these four angles will go all the way around the point.

  After this development the students are given an opportunity to draw any quadrilateral and experiment with the sum of the quadrilateral's angles by pasting them around a point. This discovery will be more surprising to the students because it is not immediately apparent that these four angles will fit around the point.

- **MATHEMATICS**

  The chief mathematical concept explored in this lesson is the reasoning behind the fact that the sum of the degree measures of the four angles of any quadrilateral is 360 degrees. This can be easily demonstrated by choosing any quadrilateral and drawing one diagonal. The diagonal divides the quadrilateral into two triangles. Since the sum of the degree measures of the angles in each triangle is 180, the sum of the degree measures of the angles of the quadrilateral will be 360. You might choose to demonstrate this for the students once they have discovered that the four angles of a quadrilateral go exactly around the point.

  The illustrations at the top of page 244 should give the students a general feeling that a quadrilateral is a closed figure that has four line segments for its sides. You may need to point out in particular that squares and rectangles are quadrilaterals that have special properties.

GEOMETRY - Lesson 7

Quadrilaterals

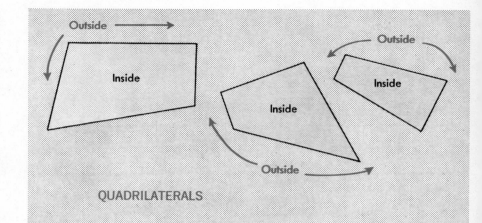

QUADRILATERALS

A quadrilateral has 4 sides. A rectangle is a quadrilateral.

1. [A] Draw a rectangle on your paper. Color each corner of your rectangle a different color.

   [B] Cut out the rectangle and tear it into 4 pieces like this.

   [C] Mark a point on another piece of paper and paste these corners around the point. Make the pieces touch but do not let them overlap. If you do your work carefully, the corners should just go around the point.

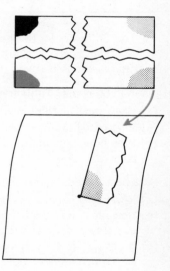

244

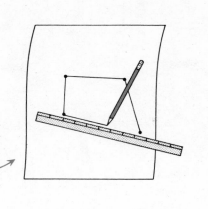

2. [A] Mark 4 points on your paper.
Be sure that no 3 of them are in
a line. Now use your ruler to
connect the points like this.
When you finish, you will have
a quadrilateral.

[B] Color each corner of your
quadrilateral a different color.
Cut it out and tear it as
you did the rectangle.

[C] Mark a point on another piece of
paper. Paste the corners around the
point as you did with the rectangle.
Do these corners go around the point
as the corners of the rectangle did?

3. Try this again with a quadrilateral of a different shape.

DIRECTIONS
PAGES 244 and 245

Study the illustrations at the top
of page 244. Emphasize the word
quadrilateral. Have the students
follow the instructions of exercise
1. Furnish whatever guidance is
necessary so that the students can
complete this exercise successfully.

For exercise 2, give as few specific
directions as possible, other than
those given in the text. Some of the
less able students will, of course,
need additional help, but you
should be alert to see that the more
able students are given an opportunity to follow the directions and
make the discovery on their own.

When the students have completed the lesson, give them an opportunity to discuss these ideas. If
time permits, you may choose to
explain, as suggested in the mathematics section, the reasoning behind the fact that the angles of a
quadrilateral go around a point.
You might even have the students
perform the experiment of drawing
a quadrilateral and one diagonal
to observe that there are two triangles. When the students cut out
these two triangles and paste the
angles around a point, they will
quickly see that the angles of the
two triangles together will go all
the way around the point just as
the angles of the quadrilateral did.

Objectives of Chapter 10

To provide experiences with even and odd numbers

To introduce some properties of number endings

To explore sums and products involving even and odd numbers

To provide additional experiences with multiples and factors

To introduce prime numbers

The opening pages of this chapter concentrate on work involving even numbers. We begin by offering an intuitive definition for even and odd numbers. This is followed with some experiences involving number endings and identification of numbers as even or odd.

Following this, students are provided with experiences in working with sums and products of even and odd numbers. Attention is then focused on multiples and factors, and material is supplied to give the students an opportunity to think about the work with these ideas. The last lesson of the chapter introduces prime numbers and some key concepts associated with prime numbers.

Mathematics of Chapter 10

We give below definitions of even, odd, and prime numbers. Following each definition, we show several examples to illustrate the set of numbers defined.

The *even numbers* are the set of all numbers x such that

$$x = 2 \times n$$

where n is a whole number.

Note that:

$$\left. \begin{array}{l} n = 0 \to x = 0 \\ n = 1 \to x = 2 \\ n = 2 \to x = 4 \\ n = 3 \to x = 6 \\ \vdots \qquad \vdots \end{array} \right\} \text{even numbers}$$

The *odd numbers* are the set of all whole numbers x such that

$$x = (2 \times n) + 1$$

where n is a whole number.

Note that:

$$\left. \begin{array}{l} n = 0 \to x = 1 \\ n = 1 \to x = 3 \\ n = 2 \to x = 5 \\ n = 3 \to x = 7 \\ \vdots \qquad \vdots \end{array} \right\} \begin{array}{l} \text{odd} \\ \text{numbers} \end{array}$$

The set of *prime numbers* is the set of all whole numbers x such that

$$x \text{ has exactly 2 factors.}$$

Thus:

2 is a prime number (factors: 2, 1).

3 is a prime number (factors: 3, 1).

5 is a prime number (factors: 5, 1).

7 is a prime number (factors: 7, 1).

11 is a prime number (factors: 11, 1).

$$\vdots$$

Note that:

1 is not prime (factor: 1).

6 is not prime (factors: 1, 2, 3, 6).

91 is not prime (factors: 1, 7, 13, 91).

Teaching Chapter 10

This chapter is designed to be covered in about one week.

In your evaluation of this material, attempt to evaluate both understanding and mastery of certain fundamental concepts: even numbers, odd numbers, multiples, factors, and primes.

You will find that the average and more able students may become quite excited in working with the ideas of this chapter. But this is not an easy chapter for the slower students. You should attempt to guide the less able students so that they do not become discouraged with this material.

Study with the students the material at the top of the page. Observe with them the even numbers shown in the blue tints and the odd numbers shown in the gray.

Now, have the students work the exercises. Although exercise 2 is starred, once the correct answer is given, the students should be able to see that by doubling a number and then adding one they always get an odd number. You may choose to have only the more able students try exercise 2. Once they have had an opportunity to work this exercise, discuss it with all the students.

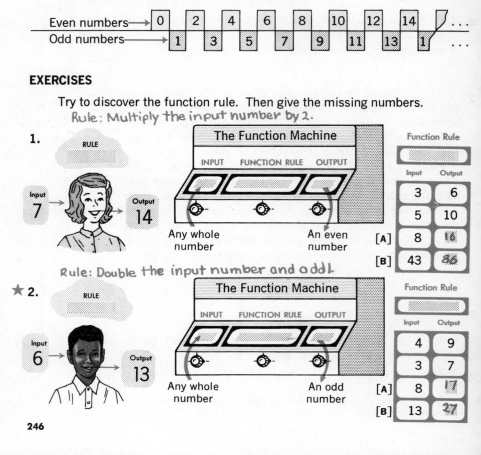

Chapter **10** **NUMBER THEORY**

Even and odd numbers

We separate the whole numbers into two sets.

Even numbers → | 0 | 2 | 4 | 6 | 8 | 10 | 12 | 14 | ...
Odd numbers → | 1 | 3 | 5 | 7 | 9 | 11 | 13 | 1 | ...

EXERCISES

Try to discover the function rule. Then give the missing numbers.

Rule: Multiply the input number by 2.

1.
RULE

Input 7 → Output 14

The Function Machine
INPUT   FUNCTION RULE   OUTPUT

Any whole number   An even number

Function Rule	
Input	Output
3	6
5	10
[A] 8	16
[B] 43	86

Rule: Double the input number and add 1.

★ 2.
RULE

Input 6 → Output 13

The Function Machine
INPUT   FUNCTION RULE   OUTPUT

Any whole number   An odd number

Function Rule	
Input	Output
4	9
3	7
[A] 8	17
[B] 13	27

246

Teaching Pages 246 and 247

- **PURPOSE**

  To introduce even and odd numbers

  To introduce identification of even and odd numbers by number endings

- **PREPARATION**

  List the numbers, 0, 2, 4, 6, in order on the chalkboard. Have the students continue this sequence through at least 30. Also list the set of odd numbers, 1, 3, 5, 7, and have the students continue this sequence through at least 29.

EXERCISES

1. Look at the picture below. Then study the table and give the missing numbers.

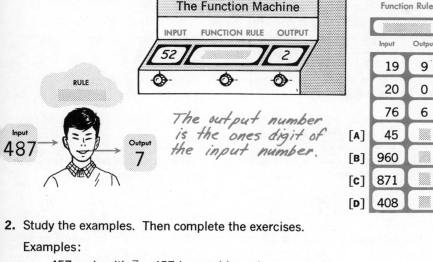

The output number is the ones digit of the input number.

Input	Output
19	9
20	0
76	6
[A] 45	5
[B] 960	0
[C] 871	1
[D] 408	8

2. Study the examples. Then complete the exercises.

Examples:

457 ends with 7.   457 is an *odd* number.

786 ends with 6.   786 is an *even* number.

[A] 34 ends with ▓.*4* Is 34 an even or odd number? *even*
[B] 43 ends with ▓.*3* Is 43 an even or odd number? *odd*
[C] 27 ends with ▓.*7* Is 27 an even or odd number? *odd*
[D] 56 ends with ▓.*6* Is 56 an even or odd number? *even*
[E] 30 ends with ▓.*0* Is 30 an even or odd number? *even*
[F] 81 ends with ▓.*1* Is 81 an even or odd number? *odd*
[G] 138 ends with ▓.*8* Is 138 an even or odd number? *even*
[H] 469 ends with ▓.*9* Is 469 an even or odd number? *odd*

3. Answer "even" or "odd."

[A] Each __?__ number ends with 0, 2, 4, 6, or 8. *even*
[B] Each __?__ number ends with 1, 3, 5, 7, or 9. *odd*

4. Answer "even" or "odd" for each number.

[A] 84 *even* [C] 27 *odd*   [E] 999 *odd* [G] 1000 *even* [I] 52,648 *even*
[B] 34 *even* [D] 772 *even* [F] 763 *odd* [H] 9284 *even* [J] 586,345 *odd*

Study with the class the material in exercise 1. If you choose, you can use this as discussion exercise. However, if you do, give the students every opportunity to discover for themselves the idea of the exercise: that in this function machine the output is always the number ending.

Now have the students study the examples in exercise 2 and then complete the page. When they have finished, allow time for checking papers and answering questions.

Point out to the students that the first sequence shows some of the even numbers and the second sequence shows some of the odd numbers.

Have the students work discussion exercise 1 by doing the additions and then attempting to tell what word goes in the blank. Be sure that all the students have an opportunity to think about the problem before the correct answer is given. Once the correct answer is given, have the students try several more examples involving the sum of two even numbers. Continue this type of discussion for exercises 2 and 3. Then have the students complete exercises 4, 5, and 6.

Have the students do all the exercises at the bottom of the page on their own. Follow up with a discussion of these exercises when they have finished.

Sums and products—even or odd

DISCUSSION EXERCISES

Find the sums and products. Then tell whether "even" or "odd" should go in the blank.

1.
6	16	60	78
+8	+28	+78	+54
14	44	138	132

The sum of two even numbers is an _?_ number. *even*

2.
5	15	37	65
+7	+1	+45	+87
12	16	82	152

The sum of two odd numbers is an _?_ number. *even*

3.
6	47	38	57
+7	+6	+11	+38
13	53	49	95

The sum of an even and an odd number is an _?_ number. *odd*

4.
4	32	46	34
×6	×2	×8	×6
24	64	368	204

The product of two even numbers is an _?_ number. *even*

5.
7	15	63	43
×3	×3	×5	×9
21	45	315	387

The product of two odd numbers, is an _?_ number. *odd*

6.
6	12	23	56
×3	×5	×8	×7
18	60	184	392

The product of an even and an odd number is an _?_ number. *even*

EXERCISES

Answer "even" or "odd."

1. The sum of an even number and 1 is an _?_ number. *odd*
2. The product of an even number and 1 is an _?_ number. *even*
3. The sum of an odd number and 1 is an _?_ number. *even*
4. The product of an odd number and 1 is an _?_ number. *odd*
5. No _?_ number is less than 1. *odd*
6. Every _?_ number is greater than 0. *odd*
7. There are two _?_ numbers less than 3. *even*
8. There is only one _?_ number less than 3. *odd*
9. The sum of 0 and an odd number is an _?_ number. *odd*
10. The product of 0 and an odd number is an _?_ number. *even*
11. The sum of an even number and 0 is an _?_ number. *even*
12. The product of an even number and 0 is an _?_ number. *even*
13. The sum of two odd numbers is an _?_ number. *even*
14. The product of two odd numbers is an _?_ number. *odd*
15. The sum of an even and an odd number is an _?_ number. *odd*
16. The product of an even and an odd number is an _?_ number. *even*

Teaching Pages 248 and 249

- **PURPOSE**

  To develop some generalizations about sums and products of even and odd numbers

  To provide additional experiences with multiples

- **PREPARATION**

  In preparation for this lesson, be sure that all students can identify even and odd numbers by number endings. That is, the students should know that the even numbers end in 0, 2, 4, 6, or 8; and the odd numbers end in 1, 3, 5, 7, and 9. Following this brief review of even and odd

Multiples

×	0	1	2	3	4	5	6	7	8	9	10	11	12	13	14
A 2	0	2	4	6	8	10	12	14	16	18	20	22	24	26	
B 3	0	3	6	9	12	15	18	21	24	27	30	33	36	39	
C 4	0	4	8	12	16	20	24	28	32	36	40	44	48	5	

The numbers in row **A**, {0, 2, 4, 6, . . .}, are multiples of 2.
The numbers in row **B**, {0, 3, 6, 9, . . .}, are multiples of 3.
The numbers in row **C**, {0, 4, 8, 12, . . .}, are multiples of 4.

EXERCISES

1. Find the missing numbers.
   [A] 14 is a multiple of 2 because $2 \times 7 = $ ■. *14*
   [B] 12 is a multiple of 3 because ■ $\times 4 = 12$. *3*
   [C] Since $4 \times 6 = 24$, we call ■ a multiple of 4. *24*
   [D] Since ■ $\times 12 = 36$, we call 36 a multiple of 3. *3*
   [E] Since $5 \times 6 = 30$, we know that ■ is a multiple of 5. *30*
   [F] 45 is a multiple of 5 since $5 \times 9 = $ ■. *45*
      (See answers at right.)

2. [A] List the multiples of 5 (through 75).
   [B] List the multiples of 6 (through 90).
   [C] List the multiples of 7 (through 70).
   [D] List the multiples of 8 (through 120).
   [E] List the multiples of 9 (through 90).

3. Find the missing numbers.
   [A] Since $3 \times 4 = 12$, 12 is a multiple of 3 and ■. *4*
   [B] Since $5 \times 6 = 30$, 30 is a multiple of ■ and 6. *5*
   [C] Since $7 \times 8 = 56$, 56 is a multiple of ■ and ■. *7; 8*
   [D] Since $4 \times 10 = 40$, ■ is a multiple of 4 and 10. *40*
   [E] Since $5 \times 9 = 45$, ■ is a multiple of ■ and ■. *45; 5; 9*
   [F] Since $6 \times$ ■ $= 42$, ■ is a multiple of ■ and ■. *7; 42; 6; 7*

DIRECTIONS PAGE 249

As you study with the class the material at the top of the page, point out that this is just a multiplication showing only three rows: the two row, the three row, and the four row. Explain that they are to think about multiplying each number in the top row by the numbers in the first column. Have them check several products to see that they are right.

Now notice with the students that in row A there are the numbers 0, 2, 4, 6, etc., and that these numbers are called multiples of two. Point out that the multiples of two are the numbers we get when multiplying by two.

Notice with them now the numbers in row B, 0, 3, 6, 9, etc., and observe that these are multiples of three. Look also at row C and observe with the students that these are multiples of four.

Now have the students work the exercises. When they have finished, allow time for a discussion and the answering of questions.

Answers, exercise 2, page 249

[A] 0, 5, 10, 15, 20, 25, 30, 35, 40, 45, 50, 55, 60, 65, 70, 75

[B] 0, 6, 12, 18, 24, 30, 36, 42, 48, 54, 60, 66, 72, 78, 84, 90

[C] 0, 7, 14, 21, 28, 35, 42, 49, 56, 63, 70

[D] 0, 8, 16, 24, 32, 40, 48, 56, 64, 72, 80, 88, 96, 104, 112, 120

[E] 0, 9, 18, 27, 36, 45, 54, 63, 72, 81, 90

numbers, give the students an opportunity to do some oral skip counting by twos, threes, fours, fives, etc. This will prepare them for the development of multiples on the second page of the lesson.

Read and study the material at the top of the page with the students. Be sure that ample opportunity is given for the students to discuss why problem C puzzled Sara. Of course, the students should see that Sara was puzzled because there are four possible answers for the two factors and she could not decide which answer Joan wanted her to give. Thus it was really incorrect for Joan to ask for *the* answer to problem C.

Following this discussion, have the students do the exercises. When they have finished, allow time for checking papers and further discussion of the ideas presented on this page.

Answer, discussion preceding exercises, page 250

There is more than one possible answer for problem C (i.e., 1, 24; 2, 12; 3, 8; and 4, 6 are the possible missing factors).

Factors and products

Joan gave Sara these problems to solve. Sara solved problems A and B easily. When she tried problem C, she stopped and looked very puzzled. Can you explain why? *(see answer at left.)*

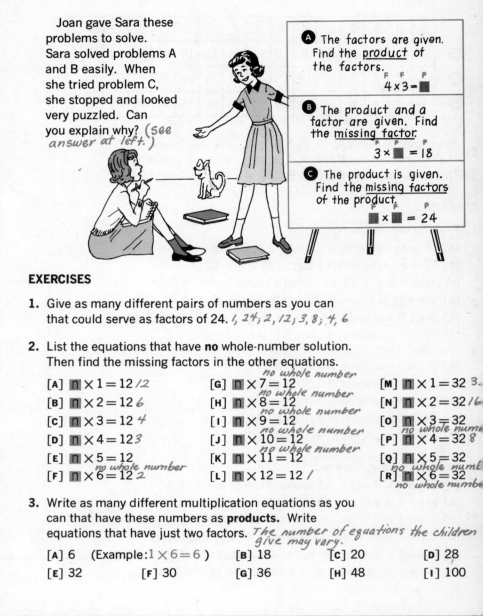

A The factors are given. Find the **product** of the factors.
$$4 \times 3 = \blacksquare$$

B The product and a factor are given. Find the **missing factor.**
$$3 \times \blacksquare = 18$$

C The product is given. Find the **missing factors** of the product.
$$\blacksquare \times \blacksquare = 24$$

EXERCISES

1. Give as many different pairs of numbers as you can that could serve as factors of 24. *1, 24; 2, 12; 3, 8; 4, 6*

2. List the equations that have **no** whole-number solution. Then find the missing factors in the other equations.

   [A] $\blacksquare \times 1 = 12$ *12*
   [B] $\blacksquare \times 2 = 12$ *6*
   [C] $\blacksquare \times 3 = 12$ *4*
   [D] $\blacksquare \times 4 = 12$ *3*
   [E] $\blacksquare \times 5 = 12$ *no whole number*
   [F] $\blacksquare \times 6 = 12$ *2*

   [G] $\blacksquare \times 7 = 12$ *no whole number*
   [H] $\blacksquare \times 8 = 12$ *no whole number*
   [I] $\blacksquare \times 9 = 12$ *no whole number*
   [J] $\blacksquare \times 10 = 12$ *no whole number*
   [K] $\blacksquare \times 11 = 12$ *no whole number*
   [L] $\blacksquare \times 12 = 12$ *1*

   [M] $\blacksquare \times 1 = 32$ *3.*
   [N] $\blacksquare \times 2 = 32$ *16*
   [O] $\blacksquare \times 3 = 32$ *no whole num*
   [P] $\blacksquare \times 4 = 32$ *8*
   [Q] $\blacksquare \times 5 = 32$
   [R] $\blacksquare \times 6 = 32$ *no whole numb*

3. Write as many different multiplication equations as you can that have these numbers as **products.** Write equations that have just two factors. *The number of equations the children give may vary.*

   [A] 6 (Example: $1 \times 6 = 6$)   [B] 18   [C] 20   [D] 28
   [E] 32   [F] 30   [G] 36   [H] 48   [I] 100

Teaching Pages 250 and 251

• **PURPOSE**

To provide experiences in working with factors
To prepare for the work on greatest common factor

• **PREPARATION**

Review with the students the meaning of *factor* and *product*. Write several multiplication equations on the chalkboard and have the students point out which numbers are factors and which are products. Encourage the students to use the language correctly. If the equation is $4 \times 3 = 12$, the students should say, "Four and three are factors of twelve," rather than "Four and three are fac-

tors." They should say, "Twelve is the product of four and three," rather than simply saying "Twelve is the product." The point to be made—not to the students necessarily, except through emphasis on correct usage—is that since the concepts of factor and product are relations, it is not quite correct to say that a number is a factor. We must say what it is a factor of. An analogous situation would be to say that "the number eight is equal." Such a statement is meaningless. Similarly when we say that the number four is a factor, the natural question arises, "A factor of what?"

Finding factors

> **A** Since ▥ × 7 = 28 has the solution 4,
> we know that 4 and 7 are factors of 28.

> **B** Since ▥ × 6 = 28 has no whole-number solution,
> we know that 6 is not a whole-number factor of 28.

EXERCISES

1. Solve the equation and give two factors of the product. *The solution to the equation is the first number in the pair.*
   [A] ▥ × 5 = 15
   (Answer: 3, 5)
   [B] ▥ × 7 = 63 *9, 7*
   [C] ▥ × 5 = 60 *12, 5*
   [D] ▥ × 12 = 48 *4, 12*
   [E] ▥ × 15 = 75 *5, 15*
   [F] ▥ × 13 = 39 *3, 13*
   [G] ▥ × 9 = 72 *8, 9*
   [H] ▥ × 18 = 72 *4, 18*
   [I] ▥ × 36 = 72 *2, 36*
   [J] ▥ × 1 = 32 *32, 1*
   [K] ▥ × 2 = 32 *16, 2*
   [L] ▥ × 4 = 32 *8, 4*
   [M] ▥ × 16 = 48 *3, 16*
   [N] ▥ × 2 = 48 *24, 2*

2. [A] Is 4 a factor of 11? *No*
   [B] Is 8 a factor of 63? *No*
   [C] Is 13 a factor of 42? *No*
   [D] Is 17 a factor of 51? *Yes*

3. Using the rule shown, you can put a **pair** of numbers into the function machine and get a single output number. Some output numbers are given below. Give as many pairs as you can that would produce each output number. *(see answers at right.)*

   The Function Machine
   INPUT   FUNCTION RULE   OUTPUT
   (2,3)   Multiply   6

   [A] 4 [Answers: (1, 4) and (2, 2)]
   [B] 12   [C] 6   [D] 5
   [E] 8   [F] 18   [G] 11   [H] 30   [I] 36   [J] 50

4. List all the factors of each number. *(see answers at right.)*
   [A] 12 (Answer: 1, 2, 3, 4, 6, 12)
   [B] 6   [C] 5
   [D] 8   [E] 18   [F] 11   [G] 30   [H] 36
   [I] 50   [J] 45   [K] 1   [L] 37   [M] 100

Read and study with the class the two statements at the top of the page, which explain how to determine whether or not a number is a factor of another number. The importance of both statements may not immediately be evident to the students, and the statements may seem to be merely a review of something they have already had. Simply point out to the students that the first statement tells them when a number *is* a factor of another number, and the second statement tells them when a number is *not* a factor of another number. Of course, the second statement may be used by the students when they are attempting to decide whether or not a given number is a factor of some number; if they cannot find a whole number that will multiply by their number to give the desired number, they conclude that this number is not a factor of the number.

Following this discussion have the students do the exercises. You may find it necessary to review the meaning of the function machine and its use in working with pairs of numbers and an operation. Following a brief review, the students should be able to do exercises 3 and 4 readily. When they have finished, allow time for checking papers and further discussion.

Answers, exercises 3 and 4, page 251

3. The number of pairs the students give will vary. Some of the possible pairs are given.
   [B] (1, 12) (3, 4) (2, 6)
   [C] (2, 3) (1, 6)
   [D] (1, 5)
   [E] (1, 8) (2, 4)
   [F] (1, 18) (2, 9) (3, 6)
   [G] (1, 11)
   [H] (1, 30) (2, 15) (3, 10) (5, 6)
   [I] (1, 36) (2, 18) (3, 12) (4, 9) (6, 6)
   [J] (1, 50) (2, 25) (5, 10)

4. [B] 1, 2, 3, 6
   [C] 1, 5
   [D] 1, 2, 4, 8
   [E] 1, 2, 3, 6, 9, 18
   [F] 1, 11
   [G] 1, 2, 3, 5, 6, 10, 15, 30
   [H] 1, 2, 3, 4, 6, 9, 12
   [I] 1, 2, 5, 10, 25, 50
   [J] 1, 3, 5, 9, 15, 45
   [K] 1
   [L] 1, 37
   [M] 1, 2, 4, 5, 10, 20, 25, 50, 100

Read and study the material at the top of the page with the class. As you discuss box A, emphasize that the numbers 1, 2, and 4 are factors of a *pair* of numbers—they are factors of both 8 and 12. Hence, we use the phrase *common factors* with respect to 1, 2, and 4 and the pair of numbers 8 and 12. We say that 1, 2, and 4 are *common factors* of 8 and 12. In box B, stress the fact that 1 and 3 are common factors of 6 and 9.

Have the students do the exercises. Note that exercise 8 has several possible solutions. That is, the students could observe that 10 is a factor of 70 but not of 105, that the number 2 is a factor of 70 but not of 105, that the number 3 is a factor of 105 but not of 70. You will note that to keep this problem from being trivial, the students are asked to give a number that is *less than* 70. Without this restriction, the students could simply answer 70 or 105.

Common factors

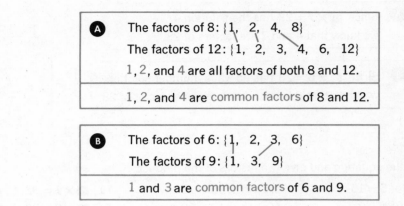

A The factors of 8: {1, 2, 4, 8}
The factors of 12: {1, 2, 3, 4, 6, 12}
1, 2, and 4 are all factors of both 8 and 12.

1, 2, and 4 are common factors of 8 and 12.

B The factors of 6: {1, 2, 3, 6}
The factors of 9: {1, 3, 9}

1 and 3 are common factors of 6 and 9.

EXERCISES

1. [A] List the factors of 9. *1, 3, 9*   [B] List the factors of 12. *1, 2, 3, 4, 6, 12*
[C] List the common factors of 9 and 12. *1, 3*

2. [A] List the factors of 6. *1, 2, 3, 6*   [B] List the factors of 8. *1, 2, 4, 8*
[C] List the common factors of 6 and 8. *1, 2*

3. [A] List the factors of 12. *1, 2, 3, 4, 6, 12* [B] List the factors of 16. *1, 2, 4, 8, 16*
[C] List the common factors of 12 and 16. *1, 2, 4*

4. [A] List the factors of 8. *1, 2, 4, 8*   [B] List the factors of 9. *1, 3, 9*
[C] List the common factors of 8 and 9. *1*

5. [A] List the factors of 12. *1, 2, 3, 4, 6, 12* [B] List the factors of 18. *1, 2, 3, 6, 9, 18*
[C] List the common factors of 12 and 18. *1, 2, 3, 6*

6. Give the number that is a factor of every number. *1*

7. Give two numbers greater than 10 that have no common factor except 1. *11, 17*

★**8.** Give a number less than 70 that is a factor of one of the numbers 70 and 105, and not of the other. Do as little computing as possible.
There are several answers. 10 is one that is obvious, without computing, since 10 is not a factor of a number ending in 5.

Teaching Pages 252 and 253

- **PURPOSE**

  To introduce the concept of a greatest common factor of two numbers

- **MATHEMATICS**

  The concept of the intersection of two sets may be more evident in this lesson than in any other portion of this textbook. We give below a formal definition for the intersection of two sets.

  If A and B are sets, then the intersection of A and B, written $A \cap B$, is the set of all elements that are in

Greatest common factors

A   The factors of 8: {1,   2,   4,   8}

The factors of 12: {1,   2,   3,   4,   6,   12}

4 is the **largest number** that is a factor of both 8 and 12.

4 is the greatest common factor of 8 and 12.

B   The factors of 6: {1,   2,   3,   6}

The factors of 9: {1,   3,   9}

3 is the greatest common factor of 6 and 9.

EXERCISES

1. Use your answers to the exercises on page 224 to help you find these numbers.
   [A] the **greatest common factor** of 9 and 12   *3*
   [B] the greatest common factor of 6 and 8   *2*
   [C] the greatest common factor of 12 and 16   *4*
   [D] the greatest common factor of 8 and 9   *1*
   [E] the greatest common factor of 12 and 8   *4*

2. [A] List the factors of 20. *1,2,4,5,10,20*   [B] List the factors of 16. *1,2,4,8,16*
   [C] List the common factors of 20 and 16. *1,2,4*
   [D] What is the greatest common factor of 20 and 16? *4*

3. [A] List the factors of 24. *1,2,3,4,6,8,12,24*   [B] List the factors of 32. *1,2,4,8,16,32*
   [C] List the common factors of 24 and 32. *1,2,4,8*
   [D] What is the greatest common factor of 24 and 32? *8*

4. Give an odd number and an even number between 10 and 20 that have 3 as the greatest common factor. *15, 18*

Read and study with the class the material in the two boxes. Observe with them that these two examples are the same as those on the previous page except that here attention is given to the *largest* number that is a factor of both of two numbers. Explain that on page 252 they saw that 1, 2, and 4 are factors of both 8 and 12, and here they learn that since 4 is the largest of these factors, it is called *the greatest common factor* of 8 and 12.

Following a discussion of these examples, have the students do the exercises. Give the more able students an opportunity to do exercise 4 without any clues. If you assign this exercise to the entire class, you might assist the other students by instructing, "Begin by listing all the numbers between 10 and 20 that have 3 as a factor; then look for one that is odd and one that is even."

When the students have finished the exercises, go back and stress again the idea of finding the greatest common factor of two numbers. Allow time for checking papers and discussion.

both *A* and *B* (that is, those elements which *A* and *B* have in common).

Of course, in this lesson, the word *common* implies the idea of the intersection of two sets, and it is not essential to define formally the concept of the union of two sets or to introduce the symbol for union. Most students will understand that the word *common* is applied to those elements which are in both of two sets.

PREPARATION

Review with the students the meaning of the factors of a number. List several numbers, such as 6, 8, and 10, on the chalkboard and have the students give the factors of these numbers.

Read and study the four sentences at the top of the page with the class.

Although the exercises on this page are labeled discussion exercises, this does not imply that the students should not be given an opportunity to attempt some exercises on their own or to write answers to some of the exercises on their papers. However, it does suggest that the greatest benefit from these exercises will come from working and then discussing them in a group situation.

Exercise 1 is of particular importance since it lays the foundation for understanding the other exercises in the set. Of course, here students should observe the generalization that any number other than one has as factors itself and one. The obvious extension of this idea is that a number which has factors other than itself and one has more than two factors.

Following exercise 1, the multiplication table is utilized to show a sequence of numbers that have a factor of two, then a sequence of numbers with a factor of three, and so on. The point here is that when a number has factors other than itself and one, it has more than two factors.

As you work through the exercises, continue to emphasize the three generalizations: that every whole number, except one, has at least two factors; that some numbers have more than two factors; and that some numbers have only two factors. Be sure that the students understand these three principles before proceeding to page 255.

How many factors?

DISCUSSION EXERCISES

▶ Every number (except 1) has at least two factors.

Since $1 \times 11 = 11$, we know that 1 and 11 are factors of 11.
Since $1 \times 28 = 28$, we know that 1 and 28 are factors of 28.
Since $1 \times 37 = 37$, we know that 1 and 37 are factors of 37.

1. Can you describe the two factors that any number (except 1) is sure to have? *1 and that number itself*

▶ Some numbers have more than two factors.

A Here is a sequence of numbers that have 2 as a factor.
B Here is a sequence of numbers that have 3 as a factor.
C Here is a sequence of numbers that have 4 as a factor.

×	0	1	2	3	4	5	6	7	8	9	10	11	12	13	14	15	16	17
0	0	0	0	0	0	0	0	0	0	0	0	0	0	0	0	0	0	0
1	0	1	2	3	4	5	6	7	8	9	10	11	12	13	14	15	16	17
2	0	2	4	6	8	10	12	14	16	18	20	22	24	26	28	30	32	34
3	0	3	6	9	12	15	18	21	24	27	30	33	36	39	42	45	48	51
4	0	4	8	12	16	20	24	28	32	36	40	44	48	52	56	60	64	68
5	0	5	10	15	20	25	30	35	40	45	50	55	60	65	70	75	80	85
6	0	6	12	18	24	30	36	42	48	54	60	66	72	78	84	90	96	102
7	0	7	14	21	28	35	42	49	56	63	70	77	84	91	98	105	112	119

2. 34 is in the 2 row of the table above. Use this fact and exercise 1 to show that 34 has more than two factors. *$1 \times 34 = 34$, $2 \times 17 = 34$*

3. 42 is in the 3 row of the table. Show that 42 has more than two factors by giving three factors of 42. *1, 3, 14*

▶ Some numbers have **only** two factors.

4. 1 and 37 are factors of 37. Can you give others? *No*

5. Give five numbers that have only two factors. *2, 3, 5, 7, 11*

Teaching Pages 254 and 255

• **PURPOSE**

To introduce prime numbers

• **MATHEMATICS**

Following is a formal definition of a prime number.

A prime number is a whole number that has exactly two factors.

The simplicity and clarity of this definition may not be immediately apparent. However, when you consider that every number except 1 has at least two factors, it then becomes obvious that this definition states the same mean-

Prime numbers

Here is a multiplication table with the 0 row and column and the 1 row and column left out.

×	2	3	4	5	6	7	8	9	10	11	12	13	14	15	16	17	18	19	20
2	4	6	8	10	12	14	16	18	20	22	24	26	28	30	32	34	36	38	
3	6	9	12	15	18	21	24	27	30	33	36	39	42	45	48	51	54		
4	8	12	16	20	24	28	32	36	40	44	48	52	56	60	64	68			
5	10	15	20	25	30	35	40	45	50	55	60	65	70	75	80				
6	12	18	24	30	36	42	48	54	60	66	72	78	84	90					
7	14	21	28	35	42	49	56	63	70	77	84	91	98						
8	16	24	32	40	48	56	64	72	80	88	96	104							
9	18	27	36	45	54	63	72	81	90	99	108								
10	20	30	40	50	60	70	80	90	100	110									
11	22	33	44	55	66	77	88	99	110										
12	24	36	48	60	72	84	96	108											
13	26	39	52	65	78	91	104												
14	28	42	56	70	84	98													
15	30	45	60	75	90														
16	32	48	64	80															
17	34	51	68																
18	36	54																	
19	38																		
20																			

Think of this table as going on without end.

EXERCISES

1. List the numbers from 2 to 40. Use the table to **mark out** the numbers in your list that have **more than two factors**. What you have left is the set of **prime numbers** less than 40.
   2,3, 5, 7, 11, 13, 17, 19, 23, 29, 31, 37
   ▸ Numbers that have **only** 2 factors are called **PRIME NUMBERS.**

2. List the prime numbers between 40 and 50. *41, 43, 47*

3. Tell why these numbers are not prime. *Because they have more than 2 factors.*
   [A] 52   [B] 54   [c] 56   [D] 55   [E] 51   ★ [F] 57
   52 = 13×4   *54 = 18×3*   *56 = 14×4*   *55 = 11×5*   *51 = 17×3*   *57 = 19×3*

4. Which of these numbers are prime?
   [A] 53   [B] 58   [c] 59   [D] 63   [E] 61   [F] 77

Discuss this multiplication table with the class. If you draw a table on the chalkboard, observe with the students that the table on the page is just like the one on the chalkboard. Remind the students that they are to think of this as a giant multiplication table that goes on and on without end. Such an idea may be beyond the comprehension of some students, but it should not surpass the imagination of others.

Following a discussion of the table and the fact that this is only a tiny corner of a giant table that continues indefinitely, have the students do the exercises. When they have finished, allow time for a discussion of each exercise. In particular, emphasize exercise 1, in which the students are asked to list the primes from 2 through 37. Also stress the statement, "Numbers that have only two factors are called prime numbers." Notice with the students that this eliminates zero and one and all the products in the table at the top of the page.

ing as does the definition, a prime number is a number greater than 1 which can be divided only by itself or 1. You may have heard some definitions which include 1 as a prime number. However, generally speaking, it is more convenient to exclude the number 1 from the set of prime numbers.

PREPARATION

Review with the students the list of factors of a number. Notice with them that some numbers have two factors and some have more than two factors. Following this discussion, construct on the chalkboard a large multiplication table similar to the one on page 255, and have the students fill in the products. Keep the table on the chalkboard for use when working page 255.

Study the function machine at the top of the page with the class. Then give them an opportunity to do exercise 1. When they have had ample time to do this exercise, follow this by checking papers and giving the students an opportunity to discuss their answers.

Discuss the function machine for exercise 2, and then have the students do the exercise. Again, when they have finished, follow up by discussing the correct answers. Repeat this procedure for exercise 3.

The function game

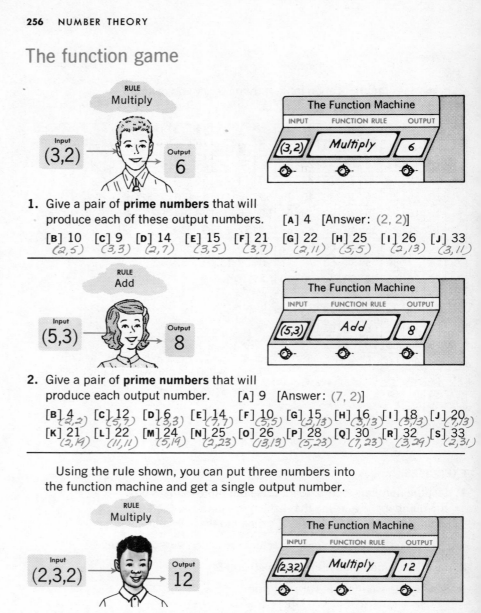

1. Give a pair of **prime numbers** that will produce each of these output numbers.   [A] 4 [Answer: (2, 2)]
   [B] 10 [C] 9 [D] 14 [E] 15 [F] 21 [G] 22 [H] 25 [I] 26 [J] 33
   (2,5)   (3,3)   (2,7)   (3,5)   (3,7)   (2,11)   (5,5)   (2,13)   (3,11)

2. Give a pair of **prime numbers** that will produce each output number.   [A] 9   [Answer: (7, 2)]
   [B] 4 [C] 12 [D] 6 [E] 14 [F] 10 [G] 15 [H] 16 [I] 18 [J] 20
   (2,2)   (5,7)   (3,3)   (7,7)   (5,5)   (2,13)   (3,13)   (5,13)   (7,13)
   [K] 21 [L] 22 [M] 24 [N] 25 [O] 26 [P] 28 [Q] 30 [R] 32 [S] 33
   (2,19)   (11,11) (5,19)   (2,23)   (13,13) (5,23)   (7,23)   (3,29)   (2,31)

Using the rule shown, you can put three numbers into the function machine and get a single output number.

3. Give the output number for each number triple.
   [A] (1, 4, 2) 8   [B] (2, 4, 2) 16   [C] (5, 3, 0) 0   [D] (1, 1, 1) 1   [E] (3, 4, 5) 60

Teaching Pages 256 and 257

- **PURPOSE**

  To provide additional experiences in working with prime numbers

  To provide experiences in working with prime factors of a number

  To introduce composite numbers

- **PREPARATION**

  Conduct an oral review of the topics covered thus far in the chapter. For example, you might give the students various numbers and ask them whether the numbers are even, odd, or prime. If you give the number seven, the

EXERCISES

(See answers at right)

1. The whole numbers greater than 1 that are not prime numbers are called **composite** numbers.

   [A] List the composite numbers less than 40.

   [B] Give a composite number between 90 and 100.

   (See answers at right)

2. [A] List all the factors of 12.

   [B] List the prime factors of 12.

   [C] List the factors of 30.

   [D] List the prime factors of 30.

Exercise for Experts

I'm such a sad odd number.
I cannot be a prime.
Since I have just one factor,
They leave me out each time.

WHO AM I?   *1*

---

3. [A] The equation $30 = 5 \times 2 \times 3$ shows that 30 is a product of prime numbers. Write an equation to show that 35 is a product of prime numbers. *$5 \times 7 = 35$*

   [B] Write an equation to show that 36 is a product of prime numbers. *$2 \times 3 \times 2 \times 3 = 36$*

4. Give the word or number for each blank.

   [A] Every prime number is odd except __?__. *2*

   [B] The number __?__ is a factor of every number. *1*

   [C] Each prime number has exactly __?__ factors. *2*

   [D] The only factor of 1 is __?__. *1*

   [E] Since the only factors of 73 are 1 and 73, 73 is a __?__ number. *prime*

   [F] Since 69 has four factors, 69 is a __?__ number. *composite*

   [G] 57 is not a prime number because $3 \times \blacksquare = 57$. *19*

   [H] __?__ is the only prime number between 61 and 71. *67*

★ [I] __?__ is the only prime number between 79 and 89. *83*

★ [J] __?__ is the only prime number between 103 and 109. *107*

★ [K] __?__ is the only prime number between 113 and 131. *127*

★ 5. The numbers 3 and 5 are called **twin primes** because their difference is 2. Another pair of twin primes is 41 and 43. Give four more pairs of twin primes. *5, 7; 11, 13; 17, 19; 29, 31*

---

students should observe that seven is an odd number and it is a prime number; for the number nine, they should observe that nine is an odd number but it is not prime. You might give them the number six and have them observe that it is an even number and not prime. Of course, the only even number you could give that would be prime would be two.

Following this oral discussion, review any other topics in the chapter with which the students may have had particular difficulty.

Have the students do the exercises. Call particular attention to exercise 1, in which the term *composite number* is defined.

Note that exercises 4I, J, and K and exercise 5 are designed primarily for the more able students. Some of the less able students will be able to do these exercises, if given enough time. These starred exercises are not conceptually difficult; they simply involve searching for larger prime numbers or pairs of prime numbers. All students will benefit from a discussion of the exercises once the correct answers are given.

Answers, exercises 1 and 2, page 257

1. [A] 4, 6, 8, 9, 10, 12, 14, 15, 16, 18, 20, 21, 22, 24, 25, 26, 27, 28, 30, 32, 33, 34, 35, 36, 38, 39

   [B] 93

2. [A] 1, 2, 3, 4, 6, 12

   [B] 2, 3

   [C] 1, 2, 3, 5, 6, 10, 15, 30

   [D] 2, 3, 5

Instruct the students to complete the exercises. When they have finished, discuss the answers and have the students check their papers. All students should benefit from a discussion of the riddle, even though some may not have been able to solve it by themselves.

Let's Review

■ ADDITION MEASUREMENT
■ SUBTRACTION PLACE VALUE
■ MULTIPLICATION INEQUALITIES
■ DIVISION ■ PRINCIPLES

1. Solve the equations.

[A] $10 \times 10 = \blacksquare$ *100*
[B] $100 \times 10 = \blacksquare$ *1000*
[C] $10 \times 1000 = \blacksquare$ *10,000*
[D] $100 \times 100 = \blacksquare$ *10,000*
[E] $100 \div 10 = \blacksquare$ *10*
[F] $1000 \div 10 = \blacksquare$ *100*
[G] $10,000 \div 10 = \blacksquare$ *1000*
[H] $10,000 \div 100 = \blacksquare$ *100*

2. Give the missing numbers.

[A] Since $5 \times 7 = 35$, we call ▦ a multiple of 7.   *35*
[B] 48 is a multiple of 6 because $\blacksquare \times 6 = 48$.   *8*
[C] ▦ is a multiple of 2 because $30 \times 2 = 60$.   *60*
[D] Since $5 \times 9 = 45$, 45 is a multiple of both 5 and ▦.   *9*
[E] Since $63 + 78 = 141$, we know that $141 - 78 = \blacksquare$.   *63*
[F] Since $156 - 79 = 77$, we know that $77 + 79 = \blacksquare$.   *156*
[G] Since $7 \times 38 = 266$, we know that $266 \div 7 = \blacksquare$.   *38*
[H] Since $147 \div 3 = 49$, we know that $49 \times 3 = \blacksquare$.   *147*
[I] Since $39 + 39 = 78$, we know that $78 - (39 + 39) = \blacksquare$.   *0*
[J] Since $11 \times 12 = 132$, we know that $132 \div (11 \times 12) = \blacksquare$.   *1*
[K] Since $39 + 61 = 100$, we know that $39 + 28 + 61 = \blacksquare$.   *128*

3. Find the sums and differences.

[A] 35	[B] 132	[C] 5076	[D] 8206	[E] 30,042
+89	−59	+3938	−39	−5,978
124	*73*	*9014*	*8167*	*24,064*

4. Find the products.

[A] 9	[B] 38	[C] 434
×6	×7	×9
54	*266*	*3906*

[D] 32	[E] 627	[F] 347
×5	×4	×2
160	*2508*	*694*

Exercise for Experts

Multiply me by myself,
Or find my sum with two.
Your answer is the same
No matter which you do.

WHO AM I? *2*

5. Find the quotients.

[A] $7\overline{)294}$ *42* [B] $8\overline{)3448}$ *431* [C] $23\overline{)2093}$ *91*

Teaching Pages 258 and 259

● **PURPOSE**

To provide a cumulative review
To provide a chapter review
To provide a sample evaluation instrument for this chapter

● **PREPARATION**

Begin by giving the students an opportunity to review any topics from the text with which they have had particular difficulty. You will notice that in this cumulative review considerable attention is focused on ordinary computation. Therefore, in preparing for this lesson you

Chapter review

1. Answer **E** if the number is even and **O** if it is odd.

[A] 68 *E* [C] 2001 *O* [E] 7642 *E*

[B] 83 *O* [D] 3958 *E* [F] 7050 *E*

2. The first even number is 0. The second is 2. The third is 4. The fourth is 6. The fifth is 8.

[A] What is the sixth even number? *10*

[B] What is the ninth even number? *16*

[C] What is the seventeenth even number? *32*

3. The first odd number is 1. The second is 3.

[A] What is the third odd number? *5*

[B] What is the eighth odd number? *15*

[C] What is the fourteenth odd number? *27*

4. List the composite numbers between 20 and 30. *21, 22, 24, 25, 26, 27, 28*

5. [A] List the factors of 18. *1, 2, 3, 6, 9, 18* [B] List the factors of 24. *1, 2, 3, 4, 6, 8, 12, 24*

[C] List the common factors of 18 and 24. *1, 2, 3, 6*

[D] What is the greatest common factor of 18 and 24? *6*

6. [A] List the factors of 30. *1, 2, 3, 5, 6, 10, 15, 30* [B] List the factors of 42. *1, 2, 3, 6, 7, 14, 21, 42*

[C] List the common factors of 30 and 42. *1, 2, 3, 6*

[D] List the common **prime** factors of 30 and 42. *2, 3*

[E] What is the greatest common factor of 30 and 42? *6*

7. [A] Write an equation to show that 38 is the product of two prime numbers. *2 × 19 = 38*

[B] Write an equation to show that 39 is the product of two prime numbers. *3 × 13 = 39*

Exercise for Experts

I'm slightly less than 30,
But more than 22.
They say that I am perfect,
And here is why they do.
Just add up all my factors,
And then divide by two.
You'll find that I'm the answer.
I'll say no more to you. *28*

WHO AM I?

Have the students work the exercises. Even though you may be using this exercise set as a test and thus choose not to have the students check their own papers, you should discuss the answers with the students immediately after they have completed the page.

The riddle brings up an interesting mathematical point—that of a perfect number. The first three perfect numbers are 6, 28, and 496; this riddle, of course, concerns the perfect number 28. You will notice that the factors of 28 are 1, 2, 4, 7, 14 and 28; and the sum of these factors is twice 28.

One definition of perfect numbers is given as follows.

A perfect number is a number such that the sum of all its factors that are less than the number is the same as the number.

That is, the sum of the factors 1, 2, 4, 7, and 14 is 28. The way the riddle is stated, however, we add up *all* the factors then divide by two and get 28.

Do not expect many, if any, of the students to unravel this riddle on their own. It is possible that some of the more able students can solve the riddle simply by trying each number between 22 and 30. However, even the more able students may not be successful with this process since it is very easy to miss one of the factors of a given number. Most of the students will understand the riddle once the correct answer is given and its factors are revealed.

---

might devote a session to some individual computing on the chalkboard by the students.

Following this, give the students an opportunity to review various concepts from the chapter. Be sure that they understand the concepts of even, odd, and prime number; greatest common factor; and finding the prime factors of a given number. Because the material on clock arithmetic is primarily for stimulus and enrichment rather than for any degree of mastery, the chapter review is devoted entirely to the material which precedes the clock-arithmetic section.

Objectives of Chapter 11

To provide a formal introduction to fraction concepts

To introduce the concept of equivalent fractions

To provide experiences in working with sets of equivalent fractions

To provide background material for a smooth transition to rational numbers

The opening pages of the chapter establish a relationship between the concept of a number pair and that of a fraction. We take the point of view formally that a fraction is a written symbol for a number pair. However, we would point out that often it is convenient to use the word *fraction* in place of *number pair,* and you will notice from time to time that we will occasionally say *fraction* when we mean number pair. However, it should be clear at all times from the context of the material whether we are speaking of the number pair or the symbol. Later, of course, it will be seen that fractions are symbols for rational numbers.

Following the introduction of fractions and number pairs, a lesson is devoted to the concept of fractional parts of an object and the fact that when speaking of one fourth of an object, we are referring to one of four parts of the same size.

Following this, the lessons cover, in order, the concepts of fractions and measurement, fractions and segments, fractions and sets, fractions and parts of an object, and the concept of equivalent fractions.

Most of the remainder of the chapter builds readiness for understanding rational-number concepts by developing understanding of equivalent fractions and providing work with sets of equivalent fractions.

The words *numerator, denominator,* and *improper fraction* are introduced. A test is provided to determine whether or not two fractions are equivalent, and then, toward the end of the chapter, the idea of lower and higher terms is introduced to lead to the fact that for each "complete" set of equivalent fractions, there is a unique fraction in the set that is called the *lowest-terms fraction* for that set.

You will note the absence of any attempt to teach particular skills for reducing fractions to lowest terms or for finding the lowest-terms fraction for another fraction. The chief emphasis here is to introduce the concept so that the students understand it completely.

Mathematics of Chapter 11

This chapter is concerned primarily with developing concepts of fractions in preparation for the introduction of rational-number concepts in the next chapter. The study of fractions is conceptually different from the study of the numbers represented by fractions (rational numbers). You will observe that, other than the mention of pairs of numbers early in the chapter, essentially nothing is said about numbers throughout Chapter 11. Fractions are considered to be symbols for number pairs in the study of this chapter, and in the next chapter they will be considered to be symbols for rational numbers.

One of the clearest explanations we can give for the concepts presented in this chapter appears at the top of page 260. The fact that on this page we introduce the idea of thinking about number pairs and writing fractions is indicative of the material which is to follow in the remainder of the chapter. We might say, therefore, that this chapter is a study of number pairs used in a certain way, and that we write fractions to symbolize these number pairs. Often we will use the word *fraction* instead of *number pair,* but it will always be clear from the context whether we are referring to the symbol or to the pair of numbers involved.

Work with equivalent fractions is the most important part of Chapter 11 in preparing for the development of rational-number concepts. We do not give a formal definition of equivalent fractions because such a definition would be too abstract for the students. What is intended is that the students recognize two fractions as being equivalent by picturing them in terms of sets or parts of a region.

We give below a formal definition of equivalent fractions.

Two fractions a/b and c/d are equivalent to each other if and only if

$$a \times d = b \times c.$$

Following are some examples of pairs of equivalent fractions. The diagrams below each example illustrate the equivalence relation with regard to part of an object.

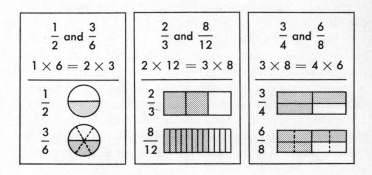

Having provided the students with experiences in working with equivalent fractions, we lead them to build sets of equivalent fractions, starting with lowest-terms fractions such as $\frac{1}{2}$, $\frac{2}{3}$, $\frac{3}{4}$, etc. The following sets are built from such fractions:

Set A {$\frac{1}{2}$, $\frac{2}{4}$, $\frac{3}{6}$, $\frac{4}{8}$, $\frac{5}{10}$, $\frac{6}{12}$, $\frac{7}{14}$, $\frac{8}{16}$, ...},

Set B {$\frac{2}{3}$, $\frac{4}{6}$, $\frac{6}{9}$, $\frac{8}{12}$, ...},

Set C {$\frac{3}{4}$, $\frac{6}{8}$, $\frac{9}{12}$, $\frac{12}{16}$, ...}.

Clearly, if we continue the established pattern indefinitely, each set contains an unlimited number of fractions. It is important to note that any fraction that is equivalent to one half is in set A (assuming an unlimited continuation of the obvious pattern) and that a fraction that is not equivalent to one half is not in set A. Of course, similar statements are true for sets B and C, as well as any other similarly constructed set of fractions. We list below points concerning equivalent fractions and sets of equivalent fractions; these points are obvious, but are essential to the general concepts of Chapter 11.

(a) The definition of equivalent fractions divides the fractions into classes.

(b) Any two fractions in one class are equivalent.

(c) A fraction from one class and a fraction from a different class are not equivalent.

(d) In every class, there is an unlimited number of fractions.

(e) Every fraction is in exactly one class.

Since this chapter is concerned only with fractions and not with rational numbers, we do not want to write equalities such as $\frac{1}{2} = \frac{2}{4}$. Eventually, we will give meaning to statements of this type, but only when one half and two fourths refer to rational numbers. Clearly, one half and two fourths are different fractions, but they are equivalent. We could, if we thought it expedient, invent a symbol for equivalence of fractions and write a mathematical sentence about the equivalence between one half and two fourths. However, this is not necessary for our study. We do want to make it clear to students that pairs of fractions, such as one half and two fourths, are in a sense the same; we use the word *equivalent* to denote this.

Teaching Chapter 11

Although most of the students' previous experiences with fractions have been in terms of working with parts of sets ($\square\square\square$, $\frac{2}{3}$) or parts of regions ($\square\square\square$, $\frac{2}{3}$), you will find it most helpful to provide additional experiences of this type. However, you should be alert to guide your students in the direction of more abstract thinking as their experiences with fractions continue at a more intense rate in this chapter. In the early parts of the chapter, use set materials as needed, and then, as the students are able to think more and more abstractly about fractions, you should reduce considerably the use of these materials. Of course, your initial use of set materials should be gauged to the abilities and needs of the students.

We attempt to play down the term *improper fraction* in this development because of the misleading connotation of the word *improper* with respect to certain types of fractions. To have the students think that there is anything wrong with a fraction such as $\frac{8}{5}$ is to be avoided. Of course, the expression *improper fraction* has historical significance much as that of *negative number*. The connotations of such words as *improper, negative,* and *irrational* simply point out that those who first thought of, used, and named these numbers had little faith in them. Attempt to expose the students to the term *improper fraction,* but play it down and use it infrequently. Whenever possible, just use the word *fraction* for the improper fraction.

Plan to cover the material in this chapter in about $4\frac{1}{2}$ to 5 weeks. Since this chapter is quite long, you must adjust this time-schedule recommendation to the needs and abilities of your students. Certainly, if your students have had considerable background material in fractions, you will be able to move through the chapter much more rapidly than if they have had very limited experiences with fractions.

We do not intend that the students attain a high level of mastery of factual material in this chapter. For example, we do not expect the students to become proficient in reducing fractions to lowest terms (finding the lowest terms fraction for a given fraction). The most important evaluation criteria in this chapter are general understanding of fraction concepts and the students' ability to construct a set of equivalent fractions with reasonable knowledge of the ideas involved. The heavy emphasis on equivalent fractions in this chapter is provided as background for understanding rational numbers, presented in the next chapter. Evaluation based primarily on understanding of concepts is difficult, and, therefore, your evaluation should primarily consist of careful daily observation of the students rather than use of cumulative test materials.

The role this chapter plays in the over-all development of rational-number concepts cannot be underplayed. The students must be provided with an opportunity to gain perception for concepts of fractions, equivalent fractions, and sets of equivalent fractions. Certainly, students must have some feeling for a quantitative relationship, or quantitative sameness, between pairs of fractions from the set {$\frac{1}{2}$, $\frac{2}{4}$, $\frac{3}{6}$, ...}. If you can build successfully students' comprehension of a certain similarity or quantitative sameness between pairs of fractions, much will be gained in terms of readiness for the more abstract concepts presented in the next chapter.

Study the material at the top of the page with the students. As you discuss each row of the table, emphasize the fact that each row shows an object or set, then the associated pair of numbers, the written fraction for this, and finally, the way in which this is read.

If additional work is needed with this type of exercise, either use the exercises at the bottom of the page or make up additional exercises before having the students do the exercises on the page.

Have the students do the exercises, if they were not previously used for discussion material. When the students have finished, allow time for further discussion and checking papers.

Chapter **11*** **FRACTIONS**

Number pairs and fractions

We see	We think	We write	We say
	3 blue parts 4 parts in all	$\frac{3}{4}$ of the region is blue.	Three fourths of the region is blue.
	2 blue dots 7 dots in all	$\frac{2}{7}$ of the dots are blue.	Two sevenths of the dots are blue.

In this column, we think about a number pair.   In this column, we write a fraction for the number pair.

EXERCISES

For each picture, write a fraction to tell what part is shaded.

1. $\frac{7}{9}$ 2. $\frac{5}{6}$ 3. $\frac{7}{12}$ 4. $\frac{3}{8}$

5. $\frac{9}{10}$ 6. $\frac{1}{4}$ 7. $\frac{3}{8}$ 8. $\frac{6}{11}$

260

* *If an exercise does not specifically call for a lowest-terms fraction answer, the students' answers should be considered correct so long as their fractions are equivalent to those given.*

Teaching Pages 260 and 261

- **PURPOSE**

  To provide introductory work with fractions and number pairs

  To provide experiences in reading fractions

  To help the students generalize the fact that for parts of an object, such as thirds or fourths, the parts must be the same size

- **MATHEMATICS**

  Although we establish in this lesson that we consider fractions to be symbols for number pairs, we will occasionally use the word *fraction* when referring to a number pair. That is, we will sometimes say *fraction* when in context it is clear that we are speaking of the number pair involved rather than the symbol. However, just as with the use of the words *number* and *numeral* when speaking of whole numbers, it will always be clear from the context whether we are referring to the number itself or the symbol for the number. When rational numbers are introduced in the next chapter, it will be seen that fractions are symbols for rational numbers. Here again, the word *fraction* will be used occasionally for rational numbers rather than for a specific symbol, but the ideas involved should always be clear from the context.

  Again, we would make the same recommendation that we made for the use of number-numeral terminology in the study of whole numbers: Use the language which will

Parts of an object

DISCUSSION EXERCISES

1. Bobby gave his little brother Alan part of his candy bar. Did Alan get half of the candy? *No*

Alan's piece

2. Mr. White planted part of his field with beans, part of it with corn, and the rest with oats. Would you say that $\frac{1}{3}$ of the field was planted with oats? *No*

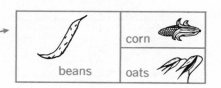

beans · corn · oats

3. Answer **true** or **false** for each exercise.

[A] *F*

$\frac{1}{2}$ of the region is blue.

[B] *T*

$\frac{1}{4}$ of the region is blue.

[C] *F*

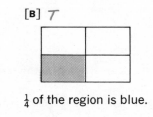

$\frac{1}{2}$ of the region is blue.

[D] *F*

$\frac{1}{4}$ of the region is blue.

[E] *T*

$\frac{1}{16}$ of the region is blue.

[F] *F*

$\frac{1}{7}$ of the region is blue.

[G] *T*

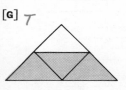

$\frac{3}{4}$ of the region is blue.

[H] *T*

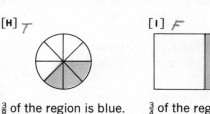

$\frac{3}{8}$ of the region is blue.

[I] *F*

$\frac{3}{4}$ of the region is blue.

Work through and discuss the first two exercises with the class. You might accompany this lesson with some estimation problems for the more able students. For example, in the first exercise, you might have these students attempt to estimate what fractional part Alan's piece of candy is. Do not insist on a high degree of accuracy for these estimations. Estimation of what part of the field is planted in oats may be quite difficult for some students. The most important aspect of exercise 3 is to recognize that the part of the field planted in oats is not one third of the whole field.

Have the students work the remaining exercises. When they have finished, allow time for discussion and checking papers. If time permits, have the students think of and draw on the chalkboard other examples similar to those in exercise 3. You might ask several students to go to the chalkboard and attempt to describe one fourth of a given circle, rectangle, or triangle. Unless the students are precise at drawing, their pictures may not be very accurate. The students in the class should recognize in these cases that one fourth has not been pictured. However, when the divisions are drawn accurately, it will be apparent to the students in the class that one fourth, or another designated fractional part of an object, is shown.

most clearly illustrate the ideas involved, even if such language is not precisely correct according to definitions. For example, just as you might tell a student to write a *number* (when, precisely, you mean *numeral*) you might also ask, "What *fraction* of the objects is blue?" Although such a question can be answered by writing a fraction, it clearly implies that you do not really mean "What *symbol* of the objects is blue?" but rather "What *part*, or give a number pair to tell what part, of the objects is blue?"

PREPARATION

The amount of set demonstrations (cutting up objects or separating sets) that you provide to illustrate ideas of number pairs and fractions in preparing for this lesson will depend largely on the backgrounds and abilities of your students. If your students are very quick and have a good background, you can limit the number of concrete demonstrations; if the students are very slow, you will need to provide a greater number of demonstrations with concrete objects.

Study the material at the top of the page with the class. Note that these diagrams reverse the procedure suggested in the Preparation Section. The first diagram shows a rectangle with eight regions, four of which have been shaded to suggest that four eighths of the region is blue. The second diagram has four less division marks to suggest that two fourths of the region is blue. Finally, two more division marks are deleted and it is observed that half of the region is blue. Of course, the same concepts apply here as in the demonstration suggested in the Preparation Section. Point out to the students that in each case the same amount of the rectangle is shaded, but that the different marks help them think of different fractions for the shaded portion.

Following this discussion, have the students do the exercises. In the discussion following completion of the exercises, point out or elicit from the students the facts that in the two parts of exercise 1 the same amount of the circle is shaded, in the three parts of exercise 2 the same amount of the rectangle is shaded, and that the division marks help them think about different fractions for a given shaded portion.

Fractions and parts of an object

We often use fractions to compare part of an object with the whole object. By dividing the same object in different ways, we can find more than one fraction for comparison.

Study these examples.

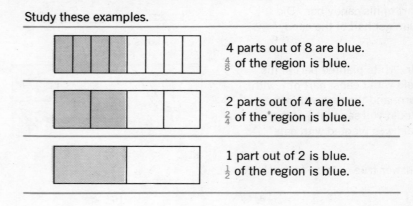

4 parts out of 8 are blue.
$\frac{4}{8}$ of the region is blue.

2 parts out of 4 are blue.
$\frac{2}{4}$ of the region is blue.

1 part out of 2 is blue.
$\frac{1}{2}$ of the region is blue.

EXERCISES

First give the missing number. Then give the fraction for the number pair.

1. [A] 3 of the ▓ parts are blue. *6*
   ▓ of the region is blue. $\frac{3}{6}$

   [B] 1 of the ▓ parts is blue. *2*
   ▓ of the region is blue. $\frac{1}{2}$

2. [A] 8 of the ▓ parts are blue. *12*
   ▓ of the region is blue. $\frac{8}{12}$

   [B] ▓ of the 6 parts are blue. *4*
   ▓ of the region is blue. $\frac{4}{6}$

   [C] ▓ of the 3 parts are blue. *2*
   ▓ of the region is blue. $\frac{2}{3}$

Teaching Pages 262 and 263

- **PURPOSE**

  To provide further experiences in working with fractions and parts of an object

  To provide experiences leading toward an understanding of equivalent-fraction concepts

- **PREPARATION**

  Provide the students with experiences similar to those introduced on page 262, either by using objects which can be readily cut apart or by showing drawings on the chalkboard. The type of materials you use should depend on the abilities of your students. If the students have a diffi-

DISCUSSION EXERCISES

1. [A] Explain how you might think if you said, "$\frac{9}{12}$ of the region is blue." *9 parts out of 12 are blue.*

   [B] Explain how you might think if you said, "$\frac{3}{4}$ of the region is blue." *3 out of 4 columns are blue.*

2. [A] Explain how you might think if you said, "$\frac{4}{24}$ of the region is blue." *4 parts out of 24 are blue*

   [B] Explain how you might think if you said, "$\frac{1}{6}$ of the region is blue." *1 out of 6 columns is blue.*

★ [C] Explain how you might think if you said, "$\frac{2}{12}$ of the region is blue."
   Group small regions by twos. There are 12 groups in all. 2 of these groups are blue $\frac{2}{4}$ of the region is blue.
   Study this example:
   $\frac{1}{2}$ of the region is blue.

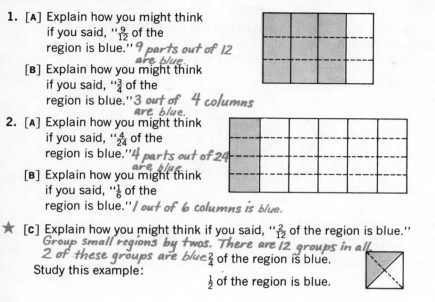

EXERCISES

Give at least two fractions to tell what part of each region is blue.

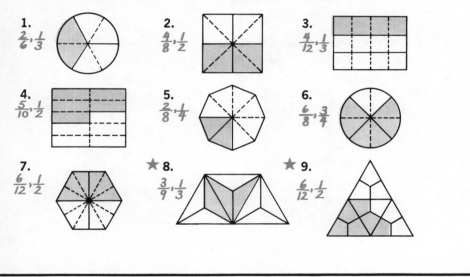

1. $\frac{2}{6}, \frac{1}{3}$

2. $\frac{4}{8}, \frac{1}{2}$

3. $\frac{4}{12}, \frac{1}{3}$

4. $\frac{5}{10}, \frac{1}{2}$

5. $\frac{2}{8}, \frac{1}{4}$

6. $\frac{6}{8}, \frac{3}{4}$

7. $\frac{6}{12}, \frac{1}{2}$

★ 8. $\frac{3}{9}, \frac{1}{3}$

★ 9. $\frac{6}{12}, \frac{1}{2}$

Lead the class through the discussion exercises. Help them see why for exercise 1 they can think of the blue region as $\frac{9}{12}$ and as $\frac{3}{4}$. Of course, for $\frac{9}{12}$ the students merely need to count to determine that there are 12 squares and that nine are shaded. However, to see that three fourths of the region is blue, the students must consider columns of the figure. They observe that three out of four columns are shaded blue; therefore, three fourths of the rectangular region is blue.

Similarly, for exercise 2, the students, by counting, can quickly observe that $\frac{4}{24}$ of the region is blue. Looking at the columns, they can see that one column out of six is shaded blue; consequently, one sixth of the region is blue. To answer exercise 2c, we would like the students to observe that they can think about the smaller regions in pairs; thus they can think of two pairs of blue regions out of a total of 12 pairs of regions.

Following this discussion, have the students complete the exercises at the bottom of the page. During the discussion which follows have the students discuss how, for each figure, they can think of more than just one fraction to describe the part of the figure that is blue.

cult time understanding the abstraction of chalkboard drawings, you may find it beneficial to use cardboard cutouts or other objects which can be cut apart to demonstrate fraction concepts. However, if your students have no difficulty understanding drawings, you will probably find this method more desirable.

The following demonstration is suggested. Draw on the chalkboard a rectangle with a dividing mark which obviously cuts the rectangle in half. Shade half the rectangle and have the students write a fraction to tell what part of the rectangle is shaded. Now draw marks which divide the rectangle in fourths, and observe with the students that half of the rectangle is still shaded, but the new lines help them think of this shaded portion as two fourths of the rectangle. Repeat this by dividing each of the four

regions into halves (thus making eight regions of the same size) and observe with the students that half or two fourths of the rectangle is still shaded, but the new division marks help them think about four eighths of the rectangle as being shaded. If you choose, you can continue this by using further division marks and the fractions $\frac{8}{16}$ and $\frac{16}{32}$.

You might also repeat this demonstration using thirds. The chief drawback to using thirds is the difficulty of drawing accurate division marks.

Discuss with the students the material at the top of the page. Point out that the same number of dots are colored for each of the three sets pictured (four of eight dots are colored in each of the three set pictures). However, in the first set picture, they think of four eighths of the dots; in the second set picture, they think of two fourths; and in the third picture, one half. Of course, the set rings form groupings to suggest two fourths and one half rather than four eighths.

If you think it necessary, provide the students with a similar demonstration to illustrate the idea that for a given part of a set, they can often think of more than one fraction simply by considering different groupings.

Following this discussion, have the students do the exercises. Allow ample time for discussion once the students have completed the page. Be sure the students see how the set rings help them think of the sets in a slightly different way, even though the same number of objects is shaded for each of the two parts of exercise 1 and for each of the three parts in exercise 2.

Fractions and sets

We often use fractions to compare part of a set with the whole set. By thinking of the same set in different ways, we may find that more than one fraction can be used for the comparison.

Study these examples.

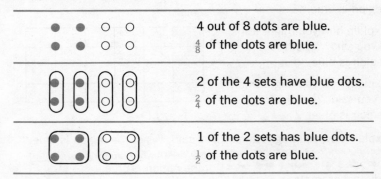

4 out of 8 dots are blue.
$\frac{4}{8}$ of the dots are blue.

2 of the 4 sets have blue dots.
$\frac{2}{4}$ of the dots are blue.

1 of the 2 sets has blue dots.
$\frac{1}{2}$ of the dots are blue.

EXERCISES

First give the missing number. Then give the fraction for the number pair.

1. [A] 3 of the ▓ triangles are blue. 6
   ▓ of the triangles are blue. $\frac{3}{6}$

   [B] 1 of the ▓ sets has blue triangles. 2
   ▓ of the triangles are blue. $\frac{1}{2}$

2. [A] 8 of the ▓ squares are blue. 12
   ▓ of the squares are blue. $\frac{8}{12}$

   [B] ▓ of the 6 sets have blue squares. 4
   ▓ of the squares are blue. $\frac{4}{6}$

   [C] ▓ of the 3 sets have blue squares. 2
   ▓ of the squares are blue. $\frac{2}{3}$

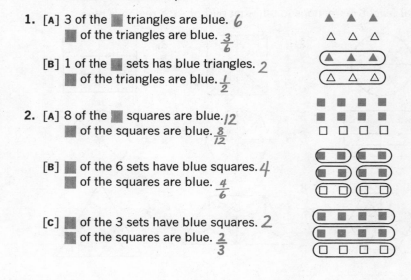

Teaching Pages 264 and 265

- **PURPOSE**

  To provide additional experiences in working with fractions and sets

  To provide experiences leading toward understanding equivalent fractions

- **PREPARATION**

  Depending on the level of maturity that is evident in your students, you may choose to provide some physical sets for them to work with in preparing for this lesson. For example, you could exhibit on a table a set of ten objects and group them in a manner that focuses attention

DISCUSSION EXERCISES

1. [A] Explain how you might think if you said, "$\frac{9}{12}$ of the squares are blue." *12 squares in all. 9 of them are blue.*

   [B] Explain how you might think if you said, "$\frac{3}{4}$ of the squares are blue." *3 of 4 columns are blue.*

2. [A] Explain how you might think if you said, "$\frac{4}{24}$ of the dots are blue." *24 dots in all. 4 of them are blue.*

   [B] Explain how you might think if you said, "$\frac{1}{6}$ of the dots are blue." *1 of 6 columns is blue.*

   ★ [C] Explain how you might think if you said, "$\frac{2}{12}$ of the dots are blue."
   Grouping by twos, there are 12 sets in all. 2 of these sets contain blue dots. $\frac{2}{4}$ of the dots are blue.
   Study this example: $\frac{1}{2}$ of the dots are blue.

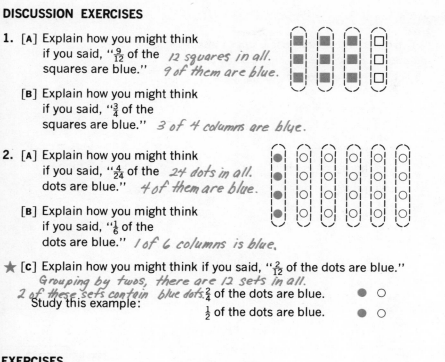

EXERCISES

For each set, give at least two different fractions to tell what part of the set is blue.

1. $\frac{2}{6}, \frac{1}{3}$

2. $\frac{4}{8}, \frac{1}{2}$

3. $\frac{4}{12}, \frac{1}{3}$

4. $\frac{3}{12}, \frac{1}{4}$

5. $\frac{5}{10}, \frac{1}{2}$

6. $\frac{4}{6}, \frac{2}{3}$

7. $\frac{6}{8}, \frac{3}{4}$

8. $\frac{6}{12}, \frac{1}{2}$

9. $\frac{3}{9}, \frac{1}{3}$

Cover the discussion exercises carefully with the class. Be sure they understand that the dotted rings around the parts of a set help them think of the set in different ways.

For discussion exercise 2c, you should elicit from the students the fact that they can think of drawing an horizontal line through the middle of the rectangular array to get 12 sets of dots with two dots in each set; there would be two sets of blue dots and 12 sets of dots in all, for which they could think "$\frac{2}{12}$ of the dots are blue." Give the students a chance to study the example and explain how they think of it for the statement "$\frac{2}{4}$ of the dots are blue" and for the statement "$\frac{1}{2}$ of the dots are blue."

Following this discussion, have the students work the exercises. As the students discuss the correct answers exhibit these fractions on the chalkboard. Of course, there are more than two correct fractions for each set. For example, for exercise 3 the students might give $\frac{1}{3}$, $\frac{2}{6}$, or $\frac{4}{12}$. Although the fraction $\frac{3}{9}$ would not be incorrect, this set picture does not suggest the fraction $\frac{3}{9}$ as telling what part of the set is blue.

on two tenths, three tenths, etc. During this discussion, have the students write the fractions on the chalkboard and group the set in other ways to demonstrate different fractions. Vary the number of objects in the set to provide a wider variety of experiences.

If your students have progressed beyond the stage of requiring experiences in handling sets, you can prepare for this lesson by having the students draw sets on the chalkboard and illustrate various fractions with their drawings.

Whether you use concrete objects or drawings on the chalkboard, you should emphasize that with certain groupings it is possible to think of more than one fraction. For example, you can group ten objects in pairs so that the students can think of two tenths and one fifth.

As you discuss the example showing the equivalent fractions one half and two fourths, be sure the students see the relationship between the pictures and the two fractions for each picture. Stress the word *equivalent* and have the students read it several times in the examples given in the table. Have the students explain how they think in one way for the set on the left and another way for the set on the right. For example, in the first row, the dotted rings in the left-hand set suggest that they think "one of the three sets is blue"; and on the right, by simply looking at the six objects, they think "two of the six are blue." Hence, one third is equivalent to two sixths. Following this discussion have the students do the exercises.

When the students have finished the exercises, allow time for checking papers and further discussion.

Equivalent fractions

Two different fractions sometimes remind us of the same number of things in a set or the same part of an object. Here is an example using $\frac{1}{2}$ and $\frac{2}{4}$.

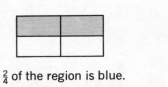

$\frac{2}{4}$ of the region is blue.
$\frac{1}{2}$ of the region is blue.

$\frac{2}{4}$ of the dots are blue.
$\frac{1}{2}$ of the dots are blue.

Such pairs of fractions are called equivalent fractions
We say that:

> $\frac{1}{2}$ **is equivalent to** $\frac{2}{4}$.

Here are some other examples.

	$\frac{1}{3}$ is equivalent to $\frac{2}{6}$.	
	$\frac{2}{3}$ is equivalent to $\frac{4}{6}$.	
	$\frac{1}{4}$ is equivalent to $\frac{2}{8}$.	

EXERCISES

1. Give the fraction for the ▒.

$\frac{4}{8}$ is equivalent to ▒ $\frac{1}{2}$

2. $\frac{2}{4}$ and $\frac{3}{6}$ are equivalent to $\frac{1}{2}$. Give another fraction that is equivalent to $\frac{1}{2}$. $\frac{4}{8}, \frac{5}{10}, \cdots$

3. Give three fractions that are equivalent to $\frac{1}{3}$. $\frac{2}{6}, \frac{3}{9}, \frac{4}{12}, \cdots$

4. Draw a picture to show that $\frac{1}{3}$ is equivalent to $\frac{2}{6}$. , etc.

Teaching Pages 266 and 267

• **PURPOSE**

To introduce formally the concept of equivalent fractions

• **MATHEMATICS**

In this lesson rather than provide a formal definition for the equivalence of two fractions, we introduce the idea in terms of sets and parts of a region in such a way that students perceive intuitively the idea of equivalent fractions.

Following is the standard definition for equivalent fractions:

The fraction a/b is equivalent to c/d if, and only if, $a \times d = b \times c$.

The fact that this definition expresses the same general idea as does the intuitive definition given in the student text requires further consideration. Certainly, using either the intuitive definition or the standard definition, we could easily observe that a fraction is equivalent to itself. Let us examine the fraction *two thirds*. Two thirds is equivalent to two thirds because $2 \times 3 = 3 \times 2$. Now, let us examine the two fractions *two thirds* and *four sixths*. Of course, if we write the numerator and denominator of four sixths in factored form, we are saying that two thirds is equivalent to the fraction $\frac{2 \times 2}{2 \times 3}$. That is, four sixths differ from two thirds only in having a factor of two in both the numerator and the denominator. Hence, $2 \times (2 \times 3) = 3 \times (2 \times 2)$. Note that the difference be-

DISCUSSION EXERCISES

1. Give a fraction to tell how much of each bar is blue. Use the fraction suggested by the dividing marks.

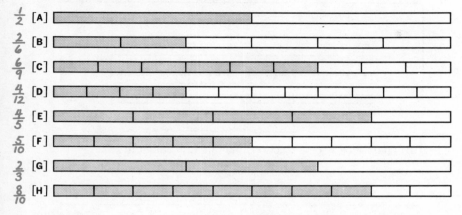

$\frac{1}{2}$ [A]

$\frac{2}{6}$ [B]

$\frac{6}{9}$ [C]

$\frac{4}{12}$ [D]

$\frac{4}{5}$ [E]

$\frac{5}{10}$ [F]

$\frac{2}{3}$ [G]

$\frac{8}{10}$ [H]

2. Explain how you can tell from the bars which fractions are equivalent.

EXERCISES

Write a pair of equivalent fractions for each picture.

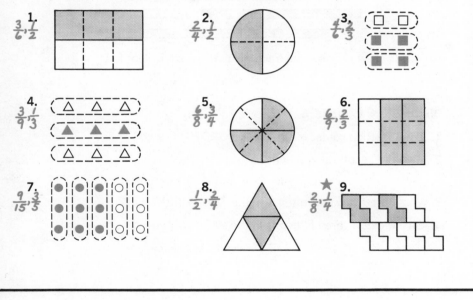

1. $\frac{3}{6}, \frac{1}{2}$

2. $\frac{2}{4}, \frac{1}{2}$

3. $\frac{4}{6}, \frac{2}{3}$

4. $\frac{3}{9}, \frac{1}{3}$

5. $\frac{6}{8}, \frac{3}{4}$

6. $\frac{6}{9}, \frac{2}{3}$

7. $\frac{9}{15}, \frac{3}{5}$

8. $\frac{1}{2}, \frac{2}{4}$

★ **9.** $\frac{2}{8}, \frac{1}{4}$

---

tween this equality and $2 \times 3 = 3 \times 2$ is simply a factor of two on each side.

It is a simple matter to illustrate the equivalence of two thirds and four sixths in a picture such as the middle row in the table on page 266. The diagrams showing two thirds of an object shaded and four sixths of an object shaded illustrate the quantitative sameness of these fractions. Of course, the importance of the idea of equivalent fractions is the fact that it allows us to separate our fractions into large classes from which we shall abstract the concept of rational number. For example, we want to associate just one number with the two fractions, two thirds and four sixths, and we will also want to observe that there are other fractions for this same number, such as $\frac{6}{9}$, $\frac{8}{12}$, $\frac{10}{15}$.

You might choose to have the students work the first exercise individually before discussing it. Have the students explain step by step how they arrive at the fraction for each bar and then how they decide which pair of fractions is equivalent. For example, the students should observe that the fractions for exercises 1A and F are equivalent because the same amount of the bar is shaded for each one; it is just that for bar F they think of five tenths because of the division marks, and for bar A they think of one half. Be sure that the students are given ample opportunity to explain these ideas.

Following this discussion, have the students do the exercises. When they have finished, ask the students to explain how they arrived at the two fractions for each exercise.

● **PREPARATION**

Conduct a review of the two previous lessons. For example, exhibit on the chalkboard or on a demonstration table a set of objects (such as six objects, three of which are blue) and have the students write two fractions for this set. Of course, for this example we would expect the students to write one half and three sixths. Do this also for a given region. You might divide a region into eighths and color two portions blue. Here, we would expect the students to write $\frac{2}{8}$ and $\frac{1}{4}$.

Study with the students the two charts on the page. Be sure the students see how in each chart the different division marks on the various bars help them think of different fractions for the same amount of shaded portion. Observe with the class that these fractions are equivalent because in each case the same amount of the bar is shaded.

Follow this discussion of the two charts by working through the discussion exercises with the students. As the students answer the exercises, attempt to get them to explain their answers.

In exercise 1, we would like the students to think about $\frac{6}{12}$ as the next fraction in the set of equivalent fractions for the *one-half* chart. There are a number of ways the students can think of this. They can think of the sequence of the numerators—{1, 2, 3, 4, 5, 6, . . .}—and the sequence of denominators—{2, 4, 6, 8, 10, 12, . . .}, or they can observe that in each case the number of divisions was two more than the number before and that six of the 12 divisions or parts would be required to make up one half. The important thing is not that the students give precise descriptions of how they decide on $\frac{6}{12}$, but rather that they consider various ways of arriving at $\frac{6}{12}$ as the next fraction in the set. Of course, we would point out that we have not said specifically that $\frac{6}{12}$ must be the next fraction in this set; it is intuitively implied as next by the pattern of the previously listed fractions. Certainly the next fraction could be $\frac{7}{14}$ or even $\frac{50}{100}$. Most of the students will arrive at the fraction $\frac{6}{12}$ as the next fraction for this set, and this, of course, is what we want them to do.

For exercise 2, again try to get the students to show how they found the next three fractions in the set. You should also follow this with similar explanations for exercises 3 and 4.

Sets of equivalent fractions

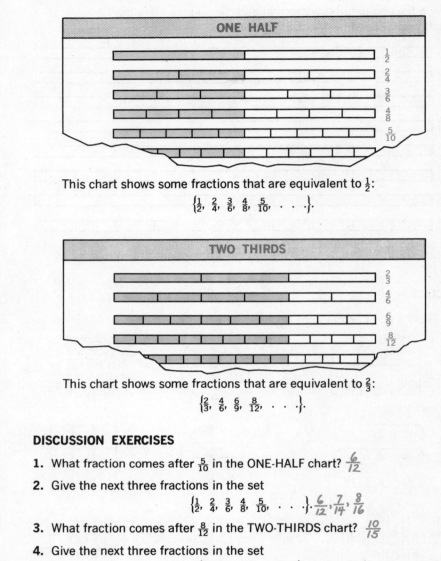

This chart shows some fractions that are equivalent to $\frac{1}{2}$:

$$\left\{\frac{1}{2}, \frac{2}{4}, \frac{3}{6}, \frac{4}{8}, \frac{5}{10}, \cdot \cdot \cdot\right\}.$$

This chart shows some fractions that are equivalent to $\frac{2}{3}$:

$$\left\{\frac{2}{3}, \frac{4}{6}, \frac{6}{9}, \frac{8}{12}, \cdot \cdot \cdot\right\}.$$

DISCUSSION EXERCISES

1. What fraction comes after $\frac{5}{10}$ in the ONE-HALF chart? $\frac{6}{12}$

2. Give the next three fractions in the set
$$\left\{\frac{1}{2}, \frac{2}{4}, \frac{3}{6}, \frac{4}{8}, \frac{5}{10}, \cdot \cdot \cdot\right\}. \frac{6}{12}, \frac{7}{14}, \frac{8}{16}$$

3. What fraction comes after $\frac{8}{12}$ in the TWO-THIRDS chart? $\frac{10}{15}$

4. Give the next three fractions in the set
$$\left\{\frac{2}{3}, \frac{4}{6}, \frac{6}{9}, \frac{8}{12}, \cdot \cdot \cdot\right\}. \frac{10}{15}, \frac{12}{18}, \frac{14}{21}$$

Teaching Pages 268 and 269

● PURPOSE

To provide further work with equivalent fractions

To introduce the concept of a set of equivalent fractions that contains an unlimited number of fractions

● PREPARATION

Exhibit on the chalkboard a long, narrow bar. Make a dividing mark at the halfway point and color the left half of the bar. Exhibit the fraction $\frac{1}{2}$ for the amount of the bar that is colored. Now, mark the bar into fourths and observe with the class that the new marks help them think about the fact that two fourths of the bar is shaded. Con-

EXERCISES

1. Study the chart and give the missing fractions.

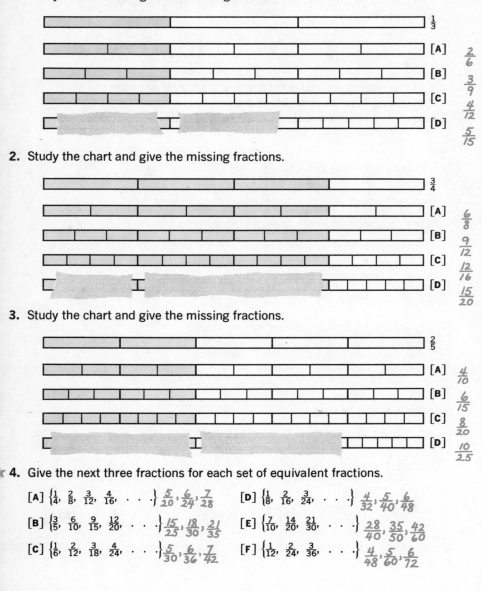

Notice with the class that in each exercise part of the last bar is covered so that they cannot count the divisions and they have to figure out for themselves what the next fraction is. Of course, in each case the first fraction is given (in a later lesson, the students will learn to call this fraction the *lowest-terms fraction* for the set). During the discussion of exercises 1 through 3, be sure that the various methods which the students used to arrive at the answer to part D are brought out for each exercise.

Exercise 4 is starred because no particular method has been given for finding the next three fractions in these sets; however, many students will be able to do this quite readily because they have an intuitive grasp of the concepts presented thus far.

2. Study the chart and give the missing fractions.

3. Study the chart and give the missing fractions.

4. Give the next three fractions for each set of equivalent fractions.

[A] $\left\{\dfrac{1}{4},\ \dfrac{2}{8},\ \dfrac{3}{12},\ \dfrac{4}{16},\ \cdots\right\}$ $\dfrac{5}{20},\dfrac{6}{24},\dfrac{7}{28}$

[D] $\left\{\dfrac{1}{8},\ \dfrac{2}{16},\ \dfrac{3}{24},\ \cdots\right\}$ $\dfrac{4}{32},\dfrac{5}{40},\dfrac{6}{48}$

[B] $\left\{\dfrac{3}{5},\ \dfrac{6}{10},\ \dfrac{9}{15},\ \dfrac{12}{20},\ \cdots\right\}$ $\dfrac{15}{25},\dfrac{18}{30},\dfrac{21}{35}$

[E] $\left\{\dfrac{7}{10},\ \dfrac{14}{20},\ \dfrac{21}{30},\ \cdots\right\}$ $\dfrac{28}{40},\dfrac{35}{50},\dfrac{42}{60}$

[C] $\left\{\dfrac{1}{6},\ \dfrac{2}{12},\ \dfrac{3}{18},\ \dfrac{4}{24},\ \cdots\right\}$ $\dfrac{5}{30},\dfrac{6}{36},\dfrac{7}{42}$

[F] $\left\{\dfrac{1}{12},\ \dfrac{2}{24},\ \dfrac{3}{36},\ \cdots\right\}$ $\dfrac{4}{48},\dfrac{5}{60},\dfrac{6}{72}$

tinue this procedure by exhibiting a picture that shows $\frac{4}{8}$ and then $\frac{8}{16}$ of the bar. Now draw another bar, shade half of it, and then mark the bar into sixths to demonstrate the fraction three sixths. You might also use this procedure to demonstrate five tenths.

Demonstrations of this type are designed to help students understand the class of equivalent fractions that begins with the fraction one half, and the fact that there is a certain quantitative similarity with respect to all fractions in this set. If necessary, repeat this for other fractions such as one third, two thirds, one fourth, etc.

Study and discuss with the class the information preceding the exercises. It may be helpful to exhibit on the chalkboard the material in the blue boxes. Be sure that the students see how these examples show that each fraction in the set can be constructed from the first fraction.

Following your discussion of the two examples presented in the blue boxes, exhibit on the chalkboard discussion exercise 1. Have the students go to the chalkboard and fill in the missing fractions. As they do this, ask them to explain how they found the fraction. It may be expedient to present another exercise, such as building a set of fractions from two thirds, as a follow-up to this lesson.

Building sets of equivalent fractions

In the last lesson, you studied sets of equivalent fractions similar to these.

In this lesson, you will learn a way of finding other fractions that belong to these sets. Study the sets of fractions in the boxes below. The blue numerals should help you understand the idea.

DISCUSSION EXERCISES

1. Give the missing fractions.

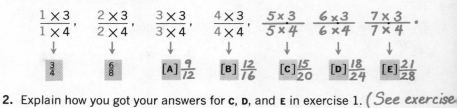

2. Explain how you got your answers for **C**, **D**, and **E** in exercise 1. *(See exercise*

Teaching Pages 270 and 271

- **PURPOSE**

  To focus further attention upon building sets of equivalent fractions

  To provide a method for building sets of equivalent fractions

- **PREPARATION**

  Review the material covered in the last lesson. Give the students an opportunity to work with several sets of equivalent fractions. For example, you can write on the chalkboard the set {½, ²⁄₄, ³⁄₆, ⁴⁄₈, . . .} and have the students write several more fractions for this set. Next present

EXERCISES

1. Find the missing fractions.

$$\frac{1\times1}{1\times6}, \quad \frac{2\times1}{2\times6}, \quad \frac{3\times1}{3\times6}, \quad \frac{4\times1}{4\times6}, \quad \frac{5\times1}{5\times6} \quad \frac{6\times1}{6\times6}$$

$\downarrow \qquad \downarrow \qquad \downarrow \qquad \downarrow \qquad \downarrow \qquad \downarrow$

$\frac{1}{6} \quad \frac{2}{12} \quad [A]\frac{3}{18} \quad [B]\frac{4}{24} \quad [C]\frac{5}{30} \quad [D]\frac{6}{36}$

$$\frac{1\times3}{1\times8}, \quad \frac{2\times3}{2\times8}, \quad \frac{3\times3}{3\times8}, \quad \frac{4\times3}{4\times8}, \quad \frac{5\times3}{5\times8} \quad \frac{6\times3}{6\times8}$$

$\downarrow \qquad \downarrow \qquad \downarrow \qquad \downarrow \qquad \downarrow \qquad \downarrow$

$\frac{3}{8} \quad \frac{6}{16} \quad [E]\frac{9}{24} \quad [F]\frac{12}{32} \quad [G]\frac{15}{40} \quad [H]\frac{18}{48}$

$$\frac{1\times4}{1\times5}, \quad \frac{2\times4}{2\times5}, \quad \frac{3\times4}{3\times5}, \quad \frac{4\times4}{4\times5}, \quad \frac{5\times4}{5\times5} \quad \frac{6\times4}{6\times5}$$

$\downarrow \qquad \downarrow \qquad \downarrow \qquad \downarrow \qquad \downarrow \qquad \downarrow$

$\frac{4}{5} \quad \frac{8}{10} \quad [I]\frac{12}{15} \quad [J]\frac{16}{20} \quad [K]\frac{20}{25} \quad [L]\frac{24}{30}$

$$\frac{1\times1}{1\times4}, \quad \frac{2\times1}{2\times4}, \quad \frac{3\times1}{3\times4}, \quad \frac{4\times1}{4\times4} \quad \frac{5\times1}{5\times4} \quad \frac{6\times1}{6\times4}$$

$\downarrow \qquad \downarrow \qquad \downarrow \qquad \downarrow \qquad \downarrow \qquad \downarrow$

$\frac{1}{4} \quad [M]\frac{2}{8} \quad [N]\frac{3}{12} \quad [O]\frac{4}{16} \quad [P]\frac{5}{20} \quad [Q]\frac{6}{24}$

2. Find the next three fractions for each set of equivalent fractions.

[A] $\{\frac{1}{3}, \frac{2}{6}, \frac{3}{9}, \frac{4}{12}, \ldots\} \frac{5}{15}, \frac{6}{18}, \frac{7}{21}$

[B] $\{\frac{1}{8}, \frac{2}{16}, \frac{3}{24}, \frac{4}{32}, \ldots\} \frac{5}{40}, \frac{6}{48}, \frac{7}{56}$

[C] $\{\frac{5}{6}, \frac{10}{12}, \frac{15}{18}, \ldots\} \frac{20}{24}, \frac{25}{30}, \frac{30}{36}$

[D] $\{\frac{2}{7}, \frac{4}{14}, \frac{6}{21}, \ldots\} \frac{8}{28}, \frac{10}{35}, \frac{12}{42}$

[E] $\{\frac{5}{9}, \frac{10}{18}, \frac{15}{27}, \ldots\} \frac{20}{36}, \frac{25}{45}, \frac{30}{54}$

[F] $\{\frac{1}{10}, \frac{2}{20}, \frac{3}{30}, \ldots\} \frac{4}{40}, \frac{5}{50}, \frac{6}{60}$

★**3.** Find the missing numbers.

$\{\frac{1}{2}, \frac{2}{4}, \frac{3}{6}, \frac{4}{8}, \ldots, [A]\frac{25}{50}, \ldots, [B]\frac{50}{100}\}$

$\{\frac{1}{3}, \frac{2}{6}, \frac{3}{9}, \frac{4}{12}, \ldots, [C]\frac{30}{90}, \ldots, [D]\frac{100}{300}\}$

$\{\frac{3}{4}, \frac{6}{8}, \frac{9}{12}, \ldots, [E]\frac{30}{40}, \ldots, [F]\frac{75}{100}, \ldots, [G]\frac{300}{400}\}$

After the students have completed exercise 1, discuss each part and exhibit one or two examples on the chalkboard. Then have the students do exercise 2. Follow up exercise 2 by writing on the chalkboard the method by which the three missing fractions can be found from those that are given. For example, in exercise 2c we would like the students to observe that the fraction $^{10}\!/_{12}$ is found by considering

$$\frac{2 \times 5}{2 \times 6}$$

and that $^{15}\!/_{18}$ is found by considering

$$\frac{3 \times 5}{3 \times 6}.$$

Then the next fraction would be

$$\frac{4 \times 5}{4 \times 6}$$

or $^{20}\!/_{24}$.

You may choose to have all the students attempt exercise 3, after cautioning the less able students that this exercise is more difficult than some of the others. Certainly many of the students will benefit from a discussion of exercise 3 once the correct answer has been given.

---

other sets of equivalent fractions and give the students an opportunity to find other fractions in the sets. You may also find it helpful to accompany the development of these sets of fractions with diagrams such as those in the last lesson. We have used the bar diagrams to help build sets of equivalent fractions simply because it is a convenient visual aid. You could, however, use rectangles, circles, etc., to continue developing the concept of equivalent fractions. It is important that the students gain some feeling for the quantitative similarity between equivalent fractions and learn how to construct sets of equivalent fractions.

Have the students read the explanation of *numerator* and *denominator*. Precise language concerning numerator and denominator would indicate that we say the numerator is the number represented by the top numeral in the fraction, and the denominator is the number represented by the bottom numeral of the fraction. This type of language, although accurate, might serve to confuse the students. Therefore, we suggest that you simply observe with the students that the numerator is the top number and the denominator is the bottom number of the fraction.

Notice also with the students that the numerator tells how many and the denominator names the fraction. Thus for ⅔, the 3 means thirds and the 2 tells how many thirds. Such an explanation is merely a further attempt to clarify and strengthen understanding of fraction concepts.

Following this discussion, have the students do the exercises and then discuss the answers. Some of the less able students may have difficulty with exercise 2, but they should understand it once the correct answers are given during the discussion period.

Numerator and denominator

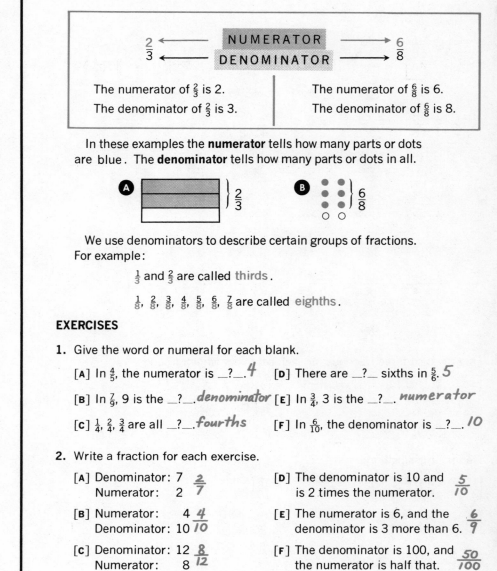

$$\frac{2}{3} \longleftarrow \boxed{\text{NUMERATOR}} \longrightarrow \frac{6}{8}$$
$$\longleftarrow \boxed{\text{DENOMINATOR}} \longrightarrow$$

The numerator of $\frac{2}{3}$ is 2.　　The numerator of $\frac{6}{8}$ is 6.
The denominator of $\frac{2}{3}$ is 3.　The denominator of $\frac{6}{8}$ is 8.

In these examples the **numerator** tells how many parts or dots are blue. The **denominator** tells how many parts or dots in all.

A $\Big\}\frac{2}{3}$　　B $\Big\}\frac{6}{8}$

We use denominators to describe certain groups of fractions. For example:

$\frac{1}{3}$ and $\frac{2}{3}$ are called thirds.

$\frac{1}{8}$, $\frac{2}{8}$, $\frac{3}{8}$, $\frac{4}{8}$, $\frac{5}{8}$, $\frac{6}{8}$, $\frac{7}{8}$ are called eighths.

EXERCISES

1. Give the word or numeral for each blank.

   [A] In $\frac{4}{5}$, the numerator is __?__. *4*　　[D] There are __?__ sixths in $\frac{5}{6}$. *5*

   [B] In $\frac{7}{9}$, 9 is the __?__. *denominator*　[E] In $\frac{3}{4}$, 3 is the __?__. *numerator*

   [C] $\frac{1}{4}$, $\frac{2}{4}$, $\frac{3}{4}$ are all __?__. *fourths*　　[F] In $\frac{6}{10}$, the denominator is __?__. *10*

2. Write a fraction for each exercise.

   [A] Denominator: 7　$\frac{2}{7}$　　[D] The denominator is 10 and　$\frac{5}{10}$
   　　Numerator:　2　　　　　　　　is 2 times the numerator.

   [B] Numerator:　　4　$\frac{4}{10}$　　[E] The numerator is 6, and the　$\frac{6}{9}$
   　　Denominator: 10　　　　　　　denominator is 3 more than 6.

   [C] Denominator: 12　$\frac{8}{12}$　　[F] The denominator is 100, and　$\frac{50}{100}$
   　　Numerator:　　8　　　　　　　the numerator is half that.

Teaching Pages 272 and 273

● **PURPOSE**

To introduce the terms numerator *and* denominator
To provide additional experiences in working with sets of equivalent fractions

● **PREPARATION**

Review the last lesson by presenting several sets of equivalent fractions on the chalkboard. You might present the set {¼, ²⁄₈, ³⁄₁₂, . . .} and have the students demonstrate how to find the next five or six fractions in this set. Their demonstration should include the breaking apart of the numerator and denominator to see how

EXERCISES

Copy each exercise on your paper. Write the missing
numerators and denominators to form a set of equivalent fractions.

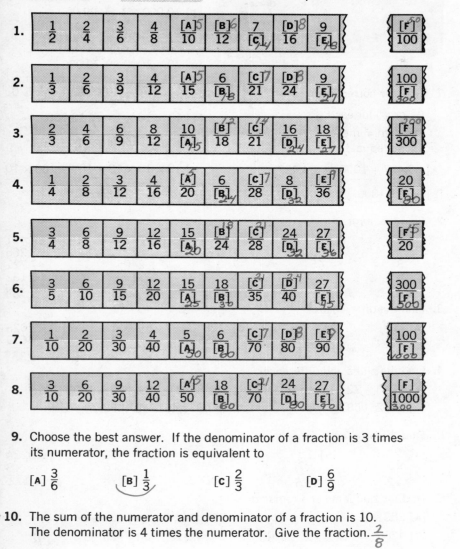

1. $\frac{1}{2}$ $\frac{2}{4}$ $\frac{3}{6}$ $\frac{4}{8}$ $\frac{[A]}{10}$ $\frac{[B]}{12}$ $\frac{7}{[C]}$ $\frac{[D]}{16}$ $\frac{9}{[E]}$ $\frac{[F]}{100}$

2. $\frac{1}{3}$ $\frac{2}{6}$ $\frac{3}{9}$ $\frac{4}{12}$ $\frac{[A]}{15}$ $\frac{6}{[B]}$ $\frac{[C]}{21}$ $\frac{[D]}{24}$ $\frac{9}{[E]}$ $\frac{100}{[F]}$

3. $\frac{2}{3}$ $\frac{4}{6}$ $\frac{6}{9}$ $\frac{8}{12}$ $\frac{10}{[A]}$ $\frac{[B]}{18}$ $\frac{[C]}{21}$ $\frac{16}{[D]}$ $\frac{18}{[E]}$ $\frac{[F]}{300}$

4. $\frac{1}{4}$ $\frac{2}{8}$ $\frac{3}{12}$ $\frac{4}{16}$ $\frac{[A]}{20}$ $\frac{6}{[B]}$ $\frac{[C]}{28}$ $\frac{8}{[D]}$ $\frac{[E]}{36}$ $\frac{20}{[E]}$

5. $\frac{3}{4}$ $\frac{6}{8}$ $\frac{9}{12}$ $\frac{12}{16}$ $\frac{15}{[A]}$ $\frac{[B]}{24}$ $\frac{[C]}{28}$ $\frac{24}{[D]}$ $\frac{27}{[E]}$ $\frac{[F]}{20}$

6. $\frac{3}{5}$ $\frac{6}{10}$ $\frac{9}{15}$ $\frac{12}{20}$ $\frac{15}{[A]}$ $\frac{18}{[B]}$ $\frac{[C]}{35}$ $\frac{[D]}{40}$ $\frac{27}{[E]}$ $\frac{300}{[F]}$

7. $\frac{1}{10}$ $\frac{2}{20}$ $\frac{3}{30}$ $\frac{4}{40}$ $\frac{5}{[A]}$ $\frac{6}{[B]}$ $\frac{[C]}{70}$ $\frac{[D]}{80}$ $\frac{[E]}{90}$ $\frac{100}{[F]}$

8. $\frac{3}{10}$ $\frac{6}{20}$ $\frac{9}{30}$ $\frac{12}{40}$ $\frac{[A]}{50}$ $\frac{18}{[B]}$ $\frac{[C]}{70}$ $\frac{24}{[D]}$ $\frac{27}{[E]}$ $\frac{[F]}{1000}$

9. Choose the best answer. If the denominator of a fraction is 3 times
its numerator, the fraction is equivalent to

[A] $\frac{3}{6}$ [B] $\frac{1}{3}$ [C] $\frac{2}{3}$ [D] $\frac{6}{9}$

10. The sum of the numerator and denominator of a fraction is 10.
The denominator is 4 times the numerator. Give the fraction. $\frac{2}{8}$

Have the students do exercises 1 and 2 on their own and then allow time for checking and presentation of these exercises on the chalkboard. Observe with the students that they are reminded again of the names *numerator* and *denominator* by the color coding of a blue screen over the word *numerator* and a corresponding blue screen over all the numerators and a gray screen over the word *denominator* and a gray screen over all the denominators in exercises 1 through 8. Simply point out to the students that this color coding is to remind them of the names *numerator* and *denominator* and their meanings. As you exhibit exercises 1 and 2 on the chalkboard with correct answers, be sure that all the students understand how these answers were found. Follow up by having the students complete the exercises on the page.

Exercise 10 is primarily for more able students, and probably the less able students will not be able to do this. However, most of the students in your class will understand the correct answer once it is given. They will be able to see that the sum of the numerator and denominator of the fraction two eighths is 10 and that the denominator eight is four times the numerator two. Be sure your more able students have time to try exercise 10 before anyone reveals the correct answer.

the additional fractions are found. For example, for ⅖ you would want the students to show

$$\frac{2 \times 1}{2 \times 4},$$

and for ³⁄₁₂ you would want them to show

$$\frac{3 \times 1}{3 \times 4}.$$

Then for the next fraction the students should show

$$\frac{4 \times 1}{4 \times 4}$$

and observe that, in fact, the next fraction in this set is ⁴⁄₁₆.

It might also be helpful as you proceed with this demonstration to show some diagrams to illustrate the equivalence of these fractions. For example, you might show a bar diagram with the first bar divided into fourths and one fourth shaded, the second divided into eighths and two eighths shaded, etc. During this preparatory lesson, you may introduce the words *numerator* and *denominator*. However, these words are introduced on page 272, and you might prefer to wait until you do the lesson on page 272 to use these words.

Have the students do the exercises. Allow time for checking papers and discussion when they have finished. In particular, discuss exercise 1 and the various ways that the students might think to answer these questions easily. The answers to exercise 1 should be relatively simple if the students are reasoning correctly. Therefore, you should attempt to have the students relate their method of thinking in arriving at their answers.

If time permits during the discussion of this page, it would be beneficial to have some of the students show their work on the chalkboard.

---

274 FRACTIONS

Let's Review

- ADDITION
- SUBTRACTION
- MULTIPLICATION
- DIVISION
- MEASUREMENT
- PLACE VALUE
- INEQUALITIES
- PRINCIPLES

1. Give the correct sign
   (= or ≠) for each ⬤
   The sign ≠ means
   "is **not** equal to."

   [A] $63,427 + 1000 = 64,427$

   [B] $100 \times 1000 \neq 1,000,000$

   [C] $872,000 \div 10 \neq 8720$

   [D] $1,000,000 = 999,999 + 1$

   [E] $10,000 - 1 \neq 99,000$

   [F] $6285 \times 100 = 628,500$

   [G] $70 \div 1000 \neq 70,000$

   [H] $832,070 - 10,000 \neq 831,070$

   [I] $10 \times 10 \times 10 \neq 10,000$

   [J] $10,000 = 100 \times 100$

   [K] $10 \times 10 \times 10 \times 10 \neq 100 \times 10$

   [L] $6322 - 302 = 6020$

2. Find the sums.

[A]	[B]	[C]	[D]	[E]
2	32	428	7465	82,471
7	58	106	8321	93,265
8	46	750	2405	47,721
6	71	623	3106	65,132
23	*207*	*1907*	*21,297*	*288,589*

3. Find the differences.

[A]	[B]	[C]	[D]	[E]
32	75	128	604	7028
−8	−37	−49	−29	−4639
24	*38*	*79*	*575*	*2389*

4. Find the sums and differences.

   [A] $6243 + 721 + 38,642 + 29$ *45,635*

   [B] $6302 - 587$ *5715*

   [C] $8432 + 36 + 285 + 1000$ *9753*

   [D] $832,461 - 87,063$ *745,398*

5. Find the products.

[A]	[B]	[C]	[D]	[E]
27	85	32	58	284
×6	×7	×5	×6	×8
162	*595*	*160*	*348*	*2,272*

6. Find the quotients and remainders.

   [A] $283 \div 6$ *47 R 1*   [C] $316 \div 13$ *24 R 4*   [E] $602 \div 86$ *7*

   [B] $4286 \div 7$ *612 R 2*   [D] $228 \div 24$ *9 R 12*   [F] $428 \div 76$ *5 R 48*

Teaching Pages 274 and 275

- **PURPOSE**

  To provide a cumulative review

  To provide word-problem experiences

- **PREPARATION**

  Use this preparatory period to strengthen the students' skills with operations. For example, this might be a good opportunity to review the division or multiplication algorithms. It might be effective to have some students work exercises on the chalkboard and other students check to see if they have done their work correctly.

Time

1. There are 24 hours in a day. How many hours are there in a year that has 365 days? *8760*

2. There are 7 days in a week. How many weeks are there in a year that has 365 days? *52 (with 1 day remaining)*

3. John said that he was 1645 days old.
   [A] How many days old will John be in another year (365 days)? *2010*
   [B] How many days old was he one year ago? *1280*

4. Some years have 365 days, and others have 366 days. How many days are there in 6 years if one of the 6 years has 366 days? *2191*

5. There are 60 seconds in one minute and 60 minutes in one hour. How many seconds are there in 24 hours (one day)? *86,400*

6. How many seconds are there in a week? *604,800*

7. March has 31 days.
   [A] Without looking at a calendar, tell what day in April is 3 weeks after March 20. *April 10*
   [B] What day in April is 4 weeks after March 10? *April 7*

Have the students work the exercises. Although exercises 5, 6, and 7 are primarily for the more able students, they contain much that can be stimulating to all students in a discussion situation. Therefore, you might have only the more able students attempt the problems but have all the students participate in a discussion of the exercises. When the students give answers to exercise 7, ask them to elaborate on the way in which they arrived at a given answer. For example, they might explain that three weeks is 21 days, and 21 and 20 are 41; March has 31 days, so they subtract 31 from 41 to find that the date for part A should be April 10. Of course, for part B starting with March 10 and adding 28 days would make 38; subtracting 31 from 38 would leave 7; hence the date would be April 7. The students will undoubtedly discover a variety of ways to think about this exercise.

You might also follow up this algorithm practice by having the students do some work in place value. For example, you might exhibit on the chalkboard a number such as 4,286,537 and have the students identify the number a given digit represents.

Study the material at the top of the page with the class. Following this discussion, have the students do the exercises. When they have finished, be sure that they see that exercises 2A through E are associated and that exercises 2F through K are also associated. Of course, this exercise is designed to illustrate the meaning of five fifths and six sixths. Understanding the meaning of these fractions will help the students understand the meaning associated with improper fractions.

For exercise 3, the students should see that in part A they are considering one more eighth in each part of the fraction sequence and one more tenth for each successive fraction in part B. Be sure that the students do not think that these are sets of equivalent fractions. The sequences are given simply to help the students understand the ideas involved in working with improper fractions. It may be worthwhile to accompany the discussion of exercise 3 with bar diagrams on the chalkboard to illustrate each fraction.

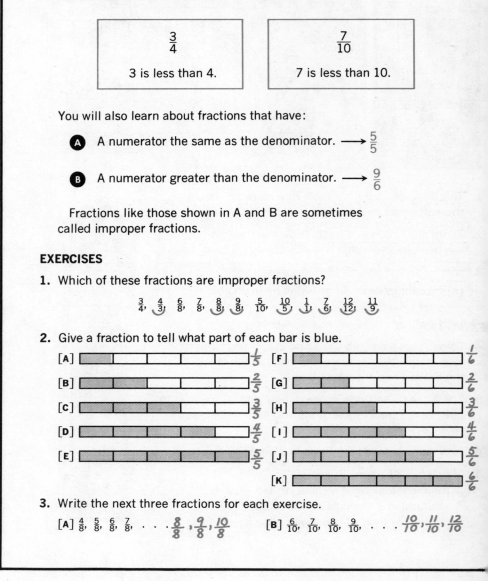

Fractions (numerator > or = denominator)

You have been learning about fractions that have numerators that are less than the denominators.

$\frac{3}{4}$

3 is less than 4.

$\frac{7}{10}$

7 is less than 10.

You will also learn about fractions that have:

A A numerator the same as the denominator. ⟶ $\frac{5}{5}$

B A numerator greater than the denominator. ⟶ $\frac{9}{6}$

Fractions like those shown in A and B are sometimes called improper fractions.

EXERCISES

1. Which of these fractions are improper fractions?

$\frac{3}{4}, \frac{4}{3}, \frac{6}{8}, \frac{7}{8}, \frac{8}{8}, \frac{9}{8}, \frac{5}{10}, \frac{10}{5}, \frac{1}{1}, \frac{7}{6}, \frac{12}{12}, \frac{11}{9}$

2. Give a fraction to tell what part of each bar is blue.

[A] ... $\frac{1}{5}$ [F] ... $\frac{1}{6}$

[B] ... $\frac{2}{5}$ [G] ... $\frac{2}{6}$

[C] ... $\frac{3}{5}$ [H] ... $\frac{3}{6}$

[D] ... $\frac{4}{5}$ [I] ... $\frac{4}{6}$

[E] ... $\frac{5}{5}$ [J] ... $\frac{5}{6}$

[K] ... $\frac{6}{6}$

3. Write the next three fractions for each exercise.

[A] $\frac{4}{8}, \frac{5}{8}, \frac{6}{8}, \frac{7}{8}, \ldots$ $\frac{8}{8}, \frac{9}{8}, \frac{10}{8}$ [B] $\frac{6}{10}, \frac{7}{10}, \frac{8}{10}, \frac{9}{10}, \ldots$ $\frac{10}{10}, \frac{11}{10}, \frac{12}{10}$

Teaching Pages 276 and 277

● **PURPOSE**

To provide experiences in working with fractions which have a numerator greater than or equal to the denominator

● **PREPARATION**

Exhibit on the chalkboard two circles and ask the students to pretend that these circles are pies. Divide both circles into fourths by drawing diameters. Shade three fourths of one circle and ask the students what part of the circle is shaded. When they respond three fourths, exhibit

More about fractions

Study these examples. Then do the exercises.

Fourths

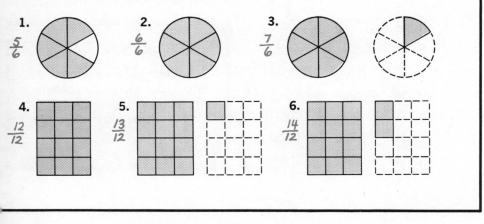

Thirds

EXERCISES

Write the fraction suggested by each exercise.

1. $\frac{5}{6}$

2. $\frac{6}{6}$

3. $\frac{7}{6}$

4. $\frac{12}{12}$

5. $\frac{13}{12}$

6. $\frac{14}{12}$

Study the examples preceding the exercises with the class. Be sure that each student understands how each fraction relates to the given picture. Ask the students to explain how the pictures of fractions are related.

Following this discussion, have the students do the exercises. Again, you should note with the students that exercises 1 through 3 are related since everything is in sixths (one more sixth is shown each time) and that exercises 4 through 6 are related since everything is in twelfths (one more twelfth is shown each time). Do not bring up mixed numerals during this discussion.

on the chalkboard the fraction ¾. Shade the other fourth of this circle and elicit from the students the fact that four fourths of the circle is shaded. Now, shade one fourth of the other circle and again elicit from the students the fact that five fourths is shaded. (If a student responds that five eighths of the two circles is shaded, say "yes" and then guide the discussion back to fourths.) Shade another part of the second circle and elicit the response that six fourths is shaded. Continue this until you have eight fourths shaded. Repeat this for other fractions using squares, rectangles, or circles. Take special care with the language. Say "⁵⁄₄ circles" or "⁹⁄₅ squares," etc. It would not make sense to speak of ⁵⁄₄ *of a* circle. For each demonstration, take special care to exhibit the fraction for each picture as you proceed.

Do not place much importance on the term *improper fraction*. Comment on this expression in passing, but, for the most part, use *fraction* rather than *improper fraction*. We do mention this term because it is in much of the arithmetic literature, and the students should be familiar with *improper fraction* as it applies to fractions having numerators equal to or greater than their denominators. We do not stress the word because we do not want the students to think that there is anything wrong with fractions having a numerator greater than or equal to the denominator. Actually, there is nothing at all "improper" about such fractions.

Have the students do the exercises. When they have finished, present several exercises on the chalkboard along with pictorial representations (similar to the bar diagrams in exercise 2, page 276) of the various equivalent fractions in a given set. For example, for exercise 1c, you can show some bars, one under the other, with the first divided into fourths and one fourth shaded; the second, into eighths with two eighths shaded, etc.

Equivalent-fraction exercises

Copy the fractions on your paper.
Write three more fractions for each set.

1. [A] $\{\frac{1}{2}, \frac{2}{4}, \frac{3}{6}, \frac{4}{8}, \ldots\}$ $\frac{5}{10}, \frac{6}{12}, \frac{7}{14}$ [E] $\{\frac{1}{6}, \frac{2}{12}, \frac{3}{18}, \ldots\}$ $\frac{4}{24}, \frac{5}{30}, \frac{6}{36}$

[B] $\{\frac{1}{3}, \frac{2}{6}, \frac{3}{9}, \frac{4}{12}, \ldots\}$ $\frac{5}{15}, \frac{6}{18}, \frac{7}{21}$ [F] $\{\frac{1}{8}, \frac{2}{16}, \frac{3}{24}, \ldots\}$ $\frac{4}{32}, \frac{5}{40}, \frac{6}{48}$

[C] $\{\frac{1}{4}, \frac{2}{8}, \frac{3}{12}, \frac{4}{16}, \ldots\}$ $\frac{5}{20}, \frac{6}{24}, \frac{7}{28}$ [G] $\{\frac{1}{10}, \frac{2}{20}, \ldots\}$ $\frac{3}{30}, \frac{4}{40}, \frac{5}{50}$

[D] $\{\frac{1}{5}, \frac{2}{10}, \frac{3}{15}, \frac{4}{20}, \ldots\}$ $\frac{5}{25}, \frac{6}{30}, \frac{7}{35}$ [H] $\{\frac{1}{12}, \frac{2}{24}, \ldots\}$ $\frac{3}{36}, \frac{4}{48}, \frac{5}{60}$

2. [A] $\{\frac{2}{3}, \frac{4}{6}, \frac{6}{9}, \frac{8}{12}, \ldots\}$ $\frac{10}{15}, \frac{12}{18}, \frac{14}{21}$ [E] $\{\frac{3}{4}, \frac{6}{8}, \frac{9}{12}, \frac{12}{16}, \ldots\}$ $\frac{15}{20}, \frac{18}{24}, \frac{21}{28}$

[B] $\{\frac{2}{5}, \frac{4}{10}, \frac{6}{15}, \frac{8}{20}, \ldots\}$ $\frac{10}{25}, \frac{12}{30}, \frac{14}{35}$ [F] $\{\frac{3}{5}, \frac{6}{10}, \frac{9}{15}, \frac{12}{20}, \ldots\}$ $\frac{15}{25}, \frac{18}{30}, \frac{21}{35}$

[C] $\{\frac{2}{7}, \frac{4}{14}, \frac{6}{21}, \ldots\}$ $\frac{8}{28}, \frac{10}{35}, \frac{12}{42}$ [G] $\{\frac{3}{7}, \frac{6}{14}, \frac{9}{21}, \ldots\}$ $\frac{12}{28}, \frac{15}{35}, \frac{18}{42}$

[D] $\{\frac{2}{9}, \frac{4}{18}, \frac{6}{27}, \ldots\}$ $\frac{8}{36}, \frac{10}{45}, \frac{12}{54}$ [H] $\{\frac{3}{10}, \frac{6}{20}, \frac{9}{30}, \ldots\}$ $\frac{12}{40}, \frac{15}{50}, \frac{18}{60}$

3. [A] $\{\frac{3}{2}, \frac{6}{4}, \frac{9}{6}, \ldots\}$ $\frac{12}{8}, \frac{15}{10}, \frac{18}{12}$ [E] $\{\frac{7}{4}, \frac{14}{8}, \frac{21}{12}, \ldots\}$ $\frac{28}{16}, \frac{35}{20}, \frac{42}{24}$

[B] $\{\frac{4}{3}, \frac{8}{6}, \frac{12}{9}, \ldots\}$ $\frac{16}{12}, \frac{20}{15}, \frac{24}{18}$ [F] $\{\frac{9}{2}, \frac{18}{4}, \frac{27}{6}, \ldots\}$ $\frac{36}{8}, \frac{45}{10}, \frac{54}{12}$

[C] $\{\frac{5}{2}, \frac{10}{4}, \frac{15}{6}, \ldots\}$ $\frac{20}{8}, \frac{25}{10}, \frac{30}{12}$ [G] $\{\frac{8}{3}, \frac{16}{6}, \frac{24}{9}, \ldots\}$ $\frac{32}{12}, \frac{40}{15}, \frac{48}{18}$

[D] $\{\frac{5}{3}, \frac{10}{6}, \frac{15}{9}, \ldots\}$ $\frac{20}{12}, \frac{25}{15}, \frac{30}{18}$ [H] $\{\frac{6}{5}, \frac{12}{10}, \frac{18}{15}, \ldots\}$ $\frac{24}{20}, \frac{30}{25}, \frac{36}{30}$

4. [A] $\{\frac{1}{1}, \frac{2}{2}, \frac{3}{3}, \ldots\}$ $\frac{4}{4}, \frac{5}{5}, \frac{6}{6}$

[B] $\{\frac{2}{1}, \frac{4}{2}, \frac{6}{3}, \ldots\}$ $\frac{8}{4}, \frac{10}{5}, \frac{12}{6}$

[C] $\{\frac{3}{1}, \frac{6}{2}, \frac{9}{3}, \ldots\}$ $\frac{12}{4}, \frac{15}{5}, \frac{18}{6}$

[D] $\{\frac{4}{1}, \frac{8}{2}, \frac{12}{3}, \ldots\}$ $\frac{16}{4}, \frac{20}{5}, \frac{24}{6}$

[E] $\{\frac{10}{1}, \frac{20}{2}, \frac{30}{3}, \ldots\}$ $\frac{40}{4}, \frac{50}{5}, \frac{60}{6}$

[F] $\{\frac{25}{1}, \frac{50}{2}, \frac{75}{3}, \ldots\}$ $\frac{100}{4}, \frac{125}{5}, \frac{150}{6}$

[G] $\{\frac{50}{1}, \frac{100}{2}, \frac{150}{3}, \ldots\}$ $\frac{200}{4}, \frac{250}{5}, \frac{300}{6}$

[H] $\{\frac{100}{1}, \frac{200}{2}, \frac{300}{3}, \ldots\}$ $\frac{400}{4}, \frac{500}{5}, \frac{600}{6}$

Exercise for Experts

Equivalent fractions you will see
When you view one half and me.
I'm thirteen above the line.
Find the name you think is mine.

WHO AM I? $\frac{13}{26}$

Teaching Pages 278 and 279

- **PURPOSE**

  To provide additional experiences in working with sets of equivalent fractions

  To introduce fractions with zero numerators

- **PREPARATION**

  Review the lesson on pages 270 and 271. For example, exhibit on the chalkboard a set of equivalent fractions such as $\{\frac{3}{4}, \frac{6}{8}, \frac{9}{12}, \frac{12}{16}, \ldots\}$. Notice with the students that they can get $\frac{6}{8}$ by thinking about

  $$\frac{2 \times 3}{2 \times 4};$$

they can get $\frac{9}{12}$ by thinking about

$$\frac{3 \times 3}{3 \times 4};$$

they can get $\frac{12}{16}$ by thinking about

$$\frac{4 \times 3}{4 \times 4};$$

they can get $\frac{15}{20}$ by thinking about

$$\frac{5 \times 3}{5 \times 4}.$$

Give the students several exercises in constructing sets of equivalent fractions.

Zero numerators

EXERCISES

1. Give a fraction to tell what part of each bar is blue.

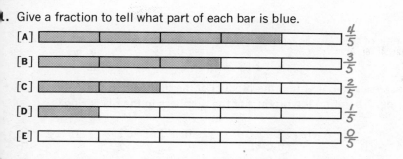

[A] $\frac{4}{5}$

[B] $\frac{3}{5}$

[C] $\frac{2}{5}$

[D] $\frac{1}{5}$

[E] $\frac{0}{5}$

2. For each bar in exercise 1, give a fraction to tell what part is white.
[A] $\frac{1}{5}$, [B] $\frac{2}{5}$, [C] $\frac{3}{5}$, [D] $\frac{4}{5}$, [E] $\frac{5}{5}$

3. Give a fraction to tell what part of each region is blue.

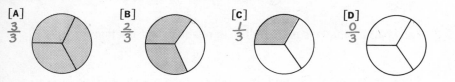

[A] $\frac{3}{3}$ [B] $\frac{2}{3}$ [C] $\frac{1}{3}$ [D] $\frac{0}{3}$

4. For each region in exercise 3, give a fraction to tell what part is white. [A] $\frac{0}{3}$, [B] $\frac{1}{3}$, [C] $\frac{2}{3}$, [D] $\frac{3}{3}$

5. Give a fraction to tell what part of each region is blue.

[A] $\frac{0}{4}$ [B] $\frac{3}{3}$ [C] $\frac{0}{6}$ [D] $\frac{8}{8}$

6. For each region in exercise 5, give a fraction to tell what part is white. [A] $\frac{4}{4}$, [B] $\frac{0}{3}$, [C] $\frac{6}{6}$, [D] $\frac{0}{8}$

7. Give five more fractions for this set.

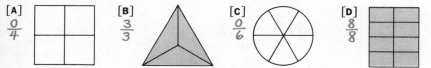

$\left\{\frac{0}{1}, \frac{0}{2}, \frac{0}{3}, \frac{0}{4}, \frac{0}{5}, \frac{0}{6}, \frac{0}{7}, \ldots\right\}$ $\frac{0}{8}, \frac{0}{9}, \frac{0}{10}, \frac{0}{11}, \frac{0}{12}$

8. Is the fraction $\frac{0}{285}$ equivalent to $\frac{0}{1}$? *Yes*

Have the students do the exercises. When they have finished, allow time for checking papers and discussion.

During the discussion of the first six exercises, stress for the students the meaning of a fraction having a zero numerator.

In exercise 7, pay particular attention to the fact that this set of equivalent fractions is much the same as previous sets of equivalent fractions. Each fraction is constructed from the first fraction, $\frac{0}{1}$, by the same method as previously. You can show this to the students by considering that the second fraction can be thought of as

$$\frac{2 \times 0}{2 \times 1};$$

the third fraction,

$$\frac{3 \times 0}{3 \times 1};$$

the fourth fraction,

$$\frac{4 \times 0}{4 \times 1}.$$

In this way, the students should see that this set of fractions is much the same as earlier sets of equivalent fractions. This is a particularly important point to make since we consider this set of fractions in our construction of the set of rational numbers in the next chapter. Of course, the students should see quickly that the answer to exercise 8 is "yes" since they can easily construct the fraction $\frac{0}{285}$ from the fraction $\frac{0}{1}$ by considering the fact that $\frac{0}{285}$ is the same as

$$\frac{285 \times 0}{285 \times 1}.$$

Follow up the last part of this preparatory lesson by giving the students an opportunity to construct sets of equivalent improper fractions. For example, you might accompany the example given above by having the students construct the set $\{\frac{5}{2}, \frac{10}{4}, \frac{15}{6}, \ldots\}$.

Next, if time permits, introduce zero numerators to the students. To do this, you can exhibit on the chalkboard a square divided into fourths, of which three fourths is shaded. Exhibit the fraction $\frac{3}{4}$ to tell what part of the square is shaded. Right beside it, exhibit a similar square with two fourths shaded. Exhibit this fraction. Then exhibit a square with only one fourth shaded and the fraction $\frac{1}{4}$. Finally, exhibit a square that is divided into fourths, with no parts shaded, and elicit from the students that for this square they can think that $\frac{0}{4}$ is shaded.

Have the students do the exercises. As you discuss them, observe with the students that in each case the product of the numbers in the blue ring is the same as the product of the numbers in the black ring and that they are working with pairs of equivalent fractions.

A check for equivalent fractions

EXERCISES

1. Each pair of fractions is from this set of equivalent fractions.

$$\left\{\frac{1}{2}, \frac{2}{4}, \frac{3}{6}, \frac{4}{8}, \frac{5}{10}, \frac{6}{12}\right\}$$

For each exercise, first find the product of the numbers in the blue ring. Then find the product of the numbers in the black ring.

[A] $\frac{2}{4} \times \frac{5}{10}$ 20,20 [B] $\frac{3}{6} \times \frac{5}{10}$ 30,30 [C] $\frac{1}{2} \times \frac{6}{12}$ 12,12 [D] $\frac{2}{4} \times \frac{3}{6}$ /.

[E] $\frac{1}{2} \times \frac{4}{8}$ 8,8 [F] $\frac{2}{4} \times \frac{5}{10}$ 20,20 [G] $\frac{1}{2} \times \frac{5}{10}$ 10,10 [H] $\frac{5}{10} \times \frac{6}{12}$

2. Each pair of fractions is from this set of equivalent fractions.

$$\left\{\frac{2}{3}, \frac{4}{6}, \frac{6}{9}, \frac{8}{12}, \frac{10}{15}, \frac{12}{18}\right\}$$

For each exercise, first find the product of the numbers in the blue ring. Then find the product of the numbers in the black ring.

[A] $\frac{2}{3} \times \frac{6}{9}$ 18,18 [B] $\frac{4}{6} \times \frac{8}{12}$ 48,48 [C] $\frac{4}{6} \times \frac{10}{15}$ 60,60 [D] $\frac{6}{9} \times \frac{8}{12}$

[E] $\frac{2}{3} \times \frac{10}{15}$ 30,30 [F] $\frac{4}{6} \times \frac{12}{18}$ 72,72 [G] $\frac{2}{3} \times \frac{12}{18}$ 36,36 [H] $\frac{8}{12} \times \frac{10}{15}$

3. Here is another set of equivalent fractions.

$$\left\{\frac{1}{4}, \frac{2}{8}, \frac{3}{12}, \frac{4}{16}, \frac{5}{20}, \frac{6}{24}\right\}$$

Read the sentence. Then find the products.

[A] $\frac{2}{8}$ is equivalent to $\frac{3}{12}$.

$2 \times 12 = \blacksquare\ 24$
$8 \times 3 = \blacksquare\ 24$

[B] $\frac{3}{12}$ is equivalent to $\frac{5}{20}$.

$3 \times 20 = \blacksquare\ 60$
$12 \times 5 = \blacksquare\ 60$

Teaching Pages 280 and 281

- **PURPOSE**

  To provide a check for determining equivalence of two fractions

  To provide the basic working definition for equivalent fractions

- **MATHEMATICS**

  The basic definition for equivalent fractions is provided in this lesson, even though previous lessons have discussed equivalent fractions. These previous discussions, however, were based primarily on intuition and pictorial demonstrations of the quantitative sameness as equivalent fractions were shown to represent the same amount of a given object. We give below the formal definition for equivalent fractions.

  The fraction a/b is equivalent to c/d if, and only if, $ad = bc$.

  Of course, you will see that in this lesson this is precisely what we are providing the students as a check for determining whether or not two fractions are equivalent.

- **PREPARATION**

  Exhibit for the students several pairs of fractions some of which are equivalent and some of which are not. Give the students an opportunity to attempt to discover whether or not the two fractions are equivalent. Assuming, of

On the opposite page, you explored a test for equivalent fractions. You can tell whether or not two fractions are equivalent by using this test. Study these examples.

$\dfrac{3}{4} \quad \dfrac{9}{12} \longrightarrow \begin{array}{l} 4 \times 9 = 36 \\ 3 \times 12 = 36 \end{array} \longrightarrow \dfrac{3}{4}$ is equivalent to $\dfrac{9}{12}$.

$\dfrac{2}{3} \quad \dfrac{6}{8} \longrightarrow \begin{array}{l} 3 \times 6 = 18 \\ 2 \times 8 = 16 \end{array} \longrightarrow \dfrac{2}{3}$ is not equivalent to $\dfrac{6}{8}$.

$\dfrac{4}{10} \quad \dfrac{10}{25} \longrightarrow \begin{array}{l} 10 \times 10 = 100 \\ 4 \times 25 = 100 \end{array} \longrightarrow \dfrac{4}{10}$ is equivalent to $\dfrac{10}{25}$.

$\dfrac{3}{8} \quad \dfrac{5}{14} \longrightarrow \begin{array}{l} 8 \times 5 = 40 \\ 3 \times 14 = 42 \end{array} \longrightarrow \dfrac{3}{8}$ is not equivalent to $\dfrac{5}{14}$.

If the two products are the same, then the fractions are equivalent.

If the two products are not the same, then the fractions are not equivalent.

We call this the product method for checking equivalence of fractions.

EXERCISES

Tell whether or not the two fractions are equivalent.

1. $\dfrac{1}{2}$ $\dfrac{7}{14}$ *Yes*   3. $\dfrac{6}{8}$ $\dfrac{7}{10}$ *No*   5. $\dfrac{12}{10}$ $\dfrac{6}{5}$ *Yes*   7. $\dfrac{6}{14}$ $\dfrac{2}{5}$ *No*   9. $\dfrac{9}{5}$ $\dfrac{18}{9}$ *No*

2. $\dfrac{3}{8}$ $\dfrac{9}{24}$ *Yes*   4. $\dfrac{6}{10}$ $\dfrac{9}{15}$ *Yes*   6. $\dfrac{3}{3}$ $\dfrac{8}{8}$ *Yes*   8. $\dfrac{0}{9}$ $\dfrac{0}{1}$ *Yes*   10. $\dfrac{15}{35}$ $\dfrac{3}{7}$ *Yes*

Read and study the material at the top of the page with the class. Point out that the students now have a method for determining whether or not two fractions are equivalent and that this method is called the *product method* for checking equivalence of fractions.

Instruct the students to work the exercises at the bottom of the page. When they have finished, allow time for checking and further discussion.

Be sure that the students understand the checking procedure involved to see whether or not two fractions are equivalent. You might also accompany this discussion by showing several illustrations of parts of objects as a double check to see that the two fractions are equivalent. For exercise 1, you might use a rectangle divided into two parts of the same size and then a rectangle divided into 14 parts of the same size. Observe with the students that seven of the 14 parts is the same amount of the rectangle as one of two parts, and therefore the product 1×14 is the same as the product 2×7.

course, that the students have not read and studied the material on pages 280 and 281, you can expect a variety of explanations concerning how they decide whether or not two fractions are equivalent. Some students may rely on pictures, while others may rely on a large set of equivalent fractions to find whether or not the two fractions are in the set. For example, if you exhibit the pair $\frac{2}{4}$ and $\frac{5}{10}$, the students may attempt to construct the set $\{\frac{1}{2}, \frac{2}{4}, \frac{3}{6}, \frac{4}{8}, \frac{5}{10}\}$ in order to recognize that these two fractions are equivalent. Other students will simply remember or refer back to having constructed this set of fractions at an earlier time. Still other students may recognize that in each fraction the denominator is twice the numerator; therefore, the two fractions are equivalent. The important point is that the students recognize that it would be

convenient to have a handy way to check whether or not two fractions are equivalent.

An important part of this preparatory lesson, then, is to provide the students an opportunity to discuss the variety of ways for finding whether or not two fractions are equivalent. It is unlikely that the students will discover the method introduced on page 280 without actually seeing it in their books. However, if someone does discover it, this is fine and will serve as additional preparation.

Study the two examples at the top of the page with the students. Be sure the students observe that the bars in the first box show that two fourths and three sixths are equivalent since the same amount of the bar is shaded in each case. Also point out that 2×6 is the same as 4×3.

Draw attention in a class discussion to the second box in which different amounts of the bar are shaded and point out that this shows that four fifths is not equivalent to six eighths. Notice also with the students that the product 4×8 is not the same as the product 5×6. Therefore, four fifths is not equivalent to six eighths. Thus, this example shows two ways for concluding that these two fractions are not equivalent.

Following this discussion, have the students do the exercises. Be sure that the students understand that in each exercise they are to tell whether or not the two fractions that they write for the pair of shaded regions are equivalent. The students have two ways to do this: one is to use the product method for checking equivalence and the other is to observe the shaded region. Of course, exercise 2 directs the students to use the product method as a check. When the students have finished the exercises, be sure that adequate time is allowed for discussion of the ideas presented here.

Answers, exercise 2, page 282

[A] $5 \times 8 = 40$
$6 \times 8 = 48$

[B] $3 \times 8 = 24$
$4 \times 6 = 24$

[C] $6 \times 12 = 72$
$8 \times 9 = 72$

[D] $5 \times 12 = 60$
$9 \times 7 = 63$

[E] $6 \times 12 = 72$
$8 \times 10 = 80$

[F] $5 \times 16 = 80$
$8 \times 10 = 80$

Equivalent fractions again

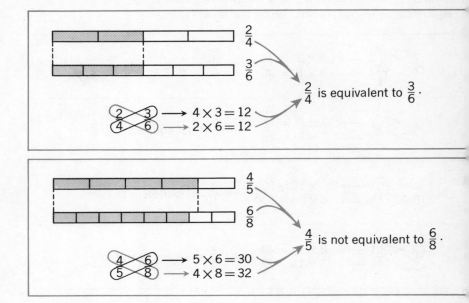

EXERCISES

1. For each exercise, write the two fractions suggested by the shaded parts of the two regions given. Then tell whether or not the two fractions are equivalent.

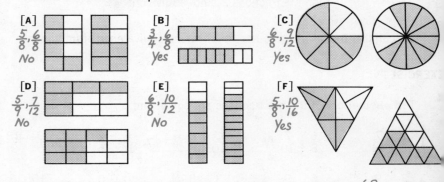

[A] $\frac{5}{8}, \frac{6}{8}$ No

[B] $\frac{3}{4}, \frac{6}{8}$ Yes

[C] $\frac{6}{8}, \frac{9}{12}$ Yes

[D] $\frac{5}{9}, \frac{7}{12}$ No

[E] $\frac{6}{8}, \frac{10}{12}$ No

[F] $\frac{5}{8}, \frac{10}{16}$ Yes

2. Use the product method to check your answers to exercise 1. *(See answer*

Teaching Pages 282 and 283

- **PURPOSE**

  To relate the association of equivalent fractions with parts of objects to the cross-product demonstration of equivalent fractions

  To provide further experiences in work with equivalent fractions

  To provide word-problem experiences in work with equivalent fractions

- **PREPARATION**

  Review the last lesson, in which students learned to check equivalence of fractions by the product method. In

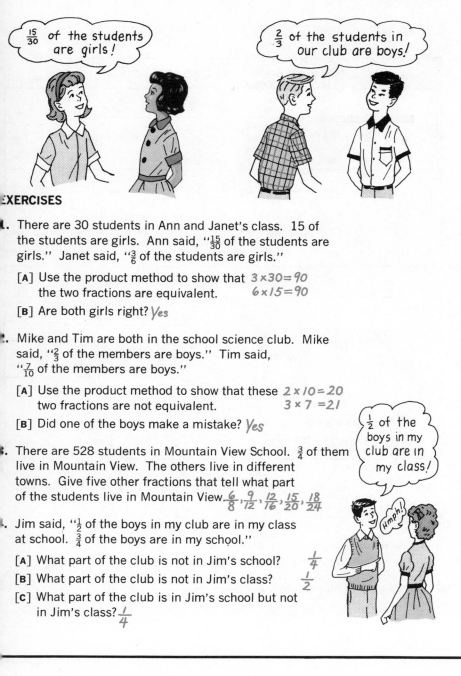

Have the students do the exercises. Follow up by discussing each exercise separately and giving the students an opportunity to express their thoughts concerning each problem.

Exercise 4 on this page is particularly difficult, and, perhaps, even the discussion of it should be restricted to only the faster students. Of course, the explanation for these exercises should go as follows. To determine what part of the club is not in Jim's school, the students should simply note that three fourths of the club is in Jim's school; therefore, one fourth of the club is not in Jim's school. For part B, the students observe that half of the boys from the club are in Jim's class; therefore, half of them are not in Jim's class. To determine what part of the club is in Jim's school but not in Jim's class, they must observe that one half is two fourths and that three fourths is one more fourth than two fourths; consequently, since three fourths of the boys are in the school, two fourths are in the class, so one fourth of the club is in the school but not in Jim's class. The diagram illustrates this pictorially.

$\frac{15}{30}$ of the students are girls!

$\frac{2}{3}$ of the students in our club are boys!

EXERCISES

1. There are 30 students in Ann and Janet's class. 15 of the students are girls. Ann said, "$\frac{15}{30}$ of the students are girls." Janet said, "$\frac{3}{6}$ of the students are girls."

 [A] Use the product method to show that the two fractions are equivalent. $3 \times 30 = 90$ $6 \times 15 = 90$

 [B] Are both girls right? Yes

2. Mike and Tim are both in the school science club. Mike said, "$\frac{2}{3}$ of the members are boys." Tim said, "$\frac{7}{10}$ of the members are boys."

 [A] Use the product method to show that these two fractions are not equivalent. $2 \times 10 = 20$ $3 \times 7 = 21$

 [B] Did one of the boys make a mistake? Yes

3. There are 528 students in Mountain View School. $\frac{3}{4}$ of them live in Mountain View. The others live in different towns. Give five other fractions that tell what part of the students live in Mountain View. $\frac{6}{8}, \frac{9}{12}, \frac{12}{16}, \frac{15}{20}, \frac{18}{24}$

4. Jim said, "$\frac{1}{2}$ of the boys in my club are in my class at school. $\frac{3}{4}$ of the boys are in my school."

 [A] What part of the club is not in Jim's school? $\frac{1}{4}$

 [B] What part of the club is not in Jim's class? $\frac{1}{2}$

 [C] What part of the club is in Jim's school but not in Jim's class? $\frac{1}{4}$

$\frac{1}{2}$ of the boys in my club are in my class!

Hmph!

eviewing this lesson, accompany each demonstration with a picture involving either shaded rectangles, circles, or a haded bar. For example, if you want to demonstrate for he students that the fractions $\frac{2}{3}$ and $\frac{6}{9}$ are equivalent, you can show a pair of bars such that the first bar is divided into three parts of the same size with two parts haded, and the other bar is divided into nine parts of the ame size with six parts shaded. The students should observe that in each case the same amount of the bar is haded, and according to the original interpretation of equivalent fractions, the two fractions are equivalent. They should then observe that 2×9 is the same as 3×6.

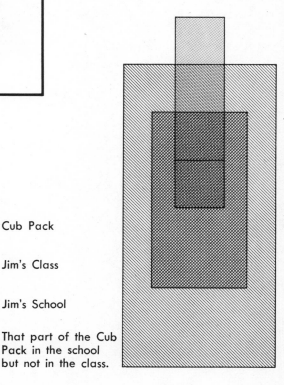

Cub Pack

Jim's Class

Jim's School

That part of the Cub Pack in the school but not in the class.

Study the material in the tables with the class. Be sure they understand that we speak of higher and lower terms only with respect to these sets of equivalent fractions. That is, we say that four eighths is in higher terms than another fraction only if four eighths is equivalent to that fraction, or we say that two fourths is in lower terms than another fraction only if two fourths is equivalent to that fraction. This should be clear to the students since the introduction here of higher and lower terms is only with respect to sets of equivalent fractions.

Follow up the discussion by assigning the exercises on the page. These exercises can be covered in a class discussion, or you can have the students do them first on their own and then discuss the answers as a class activity.

Lower and higher terms

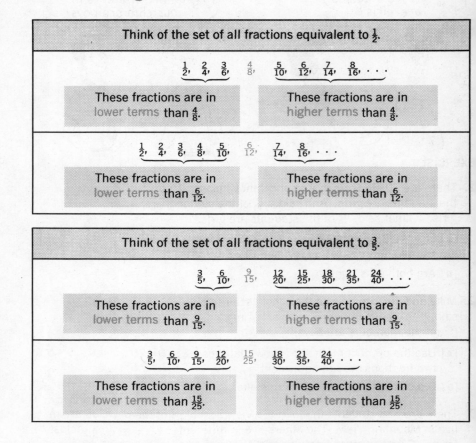

▶ We use higher and lower terms only when the fractions are equivalent.

EXERCISES

1. [A] Give four fractions in lower terms than $\frac{5}{10}$. $\frac{4}{8}, \frac{3}{6}, \frac{2}{4}, \frac{1}{2}$

   [B] Give four fractions that are in higher terms than $\frac{5}{10}$. $\frac{6}{12}, \frac{7}{14}, \frac{8}{16}, \frac{9}{18}$

2. [A] Give three fractions in lower terms than $\frac{12}{20}$. $\frac{9}{15}, \frac{6}{10}, \frac{3}{5}$

   [B] Give five fractions in higher terms than $\frac{12}{20}$. $\frac{15}{25}, \frac{18}{30}, \frac{21}{35}$

Teaching Pages 284 and 285

- **PURPOSE**

  To introduce higher and lower terms

  To provide additional experiences in working with sets of equivalent fractions

- **PREPARATION**

  If you choose, the material on page 284 and at the top of page 285 can be used as your preparatory work for this lesson. However, you may feel it necessary to give the students additional experiences in work with sets of equivalent fractions. In this case, you should exhibit several sets of equivalent fractions on the chalkboard and have the

More about lower and higher terms

On the opposite page, you learned about higher and lower terms for equivalent fractions. You should remember:

> We speak of higher and lower terms only when the fractions are equivalent.

For example:

A $\frac{3}{4}$ is equivalent to $\frac{9}{12}$. We say that $\frac{3}{4}$ is in lower terms than $\frac{9}{12}$ and that $\frac{9}{12}$ is in higher terms than $\frac{3}{4}$.

B $\frac{2}{3}$ is **not** equivalent to $\frac{6}{8}$. We do not say $\frac{2}{3}$ is in lower terms than $\frac{6}{8}$.

EXERCISES

1. 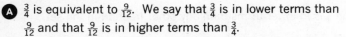 $\frac{2}{3}, \frac{4}{6}, \frac{6}{9}, \frac{8}{12}, \frac{10}{15}, \frac{12}{18}, \frac{14}{21}, \ldots$ →

[A] What fractions are in lower terms than $\frac{6}{9}$? $\frac{2}{3}, \frac{4}{6}$

[B] List two fractions that are in higher terms than $\frac{6}{9}$. $\frac{8}{12}, \frac{10}{15}$

[C] List four fractions that are in lower terms than $\frac{12}{18}$. $\frac{4}{6}, \frac{6}{9}, \frac{8}{12}, \frac{10}{15}$

[D] Give two fractions that are in higher terms than $\frac{12}{18}$. $\frac{14}{21}, \frac{16}{24}$

[E] What fraction in the set is in lower terms than any other fraction in the set? $\frac{2}{3}$

2.  ▓, $\frac{2}{16}, \frac{3}{24}$, ▓, ▓, ▓, ▓ →

[A] Give two fractions in higher terms than $\frac{2}{16}$. $\frac{3}{24}, \frac{4}{32}$

[B] Give two fractions in lower terms than $\frac{3}{24}$. $\frac{1}{8}, \frac{2}{16}$

3. ▓, $\frac{10}{12}$, ▓, ▓, ▓, →

[A] Give a fraction in higher terms than $\frac{10}{12}$. $\frac{15}{18}$

[B] Give a fraction in lower terms than $\frac{10}{12}$. $\frac{5}{6}$

Study the material preceding the exercises with the students. Again emphasize that we only speak of higher and lower terms with respect to fractions that are equivalent. Have the students do the exercises. As you discuss the answers, be sure to emphasize again that we would not say that two thirds is in lower terms than $\frac{10}{12}$ because two thirds is not equivalent to $\frac{10}{12}$ even though the numerator and denominator of two thirds are smaller than those of $\frac{10}{12}$. However, we would say that two thirds is in lower terms than $\frac{8}{12}$ because two thirds is equivalent to $\frac{8}{12}$. Be sure that the students have an opportunity and are encouraged to ask questions during the discussion of these three exercises.

students write additional fractions that belong to each set. For example, you might exhibit the set $\{\frac{3}{5}, \frac{6}{10}, \frac{9}{15}, \frac{12}{20}, \ldots\}$ and then have the students give the next three fractions. You should have the students explain how they found each fraction and, perhaps, have them select pairs of fractions from this set and, using the product method, check to see whether or not they are equivalent. From time to time, it is a good practice to have the students select pairs of fractions from the sets that they construct and test to see whether or not the two fractions are equivalent.

Study the material on this page with the students. Stress the three statements associated with the set in each blue box. Observe with the students that in the first box three fourths is in lower terms than any of the other fractions. Note also that there is no fraction that is in lower terms than three fourths. Finally, observe that we say the fraction three fourths is in lowest terms.

Conduct a similar discussion for the set of fractions equivalent to five eighths.

Following this, have the students work the exercises. In discussing these, be sure the students realize that when the correct answer is given there is no fraction that is in lower terms than the one given.

Lowest terms

In this lesson, you will learn about fractions that are in lowest terms.

Study the examples.

$$\left\{ \frac{3}{4},\ \frac{6}{8},\ \frac{9}{12},\ \frac{12}{16},\ \frac{15}{20},\ \frac{18}{24},\ \frac{21}{28},\ \cdots \right\}$$

▶ The fraction $\frac{3}{4}$ is in lower terms than any other fraction in the set.

▶ There is no fraction that is in lower terms than $\frac{3}{4}$.

▶ The fraction $\frac{3}{4}$ is in lowest terms.

$$\left\{ \frac{5}{8},\ \frac{10}{16},\ \frac{15}{24},\ \frac{20}{32},\ \frac{25}{40},\ \frac{30}{48},\ \frac{35}{56},\ \cdots \right\}$$

▶ The fraction $\frac{5}{8}$ is in lower terms than any other fraction in the set.

▶ There is no fraction that is in lower terms than $\frac{5}{8}$.

▶ The fraction $\frac{5}{8}$ is in lowest terms.

EXERCISES

Each set is a set of equivalent fractions. Each set has one fraction in lowest terms. Find that fraction.

1. $\left\{ \frac{3}{6},\ \frac{2}{4},\ \frac{5}{10},\ \frac{1}{2},\ \frac{10}{20} \right\}$ $\frac{1}{2}$

2. $\left\{ \frac{8}{12},\ \frac{20}{30},\ \frac{14}{21},\ \frac{6}{9},\ \frac{2}{3} \right\}$ $\frac{2}{3}$

3. $\left\{ \frac{7}{8},\ \frac{70}{80},\ \frac{14}{16},\ \frac{35}{40},\ \frac{21}{24} \right\}$ $\frac{7}{8}$

4. $\left\{ \frac{8}{6},\ \frac{16}{12},\ \frac{40}{30},\ \frac{4}{3},\ \frac{32}{24} \right\}$ $\frac{4}{3}$

5. $\left\{ \frac{30}{10},\ \frac{15}{5},\ \frac{3}{1},\ \frac{6}{2},\ \frac{9}{3} \right\}$ $\frac{3}{1}$

6. $\left\{ \frac{15}{20},\ \frac{3}{4},\ \frac{9}{12},\ \frac{21}{28},\ \frac{12}{16} \right\}$ $\frac{3}{4}$

7. $\left\{ \frac{10}{100},\ \frac{2}{20},\ \frac{1}{10},\ \frac{5}{50},\ \frac{7}{70} \right\}$ $\frac{1}{10}$

8. $\left\{ \frac{80}{100},\ \frac{8}{10},\ \frac{40}{50},\ \frac{16}{20},\ \frac{4}{5} \right\}$ $\frac{4}{5}$

9. $\left\{ \frac{21}{14},\ \frac{3}{2},\ \frac{30}{20},\ \frac{12}{8},\ \frac{9}{6} \right\}$ $\frac{3}{2}$

10. $\left\{ \frac{1}{4},\ \frac{4}{16},\ \frac{2}{8},\ \frac{10}{40},\ \frac{5}{20} \right\}$ $\frac{1}{4}$

Teaching Pages 286 and 287

● **PURPOSE**

To introduce the idea of fractions in lowest terms

To provide additional experiences in working with sets of equivalent fractions

To provide a test for determining whether or not a fraction is in lowest terms

● **PREPARATION**

Have the students construct on the chalkboard several sets of equivalent fractions so that each set contains at least seven fractions for that set. For each of these sets review the lesson covering higher and lower terms. Fol-

More about lowest terms

Here is a special rule for telling whether or not a fraction is in lowest terms.

Study the examples.

$\frac{3}{4}$	3 and 4 have no common factors except 1. $\longrightarrow$	$\frac{3}{4}$ is in lowest terms.
$\frac{6}{10}$	6 and 10 have 2 as a common factor. $\longrightarrow$	$\frac{6}{10}$ is not in lowest terms.
$\frac{9}{8}$	9 and 8 have no common factors except 1. $\longrightarrow$	$\frac{9}{8}$ is in lowest terms.
$\frac{9}{12}$	9 and 12 have 3 as a common factor. $\longrightarrow$	$\frac{9}{12}$ is not in lowest terms.

> If the numerator and denominator have no common factor except 1, then the fraction is in lowest terms.

> If the numerator and denominator have a common prime factor, then the fraction is not in lowest terms.

EXERCISES

1. Tell whether or not the fraction is in lowest terms. The prime factors of the numerator and denominator are given in blue.

[A] $\frac{10}{14}$ 2, 5 / 2, 7 *No*

[B] $\frac{6}{35}$ 2, 3 / 5, 7 *Yes*

[C] $\frac{12}{15}$ 2, 3 / 3, 5 *No*

[D] $\frac{7}{30}$ 7 / 2, 3, 5 *Yes*

[E] $\frac{16}{15}$ 2 / 3, 5 *Yes*

[F] $\frac{27}{24}$ 3 / 2, 3 *No*

2. Tell whether or not the fraction is in lowest terms.

[A] $\frac{3}{6}$ *No*   [B] $\frac{8}{12}$ *No*   [C] $\frac{9}{15}$ *No*   [D] $\frac{8}{9}$ *Yes*   [E] $\frac{9}{14}$ *Yes*   [F] $\frac{15}{25}$ *No*

Explain to the students that they are going to learn a rule for determining whether or not a given fraction is in lowest terms (that is, a fraction is in lowest terms only if there is no common factor other than one for the numerator and denominator). Examples are given here of fractions that are in lowest terms and of fractions that are not in lowest terms. Stress these examples and provide the students with other examples of fractions that either are in lowest terms or are not in lowest terms, as needed.

Following this discussion, stress the two statements which appear in the blue screens.

Have the students do the exercises. When they have finished, allow time for discussion. We would note that it is not expected that the students acquire any particular skill at reducing a fraction to lowest terms. The chief emphasis here is on understanding lowest terms.

lowing this review, ask the students which fraction in this set is in lower terms than any other fraction in the set. Do not mention *lowest terms* at this point. This is simply to prepare the students to focus attention on the fraction that is in lower terms than any of the others. Of course, if a set contains *all* the fractions equivalent to a given fraction, the lowest-terms fraction in that set is the fraction which is in lower terms than any other fraction. However, if the set does not contain all the fractions that are equivalent to a given fraction, the fraction in lower terms than any other is not necessarily a lowest-terms fraction. For example, in the set $\{\frac{6}{8}, \frac{9}{12}, \frac{12}{16}, \ldots\}$ the fraction six-eighths is in lower terms than any other fraction in the set, but it is not in lowest terms. Of course, there is no lowest-terms fraction for this set because we did not in-

clude three fourths in the set. Therefore, we want our sets to be complete, in the sense that we start with the lowest-terms fraction each time. For this reason, in the lesson beginning on page 286, we emphasize the fact that there is no fraction that is in lower terms than the lowest-terms fraction. Therefore, it should be seen that six eighths is not in lowest terms since there is a fraction, namely three fourths, that is in lower terms than six eighths.

Study the material at the top of the page with the students. Emphasize the fact that this example again shows the building of sets of equivalent fractions, but this time the emphasis is on the fact that, starting with the lowest-terms fraction, a set of equivalent fractions can be built in which all succeeding fractions are equivalent to this lowest-terms fraction.

Following this discussion, have the students do the exercises. When they have finished, allow time for discussion and checking papers. Be sure that the students understand how to find the correct answers for exercises 2A through F.

Exercises 2G through J could be thought of as involving reducing fractions to lowest terms, but the students are not expected to develop great skill at reducing fractions to lowest terms. Therefore do not try to teach skills in finding solutions in these exercises; rather, have the students attempt these exercises by thinking about constructing sets of equivalent fractions. The fact that they have to work backward this time should not be a deterrent to most of the students. It may be slightly more difficult, but many of the students should be able to do it. Certainly, all will understand the correct answers once they are given.

Lowest-terms fractions

You have learned how to build a set of equivalent fractions from a lowest-terms fraction. Here is an example.

$$\frac{3}{4} \longrightarrow \frac{2 \times 3}{2 \times 4} \longrightarrow \frac{3 \times 3}{3 \times 4} \longrightarrow \frac{4 \times 3}{4 \times 4} \longrightarrow \frac{5 \times 3}{5 \times 4} \longrightarrow \cdots$$

This process gives the set:

$$\left\{ \frac{3}{4}, \frac{6}{8}, \frac{9}{12}, \frac{12}{16}, \frac{15}{20}, \cdots \right\}$$

Choose two fractions from this set and show that they are equivalent. *24, 24*

EXERCISES

1. Build a set of equivalent fractions from each lowest-terms fraction. Find at least six fractions for each set.

[A] $\frac{1}{2}$ $\frac{2}{4}, \frac{3}{6}, \frac{4}{8},$ [B] $\frac{2}{3}$ $\frac{6}{9}, \frac{8}{12}, \frac{10}{15},$ [C] $\frac{1}{5}$ $\frac{2}{10}, \frac{3}{15}, \frac{4}{20},$ [D] $\frac{3}{10}$ $\frac{6}{20}, \frac{9}{30}, \frac{12}{40},$ [E] $\frac{5}{6}$ $\frac{10}{12}, \frac{15}{18}, \frac{20}{24},$ [F] $\frac{7}{4}, \frac{14}{8},$
$\frac{5}{10}, \frac{6}{12}$ $\frac{12}{18}, \frac{14}{21}, \frac{16}{24}$ $\frac{5}{25}, \frac{6}{30}, \frac{7}{35}$ $\frac{15}{50}, \frac{18}{60}, \frac{21}{70}$ $\frac{25}{30}, \frac{30}{36}, \frac{35}{42}$ $\frac{35}{20}$

2. In each exercise, find the fraction for the ▨ .

[A] $\left\{ \frac{1}{8}, \frac{2}{16}, \frac{3}{24}, \frac{4}{32}, \cdots \right\}$

[B] $\left\{ \frac{5}{4}, \frac{10}{8}, \frac{15}{12}, \frac{20}{16}, \cdots \right\}$

[C] $\left\{ \frac{1}{1}, \frac{2}{2}, \frac{3}{3}, \frac{4}{4}, \cdots \right\}$

[D] $\left\{ \frac{0}{1}, \frac{0}{2}, \frac{0}{3}, \frac{0}{4}, \cdots \right\}$

[E] $\left\{ \frac{2}{1}, \frac{4}{2}, \frac{6}{3}, \frac{8}{4}, \cdots \right\}$

[F] $\left\{ \frac{5}{8}, \frac{10}{16}, \frac{15}{24}, \cdots \right\}$

[G] $\left\{ \frac{1}{9}, \frac{2}{18}, \frac{3}{27}, \cdots \right\}$

[H] $\left\{ \frac{2}{7}, \frac{4}{14}, \frac{6}{21}, \cdots \right\}$ *5*

[I] $\left\{ \frac{3}{2}, \frac{6}{4}, \frac{9}{6}, \cdots \right\}$

[J] $\left\{ \frac{6}{5}, \frac{12}{10}, \frac{18}{15}, \cdots \right\}$

3. Give the lowest-terms fraction for each part of exercise 2.

(A) $\frac{1}{8}$ (B) $\frac{5}{4}$ (C) $\frac{1}{1}$ (D) $\frac{0}{1}$ (E) $\frac{2}{1}$ (F) $\frac{5}{8}$ (G) $\frac{1}{9}$
(H) $\frac{2}{7}$ (I) $\frac{3}{2}$ (J) $\frac{6}{5}$

Exercise for Experts

My head and feet are just alike.
My terms, as low as they can be.
As a fraction, I'm not proper.
I'm one you seldom see. $\frac{1}{1}$
WHO AM I?

Teaching Pages 288 and 289

● **PURPOSE**

To provide additional experiences in working with sets of equivalent fractions

To provide additional experiences in finding lowest-terms fractions

To provide experiences in work with fractions in practical situations

To provide experiences in work with number pairs and fractions

● **PREPARATION**

Review with the students the material on lower and higher terms and on lowest terms. Emphasize again that we think of lower and higher terms only if the fractions involved are equivalent. Observe with the students also that the lowest-terms fraction is in lower terms than any other fraction in the set of fractions that are equivalent to it. Be sure to review also that we can tell most easily whether or not a fraction is in lowest terms by finding out whether or not the numerator and denominator have a common factor greater than one.

Following this review, provide the students with several fractions and ask them to determine whether or not these fractions are in lowest terms. In each case, whether their

Fraction exercises

1. Ann has 12 fish. 5 of the fish have black spots. What fraction of the fish have black spots? $\frac{5}{12}$

2. Jim said, "Two thirds of my fish have black spots." Jim has 3 gold fish. How many have black spots? 2

3. Write a fraction for each number-pair story.

[A] Tom said, "5 of the 8 birds in our yard are bluebirds." What fraction of the birds are bluebirds? $\frac{5}{8}$

[B] Sue has 9 coins in her purse. 4 of them are nickels. What fraction of the coins are nickels? $\frac{4}{9}$

4. Write a fraction for each ▓. (A second is $\frac{1}{60}$ of a minute.)

[A] A minute is ▓ of an hour.
[B] An hour is ▓ of a day.
[C] A day is ▓ of a week.
[D] A month is ▓ of a year.
[E] A year is a ▓ of a decade.
[F] A decade is ▓ of a century.
[G] An inch is ▓ of a foot.
[H] A foot is ▓ of a yard.
[I] A yard is ▓ of a mile.
[J] An ounce is ▓ of a pint.
[K] A pint is ▓ of a quart.
[L] A quart is ▓ of a gallon.
[M] An ounce is ▓ of a pound.
[N] A pound is ▓ of a ton.

★5. Give the lowest-terms fraction for each ▓.

[A] 4 months is ▓ of a year.
[B] 40 minutes is ▓ of an hour.
[C] A 12-ounce steak weighs ▓ of a pound.
[D] 9 inches is ▓ of a foot.
[E] 9 inches is ▓ of a yard.
[F] 880 yards is ▓ of a mile.
[G] A quarter is ▓ of a dollar.
[H] A dime is ▓ of a dollar.
[I] A nickel is ▓ of a dollar.
[J] A half foot is ▓ of a yard.
[K] 12 seconds is ▓ of an hour.
[L] A half centimeter is about ▓ of an inch.

Have the students do the exercises. Note that exercise 5 is primarily for the more able students, since the students are asked to give the lowest-terms fraction to complete each sentence. If you choose, you can have all the students do the exercise but have only the more able students attempt to give the lowest-terms fraction for their answer. Of course, in exercise 5A, it will be easy for all students to observe that four months is $\frac{4}{12}$ of a year. The more difficult part is for them to determine that four months is one third of a year. Again, we would emphasize that you should not attempt to teach the students rules for reducing a fraction to lowest terms. This should be experimental activity; if the students are unable to discover a method for reducing to lowest terms, they will have to figure it out the long way.

We would note also that in doing these exercises, the students may sometimes need data which are not given on the page. This is an excellent time to point out to the students that in some instances they must look up information in order to solve a problem. Therefore, this is a fine opportunity for you to involve the students in elementary research to find out such things as the number of pints in a quart, the number of ounces in a pound, etc. All the required information can be found quickly in the Table of Measures.

answers are right or wrong, give the students an opportunity to explain how they arrived at a given decision. The other students in the class will likely catch any mistakes that are made.

We would emphasize the importance of making careful and accurate judgments concerning the students' ability to progress with these ideas. The material provided in these early lessons is of utmost importance, but you should move ahead rapidly if the students are ready.

Have the students do the exercises. When they have finished, allow time for checking papers and discussion. It might be helpful to have some part of exercises 3 and 4 put on the chalkboard and explained to the entire class. Also, you may find it effective to have the more able students explain individually to some less able students the measurements obtained in exercise 2.

Let's Review

- ■ ADDITION
- ■ SUBTRACTION
- ■ MULTIPLICATION
- ■ DIVISION
- ■ MEASUREMENT
- **PLACE VALUE**
- ■ INEQUALITIES
- **PRINCIPLES**

1. Give the correct sign (+, −, ×, ÷) for each ⬤

[A] 48 ⊗ 48 > 100 [C] 564 ⬤ 1 > 564 [M] 10 ⊗ 100 = 1000

[B] 127 ⬤ 29 = 98 [D] 329 ⊗ 0 ≠ 329 [N] 1000 ⬤ 1 = 999

[E] 0 ⬤ 28 > 0
[F] 764 ⬤ 764 < 1
[G] 168 ⬤ 1 < 168
[H] 67 ⬤ 35 = 102
[I] 369 ⊗ 7 > 376
[J] 0 ⬤ 1 > 0
[K] 1 ⬤ 1 < 1
[L] 4500 ⬤ 2 < 4000

2. Find the length of each segment to the nearest half centimeter.

[A] ——————————————————— 8
[B] ————————————— 5½
[C] ——————————————— 6½
[D] ———————————————————— 11
[E] ——————— 5
[F] ——————————————————— 9½

3. Find the sums and differences.

[A] 34
+68
102

[B] 82
−43
39

[C] 80
−26
54

[D] 865
+728
1593

[E] 140
−65
75

[F] 84
−76
8

[G] 927
+849
1776

[H] 60
−47
13

[I] 120
−35
85

[J] 9830
+7692
17,522

4. Find the products and quotients.

[A] 83 × 5 *415*   [G] 545 ÷ 5 *109*   [M] 128 ÷ 4 *32*   [S] 522 ÷ 6 *87*

[B] 64 ÷ 4 *16*   [H] 205 ÷ 5 *41*   [N] 3276 × 1 *3276*   [T] 1346 × 3 *403*

[C] 76 × 3 *228*   [I] 816 × 2 *1632*   [O] 600 ÷ 6 *100*   [U] 435 × 6 *2610*

[D] 108 ÷ 2 *54*   [J] 264 ÷ 4 *66*   [P] 437 × 6 *2622*   [V] 252 ÷ 3 *84*

[E] 319 × 7 *2233*   [K] 902 × 3 *2706*   [Q] 700 ÷ 7 *100*   [W] 3412 × 5 *17,06*

[F] 428 × 3 *1284*   [L] 392 ÷ 7 *56*   [R] 3269 × 4 *13,076*   [X] 44 ÷ 4 *11*

Teaching Pages 290 and 291

● **PURPOSE**

To provide a cumulative review of the material covered thus far in the text

To provide a review of word problems

● **PREPARATION**

Give the students an opportunity to review any text material with which they have had particular difficulty. If you feel the students have had adequate exposure to the whole-number algorithms, you might use this period to provide experiences in making up word problems. You might exhibit on the chalkboard a given equation involv-

Weights

TRUCK WEIGHING STATION —

1 pound (lb) is 16 ounces (oz).   1 ton is 2000 pounds.

1. [A] How many ounces are in 5 pounds? *80*
    [B] How many pounds are in 5 tons? *10,000*
    [C] How many ounces are in 8 pounds? *128*
    [D] How many pounds are in 7 tons? *14,000*
    [E] How many pounds are in 10 tons? *20,000*

2. [A] How many ounces does a 7-pound beef roast weigh? *112*
    [B] How many ounces does a 9-pound ham weigh? *144*
    [C] If a turkey weighs 10 pounds and 7 ounces, how many ounces does it weigh? *167*
    [D] If a car weighs 1 ton and 1287 pounds, how many pounds does it weigh? *3287*

3. [A] 2 pounds is how many ounces? *32* [D] 9 pounds is how many ounces? *144*
    [B] 3 pounds is how many ounces? *48* [E] 10 pounds is how many ounces? *160*
    [C] 5 pounds is how many ounces? *80* [F] 100 pounds is how many ounces? *1600*

★4. Tell what should go in each ▥.
    [A] 41 ounces is 2 pounds and ▥ ounces.
    [B] 82 ounces is ▥ pounds and 2 ounces.
    [C] 20 ounces is ▥ pounds and ▥ ounces.

DIRECTIONS PAGE 291

Have the students read the statement that a pound is 16 ounces and that a ton is 2000 pounds. Following this have the students do the exercises. Exercise 4 is primarily for the more able students since parts B and C involve fairly complicated division, and the students may have some difficulty in understanding how the remainder relates to the number of ounces. When the students divide the number of ounces by 16 in part B and come out with the correct quotient and a remainder of 13, they may not understand that 13 is the number of ounces. It should help the students understand why the remainder tells the number of ounces if they check the answer by multiplication. Give all students an opportunity to participate in a discussion of exercises 1 through 3.

ing one of the operations, addition, subtraction, multiplication, or division, and instruct the students to make up a word problem about this equation. For example, if you give the equation $38 + 79 = n$, the students can make up a word problem in which the numbers 38 and 79 are involved and the addition operation is to be performed.

Instruct the students to do the exercises. If you decide to use this as a chapter test, you will want to check the papers yourself. If not, have the students discuss their answers after they have completed the page. Of course, if the page is used as a test, you will want to hold a discussion of the exercises when you return the corrected papers.

Answers, exercise 7, page 292

[A] $\frac{2}{4}$, $\frac{3}{6}$, $\frac{4}{8}$, $\frac{5}{10}$, $\frac{6}{12}$, $\frac{7}{14}$

[B] $\frac{2}{8}$, $\frac{3}{12}$, $\frac{4}{16}$, $\frac{5}{20}$, $\frac{6}{24}$, $\frac{7}{28}$

[C] $\frac{4}{6}$, $\frac{6}{9}$, $\frac{8}{12}$, $\frac{10}{15}$, $\frac{12}{18}$, $\frac{14}{21}$

[D] $\frac{6}{8}$, $\frac{9}{12}$, $\frac{12}{16}$, $\frac{15}{20}$, $\frac{18}{24}$, $\frac{21}{28}$

[E] $\frac{14}{16}$, $\frac{21}{24}$, $\frac{28}{32}$, $\frac{35}{40}$, $\frac{42}{48}$, $\frac{49}{56}$

[F] $\frac{6}{20}$, $\frac{9}{30}$, $\frac{12}{40}$, $\frac{15}{50}$, $\frac{18}{60}$, $\frac{21}{70}$

Chapter review

1. Give a fraction to tell what part of each picture is blue.

[A] $\frac{3}{10}$ [B] $\frac{7}{16}$ [c] $\frac{17}{18}$

2. Give a fraction to tell what part of each bar is blue.

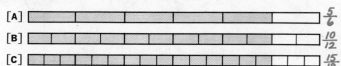

[A] $\frac{5}{6}$

[B] $\frac{10}{12}$

[c] $\frac{15}{18}$

3. Use the product method to show that your fractions in exercise 2 are equivalent.

$5 \times 12 = 60$ $10 \times 18 = 180$ $5 \times 18 = 90$
$6 \times 10 = 60$ $12 \times 15 = 180$ $15 \times 6 = 90$

4. Give three more fractions for each set.

[A] $\left\{\frac{3}{7}, \frac{6}{14}, \frac{9}{21}, \cdots\right\}$ $\frac{12}{28}, \frac{15}{35}, \frac{18}{42}$

[B] $\left\{\frac{4}{5}, \frac{8}{10}, \frac{12}{15}, \cdots\right\}$ $\frac{16}{20}, \frac{20}{25}, \frac{24}{30}$

> **Exercise for Experts**
> I like to think that I am big,
> But no one will agree.
> One in a million is your clue.
> Use lowest terms for me.
> WHO AM I? $\frac{1}{1,000,000}$

5. Tell whether or not the two fractions are equivalent.

[A] $\frac{2}{4}$ $\frac{8}{16}$ [B] $\frac{8}{3}$ $\frac{25}{9}$ [c] $\frac{10}{8}$ $\frac{15}{12}$ [D] $\frac{7}{8}$ $\frac{21}{16}$
   equiv.   *not equiv.*   *equiv.*   *not equiv.*

6. Write an improper fraction for each exercise.

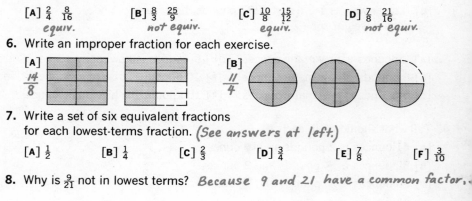

[A] $\frac{14}{8}$ [B] $\frac{11}{4}$

7. Write a set of six equivalent fractions for each lowest-terms fraction. *(See answers at left.)*

[A] $\frac{1}{2}$ [B] $\frac{1}{4}$ [C] $\frac{2}{3}$ [D] $\frac{3}{4}$ [E] $\frac{7}{8}$ [F] $\frac{3}{10}$

8. Why is $\frac{9}{21}$ not in lowest terms? *Because 9 and 21 have a common factor.*

Teaching Pages 292 and 293

● **PURPOSE**

To provide a chapter review
To provide a sample evaluation instrument

● **PREPARATION**

Give the students an opportunity to review the chapter topics. Focus attention on any topics with which the students have had difficulty. In particular, review the construction of sets of equivalent fractions beginning with the lowest-terms fraction (one of the most important topics of the chapter). During the construction of these sets, present several diagrams to illustrate the equivalence of

The 50 states

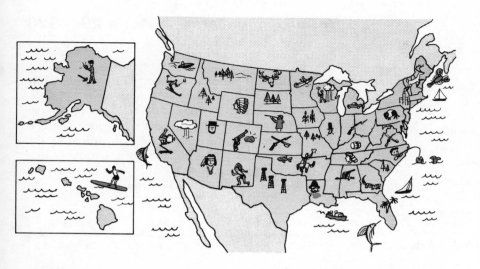

1. The United States has 50 states. Two of them do not border on any other states. Give two fractions that tell what part of the states do not border on other states. $\frac{2}{50}$, $\frac{1}{25}$

2. Michigan touches four of the five Great Lakes. What fraction of the lakes touch Michigan? $\frac{4}{5}$ What fraction of the lakes do not touch Michigan? $\frac{1}{5}$

3. Eight of the 50 states touch at least one of the Great Lakes. Give two fractions to tell what part of the states this is. $\frac{8}{50}$, $\frac{4}{25}$

4. Ten of the states border Canada. Give three fractions to tell what part of the states border Canada. $\frac{10}{50}$, $\frac{5}{25}$, $\frac{1}{5}$

5. Five of the states border the Gulf of Mexico. Give two fractions to tell what part of the states border the Gulf of Mexico. $\frac{5}{50}$, $\frac{1}{10}$

★6. Four states border on Mexico, and three states border on the Pacific Ocean. California borders on both Mexico and the Pacific Ocean. What part of the 50 states border on Mexico or on the Pacific Ocean or both? $\frac{6}{50}$

These word problems are considered part of the chapter review; therefore, you may choose to use some or all of them as part of your evaluation.

Although exercise 6 is primarily for the more able students, all students will probably understand the exercise once the correct answer is given, especially if you refer to the map and help them count the states bordering on both Mexico and the Pacific Ocean. One point to be made concerning this problem is that it concerns the union of two sets which are not disjoint. Since one set contains four and the other set contains three, one would normally expect that the union of the two sets would contain seven. However, since California is in both sets (it borders on both Mexico and the Pacific Ocean), the union of these two sets contains only six states. This is easy enough to see by looking at the map and simply counting the states which border on Mexico or the Pacific Ocean or both.

Keep in mind during the discussion of these exercises that one value of such an exercise set is that it encourages students to develop interest in other topics and in the application of arithmetic to these topics. For this reason, you should encourage discussion of the geography of the United States and, perhaps, give the students an opportunity to make up some problems of their own with respect to the map on this page.

pairs of fractions within the set. You should also have the students select two fractions from a given set of equivalent fractions and check them for equivalence by using the product method.

Objectives of Chapter 12

To introduce rational numbers

To provide a transition from sets of equivalent fractions to rational numbers

To introduce the rational number line

To establish the fact that each whole number is also a rational number

To introduce equality and inequality for rational numbers

To introduce informally addition of rational numbers

To introduce mixed numerals

To provide word-problem experiences with rational numbers

The opening pages of the chapter are devoted to material which helps the students begin a left-to-right orientation in fraction concepts as preparation for locating rational numbers on the number line. The concept of relating each set of equivalent fractions to exactly one point on the number line, and thus to one rational number, is introduced and stressed in a considerable part of the chapter. The number line is used as the chief tool for providing experiences with these new rational-number concepts.

Following considerable work with rational numbers on the number line, the concept of equality is introduced. It is emphasized that any fraction from the set of equivalent fractions for a given rational number can be used to name the number; thus when we write a statement such as $3/9 = 1/3$, we simply mean that three ninths and one third are names for the same rational number.

Following work with equality of rational numbers, additional work is provided in relating rational numbers to the number line and focusing greater attention on the lowest-terms fraction as the name often used for a rational number.

The next topic is inequalities, and work is provided to help the students understand inequality concepts for rational numbers. This is followed by considering rational numbers greater than one and rational numbers that are whole numbers. Finally, addition of rational numbers is introduced intuitively through number-line experiences, and this is followed by introducing mixed numerals. The final part of the chapter is concerned with rational numbers in measurement, more on addition, and, finally, some rational-number problems.

Mathematics of Chapter 12

As you saw in the last chapter, we can start with any lowest-terms fraction and imagine an infinite set of equivalent fractions. Of course, with each of the sets, we

associate a different rational number. The number line is very effective for illustrating these ideas. For example, the number-line charts on page 301 of the text demonstrate that for each set of equivalent fractions there is one and only one rational number. As illustrated by the following number line, showing more of the number line and labeling fourths help give meaning to improper fractions and corresponding rational numbers.

The number line also helps illustrate that each whole number can be considered a rational number. That is, whole numbers are a subset of rational numbers.

Although we think of exactly one number for a given point on the number line (and exactly one point for a given rational number), we may label the point with any fraction from the set of equivalent fractions for that point. Thus, the point associated with one half could be labeled with any fraction from the set $\{1/2, 2/4, 3/6, 4/8, 5/10, 6/12, \ldots\}$.

The fact that each rational number has many different names (any fraction in the set) leads us to consider the concept of equality for rational numbers. When we write

$$1/2 = 4/8$$

we are indicating that $1/2$ and $4/8$ represent the same rational number. Of course, this would indicate also that the fractions are equivalent. Keep in mind, however, that

$$1/2 = 4/8$$

is to be considered as a statement about *numbers,* not about *fractions.* In general, we would say that

$$a/b = c/d$$

means that a/b and c/d name the same rational number. Again we observe that:

Two fractions name the same rational number if and only if they are equivalent.

Therefore,

$$a/b = c/d \text{ if and only if } ad = bc.$$

If we wish to compare two rational numbers such as $3/8$ and $5/8$, we would easily arrive at $3/8 < 5/8$ by simply considering the physical interpretations from which the fractions $3/8$ and $5/8$ arise. Several examples will make the following definition seem plausible:

$$a/b > c/d \text{ if and only if } ad > bc.$$

Consider these examples.

Example 1.

$$\tfrac{3}{8} > \tfrac{5}{14} \text{ since } 3 \times 14 > 8 \times 5$$

Example 2.

$$\tfrac{9}{15} < \tfrac{4}{6} \text{ since } 9 \times 6 < 15 \times 4$$

Using the number line or some physical interpretation, we could make the examples above seem obvious. Also, we could find fractions with common denominators for the two rational numbers. Again, the inequality becomes obvious when we do this. Consider Example 2.

Since $\tfrac{9}{15} = \tfrac{18}{30}$ and $\tfrac{4}{6} = \tfrac{20}{30}$ and $\tfrac{18}{30} < \tfrac{20}{30}$, it is clear that $\tfrac{9}{15} < \tfrac{4}{6}$.

As in this example, it often is inconvenient to use physical objects or the number line to consider inequality, but it is often helpful, especially with students, to use other interpretations for certain simple pairs of fractions. For example, to demonstrate that $\tfrac{1}{2} = \tfrac{1}{3}$, we could examine the scale on a measuring cup. To see that $\tfrac{1}{5} < \tfrac{1}{4}$ we could use a number line or some physical object. Keep in mind, however, that such demonstrations simply serve to strengthen understanding of the definition with respect to the generally accepted notion of "less than" and "greater than."

Teaching Chapter 12

It is most important that you relate the fraction concepts developed in Chapter 11 to the rational-number concepts developed in this chapter; this is done primarily in an abstract way, using number-line pictures. It might be convenient to have a large display number line drawn and left on the chalkboard, since you will need to display number lines frequently.

In working problems later in the chapter, it may be helpful to have cutouts which can be used to demonstrate certain fraction and rational-number concepts as suggested by the problems in the text. The suggested map can be used in conjunction with the airline distances listed in the lesson on page 325.

You will notice that we use the term *mixed numeral* rather than the traditional term *mixed number* to refer to numbers represented by symbols such as $3\tfrac{1}{2}$, $4\tfrac{1}{8}$, etc. We make this distinction because it is the symbol that is "mixed," not the number.

Plan to cover this material in about $3\tfrac{1}{2}$ to 4 weeks. Naturally, you will want to adjust your time schedule to the needs and abilities of your students and according to the time remaining in the school year.

Evaluating students' achievement may be more difficult for this chapter than for any other chapter in the text. We do not expect the students to achieve a great deal of mastery of any particular skill in this chapter. Your primary evaluation criterion should be the students' understanding of the general concept of rational numbers, their relation to whole numbers, and their location on the number line. Of course, associated with this is the concept of equality and inequality for rational numbers. The best method for such evaluation is through a day-to-day consideration of students' responses and participation during a given discussion.

Keep in mind, while teaching this chapter, that we do not expect that all students completely master the rational-number concepts on this first exposure. Do not be overly concerned if some students have difficulty grasping the idea that there is exactly one number and exactly one point on the number line associated with each complete set of equivalent fractions. These students can continue to study rational numbers without fully abstracting the idea from the class of equivalent fractions. Certainly, many students experienced some insight for certain rational-number concepts when they were working with fractions. At that point, however, we focused attention on number pairs rather than on a single number. Now that we are considering a single number, the concepts involved become more complex. Of course, a chief difficulty in the study of rational numbers is the fact that there are so many different names to represent each rational number.

If you choose, you can use the exercises on this page as class-discussion exercises. However, it may be more informative to have the students go through and try to work the exercises on their own before discussing each one separately.

Most of the exercises are quite easy, and the students should be able to work them fairly quickly. It is important that they understand the idea presented here: that they begin at the left and think about moving across to the right a certain fractional part of the way.

So that the students will be more inclined to count spaces rather than dots as they work exercises 3 through 6, it may help them to think about the jet landing at each city.

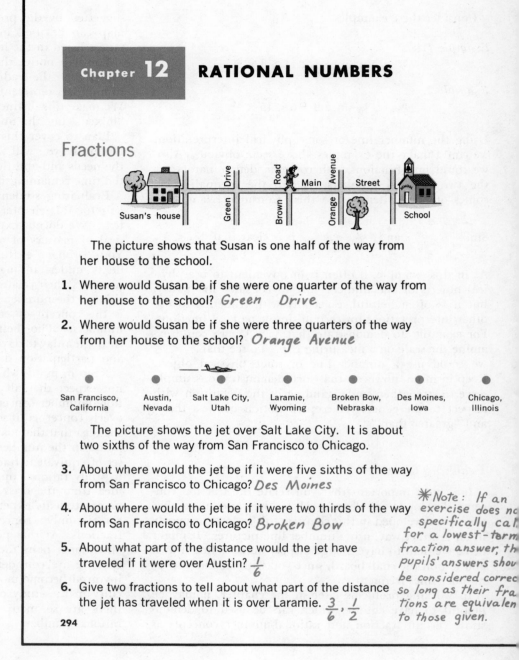

Chapter **12** **RATIONAL NUMBERS**

Fractions

The picture shows that Susan is one half of the way from her house to the school.

1. Where would Susan be if she were one quarter of the way from her house to the school? *Green Drive*

2. Where would Susan be if she were three quarters of the way from her house to the school? *Orange Avenue*

San Francisco, California   Austin, Nevada   Salt Lake City, Utah   Laramie, Wyoming   Broken Bow, Nebraska   Des Moines, Iowa   Chicago, Illinois

The picture shows the jet over Salt Lake City. It is about two sixths of the way from San Francisco to Chicago.

3. About where would the jet be if it were five sixths of the way from San Francisco to Chicago? *Des Moines*

4. About where would the jet be if it were two thirds of the way from San Francisco to Chicago? *Broken Bow*

5. About what part of the distance would the jet have traveled if it were over Austin? $\frac{1}{6}$

6. Give two fractions to tell about what part of the distance the jet has traveled when it is over Laramie. $\frac{3}{6}, \frac{1}{2}$

✳Note: If an exercise does no specifically call for a lowest-term fraction answer, th pupils' answers shou be considered correc so long as their fra tions are equivalen to those given.

294

Teaching Pages 294 and 295

● **PURPOSE**

To provide additional work with fractions to lead toward an introduction of rational numbers on a number line

● **PREPARATION**

Review with the students various common fractions such as fourths, thirds, fifths, and eighths. Following this, ask a student to go to the left side (as you face the front) of the room and then instruct him to walk one fourth of the way across the room. After he does this, point out to the students that if they think of the fraction one fourth as starting at one place and going one fourth of the way, then they would have three fourths left to go. Have other stu-

EXERCISES

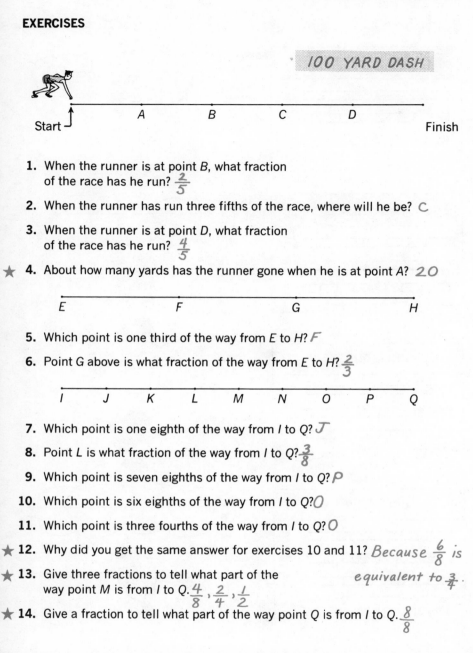

100 YARD DASH

Start ⌐   A   B   C   D   Finish

1. When the runner is at point B, what fraction of the race has he run? $\frac{2}{5}$

2. When the runner has run three fifths of the race, where will he be? C

3. When the runner is at point D, what fraction of the race has he run? $\frac{4}{5}$

★ 4. About how many yards has the runner gone when he is at point A? 20

E   F   G   H

5. Which point is one third of the way from E to H? F

6. Point G above is what fraction of the way from E to H? $\frac{2}{3}$

I   J   K   L   M   N   O   P   Q

7. Which point is one eighth of the way from I to Q? J

8. Point L is what fraction of the way from I to Q? $\frac{3}{8}$

9. Which point is seven eighths of the way from I to Q? P

10. Which point is six eighths of the way from I to Q? O

11. Which point is three fourths of the way from I to Q? O

★ 12. Why did you get the same answer for exercises 10 and 11? Because $\frac{6}{8}$ is equivalent to $\frac{3}{4}$.

★ 13. Give three fractions to tell what part of the way point M is from I to Q. $\frac{4}{8}$, $\frac{2}{4}$, $\frac{1}{2}$

★ 14. Give a fraction to tell what part of the way point Q is from I to Q. $\frac{8}{8}$

Have the students work the exercises. Although exercises 4, 12, 13, and 14 are primarily for the more able students, you may find that these exercises will benefit all the students in a class-discussion situation. The essential point is that you give the more proficient students an opportunity to try these exercises prior to discussing them in class.

It may seem that exercise 4 involves a multiplication problem (that is, one fifth of one hundred). Since the students know nothing about multiplying fractions, they may simply divide 100 by 5, or, through experimentation and observation, find that if each space is 20 yards, then the five spaces would make up 100 yards and point A would be 20 yards from the starting point.

Of course, the answer for exercise 12 is that six parts out of eight is the same as three parts out of four if we are considering the same object.

dents walk different fractional parts of the way across the room (such as two thirds, four fifths, etc.). One purpose of this demonstration is to accustom the students to a left-to-right orientation in selecting a point and moving a certain fractional part of the way. During this discussion, ask the students each time what fraction of the way they have yet to go. For example, if you have a student walk one third of the way across the room, you should then ask him what fraction of the way remains to be covered. You might also provide similar demonstrations with drawings on the chalkboard.

Ask the students to study the first diagram which shows the one-half chart. Explain that the torn bottom edge of this chart means that they should think of the chart as going on indefinitely. Now observe with the students that the girl is looking at the chart and thinking about a point on the number line. That is, she is looking at the chart labeled "one half" and she is thinking about exactly one number. Have the students tell whether or not they think she has found the right location for the number.

Now, move to the second diagram and observe with the class that the boy is looking at this number chart and thinking about one number and one point on the number line.

Have the students continue to discuss the third and fourth pictures on this page in the same way.

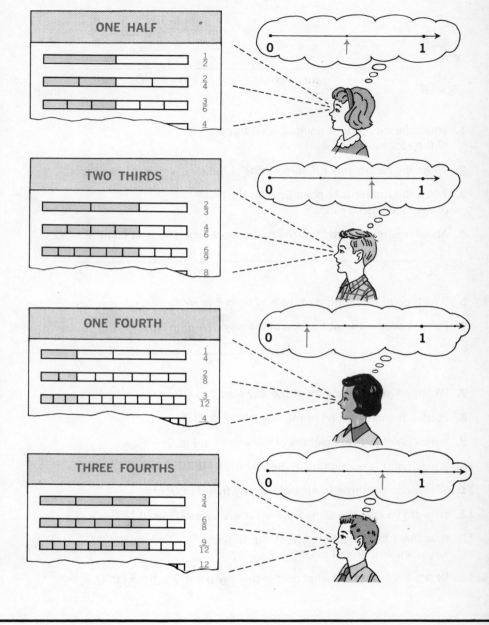

From fractions to numbers

Teaching Pages 296 and 297

• PURPOSE

To introduce rational numbers

To associate with each class of equivalent fractions exactly one rational number and one point on the number line

• MATHEMATICS

This lesson contains the heart of the mathematical development of the rational-number concept. The four charts on page 296 show the idea of a class of equivalent fractions, the fact that these fractions are equivalent (illustrated by showing that they represent the same part of a bar), and the fact that each class continues indefinitely (illustrated by the torn-off bottom edge of each chart). Of course, the picture of a student looking at a chart and then thinking of exactly one point on the number line indicates the general idea of rational number. That is, there is exactly one quantitative idea associated with each chart (set of fractions). We indicate this association with a point on the number line to show that we consider this idea as a number in much the same way as we have thought about whole numbers. You will note that up to this point we have reserved the number line for numbers; we have not put fractions on the number line. In future lessons we shall indicate numbers by using fractions on the number line.

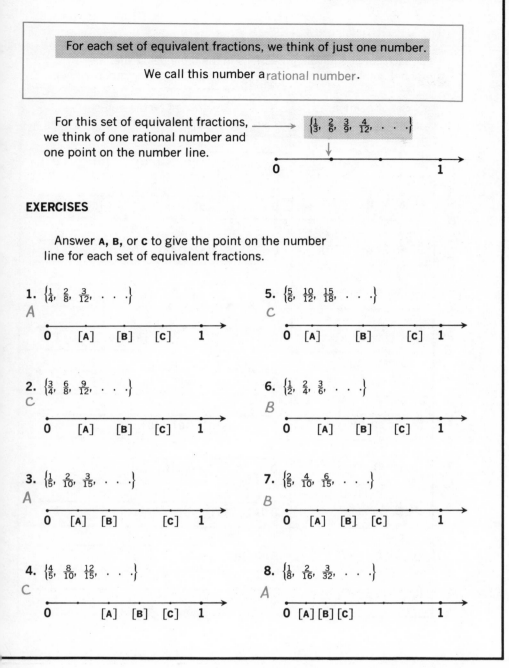

For each set of equivalent fractions, we think of just one number.

We call this number a rational number.

For this set of equivalent fractions, we think of one rational number and one point on the number line.

$$\left\{\frac{1}{3}, \frac{2}{6}, \frac{3}{9}, \frac{4}{12}, \cdots\right\}$$

0   1

EXERCISES

Answer **A**, **B**, or **C** to give the point on the number line for each set of equivalent fractions.

1. $\left\{\frac{1}{4}, \frac{2}{8}, \frac{3}{12}, \cdots\right\}$

A

0   [A]   [B]   [C]   1

2. $\left\{\frac{3}{4}, \frac{6}{8}, \frac{9}{12}, \cdots\right\}$

C

0   [A]   [B]   [C]   1

3. $\left\{\frac{1}{5}, \frac{2}{10}, \frac{3}{15}, \cdots\right\}$

A

0   [A]   [B]   [C]   1

4. $\left\{\frac{4}{5}, \frac{8}{10}, \frac{12}{15}, \cdots\right\}$

C

0   [A]   [B]   [C]   1

5. $\left\{\frac{5}{6}, \frac{10}{12}, \frac{15}{18}, \cdots\right\}$

C

0   [A]   [B]   [C]   1

6. $\left\{\frac{1}{2}, \frac{2}{4}, \frac{3}{6}, \cdots\right\}$

B

0   [A]   [B]   [C]   1

7. $\left\{\frac{2}{5}, \frac{4}{10}, \frac{6}{15}, \cdots\right\}$

B

0   [A]   [B]   [C]   1

8. $\left\{\frac{1}{8}, \frac{2}{16}, \frac{3}{32}, \cdots\right\}$

A

0 [A][B][C]   1

Study the material at the top of the page with the class. In particular, stress the statement, "For each set of equivalent fractions, we think of just one number," and that this number is called a rational number. Remind the students that the numbers they have studied so far are called whole numbers and then remark that now they are going to study numbers that are called rational numbers.

Study with the students the diagram showing the set of fractions $\{\frac{1}{3}, \frac{2}{6}, \frac{3}{9}, \frac{4}{12}, \ldots\}$ and its location on the number line. Observe with the students that for this set of equivalent fractions they are to think of just one number and that its location on the number line is indicated in the picture.

Give the students an opportunity to do exercises 1 through 8 on their own.

When the students have completed these exercises, you may exhibit several on the chalkboard and give the students an opportunity to discuss each one. As a follow-up to this lesson and as preparation for the next lesson, you might observe with the students that in exercise 1 the correct answer is A. However, by putting in additional division marks they could think of point A as $\frac{2}{8}$ or $\frac{3}{12}$, etc. Hence, point A is associated with each of these fractions. That is, for this set of equivalent fractions, we have exactly one point on the number line and, of course, one rational number.

PREPARATION

Have the students construct several sets of equivalent fractions, including sets containing one half, two thirds, one fourth, and three fourths (these are the rational numbers developed first, on page 296). With the set of equivalent fractions for one half, you should have an accompanying picture to illustrate that these fractions are equivalent. You can use a picture similar to that found on page 296, or you might choose to use a circle or a rectangle. The purpose of this preparatory lesson is to ready the students for the introduction of rational numbers and to give them some background for the idea of a quantitative sameness between any of the fractions in a given set.

If the students are successful in locating points for sets of fractions during the preparation period, you might have them do these exercises without further instruction. If you feel that more practice is needed, you might work through the first one or two exercises with the students. You can do this by exhibiting on the chalkboard the sets of fractions along with a number-line picture and having the students show where the rational number is located. Following this, have the students complete the exercises. When they have finished, allow time for checking papers and further discussion. It might be effective to have several of these exercises presented on the chalkboard and explained.

The students may observe that exercises 2 and 11 are the same. However, you should note with them that in exercise 2 the segment between zero and one is divided into six parts, and in exercise 11 it is divided into 12 parts.

If the students have difficulty with this set of exercises, you might point out, during the discussion period, that they can find the number of divisions for the segment between zero and one and then look for the fraction that corresponds to this number of divisions. For example, in exercise 5 the students should see that the segment is divided into eighths, and they should look at the fraction $\frac{6}{8}$. Or in exercise 6 they see that the segment is divided into tenths, and they can look at the fraction $\frac{8}{10}$. Therefore, in doing exercise 11, the students may find it helpful to look at the fraction $\frac{4}{12}$ in order to locate the point for this rational number.

Rational-number exercises

For each set of equivalent fractions in the table below there is a rational number. Give the point for the number on the number line.

	Set of fractions for the number	Which point on the number line goes with the number?
1. B	$\{\frac{2}{5}, \frac{4}{10}, \frac{6}{15}, \frac{8}{20} \cdots\}$	0 [A] [B] [C] [D] 1
2. B	$\{\frac{1}{3}, \frac{2}{6}, \frac{3}{9}, \frac{4}{12} \cdots\}$	0 [A] [B] [C] 1
3. C	$\{\frac{2}{3}, \frac{4}{6}, \frac{6}{9}, \frac{8}{12} \cdots\}$	0 [A] [B] [C] 1
4. B	$\{\frac{3}{5}, \frac{6}{10}, \frac{9}{15}, \frac{12}{20} \cdots\}$	0 [A] [B] [C] 1
5. C	$\{\frac{3}{4}, \frac{6}{8}, \frac{9}{12}, \frac{12}{16} \cdots\}$	0 [A] [B] [C] 1
6. C	$\{\frac{4}{5}, \frac{8}{10}, \frac{12}{15}, \frac{16}{20} \cdots\}$	0 [A] [B] [C] 1
7. B	$\{\frac{3}{7}, \frac{6}{14}, \frac{9}{21}, \frac{12}{28} \cdots\}$	0 [A] [B] [C] 1
8. C	$\{\frac{5}{8}, \frac{10}{16}, \frac{15}{24}, \frac{20}{32} \cdots\}$	0 [A] [B] [C] 1
9. B	$\{\frac{1}{4}, \frac{2}{8}, \frac{3}{12}, \frac{4}{16} \cdots\}$	0 [A] [B] [C] 1
10. B	$\{\frac{1}{6}, \frac{2}{12}, \frac{3}{18}, \frac{4}{24} \cdots\}$	0 [A][B] [C] 1
11. B	$\{\frac{1}{3}, \frac{2}{6}, \frac{3}{9}, \frac{4}{12} \cdots\}$	0 [A][B] [C] 1

Teaching Pages 298 and 299

- **PURPOSE**

  To provide additional experiences in assigning a set of equivalent fractions to a point on the number line and, consequently, to a given rational number

- **PREPARATION**

  Provide the students with experiences in constructing sets of equivalent fractions, starting with the lowest-terms fraction. For example, have the students start with the fraction two thirds and build the first six or eight fractions in this set. Now place some illustrations on the chalkboard to demonstrate that each fraction may be used to

EXERCISES

1. Match the sets of fractions with the number-line pictures.

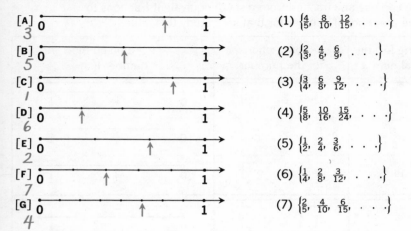

(1) $\left\{\frac{4}{5}, \frac{8}{10}, \frac{12}{15}, \ldots \right\}$

(2) $\left\{\frac{2}{3}, \frac{4}{6}, \frac{6}{9}, \ldots \right\}$

(3) $\left\{\frac{3}{4}, \frac{6}{8}, \frac{9}{12}, \ldots \right\}$

(4) $\left\{\frac{5}{8}, \frac{10}{16}, \frac{15}{24}, \ldots \right\}$

(5) $\left\{\frac{1}{2}, \frac{2}{4}, \frac{3}{6}, \ldots \right\}$

(6) $\left\{\frac{1}{4}, \frac{2}{8}, \frac{3}{12}, \ldots \right\}$

(7) $\left\{\frac{2}{5}, \frac{4}{10}, \frac{6}{15}, \ldots \right\}$

2. Choose the fraction that is from the set of equivalent fractions for the point over the blue arrow.

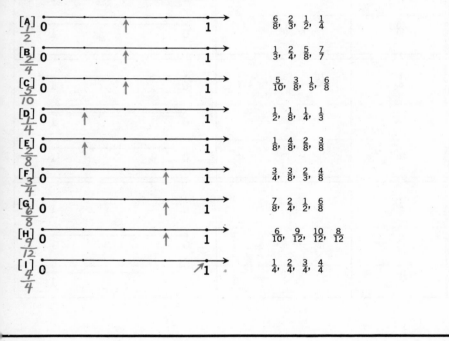

$\frac{6}{8}, \frac{2}{3}, \frac{1}{2}, \frac{1}{4}$

$\frac{1}{3}, \frac{2}{4}, \frac{5}{8}, \frac{7}{7}$

$\frac{5}{10}, \frac{3}{8}, \frac{1}{5}, \frac{6}{8}$

$\frac{1}{2}, \frac{1}{8}, \frac{1}{4}, \frac{1}{3}$

$\frac{1}{8}, \frac{4}{8}, \frac{2}{8}, \frac{3}{8}$

$\frac{3}{4}, \frac{3}{8}, \frac{2}{3}, \frac{4}{8}$

$\frac{7}{8}, \frac{2}{4}, \frac{1}{2}, \frac{6}{8}$

$\frac{6}{10}, \frac{9}{12}, \frac{10}{12}, \frac{8}{12}$

$\frac{1}{4}, \frac{2}{4}, \frac{3}{4}, \frac{4}{4}$

Explain to the students that in exercise 1 they need to figure out a fraction for the point indicated by the blue arrow and then look for that fraction within one of the sets. They can be assured that when they find the given fraction in the set, it is that set which belongs to that rational-number point.

Have the students do the exercises. When they have finished, allow time for checking papers and discussion. It will be beneficial to place several of these exercises on the chalkboard and have students explain them to the class.

In exercise 2, the students should observe that the exercises are grouped so that exercises 2A, B, and C all indicate the same point. However, the students must give a different fraction for each. Note that parts D and E and parts F, G, and H indicate the same point. Exercise 2I indicates the point *one*; consequently, the answer is ¼. Since the segment is divided into fourths, the students should have no trouble in arriving at the correct answer. If they merely use the process of elimination, the students should see that the correct answer could not be ¼, ²⁄₄, or ¾; therefore, it must be ⁴⁄₄.

indicate the same amount of a given object. Try to get the students to explain this quantitative similarity for each fraction in the set. Of course, it is this idea which helps the students understand the reasoning behind saying that there is exactly one number for this entire set of fractions and, of course, one location on the number line.

After you have constructed and demonstrated several such sets of fractions, exhibit on the chalkboard a number line with no labels between zero and one. Be sure there is enough space for the students to indicate various points between zero and one. Now have the students estimate the point for the rational number for each set of fractions they have constructed. Do not insist upon a high degree of accuracy for these estimations.

Read the first sentence with the class. To speak of naming a number may be somewhat strange to the students. However, you can tell the students that when they were preschoolers or in kindergarten they had to find names for the numbers *two*, *three*, and *four*, and they also had to find numerals, or symbols, to write for these numbers. Tell them that this is what they are learning now with rational numbers: they are finding names and symbols to write for these numbers.

Study the table row by row with the students. Point out that the first column of the first three rows gives three names for the same rational number. That is, in the middle column the students will note that the set of fractions is the same for the first three rows; they will also note that the point on the number line is the same for these rows. Now move back to the left column and notice with the students that in the first row this rational number is named one half; in the second row, two fourths; and in the third row, five tenths. Notice now with the students that in the right column these names are indicated on the number line. At this point you should stress that it is correct to use any fraction from the set of equivalent fractions to name the rational number. You might observe with the students that the simplest name and, in fact, the most common name for this rational number is one half, but if we choose, we can use the names two fourths, three sixths, four eighths, five tenths, etc.

Continue with this type of discussion for the remaining part of the table. Be sure to study the rows of the table in groups of three, as indicated by the wider gray dividing lines which separate the four different rational numbers.

Names for rational numbers

We can use any fraction from a set of equivalent fractions to name the rational number for that set. Study this table.

A name for the rational number	Set of fractions for the number	Position on the number line
$\frac{1}{2}$	$\left\{\frac{1}{2}, \frac{2}{4}, \frac{3}{6}, \cdots\right\}$	0 — $\frac{1}{2}$ — 1
$\frac{2}{4}$	$\left\{\frac{1}{2}, \frac{2}{4}, \frac{3}{6}, \cdots\right\}$	0 — $\frac{2}{4}$ — 1
$\frac{5}{10}$	$\left\{\frac{1}{2}, \frac{2}{4}, \frac{3}{6}, \cdots\right\}$	0 — $\frac{5}{10}$ — 1
$\frac{2}{3}$	$\left\{\frac{2}{3}, \frac{4}{6}, \frac{6}{9}, \cdots\right\}$	0 — $\frac{2}{3}$ — 1
$\frac{4}{6}$	$\left\{\frac{2}{3}, \frac{4}{6}, \frac{6}{9}, \cdots\right\}$	0 — $\frac{4}{6}$ — 1
$\frac{20}{30}$	$\left\{\frac{2}{3}, \frac{4}{6}, \frac{6}{9}, \cdots\right\}$	0 — $\frac{20}{30}$ — 1
$\frac{1}{4}$	$\left\{\frac{1}{4}, \frac{2}{8}, \frac{3}{12}, \cdots\right\}$	0 — $\frac{1}{4}$ — 1
$\frac{3}{12}$	$\left\{\frac{1}{4}, \frac{2}{8}, \frac{3}{12}, \cdots\right\}$	0 — $\frac{3}{12}$ — 1
$\frac{5}{20}$	$\left\{\frac{1}{4}, \frac{2}{8}, \frac{3}{12}, \cdots\right\}$	0 — $\frac{5}{20}$ — 1
$\frac{3}{5}$	$\left\{\frac{3}{5}, \frac{6}{10}, \frac{9}{15}, \cdots\right\}$	0 — $\frac{3}{5}$ — 1
$\frac{6}{10}$	$\left\{\frac{3}{5}, \frac{6}{10}, \frac{9}{15}, \cdots\right\}$	0 — $\frac{6}{10}$ — 1
$\frac{18}{30}$	$\left\{\frac{3}{5}, \frac{6}{10}, \frac{9}{15}, \cdots\right\}$	0 — $\frac{18}{30}$ — 1

Teaching Pages 300 and 301

● **PURPOSE**

To provide additional experiences in thinking of one rational number for a set of equivalent fractions and in locating corresponding points on the rational number line

To introduce the idea that any fraction in the set may be used as a name for the rational number of that set

● **PREPARATION**

One of the best ways to prepare the students for this lesson is to review carefully the first eight parts of exercise 2, page 299, in which the students must identify a single

EXERCISES

1. Just one rational number goes with each point. Some of the fractions that name the rational number are given. Give the missing fractions.

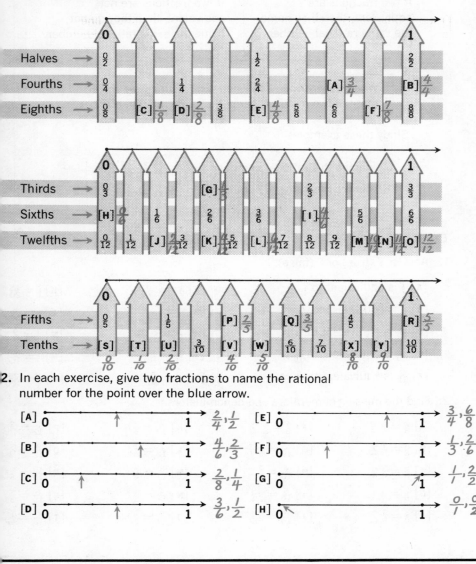

2. In each exercise, give two fractions to name the rational number for the point over the blue arrow.

[A] 0 — ↑ — 1 $\frac{2}{4}, \frac{1}{2}$ [E] 0 — ↑ — 1 $\frac{3}{4}, \frac{6}{8}$

[B] 0 — ↑ — 1 $\frac{4}{6}, \frac{2}{3}$ [F] 0 — ↑ — 1 $\frac{1}{3}, \frac{2}{6}$

[C] 0 — ↑ — 1 $\frac{2}{8}, \frac{1}{4}$ [G] 0 — ↗ 1 $\frac{1}{1}, \frac{2}{2}$

[D] 0 — ↑ — 1 $\frac{3}{6}, \frac{1}{2}$ [H] 0 ↖ — 1 $\frac{0}{1}, \frac{0}{2}$

fraction for a given point on the number line. Identifying one fraction for this point is similar to what is to be done in this lesson. Of course, in exercise 2, page 299, the students were to observe which fraction was from the set of fractions for that point. In the current lesson, the important fact to be stressed is that there are many fractions which can be associated with a given point on the number line. If you choose, you can use the table on page 300 as part of your preparatory lesson for the material which is covered on page 301.

It may be helpful to work through exercises 1A through G with the students before having them complete the page on their own. This will give them an idea of what is expected in these exercises. During a discussion of exercises 1A through G, be sure to point out to the students the concepts involved. That is, they are using different fractions to name the points on the number line.

Following this discussion, have the students complete the exercises. When they have finished, allow time for checking papers and further discussion. Take this opportunity again to stress that they are learning to associate, with a given point on the number line, not only a rational number and a set of equivalent fractions but any one fraction from the set of equivalent fractions.

Study the two statements at the top of the page with the class. Making these two statements may, at this time, seem unimportant and trivial since we have defined rational number in such a way as to be associated with sets of equivalent fractions. However, stressing these statements will help give meaning to the concept of equality for rational numbers in the following exercises. Since the students know how to test to see whether or not two fractions are equivalent, these statements will also remind them that the test for determining equivalence of fractions will help them determine whether or not $\frac{1}{2}$ and $\frac{2}{4}$ in exercise 1A and $\frac{2}{3}$ and $\frac{8}{12}$ in part B name the same rational number.

Following a brief review of these ideas, instruct the students to do the exercises on the page.

The students might have difficulty with exercise 2 in which they must find a missing numerator or a missing denominator. They do, however, have clues for finding these missing numbers. For example, in exercise 2A, the students should be able to find the missing numerator since if the two fractions are to represent the same rational number, they must be equivalent. Therefore, from the test for equivalence they learned in Chapter 10, they can see that 2×4 must be equal to 8 times some number, or 1. Also, the students may be able to find this missing numerator by a more thoughtful approach by remembering that two eighths and one fourth belong to the same set of equivalent fractions, and hence the answer must be one.

Equality

Study this definition.

If two fractions are equivalent, then they name the same rational number.	If two fractions are not equivalent, then they do not name the same rational number.

When we write "=" between two fractions, we mean that the two fractions name the same rational number.

Study these examples.

$\frac{2}{4}$ names this rational number $\longrightarrow \left\{\frac{1}{2}, \frac{2}{4}, \frac{3}{6}, \frac{4}{8}, \ldots \right\}$.

$\frac{3}{6}$ names this rational number $\longrightarrow \left\{\frac{1}{2}, \frac{2}{4}, \frac{3}{6}, \frac{4}{8}, \ldots \right\}$.

We write: $\frac{2}{4} = \frac{3}{6}$.

EXERCISES

1. Answer **T** (true) or **F** (false).

[A] $\frac{1}{2}$ is equivalent to $\frac{2}{4}$. T   [F] $\frac{1}{2} = \frac{2}{4}$ T   [K] $\frac{3}{4} = \frac{15}{20}$ T

[B] $\frac{3}{8}$ is equivalent to $\frac{7}{16}$. F   [G] $\frac{3}{8} = \frac{7}{16}$ F   [L] $\frac{1}{8} = \frac{8}{64}$ T

[C] $\frac{8}{12}$ is equivalent to $\frac{2}{3}$. T   [H] $\frac{8}{12} = \frac{2}{3}$ T   [M] $\frac{3}{5} = \frac{9}{10}$ F

[D] $\frac{12}{30}$ is equivalent to $\frac{3}{10}$. F   [I] $\frac{12}{30} = \frac{3}{10}$ F   [N] $\frac{1}{2} = \frac{50}{100}$ T

[E] $\frac{2}{12}$ is equivalent to $\frac{5}{30}$. T   [J] $\frac{2}{12} = \frac{5}{30}$ T   [O] $\frac{1}{4} = \frac{25}{100}$ T

2. Find the missing numerators and denominators.

[A] $\frac{2}{8} = \frac{\square}{4}$ 1   [F] $\frac{4}{6} = \frac{\square}{3}$ 2   [K] $\frac{8}{10} = \frac{\square}{5}$ 4   [P] $\frac{8}{12} = \frac{2}{\square}$ 3

[B] $\frac{4}{8} = \frac{1}{\square}$ 2   [G] $\frac{2}{10} = \frac{\square}{5}$ 1   [L] $\frac{2}{12} = \frac{1}{\square}$ 6   [Q] $\frac{9}{12} = \frac{3}{\square}$ 4

[C] $\frac{6}{8} = \frac{\square}{4}$ 3   [H] $\frac{4}{10} = \frac{2}{\square}$ 5   [M] $\frac{3}{12} = \frac{\square}{4}$ 1   [R] $\frac{10}{12} = \frac{\square}{6}$ 5

[D] $\frac{2}{6} = \frac{\square}{3}$ 1   [I] $\frac{5}{10} = \frac{1}{\square}$ 2   [N] $\frac{4}{12} = \frac{\square}{3}$ 1   [S] $\frac{5}{15} = \frac{\square}{3}$ 1

[E] $\frac{3}{6} = \frac{1}{\square}$ 2   [J] $\frac{6}{10} = \frac{\square}{5}$ 3   [O] $\frac{6}{12} = \frac{\square}{2}$ 1   [T] $\frac{6}{18} = \frac{1}{\square}$ 3

Teaching Pages 302 and 303

● **PURPOSE**

To provide additional experiences in working with rational numbers and names for rational numbers

To introduce equality for rational numbers

● **PREPARATION**

Tell the students that you are going to name a rational number and that they are to write a set of equivalent fractions for this rational number (have them write the first five fractions, beginning with the lowest-terms fraction, in the set). Start by giving several fractions in lowest terms, such as $\frac{1}{2}$, $\frac{2}{3}$, $\frac{3}{4}$, and $\frac{2}{5}$. Now give them several fractions

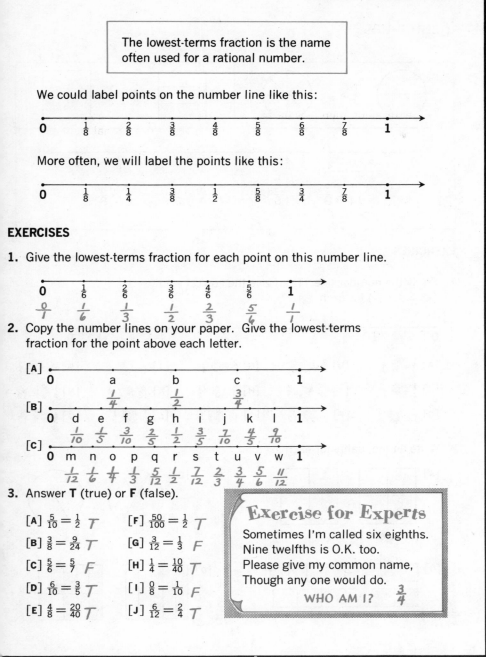

The lowest-terms fraction is the name often used for a rational number.

We could label points on the number line like this:

0 $\frac{1}{8}$ $\frac{2}{8}$ $\frac{3}{8}$ $\frac{4}{8}$ $\frac{5}{8}$ $\frac{6}{8}$ $\frac{7}{8}$ 1

More often, we will label the points like this:

0 $\frac{1}{8}$ $\frac{1}{4}$ $\frac{3}{8}$ $\frac{1}{2}$ $\frac{5}{8}$ $\frac{3}{4}$ $\frac{7}{8}$ 1

EXERCISES

1. Give the lowest-terms fraction for each point on this number line.

0 $\frac{1}{6}$ $\frac{2}{6}$ $\frac{3}{6}$ $\frac{4}{6}$ $\frac{5}{6}$ 1
$\frac{0}{1}$ $\frac{1}{6}$ $\frac{1}{3}$ $\frac{1}{2}$ $\frac{2}{3}$ $\frac{5}{6}$ $\frac{1}{1}$

2. Copy the number lines on your paper. Give the lowest-terms fraction for the point above each letter.

[A] 0 a b c 1

[B] 0 d e f g h i j k l 1
     $\frac{1}{4}$ $\frac{1}{2}$ $\frac{3}{4}$

[B] $\frac{1}{10}$ $\frac{1}{5}$ $\frac{3}{10}$ $\frac{2}{5}$ $\frac{1}{2}$ $\frac{3}{5}$ $\frac{7}{10}$ $\frac{4}{5}$ $\frac{9}{10}$

[C] 0 m n o p q r s t u v w 1
     $\frac{1}{12}$ $\frac{1}{6}$ $\frac{1}{4}$ $\frac{1}{3}$ $\frac{5}{12}$ $\frac{1}{2}$ $\frac{7}{12}$ $\frac{2}{3}$ $\frac{3}{4}$ $\frac{5}{6}$ $\frac{11}{12}$

3. Answer T (true) or F (false).

[A] $\frac{5}{10} = \frac{1}{2}$ T
[B] $\frac{3}{8} = \frac{9}{24}$ T
[C] $\frac{5}{6} = \frac{5}{7}$ F
[D] $\frac{6}{10} = \frac{3}{5}$ T
[E] $\frac{4}{8} = \frac{20}{40}$ T

[F] $\frac{50}{100} = \frac{1}{2}$ T
[G] $\frac{3}{12} = \frac{1}{3}$ F
[H] $\frac{1}{4} = \frac{10}{40}$ T
[I] $\frac{0}{8} = \frac{1}{10}$ F
[J] $\frac{6}{12} = \frac{2}{4}$ T

Exercise for Experts

Sometimes I'm called six eighths.
Nine twelfths is O.K. too.
Please give my common name,
Though any one would do.

WHO AM I? $\frac{3}{4}$

Study the material preceding the exercises with the class. Observe that we do not use the lowest-terms fraction to label the points on the first number line, and that we do use it on the second number line. Simply point out to the students that it is more common to label the middle point $\frac{1}{2}$ than it is to label it $\frac{4}{8}$. However, you should stress for the students that it is not incorrect to label this point $\frac{4}{8}$.

Following this discussion, have the students do the exercises. When they have finished, allow time for checking papers and discussion. At this time, it may be effective to exhibit exercises 2A, B, and C on the chalkboard and to give the students an opportunity to label these number lines using both the first method shown at the top of the page (which shows fractions which are not in lowest terms) and the second method (which shows lowest-terms fractions). For example, in 2B, the first labeling would be $\frac{1}{10}, \frac{2}{10}, \ldots, \frac{9}{10}$, and the second labeling would be $\frac{1}{10}, \frac{1}{5}, \frac{3}{10}, \frac{2}{5}, \frac{1}{2}, \frac{3}{5}, \frac{7}{10}, \frac{4}{5}, \frac{9}{10}$.

that are not in lowest terms, such as $\frac{4}{12}, \frac{12}{16}, \frac{9}{15}$, etc. During this discussion, stress the fact that the fraction you give names the rational number that they indicate with their sets of equivalent fractions. Now, demonstrate the location of these rational numbers on the number line.

Provide the students with a review of the test for equivalence of fractions. Based on the abilities of your students, you may decide to accompany this review with diagrams to help the students decide whether or not two fractions are equivalent. For example, if you have the students test to see if $\frac{3}{6}$ is equivalent to $\frac{5}{10}$, an accompanying diagram might illustrate the fact that each fraction indicates half of any object. Certainly, if your students are quite advanced in work with fractions and equivalent fractions, such a diagram may not be needed. However, it is usually

true that the less able students benefit from these pictorials. Give the students opportunities to test several pairs of fractions to see whether or not they are equivalent. Once the students have completed the test, you can have them write the equality sign between the equivalent fractions and the inequality sign ($\neq$) if they are not equivalent. Do not ask the students to indicate less than and greater than. You might explain that $\frac{1}{2} \neq \frac{1}{3}$, simply means that one half and one third represent different rational numbers.

Study the three examples at the top of the page with the students. Give them an opportunity to discuss the various inequalities demonstrated first by the pictures in the top two boxes and then by the number line at the bottom of the illustration.

Have the students do the exercises. You might point out that all the inequalities in the first exercise can be answered by studying the number-line picture.

After the class has completed the exercises, allow time for a discussion and checking papers. Observe with the students that there are several correct answers for exercise 2, depending upon which name they use for the rational number and upon which inequality sign they use. For example, for exercise 2B they might well say that $\frac{1}{3} < \frac{4}{6}$ or $\frac{1}{3} < \frac{2}{3}$ or $\frac{4}{6} > \frac{1}{3}$ or $\frac{2}{3} > \frac{1}{3}$.

Inequalities

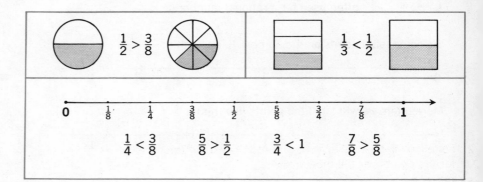

EXERCISES

1. Study the number line. Then give the correct sign (<, =, or >) for each .

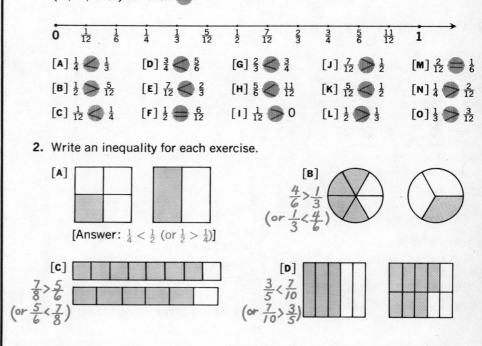

2. Write an inequality for each exercise.

Teaching Pages 304 and 305

- **PURPOSE**

  To introduce inequalities for rational numbers

- **MATHEMATICS**

  In this lesson, we present informally, through the use of pictures of various objects, the general concept of inequalities for rational numbers. Such a concept involves a precise definition (which is not presented to the students at this time):

  $$a/b > c/d \text{ if and only if } ad > bc.$$

EXERCISES

1. Give the missing fractions.

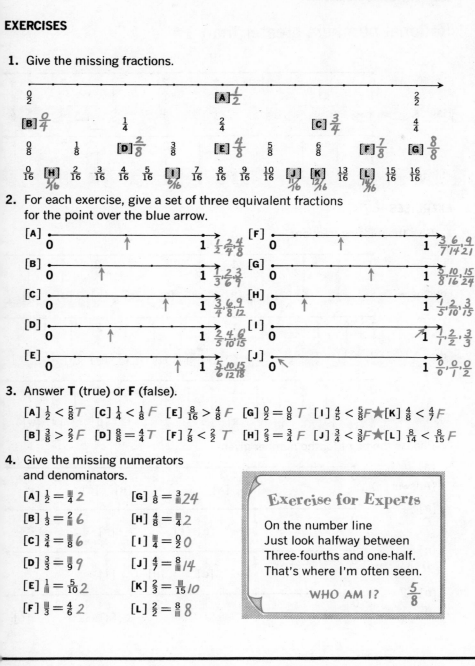

$\frac{0}{2}$ [A]$\frac{1}{2}$ $\frac{2}{2}$

[B]$\frac{0}{4}$ $\frac{1}{4}$ $\frac{2}{4}$ [C]$\frac{3}{4}$ $\frac{4}{4}$

$\frac{0}{8}$ $\frac{1}{8}$ [D]$\frac{2}{8}$ $\frac{3}{8}$ [E]$\frac{4}{8}$ $\frac{5}{8}$ $\frac{6}{8}$ [F]$\frac{7}{8}$ [G]$\frac{8}{8}$

$\frac{0}{16}$ [H]$\frac{1}{16}$ $\frac{2}{16}$ $\frac{3}{16}$ $\frac{4}{16}$ $\frac{5}{16}$ [I]$\frac{6}{16}$ $\frac{7}{16}$ $\frac{8}{16}$ $\frac{9}{16}$ $\frac{10}{16}$ [J]$\frac{11}{16}$ [K]$\frac{12}{16}$ $\frac{13}{16}$ [L]$\frac{14}{16}$ $\frac{15}{16}$ $\frac{16}{16}$

2. For each exercise, give a set of three equivalent fractions for the point over the blue arrow.

[A] 0 ——↑—— 1 $\frac{1}{2}, \frac{2}{4}, \frac{4}{8}$

[B] 0 —↑——— 1 $\frac{1}{3}, \frac{2}{6}, \frac{3}{9}$

[C] 0 ————↑—— 1 $\frac{3}{4}, \frac{6}{8}, \frac{9}{12}$

[D] 0 —↑——— 1 $\frac{2}{5}, \frac{4}{10}, \frac{6}{15}$

[E] 0 ——————↑ 1 $\frac{5}{6}, \frac{10}{12}, \frac{15}{18}$

[F] 0 ———↑——— 1 $\frac{3}{7}, \frac{6}{14}, \frac{9}{21}$

[G] 0 —————↑— 1 $\frac{5}{8}, \frac{10}{16}, \frac{15}{24}$

[H] 0 —↑——— 1 $\frac{1}{5}, \frac{2}{10}, \frac{3}{15}$

[I] 0 ——————↗ 1 $\frac{1}{1}, \frac{2}{2}, \frac{3}{3}$

[J] 0 ↖ 1 $\frac{0}{0}, \frac{0}{1}, \frac{0}{2}$

3. Answer **T** (true) or **F** (false).

[A] $\frac{1}{2} < \frac{5}{8}$ *T* [C] $\frac{1}{4} < \frac{1}{8}$ *F* [E] $\frac{8}{16} > \frac{4}{8}$ *F* [G] $\frac{0}{2} = \frac{0}{8}$ *T* [I] $\frac{4}{5} < \frac{5}{8}$ *F*★[K] $\frac{4}{8} < \frac{4}{7}$ *F*

[B] $\frac{3}{8} > \frac{2}{2}$ *F* [D] $\frac{8}{8} = \frac{4}{4}$ *T* [F] $\frac{7}{8} < \frac{2}{2}$ *T* [H] $\frac{2}{3} = \frac{3}{4}$ *F* [J] $\frac{3}{4} < \frac{3}{8}$ *F*★[L] $\frac{8}{14} < \frac{8}{15}$ *F*

4. Give the missing numerators and denominators.

[A] $\frac{1}{2} = \frac{1}{4}$ *2*   [G] $\frac{1}{8} = \frac{3}{24}$ *24*

[B] $\frac{1}{3} = \frac{2}{6}$ *6*   [H] $\frac{4}{8} = \frac{1}{2}$ *2*

[C] $\frac{3}{4} = \frac{6}{8}$ *6*   [I] $\frac{1}{4} = \frac{0}{2}$ *0*

[D] $\frac{3}{3} = \frac{9}{9}$ *9*   [J] $\frac{4}{7} = \frac{8}{14}$ *14*

[E] $\frac{1}{1} = \frac{5}{10}$ *2*   [K] $\frac{2}{3} = \frac{10}{15}$ *10*

[F] $\frac{2}{3} = \frac{4}{6}$ *2*   [L] $\frac{2}{2} = \frac{8}{8}$ *8*

> ### Exercise for Experts
>
> On the number line
> Just look halfway between
> Three-fourths and one-half.
> That's where I'm often seen.
>
> WHO AM I? $\frac{5}{8}$

PREPARATION

Use a measuring cup to demonstrate for the students the idea associated with saying that a half is greater than a fourth, a half is greater than a third, or a third is greater than a fourth. Of course, these inequalities can be demonstrated with pictures, but using a physical object, such as a measuring cup, to demonstrate these concepts will additionally strengthen the students' perception of these ideas. In addition to the measuring-cup demonstration, you will want to use other illustrations involving inequalities with rational numbers less than one.

Have the students do the exercises. When they have finished, allow time for checking papers and for discussion. During the discussion, you should make several interesting observations concerning exercise 3 with the students. For example, you might ask the students why exercise 3L is false. Of course, the point to note is that the smaller the denominator, the larger the rational number for a given numerator. This will be obvious to the students when they consider that $\frac{1}{14}$ of an object would be more than $\frac{1}{15}$ of the same object; hence, $\frac{8}{14}$ of the object would be more than $\frac{8}{15}$ of the object; therefore, it is false that $\frac{8}{14}$ is less than $\frac{8}{15}$. Observe also that in exercises 3J and K the numerators are the same but the denominators are different. Of course, in exercise 3K, the inequality is correct since $\frac{4}{8}$ is, in fact, less than $\frac{4}{7}$ because one eighth of an object is certainly less than one seventh of the object.

Again, we would point out that the students have the machinery to find the numerators and denominators in exercise 4. Hence we would stress the importance of allowing them to work with these exercises without the benefit of any particular rules.

The riddle is not particularly difficult, especially if the students refer to a labeled number line. The number line at the top of page 304 should suffice to give the students the answer to this riddle. Certainly all the students will understand the answer to the riddle once it is given and demonstrated on the number line.

Supplementary exercises, Set 53 (page 352) may be assigned as necessary beyond this page.

Study the material at the top of the page with the students. Observe with them that another name for the number one is $\frac{2}{2}$; another name for two is $\frac{4}{2}$; and for three, $\frac{6}{2}$. Note also with the students that the point that is halfway between the numbers one and two is $\frac{3}{2}$ and that $\frac{5}{2}$ is halfway between two and three.

Following this discussion, have the students do the exercises. When they have finished, allow time for checking papers and for discussion. You might point out to the students that these exercises are much the same as exercises they have done before and the only difference is that they are now working with rational numbers that are greater than one. Also stress the relationship between whole numbers and rational numbers (e.g., each whole number is also a rational number).

Rational numbers greater than 1

Halves → $\frac{0}{2}$ $\frac{1}{2}$ $\frac{2}{2}$ $\frac{3}{2}$ $\frac{4}{2}$ $\frac{5}{2}$ $\frac{6}{2}$ $\frac{7}{2}$

Thirds → $\frac{0}{3}$ $\frac{1}{3}$ $\frac{2}{3}$ $\frac{3}{3}$ $\frac{4}{3}$ $\frac{5}{3}$ $\frac{6}{3}$ $\frac{7}{3}$ $\frac{8}{3}$ $\frac{9}{3}$ $\frac{10}{3}$

EXERCISES

1. Give the missing fractions.

Fourths → $\frac{0}{4}$ $\frac{1}{4}$ $\frac{2}{4}$ [A] $\frac{3}{4}$ [B] $\frac{4}{4}$ [C] $\frac{5}{4}$ [D] $\frac{6}{4}$ [E] $\frac{7}{4}$ [F] $\frac{8}{4}$ [G] $\frac{9}{4}$ [H] $\frac{10}{4}$

Fifths → $\frac{0}{5}$ $\frac{1}{5}$ $\frac{2}{5}$ $\frac{3}{5}$ $\frac{4}{5}$ $\frac{5}{5}$ [I] $\frac{6}{5}$ [J] $\frac{7}{5}$ [K] $\frac{8}{5}$ [L] $\frac{9}{5}$ [M] $\frac{10}{5}$ [N] $\frac{11}{5}$ [O] $\frac{12}{5}$ [P]

Sixths → $\frac{0}{6}$ $\frac{1}{6}$ [Q] $\frac{3}{6}$ $\frac{4}{6}$ $\frac{5}{6}$ [R] $\frac{7}{6}$ $\frac{8}{6}$ $\frac{9}{6}$ [S] [T] [U] $\frac{13}{6}$ [V] [W]

$\frac{10}{6}$ $\frac{11}{6}$ $\frac{12}{6}$ $\frac{14}{6}$ $\frac{15}{6}$

2. Choose the point for the number given.

[A] $\frac{7}{3}$
(Answer: B)

0 ... 1 [A] 2 [B] [C] 3

[B] $\frac{12}{8}$
D

0 ... 1 [D] [E] 2 [F] 3

[C] $\frac{16}{8}$
H

0 ... 1 [G] [H] [I] 3

[D] $\frac{10}{4}$
K

0 ... 1 [J] 2 [K] 3 [L]

Teaching Pages 306 and 307

- **PURPOSE**

  To introduce rational numbers greater than one

  To establish the fact that each whole number is also a rational number

- **PREPARATION**

  You can center your preparation activities around the presentation of examples similar to those at the top of page 306. For example, you might illustrate on the chalkboard a number line with labels 0, 1, 2, and 3. Then mark off fourths between these labels and label the points you have marked $\frac{0}{4}$, $\frac{1}{4}$, $\frac{2}{4}$, $\frac{3}{4}$, $\frac{4}{4}$, $\frac{5}{4}$, etc., up to

Give the missing fractions.

Number line from 0 to 3 with fractions:

$\frac{0}{2}$ $\frac{1}{2}$ $\frac{2}{2}$ **[A]**$\frac{3}{2}$ **[B]**$\frac{4}{2}$ **[C]**$\frac{5}{2}$ $\frac{6}{2}$

[D]$\frac{0}{3}$ $\frac{1}{3}$ $\frac{2}{3}$ **[E]**$\frac{3}{3}$ $\frac{4}{3}$ **[F]**$\frac{5}{3}$ $\frac{6}{3}$ $\frac{7}{3}$ $\frac{8}{3}$ **[G]**$\frac{9}{3}$

$\frac{0}{6}$ **[H]**$\frac{2}{6}$ $\frac{3}{6}$ $\frac{4}{6}$ $\frac{5}{6}$ $\frac{6}{6}$ $\frac{7}{6}$ **[I]**$\frac{9}{6}$ $\frac{10}{6}$ $\frac{11}{6}$ **[J]**$\frac{13}{6}$ $\frac{14}{6}$ **[K]**$\frac{16}{6}$ **[L]**$\frac{18}{6}$

(handwritten) $\frac{1}{6}$ $\frac{8}{6}$ $\frac{12}{6}$ $\frac{15}{6}$ $\frac{17}{6}$

Give a set of three equivalent fractions that name the rational number for the point above the blue arrow.

[A] (number line 0 to 3, arrow below point between 2 and 3) $\frac{5}{2}, \frac{10}{4}, \frac{15}{6}$

[B] (number line 0 to 3, arrow below point between 1 and 2) $\frac{7}{4}, \frac{14}{8}, \frac{21}{12}$

[C] (number line 0 to 3, arrow below point after 2) $\frac{11}{5}, \frac{22}{10}, \frac{33}{15}$

Answer **T** (true) or **F** (false).

[A] $\frac{2}{2} > \frac{1}{2}$ _T_   **[D]** $\frac{5}{2} > 2$ _T_   **[G]** $\frac{6}{4} = \frac{3}{2}$ _T_   **[J]** $\frac{12}{4} < 3$ _F_

[B] $\frac{2}{2} < \frac{3}{2}$ _T_   **[E]** $\frac{6}{8} = \frac{9}{12}$ _T_   **[H]** $\frac{9}{4} < 2$ _F_   **[K]** $\frac{8}{8} > \frac{4}{4}$ _F_

[C] $\frac{3}{4} > \frac{3}{2}$ _F_   **[F]** $\frac{5}{2} < 3$ _T_   **[I]** $\frac{11}{4} > \frac{5}{2}$ _T_   **[L]** $\frac{6}{3} > \frac{5}{2}$ _F_

Give the missing numerators and denominators.

[A] $\frac{3}{2} = \frac{}{4}$ _6_   **[D]** $\frac{10}{4} = \frac{5}{}$ _2_   **[G]** $\frac{11}{3} = \frac{}{9}$ _33_   **[J]** $\frac{18}{6} = \frac{}{2}$ _6_

[B] $\frac{5}{4} = \frac{10}{}$ _8_   **[E]** $\frac{4}{2} = \frac{8}{}$ _4_   **[H]** $\frac{0}{4} = \frac{}{2}$ _0_   **[K]** $\frac{14}{6} = \frac{7}{}$ _3_

[C] $\frac{5}{3} = \frac{}{6}$ _10_   **[F]** $\frac{3}{3} = \frac{}{9}$ _9_   **[I]** $\frac{6}{2} = \frac{}{4}$ _12_   **[L]** $\frac{15}{6} = \frac{5}{}$ _2_

Find the missing numerators.

[A] (number line: 0 $\frac{1}{2}$ 1 $\frac{3}{2}$ 2 $\frac{5}{2}$ 3 ... 15 $\frac{}{2}$31 16 $\frac{}{2}$33)

[B] (number line: 0 $\frac{1}{3}$ $\frac{2}{3}$ 1 $\frac{4}{3}$ $\frac{5}{3}$ 2 $\frac{7}{3}$ $\frac{8}{3}$ 3 ... 20 $\frac{}{3}$ $\frac{}{3}$ 21 $\frac{}{3}$)

(handwritten) 61 62   64

DIRECTIONS PAGE 307

Have the students do the exercises, and allow time for checking papers and for discussion when they have finished.

Note that exercise 7 is designed primarily for more able students. You may have to call attention to the fact that a considerable portion of the number line is missing. That is, in exercise 7A, the part of the number line between 3 and 15 is to be thought of as missing, and the students must decide how many halves there are between 15 and 16 and how many halves there are between 16 and 17. If they observe that one half is between 0 and 1, three halves is between 1 and 2, and five halves is between 2 and 3, they can extend this idea to determine that 31 halves is between 15 and 16, and 33 halves is between 16 and 17. Of course, this reasoning applies to part B of exercise 7. All students will benefit from a discussion of this exercise, and you may even choose to have all the students try it prior to a discussion.

---

4. You might have the students do this labeling. The important element here is that the students observe the transition in moving beyond the number one to $\frac{5}{4}$, $\frac{6}{4}$, etc., and that they see the association between $\frac{0}{4}$ and zero, between $\frac{4}{4}$ and one, between $\frac{8}{4}$ and two, etc. Repeat similar examples until the students understand the idea of rational numbers greater than one.

With the class, read and study the material at the top of the page. Give them an opportunity to discuss for each number line the two jumps and the equation associated with these jumps. You may find it helpful to have these two exercises put on the chalkboard. Afterward, have the students do the exercises at the bottom of the page. When they have finished, allow time for checking papers and further discussion.

Addition and subtraction

You have learned that some rational numbers are the same as whole numbers:

$$\tfrac{6}{3}=2, \quad \tfrac{20}{4}=5, \quad \tfrac{19}{1}=19, \quad \text{and so on.}$$

Because of this, the operations (addition, subtraction, multiplication, and division) with rational numbers are much like operations with whole numbers. You can use jumps on the number line to help you understand addition and subtraction of rational numbers.

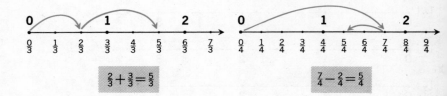

$$\tfrac{2}{3}+\tfrac{3}{3}=\tfrac{5}{3} \qquad\qquad \tfrac{7}{4}-\tfrac{2}{4}=\tfrac{5}{4}$$

EXERCISES

1. Write an equation for each number-line picture.

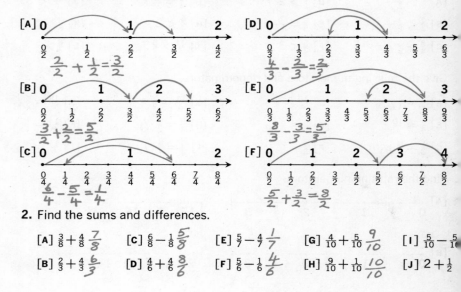

[A] $\tfrac{2}{2}+\tfrac{1}{2}=\tfrac{3}{2}$

[B] $\tfrac{3}{2}+\tfrac{2}{2}=\tfrac{5}{2}$

[C] $\tfrac{6}{4}-\tfrac{5}{4}=\tfrac{1}{4}$

[D] $\tfrac{4}{3}-\tfrac{2}{3}=\tfrac{2}{3}$

[E] $\tfrac{8}{3}-\tfrac{3}{3}=\tfrac{5}{3}$

[F] $\tfrac{5}{2}+\tfrac{3}{2}=\tfrac{8}{2}$

2. Find the sums and differences.

[A] $\tfrac{3}{8}+\tfrac{4}{8}$ $\tfrac{7}{8}$

[B] $\tfrac{2}{3}+\tfrac{4}{3}$ $\tfrac{6}{3}$

[C] $\tfrac{6}{8}-\tfrac{1}{8}$ $\tfrac{5}{8}$

[D] $\tfrac{4}{6}+\tfrac{4}{6}$ $\tfrac{8}{6}$

[E] $\tfrac{5}{7}-\tfrac{4}{7}$ $\tfrac{1}{7}$

[F] $\tfrac{5}{6}-\tfrac{1}{6}$ $\tfrac{4}{6}$

[G] $\tfrac{4}{10}+\tfrac{5}{10}$ $\tfrac{9}{10}$

[H] $\tfrac{9}{10}+\tfrac{1}{10}$ $\tfrac{10}{10}$

[I] $\tfrac{5}{10}-\tfrac{5}{10}$

[J] $2+\tfrac{1}{2}$

Teaching Pages 308 and 309

● **PURPOSE**

To introduce addition and subtraction of rational numbers using the number-line model and regions

● **PREPARATION**

Exhibit on the chalkboard a number line and label it with halves. You should show enough of the number line to label up to about six or eight halves. Show another number line and label it with thirds up to about 12 thirds. Draw other lines for fourths and sixths. Now, demonstrate for the students several examples similar to those on page 308. Be sure to restrict the writing of equations to

We often think of addition of whole numbers when we bring objects together and of subtraction when we take objects away. Since each whole number is equal to a rational number, the use of objects should also help you think about addition and subtraction of rational numbers. Study the following examples.

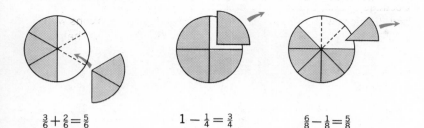

$$\frac{3}{6} + \frac{2}{6} = \frac{5}{6} \qquad 1 - \frac{1}{4} = \frac{3}{4} \qquad \frac{6}{8} - \frac{1}{8} = \frac{5}{8}$$

EXERCISES

. Solve the equations.

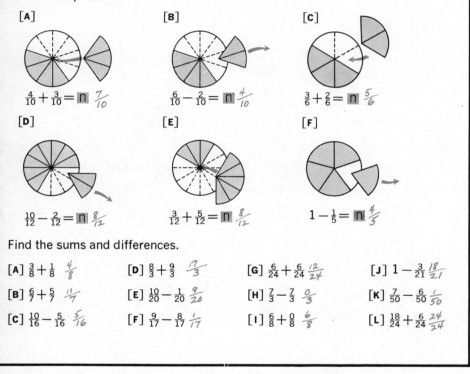

[A] $\frac{4}{10} + \frac{3}{10} = \blacksquare \; \frac{7}{10}$ [B] $\frac{6}{10} - \frac{2}{10} = \blacksquare \; \frac{4}{10}$ [C] $\frac{3}{6} + \frac{2}{6} = \blacksquare \; \frac{5}{6}$

[D] $\frac{10}{12} - \frac{2}{12} = \blacksquare \; \frac{8}{12}$ [E] $\frac{3}{12} + \frac{5}{12} = \blacksquare \; \frac{8}{12}$ [F] $1 - \frac{1}{5} = \blacksquare \; \frac{4}{5}$

. Find the sums and differences.

[A] $\frac{3}{8} + \frac{1}{8}$ $\frac{4}{8}$ [D] $\frac{8}{3} + \frac{9}{3}$ $\frac{17}{3}$ [G] $\frac{6}{24} + \frac{6}{24}$ $\frac{12}{24}$ [J] $1 - \frac{3}{21}$ $\frac{18}{21}$

[B] $\frac{6}{7} + \frac{5}{7}$ $\frac{11}{7}$ [E] $\frac{10}{20} - \frac{1}{20}$ $\frac{9}{20}$ [H] $\frac{7}{3} - \frac{7}{3}$ $\frac{0}{3}$ [K] $\frac{7}{50} - \frac{6}{50}$ $\frac{1}{50}$

[C] $\frac{10}{16} - \frac{5}{16}$ $\frac{5}{16}$ [F] $\frac{9}{17} - \frac{8}{17}$ $\frac{1}{17}$ [I] $\frac{6}{8} + \frac{0}{8}$ $\frac{6}{8}$ [L] $\frac{18}{24} + \frac{6}{24}$ $\frac{24}{24}$

Read and study the material at the top of the page with the students. It may be helpful, especially for the less able students, to have cutouts available similar to the examples shown here. Following this discussion, have the students do the exercises. When they have finished, allow time for discussion and checking papers. If time permits, you may find it helpful to demonstrate several parts of exercise 2, using either number lines or regions.

se of fractions having the same denominator. Do not, uring this lesson, attempt to reduce any of the fractions o lowest terms; merely write equations similar to those n the blue screens on page 308.

Follow this demonstration either by drawing on the halkboard pictures similar to those on page 309 or by aving actual cutouts which offer the students an opportunity to take apart and put together various parts of regions, perhaps as suggested by the examples on page 09. For each example illustrated by a figure or cutout, xhibit the corresponding equation.

At this time, the point of chief concern is to bring out he idea of adding rational numbers using fractions that ave the same denominator. Therefore, do not attempt to educe any of the answers to lowest terms; simply leave

the answers as they turn out. All the numbers involved should be represented by fractions having the same denominator. During this discussion, bring out for the class the fact that the whole numbers are also rational numbers. You will need to review this idea from time to time by exhibiting statements of equality similar to those at the top of page 308 (e.g., emphasize for the students that two is a rational number since we can write two as $\frac{6}{3}$, five is a rational number since we can write five as $\frac{20}{4}$ or $\frac{10}{2}$, etc.).

Have the students do the exercises. When they have finished, allow time for checking papers and for discussion. You will observe that a chief purpose of this page is to help the students relate certain rational numbers to whole numbers. Therefore, in the discussion period, you should make a special effort to determine that the students establish a feeling for the rational-number labels for whole numbers. For this reason, place particular emphasis on exercise 3. Rather than giving specific rules for doing exercise 3, refer the students to number-line pictures or any other physical devices that might be useful in arriving at the correct answers. Of course, one possibility for exercise 3 is to remind the students that every whole number also has a fraction name, six has the name $6/1$, etc. Using this idea, the students will then see for an exercise such as 3A that three can be thought of as $3/1 = 6/n$ and hence observe that in order to have the product $1 \times 6 = 3 \times n$ they must have $6/2$. Of course, this applies to exercise 3L, where the students might think $10/1 = n/2$, hence 10×2 must be $n \times 1$, or 20×1, so the fraction is $20/2$.

Whole numbers and rational numbers

EXERCISES

1. Give the missing fractions.

Number line labeled 0, 1, 2, 3, 4, 5, 6, 7, 8

Row: $\frac{0}{1}$, $\frac{1}{1}$, [A] $\frac{2}{1}$, $\frac{3}{1}$, $\frac{4}{1}$, $\frac{5}{1}$, [B] $\frac{6}{1}$, $\frac{7}{1}$, $\frac{8}{1}$

Row: $\frac{0}{2}$, [C] $\frac{2}{2}$, $\frac{4}{2}$, [D] $\frac{6}{2}$, $\frac{8}{2}$, [E] $\frac{10}{2}$, $\frac{12}{2}$, [F] $\frac{14}{2}$, $\frac{16}{2}$

Row: [G] $\frac{0}{3}$, $\frac{3}{3}$, $\frac{6}{3}$, $\frac{9}{3}$, [H] $\frac{12}{3}$, $\frac{15}{3}$, $\frac{18}{3}$, $\frac{21}{3}$, [I] $\frac{24}{3}$

2. Match each whole number with a set of equivalent fractions.

[A] 3 (Answer: Set 4)   (1) $\left\{\frac{9}{1}, \frac{18}{2}, \frac{27}{3}, \frac{36}{4}, \ldots\right\}$

[B] 6 *Set 3*   (2) $\left\{\frac{15}{1}, \frac{30}{2}, \frac{45}{3}, \frac{60}{4}, \ldots\right\}$

[C] 1 *Set 5*   (3) $\left\{\frac{6}{1}, \frac{12}{2}, \frac{18}{3}, \frac{24}{4}, \ldots\right\}$

[D] 9 *Set 1*   (4) $\left\{\frac{3}{1}, \frac{6}{2}, \frac{9}{3}, \frac{12}{4}, \ldots\right\}$

[E] 0 *Set 6*   (5) $\left\{\frac{1}{1}, \frac{2}{2}, \frac{3}{3}, \frac{4}{4}, \ldots\right\}$

[F] 15 *Set 2*   (6) $\left\{\frac{0}{1}, \frac{0}{2}, \frac{0}{3}, \frac{0}{4}, \ldots\right\}$

3. Give the missing numerators and denominators.

[A] $3 = \frac{6}{▦}$ *2*   [E] $0 = \frac{▦}{6}$ *0*   [I] $5 = \frac{15}{▦}$ *3*   [M] $12 = \frac{▦}{1}$ *12*   [Q] $\frac{1}{4} = \frac{▦}{3}$ *3*

[B] $6 = \frac{6}{▦}$ *1*   [F] $15 = \frac{30}{▦}$ *2*   [J] $8 = \frac{▦}{3}$ *24*   [N] $20 = \frac{40}{▦}$ *2*   [R] $\frac{1}{2} = \frac{▦}{1}$

[C] $1 = \frac{▦}{5}$ *5*   [G] $2 = \frac{▦}{4}$ *8*   [K] $4 = \frac{12}{▦}$ *3*   [O] $11 = \frac{77}{▦}$ *7*   [S] $\frac{2}{3} = \frac{▦}{8}$

[D] $9 = \frac{▦}{1}$ *9*   [H] $7 = \frac{▦}{2}$ *14*   [L] $10 = \frac{▦}{2}$ *20*   [P] $\frac{1}{2} = \frac{▦}{10}$ *5*   [T] $\frac{3}{4} = \frac{▦}{9}$

4. Find the sums.

[A] $\frac{4}{2} + \frac{1}{2}$ *$\frac{5}{2}$*   [D] $\frac{6}{3} + \frac{1}{3}$ *$\frac{7}{3}$*   [G] $3 + \frac{1}{3}$ *$\frac{10}{3}$*   [J] $\frac{12}{2} + \frac{3}{2}$ *$\frac{15}{2}$*   [M] $2 + \frac{3}{4}$

[B] $\frac{6}{2} + \frac{1}{2}$ *$\frac{7}{2}$*   [E] $2 + \frac{1}{3}$ *$\frac{7}{3}$*   [H] $\frac{12}{3} + \frac{2}{3}$ *$\frac{14}{3}$*   [K] $6 + \frac{3}{2}$ *$\frac{15}{2}$*   [N] $\frac{8}{8} + \frac{5}{8}$

[C] $3 + \frac{1}{2}$ *$\frac{7}{2}$*   [F] $\frac{9}{3} + \frac{1}{3}$ *$\frac{10}{3}$*   [I] $4 + \frac{2}{3}$ *$\frac{14}{3}$*   [L] $\frac{8}{4} + \frac{3}{4}$ *$\frac{11}{4}$*   [O] $1 + \frac{5}{8}$

Teaching Pages 310 and 311

- **PURPOSE**

  To provide additional experiences in working with rational numbers greater than one

  To provide further experiences in working with addition of rational numbers

  To introduce mixed-numeral notation for rational numbers

- **PREPARATION**

  Provide the students with a brief review of exercise similar to those on page 310. For example, draw on the

Study these examples.

$2\frac{1}{2}$ means $2 + \frac{1}{2}$ $3\frac{1}{4}$ means $3 + \frac{1}{4}$ $5\frac{1}{3}$ means $5 + \frac{1}{3}$

We write:

$2\frac{1}{2} = 2 + \frac{1}{2}$ $3\frac{1}{4} = 3 + \frac{1}{4}$ $5\frac{1}{3} = 5 + \frac{1}{3}$

Explain these examples.

A $\frac{3}{2} = \frac{2}{2} + \frac{1}{2} = 1 + \frac{1}{2} = 1\frac{1}{2}$	**B** $\frac{10}{4} = \frac{8}{4} + \frac{2}{4} = 2 + \frac{2}{4} = 2\frac{2}{4}$
C $\frac{7}{3} = \frac{6}{3} + \frac{1}{3} = 2 + \frac{1}{3} = 2\frac{1}{3}$	**D** $\frac{15}{14} = \frac{12}{4} + \frac{3}{4} = 3 + \frac{3}{4} = 3\frac{3}{4}$

Symbols like $1\frac{1}{2}$, $2\frac{1}{3}$, $2\frac{3}{4}$, $3\frac{3}{4}$ are called mixed numerals.

EXERCISES

1. Give the correct mixed numeral for each sum.

[A] $2 + \frac{1}{4}$
(Answer: $2\frac{1}{4}$)

[B] $\frac{8}{4} + \frac{1}{4}$
(Answer: $2\frac{1}{4}$)

[C] $3 + \frac{1}{5}$ $3\frac{1}{5}$

[D] $\frac{15}{5} + \frac{1}{5}$ $3\frac{1}{5}$
[E] $1 + \frac{1}{8}$ $1\frac{1}{8}$
[F] $\frac{8}{8} + \frac{1}{8}$ $1\frac{1}{8}$
[G] $5 + \frac{1}{2}$ $5\frac{1}{2}$
[H] $\frac{10}{2} + \frac{1}{2}$ $5\frac{1}{2}$

[I] $1 + \frac{5}{6}$ $1\frac{5}{6}$
[J] $\frac{6}{6} + \frac{5}{6}$ $1\frac{5}{6}$
[K] $1 + \frac{3}{5}$ $1\frac{3}{5}$
[L] $\frac{5}{5} + \frac{3}{5}$ $1\frac{3}{5}$
[M] $8 + \frac{1}{4}$ $8\frac{1}{4}$

[N] $\frac{32}{4} + \frac{1}{4}$ $8\frac{1}{4}$
[O] $\frac{4}{9} + \frac{6}{9}$ $1\frac{1}{9}$
[P] $\frac{4}{9} + \frac{15}{9}$ $2\frac{1}{9}$
[Q] $\frac{6}{10} + \frac{7}{10}$ $1\frac{3}{10}$
[R] $\frac{10}{10} + \frac{9}{10}$ $1\frac{9}{10}$

2. Give a mixed numeral for each fraction. Use exercise 1.

[A] $\frac{9}{4}$ $2\frac{1}{4}$ [B] $\frac{16}{5}$ $3\frac{1}{5}$ [C] $\frac{11}{6}$ $1\frac{5}{6}$ [D] $\frac{33}{4}$ $8\frac{1}{4}$ [E] $\frac{8}{5}$ $1\frac{3}{5}$ [F] $\frac{9}{8}$ $1\frac{1}{8}$ [G] $\frac{11}{2}$ $5\frac{1}{2}$

3. Give a mixed numeral for each point **A** through **D**.

[A] $1\frac{1}{4}$ [B] $1\frac{3}{4}$ [C] $2\frac{1}{2}$ [D] $3\frac{3}{4}$

chalkboard a number line labeled 0 to 6, and divide the units into thirds.

Have the students take turns coming to the chalkboard and labeling the various points.

Follow this by repeating the same number line with only the whole-number points marked and labeled. Begin by writing $\frac{0}{4}$ under the 0 label, $\frac{4}{4}$ under the 1, and $\frac{8}{4}$ under the 2, and then have the students continue labeling the whole-number points with fractions.

Next provide the students with several exercises similar to exercise 3 to work on the chalkboard. If time permits, give them additional experiences in working with sums. If possible, accompany each addition equation with a demonstration, preferably one involving jumps on the number line.

As you study the examples with the students, stress that they are to think about new symbols for certain rational numbers. That is, they think of the rational number $2\frac{1}{2}$ as $2 + \frac{1}{2}$ and read the symbol as "two and one half." You might remind the students that they can also think of $\frac{5}{2}$ as a symbol for $2\frac{1}{2}$. This can be easily demonstrated on the number line. We would point out that the number line is most effective in demonstrating the mixed numerals shown for the four examples A, B, C, and D. For example, you could picture on the number line the point for rational number $\frac{7}{3}$ and then observe with the students that this is $\frac{1}{3}$ of a unit beyond the whole-number two. Therefore, they could think of this as $2 + \frac{1}{3}$ or simply as $2\frac{1}{3}$.

Following this discussion, have the students do the exercises. When they have finished, allow time for checking papers and discussion. Involve the students in a discussion and emphasize for them the fact that these mixed-numeral symbols are simply new ways of writing numerals for rational numbers.

Also, during the discussion pay particular attention to exercise 3 since this is the type of exercise to which mixed numerals lend themselves readily. That is, by looking at a number-line picture, it is quite easy to see that point **D**, for example, represents $3\frac{1}{4}$. You might conclude this lesson by presenting other number lines and, using mixed-numeral notation, giving the students an opportunity to identify other points.

Supplementary exercises, Set 54 (page 352) may be assigned as necessary beyond this page.

Study the material preceding the exercises with the class. When instructing the students to do the exercises, you might note that for exercise 1 only a part of the number line is shown and all of it from zero up to the first indicated point has been deleted. Explain that this is indicated on the number lines with the small, wavy line. The students should observe that dots shown for each number line give the division marks for the units. That is, they can see that the unit has been divided into thirds in exercise 1A, into halves in exercise 1B, into halves in exercise 1C, etc.

When the students have completed the exercises, allow time for discussion and checking papers. Most students will have little difficulty with exercise 2 and the inequalities involved. Inequalities are much easier when using mixed-numeral notation than when using fractional notation, especially fractional notation in which the denominators are not the same. It is quite simple for the students to observe that $6 > 5\frac{3}{4}$ or that $2\frac{1}{2} > 2$.

Most students will be able to solve the riddle satisfactorily, and, certainly, all will understand the riddle once the correct answer is given.

Mixed numerals

Often it is easier to think of a number for a point by thinking of a mixed numeral rather than an improper fraction.

To find the number for the point over the arrow, you could count by fourths and find 21 fourths. It may be easier just to think $5\frac{1}{4}$.

EXERCISES

1. Give a mixed numeral for each exercise.

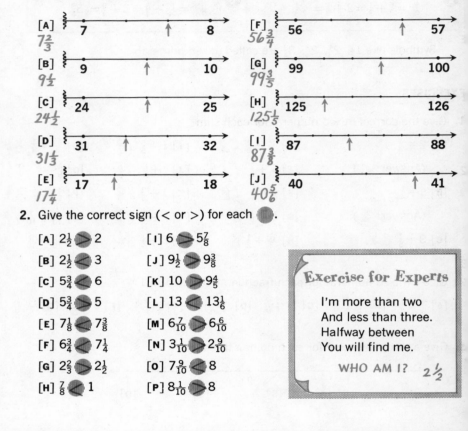

2. Give the correct sign ($<$ or $>$) for each ●.

[A] $2\frac{1}{2}$ ⊜ 2 [I] 6 ⊜ $5\frac{7}{8}$

[B] $2\frac{1}{2}$ ⊜ 3 [J] $9\frac{1}{2}$ ⊜ $9\frac{3}{8}$

[C] $5\frac{3}{4}$ ⊜ 6 [K] 10 ⊜ $9\frac{4}{5}$

[D] $5\frac{3}{4}$ ⊜ 5 [L] 13 ⊜ $13\frac{1}{6}$

[E] $7\frac{1}{8}$ ⊜ $7\frac{3}{8}$ [M] $6\frac{7}{10}$ ⊜ $6\frac{6}{10}$

[F] $6\frac{3}{4}$ ⊜ $7\frac{1}{4}$ [N] $3\frac{1}{10}$ ⊜ $2\frac{9}{10}$

[G] $2\frac{2}{3}$ ⊜ $2\frac{1}{2}$ [O] $7\frac{9}{10}$ ⊜ 8

[H] $\frac{7}{8}$ ⊜ 1 [P] $8\frac{1}{10}$ ⊜ 8

Exercise for Experts

I'm more than two
And less than three.
Halfway between
You will find me.

WHO AM I? $2\frac{1}{2}$

Teaching Pages 312 and 313

● **PURPOSE**

To provide additional experiences in working with mixed-numeral notation

To provide experiences in working with measurement concepts and rational numbers

To associate the mixed-numeral notation introduced in connection with measurements (Chapter 6) with the rational-number concepts presented in this chapter

● **PREPARATION**

Have the students measure, to the nearest half unit, various objects around the room. Measuring to the nearest

Measurement using mixed numerals

Using mixed numerals is very helpful in giving lengths. You can think of your ruler in the same way you think of a number line.

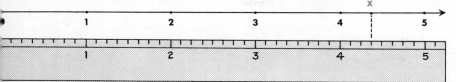

On most rulers the units are divided into eighths or sixteenths. Check to see how the units on the ruler above are divided. Now check your own ruler to see how it is divided. Notice in the picture that point X is $4\frac{3}{8}$ inches from the 0 point.

EXERCISES

The units on each number line are divided into eighths. Use mixed numerals to give the length of each object.

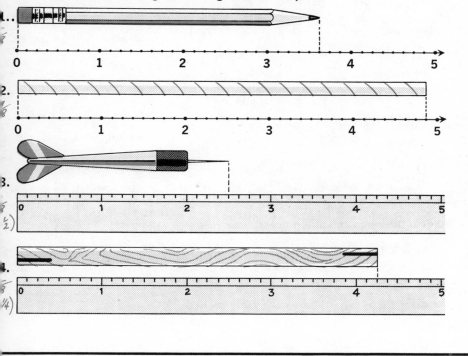

DIRECTIONS PAGE 313

As the students study and discuss the material at the top of the page, be sure they notice the similarity between the number line and the way in which the ruler is marked. Following a discussion that emphasizes these similarities, have the students do the exercises.

The exercises should go fairly rapidly and, in many respects, be routine for the students. It is important that the students see that finding measurements by using number lines in exercises 1 and 2 is essentially the same as finding the measurements by using the rulers in exercises 3 and 4.

half unit and writing the lengths on the chalkboard will give the students practice in writing mixed-numeral notation. Of course, they encountered mixed-numeral notation when measuring to the nearest half unit was introduced in Chapter 6, but at that time the students thought of the physical concept of, say, four units and a half unit more, rather than about a rational-number concept. It is important at this stage to relate the new rational-number notation for mixed numerals to the previous experiences the students have had with these mixed numerals in measurement application.

Have the students do the exercises. When they have finished, allow time for discussion and checking papers. It may be beneficial to have several students write exercises on the board and explain them to the class.

We stress the importance of your not insisting that the students give their sums in lowest terms. The goal for this lesson is to have the students begin to understand the idea of finding the sum or difference of two rational numbers even when the fractions given do not have the same denominator. Therefore, you should place all of your efforts on this particular point rather than upon reducing the sum or difference to lowest terms, which will be covered later. Be sure to point out repeatedly throughout this lesson that subtraction of rational numbers has the same relation to addition of rational numbers as subtraction of whole numbers has to addition of whole numbers.

More about addition and subtraction

Study this example.

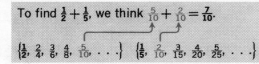

To find $\frac{1}{2} + \frac{1}{5}$, we think $\frac{5}{10} + \frac{2}{10} = \frac{7}{10}$.

$\{\frac{1}{2}, \frac{2}{4}, \frac{3}{6}, \frac{4}{8}, \frac{5}{10}, \cdots\}$ $\{\frac{1}{5}, \frac{2}{10}, \frac{3}{15}, \frac{4}{20}, \frac{5}{25}, \cdots\}$

EXERCISES

1. For each exercise, write an equation using fractions that have the same denominator.

[A] To find $\frac{1}{2} + \frac{1}{4}$, $\{\frac{1}{2}, \frac{2}{4}, \frac{3}{6}, \frac{4}{8}, \frac{5}{10}, \cdots\}$
we think ▨. $\{\frac{1}{4}, \frac{2}{8}, \frac{3}{12}, \frac{4}{16}, \frac{5}{20}, \cdots\}$
(Answer: $\frac{2}{4} + \frac{1}{4} = \frac{3}{4}$)

[B] To find $\frac{3}{4} + \frac{1}{2}$, $\{\frac{3}{4}, \frac{6}{8}, \frac{9}{12}, \frac{12}{16}, \frac{15}{20}, \cdots\}$
we think $\frac{3}{4} + \frac{2}{4} = \frac{5}{4}$. $\{\frac{1}{2}, \frac{2}{4}, \frac{3}{6}, \frac{4}{8}, \frac{5}{10}, \cdots\}$

[C] To find $\frac{3}{4} + \frac{1}{6}$, $\{\frac{3}{4}, \frac{6}{8}, \frac{9}{12}, \frac{12}{16}, \frac{15}{20}, \cdots\}$
we think $\frac{9}{12} + \frac{2}{12} = \frac{11}{12}$. $\{\frac{1}{6}, \frac{2}{12}, \frac{3}{18}, \frac{4}{24}, \frac{5}{30}, \cdots\}$

[D] To find $\frac{1}{2} - \frac{1}{4}$, $\{\frac{1}{2}, \frac{2}{4}, \frac{3}{6}, \frac{4}{8}, \cdots\}$
we think $\frac{2}{4} - \frac{1}{4} = \frac{1}{4}$. $\{\frac{1}{4}, \frac{2}{8}, \frac{3}{12}, \frac{4}{16}, \cdots\}$

[E] To find $\frac{1}{2} - \frac{1}{3}$, $\{\frac{1}{2}, \frac{2}{4}, \frac{3}{6}, \frac{4}{8}, \cdots\}$
we think $\frac{3}{6} - \frac{2}{6} = \frac{1}{6}$. $\{\frac{1}{3}, \frac{2}{6}, \frac{3}{9}, \frac{4}{12}, \cdots\}$

[F] To find $\frac{3}{4} - \frac{1}{6}$, $\{\frac{3}{4}, \frac{6}{8}, \frac{9}{12}, \frac{12}{16}, \cdots\}$
we think $\frac{9}{12} - \frac{2}{12} = \frac{7}{12}$. $\{\frac{1}{6}, \frac{2}{12}, \frac{3}{18}, \frac{4}{24}, \cdots\}$

2. Solve the equations.

[A] Since $\frac{1}{2} = \frac{2}{4}$,
we know that $\frac{1}{2} + \frac{1}{4} + n$. $\frac{3}{4}$

[B] Since $\frac{1}{2} = \frac{2}{4}$,
we know that $\frac{3}{4} + \frac{1}{2} = n$. $\frac{5}{4}$

[C] Since $\frac{3}{4} = \frac{9}{12}$ and $\frac{1}{6} = \frac{2}{12}$,
we know that $\frac{3}{4} + \frac{1}{6} = n$. $\frac{11}{12}$

[D] Since $\frac{1}{2} = \frac{2}{4}$,
we know that $\frac{1}{2} - \frac{1}{4} = n$. $\frac{1}{4}$

[E] Since $\frac{1}{2} = \frac{3}{6}$ and $\frac{1}{3} = \frac{2}{6}$,
we know that $\frac{1}{2} - \frac{1}{3} = n$. $\frac{1}{6}$

[F] Since $\frac{3}{4} = \frac{9}{12}$ and $\frac{1}{6} = \frac{2}{12}$,
we know that $\frac{3}{4} - \frac{1}{6} = n$. $\frac{7}{12}$

3. Find the sums and differences.

[A] Since $\frac{2}{3} = \frac{8}{12}$ and $\frac{1}{4} = \frac{3}{12}$, we know that $\frac{2}{3} + \frac{1}{4} = n$. $\frac{11}{12}$
[B] Since $\frac{1}{2} + \frac{1}{3} = \frac{5}{6}$, we know that $5\frac{1}{2} + 2\frac{1}{3} = n$. $7\frac{5}{6}$
[C] Since $\frac{1}{2} = \frac{4}{8}$, we know that $\frac{1}{2} - \frac{1}{8} = n$. $\frac{3}{8}$
[D] Since $5\frac{3}{4} = 5\frac{9}{12}$ and $\frac{2}{3} = \frac{8}{12}$, we know that $5\frac{3}{4} - \frac{2}{3} = n$. $5\frac{1}{12}$

Teaching Pages 314 and 315

● PURPOSE

To provide material leading toward finding the sum of two rational numbers which are represented by fractions having different denominators

To define subtraction of rational numbers, using the same, familiar inverse relationship that exists between addition and subtraction of whole numbers

To provide word problems involving work with rational numbers

Rational-number problems

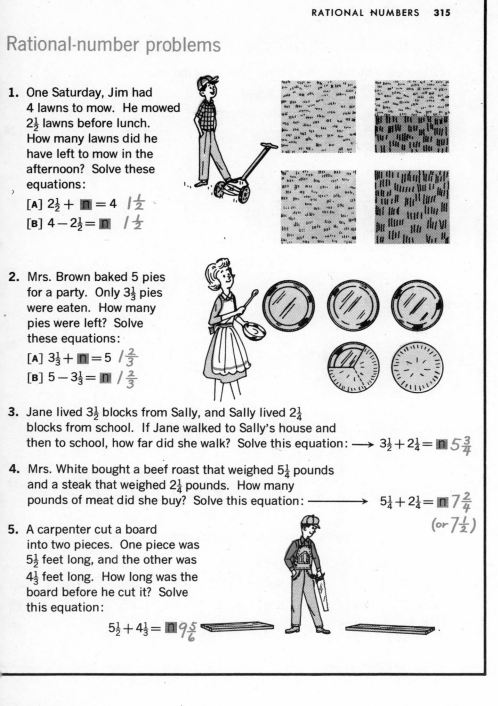

1. One Saturday, Jim had 4 lawns to mow. He mowed $2\frac{1}{2}$ lawns before lunch. How many lawns did he have left to mow in the afternoon? Solve these equations:

   [A] $2\frac{1}{2} + \blacksquare = 4$ $1\frac{1}{2}$

   [B] $4 - 2\frac{1}{2} = \blacksquare$ $1\frac{1}{2}$

2. Mrs. Brown baked 5 pies for a party. Only $3\frac{1}{3}$ pies were eaten. How many pies were left? Solve these equations:

   [A] $3\frac{1}{3} + \blacksquare = 5$ $1\frac{2}{3}$

   [B] $5 - 3\frac{1}{3} = \blacksquare$ $1\frac{2}{3}$

3. Jane lived $3\frac{1}{2}$ blocks from Sally, and Sally lived $2\frac{1}{4}$ blocks from school. If Jane walked to Sally's house and then to school, how far did she walk? Solve this equation: $\longrightarrow$ $3\frac{1}{2} + 2\frac{1}{4} = \blacksquare$ $5\frac{3}{4}$

4. Mrs. White bought a beef roast that weighed $5\frac{1}{4}$ pounds and a steak that weighed $2\frac{1}{4}$ pounds. How many pounds of meat did she buy? Solve this equation: $\longrightarrow$ $5\frac{1}{4} + 2\frac{1}{4} = \blacksquare$ $7\frac{2}{4}$ (or $7\frac{1}{2}$)

5. A carpenter cut a board into two pieces. One piece was $5\frac{1}{2}$ feet long, and the other was $4\frac{1}{3}$ feet long. How long was the board before he cut it? Solve this equation:

   $5\frac{1}{2} + 4\frac{1}{3} = \blacksquare$ $9\frac{5}{6}$

Have the students do the exercises. As you discuss the answers, observe with the class that the two equations given for exercises 1 and 2 show the relationship between addition and subtraction. If time permits following discussion of these exercises, give the students an opportunity to make up some rational-number word problems of their own to present to the class either orally or on the chalkboard.

PREPARATION

Provide the students with an opportunity to list several members of sets of equivalent fractions beginning with a lowest-terms fraction. For example, you can exhibit on the chalkboard lowest-term fractions such as $\frac{1}{2}$, $\frac{1}{3}$, $\frac{2}{3}$, $\frac{3}{4}$, and $\frac{5}{6}$. Have the students build the first six or eight equivalent fractions for each of these lowest-terms fractions.

Building sets of equivalent fractions for the two rational numbers to be added is the technique used in this lesson to find common-denominator fractions. For instance, if the students are to add $\frac{3}{4}$ and $\frac{1}{6}$, they are expected to list several fractions in the set containing $\frac{3}{4}$ and several fractions in the set containing $\frac{1}{6}$, at least until they arrive at a pair of fractions (one for each number) that have the same denominator. After this activity, review with the students the method for finding the sum of two rational numbers when they are represented by fractions that have the same denominator.

Review with the students the relationship between addition and subtraction of whole numbers. Exhibit on the chalkboard several addition equations and have the students write two subtraction equations for each addition equation. Now, exhibit some addition equations in which the students are required to find a missing addend. Once they find the missing addend, have other students explain how this relates to the idea of subtraction, by writing the corresponding subtraction equation for the missing-addend problem.

Have the students do exercise 1. When they have finished, allow time for discussion and checking papers. Follow up by reading the directions to exercise 2 and by exhibiting the four examples on the chalkboard. Give the students an opportunity to discuss the colored numerals. Elicit from them the observation that, in multiplication of the first type shown here, we simply use the whole number as the numerator and we use the denominator of the fraction as the denominator in our answer; and for the second type shown here, we simply use *one* as the numerator and we use the product of the denominators as the denominator of the answer. Of course, every effort should be made to give students an opportunity not only to discover this rule but also to understand it by use of regions and number-line examples. However, it is important for future work that the students become familiar with the quick and easy way to find products as indicated in this exercise set.

Following a discussion of the four examples, have the students complete exercise 2. When they have finished, allow time for discussion and checking papers.

Supplementary exercises, Set 55 (page 352) may be assigned as necessary beyond this page.

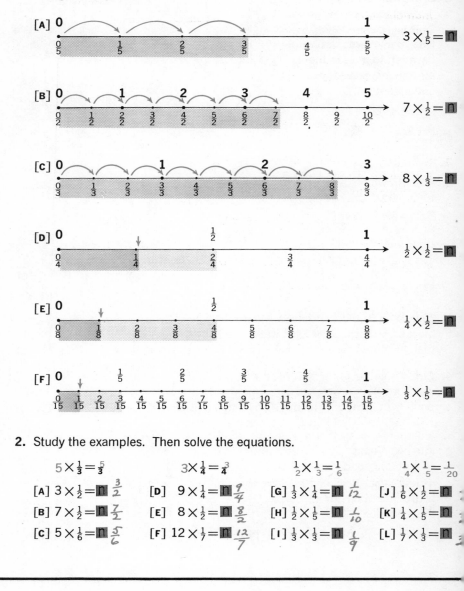

Multiplication of rational numbers

1. Study the number-line picture. Then copy the equation and give the product.

[A] $3 \times \frac{1}{5} = \blacksquare$

[B] $7 \times \frac{1}{2} = \blacksquare$

[C] $8 \times \frac{1}{3} = \blacksquare$

[D] $\frac{1}{2} \times \frac{1}{2} = \blacksquare$

[E] $\frac{1}{4} \times \frac{1}{2} = \blacksquare$

[F] $\frac{1}{3} \times \frac{1}{5} = \blacksquare$

2. Study the examples. Then solve the equations.

$$5 \times \frac{1}{3} = \frac{5}{3} \qquad 3 \times \frac{1}{4} = \frac{3}{4} \qquad \frac{1}{2} \times \frac{1}{3} = \frac{1}{6} \qquad \frac{1}{4} \times \frac{1}{5} = \frac{1}{20}$$

[A] $3 \times \frac{1}{2} = \blacksquare \; \frac{3}{2}$

[B] $7 \times \frac{1}{2} = \blacksquare \; \frac{7}{2}$

[C] $5 \times \frac{1}{6} = \blacksquare \; \frac{5}{6}$

[D] $9 \times \frac{1}{4} = \blacksquare \; \frac{9}{4}$

[E] $8 \times \frac{1}{2} = \blacksquare \; \frac{8}{2}$

[F] $12 \times \frac{1}{7} = \blacksquare \; \frac{12}{7}$

[G] $\frac{1}{3} \times \frac{1}{4} = \blacksquare \; \frac{1}{12}$

[H] $\frac{1}{2} \times \frac{1}{5} = \blacksquare \; \frac{1}{10}$

[I] $\frac{1}{3} \times \frac{1}{3} = \blacksquare \; \frac{1}{9}$

[J] $\frac{1}{6} \times \frac{1}{2} = \blacksquare$

[K] $\frac{1}{4} \times \frac{1}{5} = \blacksquare$

[L] $\frac{1}{7} \times \frac{1}{3} = \blacksquare$

Teaching Pages 316 and 317

- ### PURPOSE

  To provide additional experiences in work with finding products of rational numbers

  To provide additional activity leading toward the general rule for finding the product of any two rational numbers

  To introduce the number line as a model for illustrating products involving a whole number and a rational number that can be represented by a unit fraction

  To introduce the number line as a model for finding the product of two rational numbers that can each be represented by unit fractions

  To develop skill in finding the product of a whole number and a rational number represented as a unit fraction

  To develop skill in finding the product of two rational numbers each of which can be represented as a unit fraction

- ### PREPARATION

  Exhibit on the chalkboard two number lines, one divided into fifths and the other into sixths. Use these number lines to demonstrate a given number of jumps of a fifth and of a sixth. For example, you might show three jumps of a fifth by using arrows from $\frac{0}{5}$ to $\frac{1}{5}$ to $\frac{2}{5}$ to $\frac{3}{5}$. Now write on the chalkboard the appropriate equation, $3 \times \frac{1}{5} = \frac{3}{5}$. On the other number line you can show 11

Finding products

Because of the **order** and **grouping** principles of multiplication of rational numbers, you can rearrange the factors when you multiply. The diagram will help you see how to use this idea to find products such as $\frac{2}{3} \times \frac{3}{4}$.

Find the product of these factors.

Find the product of these factors.

$$\frac{2}{3} \times \frac{3}{4} = \left(2 \times \frac{1}{3}\right) \times \left(3 \times \frac{1}{4}\right) = 6 \times \frac{1}{12} = \frac{6}{12}$$

EXERCISES

1. Give the whole number for ▓. Give the fraction for **N**. Then give the missing product.

[A] $\frac{3}{5} \times \frac{2}{5} = \left(3 \times \frac{1}{5}\right) \times \left(2 \times \frac{1}{5}\right) = $ ▓ $\times$ **N** $= $ ▓
(Answer: $6, \frac{1}{10}, \frac{6}{10}$)

[B] $\frac{4}{5} \times \frac{2}{3} = \left(4 \times \frac{1}{5}\right) \times \left(2 \times \frac{1}{3}\right) = $ ▓ $\times$ **N** $= $ ▓
$8, \frac{1}{15}, \frac{8}{15}$

[C] $\frac{3}{4} \times \frac{5}{2} = \left(3 \times \frac{1}{4}\right) \times \left(5 \times \frac{1}{2}\right) = $ ▓ $\times$ **N** $= $ ▓
$15, \frac{1}{8}, \frac{15}{8}$

[D] $\frac{2}{7} \times \frac{4}{3} = \left(2 \times \frac{1}{7}\right) \times \left(4 \times \frac{1}{3}\right) = $ ▓ $\times$ **N** $= $ ▓
$8, \frac{1}{21}, \frac{8}{21}$

[E] $\frac{3}{5} \times \frac{3}{2} = \left(3 \times \frac{1}{5}\right) \times \left(3 \times \frac{1}{2}\right) = $ ▓ $\times$ **N** $= $ ▓
$9, \frac{1}{10}, \frac{9}{10}$

[F] $\frac{4}{7} \times \frac{2}{5} = \left(4 \times \frac{1}{7}\right) \times \left(2 \times \frac{1}{5}\right) = $ ▓ $\times$ **N** $= $ ▓
$8, \frac{1}{35}, \frac{8}{35}$

[G] $\frac{5}{8} \times \frac{3}{2} = \left(5 \times \frac{1}{8}\right) \times \left(3 \times \frac{1}{2}\right) = $ ▓ $\times$ **N** $= $ ▓
$15, \frac{1}{16}, \frac{15}{16}$

[H] $\frac{5}{6} \times \frac{2}{3} = \left(5 \times \frac{1}{6}\right) \times \left(2 \times \frac{1}{3}\right) = $ ▓ $\times$ **N** $= $ ▓
$10, \frac{1}{18}, \frac{10}{18}$

2. Give the products.

[A] $\frac{3}{4} \times \frac{2}{3} = \left(3 \times 2\right) \times \left(\frac{1}{4} \times \frac{1}{3}\right) = $ ▓ $\frac{6}{12}$

[B] $\frac{4}{3} \times \frac{5}{2} = \left(4 \times 5\right) \times \left(\frac{1}{3} \times \frac{1}{2}\right) = $ ▓ $\frac{20}{6}$

[C] $\frac{4}{5} \times \frac{2}{3} = \left(4 \times 2\right) \times \left(\frac{1}{5} \times \frac{1}{3}\right) = $ ▓ $\frac{8}{15}$

[D] $\frac{3}{4} \times \frac{7}{2} = \left(3 \times 7\right) \times \left(\frac{1}{4} \times \frac{1}{2}\right) = $ ▓ $\frac{21}{8}$

[E] $\frac{5}{6} \times \frac{5}{4} = \left(5 \times 5\right) \times \left(\frac{1}{6} \times \frac{1}{4}\right) = $ ▓ $\frac{25}{24}$

[F] $\frac{4}{3} \times \frac{3}{7} = \left(4 \times 3\right) \times \left(\frac{1}{3} \times \frac{1}{7}\right) = $ ▓ $\frac{12}{21}$

3. Give the products.

[A] $\frac{3}{4} \times \frac{2}{5} \quad \frac{6}{20}$

[B] $\frac{5}{3} \times \frac{3}{2} \quad \frac{15}{6}$

[C] $\frac{2}{7} \times \frac{5}{2} \quad \frac{10}{14}$

[D] $\frac{4}{5} \times \frac{7}{3} \quad \frac{28}{15}$

[E] $\frac{3}{8} \times \frac{5}{5} \quad \frac{6}{40}$

[F] $\frac{5}{4} \times \frac{3}{5} \quad \frac{15}{20}$

[G] $\frac{2}{3} \times \frac{2}{3} \quad \frac{4}{9}$

[H] $\frac{5}{6} \times \frac{3}{8} \quad \frac{15}{48}$

[I] $\frac{8}{3} \times \frac{3}{4} \quad \frac{24}{12}$

[J] $\frac{3}{4} \times \frac{5}{8} \quad \frac{15}{32}$

[K] $\frac{5}{6} \times \frac{7}{4} \quad \frac{35}{24}$

[L] $\frac{4}{7} \times \frac{7}{4} \quad \frac{28}{28}$

[M] $\frac{5}{5} \times \frac{3}{5} \quad \frac{15}{25}$

[N] $\frac{9}{7} \times \frac{3}{8} \quad \frac{27}{56}$

Read and study the material at the top of the page with the class. Use the chalkboard to exhibit the equation at the top of the page. Go through this equation a step at a time and discuss it with the students. Have the students point out that $2 \times \frac{1}{3}$ is simply $\frac{2}{3}$ and that $3 \times \frac{1}{4}$ is simply $\frac{3}{4}$. Now, notice with the students that we rearrange the factors and multiply 2×3 to get six. We rearrange the factors and multiply $\frac{1}{3} \times \frac{1}{4}$ to get $\frac{1}{12}$. We then multiply $6 \times \frac{1}{12}$, and we get our final answer, $\frac{6}{12}$. Be sure to emphasize for the students that we have gone through some intermediate steps but that the $\frac{6}{12}$ that we found is the product of the first two factors, $\frac{2}{3}$ and $\frac{3}{4}$. This is extremely important. Therefore, you might find it helpful to exhibit, at the end of this discussion, the equation $\frac{2}{3} \times \frac{3}{4} = \frac{6}{12}$.

Have the students do exercise 1. Emphasize again and again as the students work the various parts of exercise 1 that they are finding the product of the first two factors. When the students have finished, you may find it helpful to select several parts of exercise 1 and present them and discuss them as you did the example at the top of the page. Again, we would emphasize the importance, once you have completed the discussion of these parts of exercise 1, of exhibiting the final equation on the chalkboard.

You should keep in mind, as you have the students do these exercises and as you discuss them, that every effort is made here to help the students discover the general rule for finding the product of two rational numbers. Notice that exercise 2 is color-coded to assist the students in observing that they multiply numerators and denominators together in order to find the product of the two rational numbers.

jumps of $\frac{1}{6}$ with a curved arrow from $\frac{0}{6}$ to $\frac{1}{6}$ to $\frac{2}{6}$ and so on up to $\frac{11}{6}$; exhibit for the students the corresponding equation, $11 \times \frac{1}{6} = \frac{11}{6}$.

After this activity, exhibit on the chalkboard an expanded form of the number line. You might have your number line divided into eighths and show only the portion between zero and one. Observe a given number of eighths with the students and then, say, half of this or a third of this. Of course, it will be necessary that you divide your number line so that you have an example that will give an answer that can easily be read by the students. You might show $\frac{1}{4}$ of the number line and then $\frac{1}{2}$ of $\frac{1}{4}$, which would, of course, be $\frac{1}{8}$. You would then want to show the corresponding equation, $\frac{1}{2} \times \frac{1}{4} = \frac{1}{8}$.

Read and study the material at the top of the page with the class. Be sure to stress each row of the chart. Point out to the students that in the first column they see the objects; in the second column, they think about the number of tens, ones, and then the number of tenths; and in the third column, they see two different ways to write this number (in the first way, with fractions; in the second way, with decimals). Emphasize for the students that they are learning a new way to write a symbol for rational numbers. For example, the old form was $23\frac{8}{10}$, and the new form is 23.8. Of course, we say the same words for both of these: *twenty-three and eight tenths*.

After you have discussed with the students the diagram and explanation following the table, have them take turns reading the decimals given in the oral exercises.

Decimals

In this lesson you will learn about **decimals.** The examples below will help you understand how decimals are used to name rational numbers. The dot is called the **decimal point.**

We see	We think	We write		We say
		Using fractions	Using decimals	
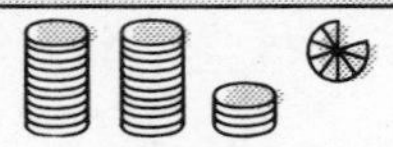 (objects)	2 tens, 3 ones, and 8 tenths	$23\frac{8}{10}$	**23.8**	twenty-three and eight tenths
 (objects)	1 ten, 8 ones, and 4 tenths	$18\frac{4}{10}$	**18.4**	eighteen and four tenths
 (objects)	1 and 2 tenths	$1\frac{2}{10}$	**1.2**	one and two tenths
 (objects)	7 tenths	$\frac{7}{10}$	**.7**	seven tenths

The following diagram shows how decimals are an extension of our place-value system.

hundreds tens ones tenths hundredths

5 2 7 . 6 8

The 6 in the **tenths** place means $\frac{6}{10}$ or $\frac{60}{100}$.

The 8 in the **hundredths** place means $\frac{8}{100}$.

The numeral 527.68 means $\rightarrow 500 + 20 + 7 + \frac{6}{10} + \frac{8}{100}$.
$\rightarrow 500 + 20 + 7 + \frac{68}{100}$.

We read, "five hundred twenty-seven and sixty-eight hundredths".

ORAL EXERCISES

Read these decimals.

1. 25.6	3. 172.6	5. 35.25	7. 327.68	9. 638.17
2. 38.3	4. 517.8	6. 15.68	8. 521.52	10. 908.92

Teaching Pages 318 and 319

- **PURPOSE**

  To introduce decimal notation for rational numbers

  To extend place-value concepts to include tenths, hundredths, and thousandths

- **PREPARATION**

  Because much of the work in this chapter presents to the students new notation for the same numbers that they have worked with in the past, you might center most of your preparation activities on the material introduced in the table on page 318. Also, since work with decimals is concerned with tenths, hundredths, and thousandths, you

EXERCISES

1. Give the missing numerators.

[A] $5.6 = 5 + \frac{\text{\textbar\textbar\textbar}}{10}$ *6*   [G] $15.6 = 15 + \frac{\text{\textbar\textbar\textbar}}{10}$ *6*   [M] $2.68 = 2 + \frac{\text{\textbar\textbar\textbar}}{10} + \frac{8}{100}$ *6*

[B] $7.3 = 7 + \frac{\text{\textbar\textbar\textbar}}{10}$ *3*   [H] $1.56 = 1 + \frac{\text{\textbar\textbar\textbar}}{100}$ *56*   [N] $3.75 = 3 + \frac{7}{10} + \frac{\text{\textbar\textbar\textbar}}{100}$ *5*

[C] $6.2 = 6 + \frac{\text{\textbar\textbar\textbar}}{10}$ *2*   [I] $3.27 = 3 + \frac{\text{\textbar\textbar\textbar}}{100}$ *27*   [O] $5.62 = 5 + \frac{\text{\textbar\textbar\textbar}}{10} + \frac{2}{100}$ *6*

[D] $5.7 = 5 + \frac{\text{\textbar\textbar\textbar}}{10}$ *7*   [J] $32.7 = 32 + \frac{\text{\textbar\textbar\textbar}}{10}$ *7*   [P] $9.38 = 9 + \frac{3}{10} + \frac{\text{\textbar\textbar\textbar}}{100}$ *8*

[E] $9.1 = 9 + \frac{\text{\textbar\textbar\textbar}}{10}$ *1*   [K] $58.6 = 58 + \frac{\text{\textbar\textbar\textbar}}{10}$ *6*   [Q] $7.64 = 7 + \frac{6}{10} + \frac{\text{\textbar\textbar\textbar}}{100}$ *4*

[F] $8.5 = 8 + \frac{\text{\textbar\textbar\textbar}}{10}$ *5*   [L] $5.86 = 5 + \frac{\text{\textbar\textbar\textbar}}{100}$ *86*   [R] $8.32 = 8 + \frac{\text{\textbar\textbar\textbar}}{10} + \frac{2}{100}$ *3*

2. Give the missing fractions.

[A] $53.6 = 53 + $ *6/10*   [E] $27.63 = 27 + $ *63/100*   [I] $52.34 = 52 + \frac{3}{10} + $ *4/100*

[B] $27.3 = 27 + $ *3/10*   [F] $51.26 = 51 + $ *26/100*   [J] $16.75 = 16 + $ *7/10* $ + \frac{5}{100}$

[C] $19.9 = 19 + $ *9/10*   [G] $43.95 = 43 + $ *95/100*   [K] $81.62 = 81 + $ *6/10* $ + \frac{2}{100}$

[D] $57.5 = 57 + $ *5/10*   [H] $18.98 = 18 + $ *98/100*   [L] $36.78 = 36 + \frac{7}{10} + $ *8/100*

3. Write a decimal for each sum.

[A] $56 + \frac{7}{10}$ *56.7*   [E] $58 + \frac{33}{100}$ *58.33*   [I] $56 + \frac{2}{10} + \frac{3}{100}$ *56,23*

[B] $37 + \frac{2}{10}$ *37.2*   [F] $25 + \frac{67}{100}$ *25.67*   [J] $27 + \frac{3}{10} + \frac{7}{100}$ *27.37*

[C] $51 + \frac{1}{10}$ *51.1*   [G] $28 + \frac{42}{100}$ *28.42*   [K] $58 + \frac{6}{10} + \frac{9}{100}$ *58.69*

[D] $76 + \frac{9}{10}$ *76.9*   [H] $65 + \frac{79}{100}$ *65.79*   [L] $42 + \frac{9}{10} + \frac{8}{100}$ *42.98*

4. Write each rational number as in the examples. *(See answers at right.)*

(Example 1: $16.7 = 16 + \frac{7}{10}$ Example 2: $52.64 = 52 + \frac{6}{10} + \frac{4}{100}$)

[A] 63.4	[E] 39.2	[I] 3.25	[M] 46.2	[Q] 56.4	[U] 643.7
[B] 52.7	[F] 84.6	[J] 1.76	[N] 9.16	[R] 23.4	[V] 81.26
[C] 16.5	[G] 72.1	[K] 8.43	[O] 84.7	[S] 7.11	[W] 513.4
[D] 27.8	[H] 56.4	[L] 2.79	[P] 3.21	[T] 84.2	[X] 92.86

★**5.** Give the correct sign (< or >) for each ⬤.

[A] 3.7 ⬤ 37 [C] 61.3 ⬤ 6.13 [E] 43.1 ⬤ 4.31 [G] 8.37 ⬤ 83.7

[B] 58 ⬤ 5.8 [D] 2.75 ⬤ 27.5 [F] 6.52 ⬤ 65.2 [H] 6.24 ⬤ 62.4

Work through one or two problems from each exercise with the students and then have them complete the exercises on their own.

Note that exercise 5 is designed for the more able students. All students should benefit from a discussion of the correct answers to these problems.

Answers, exercise 4, page 319

4. [A] $63.4 = 63 + \frac{4}{10}$
  [B] $52.7 = 52 + \frac{7}{10}$
  [C] $16.5 = 16 + \frac{5}{10}$
  [D] $27.8 = 27 + \frac{8}{10}$
  [E] $39.2 = 39 + \frac{2}{10}$
  [F] $84.6 = 84 + \frac{6}{10}$
  [G] $72.1 = 72 + \frac{1}{10}$
  [H] $56.4 = 56 + \frac{4}{10}$
  [I] $3.25 = 3 + \frac{2}{10} + \frac{5}{100}$
  [J] $1.76 = 1 + \frac{7}{10} + \frac{6}{100}$
  [K] $8.43 = 8 + \frac{4}{10} + \frac{3}{100}$
  [L] $2.79 = 2 + \frac{7}{10} + \frac{9}{100}$
  [M] $46.2 = 46 + \frac{2}{10}$
  [N] $9.16 = 9 + \frac{1}{10} + \frac{6}{100}$
  [O] $84.7 = 84 + \frac{7}{10}$
  [P] $3.21 = 3 + \frac{2}{10} + \frac{1}{100}$
  [Q] $56.4 = 56 + \frac{4}{10}$
  [R] $23.4 = 23 + \frac{4}{10}$
  [S] $7.11 = 7 + \frac{1}{10} + \frac{1}{100}$
  [T] $84.2 = 84 + \frac{2}{10}$
  [U] $643.7 = 643 + \frac{7}{10}$
  [V] $81.26 = 81 + \frac{2}{10} + \frac{6}{100}$
  [W] $513.4 = 513 + \frac{4}{10}$
  [X] $92.86 = 92 + \frac{8}{10} + \frac{6}{100}$

may find it helpful to review with the students some fractions having denominators of ten, one hundred, and one thousand. You can also provide the students with some practice in giving the numerator for the following type of exercise:

$$\frac{4}{10} = \frac{}{100} \qquad \frac{3}{100} = \frac{}{1000}.$$

Have the students do the exercises. When they have finished, allow time for discussion and checking papers. Be sure, during the discussion, to bring out the similarities between pairs of exercises in each part of exercises 1 and 2. Stress that adding rational numbers using decimals is the same as adding rational numbers using fractions except that the work looks a little different on paper.

Addition and subtraction using decimals

EXERCISES

1. Find the sums and differences.

[A] $\frac{6}{10} - \frac{3}{10} = \blacksquare\,\frac{3}{10}$ [B] $\frac{2}{10} + \frac{5}{10} = \blacksquare\,\frac{7}{10}$ [C] $\frac{23}{100} + \frac{34}{100} = \blacksquare\,\frac{57}{100}$ [D] $\frac{15}{100} + \frac{63}{100} = \blacksquare\,\frac{78}{100}$

$.6 - .3 = \blacksquare\ .3$ $.2 + .5 = \blacksquare\ .7$ $.23 + .34 = \blacksquare\ .57$ $.15 + .63 = \blacksquare\ .78$

[E] $\frac{25}{100} - \frac{15}{100} = \blacksquare\,\frac{10}{100}$ [F] $\frac{38}{100} + \frac{15}{100} = \blacksquare\,\frac{53}{100}$ [G] $\frac{37}{100} - \frac{19}{100} = \blacksquare\,\frac{18}{100}$ [H] $\frac{56}{100} + \frac{24}{100} = \blacksquare\,\frac{80}{100}$

$.25 - .15 = \blacksquare\ .10$ $.18 + .15 = \blacksquare\ .53$ $.37 - .19 = \blacksquare\ .18$ $.56 + .24 = \blacksquare\ .80$

[I] $\frac{3}{10}$ .3   [J] $\frac{7}{10}$ .7   [K] $\frac{16}{100}$ .16   [L] $\frac{82}{100}$ .82
$\quad +\frac{5}{10}$ +.5 $\quad -\frac{2}{10}$ −.2 $\quad +\frac{42}{100}$ +.42 $\quad -\frac{26}{100}$ −.26
$\quad \overline{\frac{8}{10}}$ $\overline{.8}$ $\quad \overline{\frac{5}{10}}$ $\overline{.5}$ $\quad \overline{\frac{58}{100}}$ $\overline{.58}$ $\quad \overline{\frac{56}{100}}$ $\overline{.56}$

[M] $\frac{29}{100}$ .29   [N] $\frac{58}{100}$ .58   [O] $\frac{27}{100}$ .27   [P] $\frac{5}{10}$ .50
$\quad +\frac{17}{100}$ +.17 $\quad -\frac{28}{100}$ −.28 $\quad +\frac{7}{10}$ +.70 $\quad +\frac{32}{100}$ +.32
$\quad \overline{\frac{46}{100}}$ $\overline{.46}$ $\quad \overline{\frac{30}{100}}$ $\overline{.30}$ $\quad \overline{\frac{97}{100}}$ $\overline{.97}$ $\quad \overline{\frac{82}{100}}$ $\overline{.82}$

2. In each exercise, copy the first equation and give the missing numerators. Then give the correct decimal for the sum or difference in the second equation.

[A] $\frac{6}{10} + \frac{7}{10} = \frac{10}{10} + \frac{3}{10} = 1 + \frac{3}{10}$ [E] $\frac{5}{10} + \frac{8}{10} = \frac{10}{10} + \frac{3}{10} = 1 + \frac{3}{10}$
$.6 + .7 = \blacksquare\ 1.3$ $.5 + .8 = \blacksquare\ 1.3$

[B] $\frac{5}{10} + \frac{9}{10} = \frac{10}{10} + \frac{4}{10} = 1 + \frac{4}{10}$ [F] $\frac{9}{10} + \frac{4}{10} = \frac{10}{10} + \frac{3}{10} = 1 + \frac{3}{10}$
$.5 + .9 = \blacksquare\ 1.4$ $.9 + .4 = \blacksquare\ 1.3$

[C] $\frac{8}{10} + \frac{6}{10} = \frac{10}{10} + \frac{4}{10} = 1 + \frac{4}{10}$ [G] $1\frac{5}{10} - \frac{7}{10} = \frac{15}{10} - \frac{7}{10}$
$.8 + .6 = \blacksquare\ 1.4$ $1.5 - .7 = \blacksquare\ 8$

[D] $\frac{4}{10} + \frac{7}{10} = \frac{10}{10} + \frac{1}{10} = 1 + \frac{1}{10}$ [H] $1\frac{2}{10} - \frac{8}{10} = \frac{12}{10} - \frac{8}{10}$
$.4 + .7 = \blacksquare\ 1.1$ $1.2 - .8 = \blacksquare\ 4$

3. Answer a, b, or c for each exercise.

[A] $.6 + .5 = \blacksquare$ (a) .11   (b) 1.1   (c) 11
[B] $.7 + .7 = \blacksquare$ (a) 1.4   (b) 14   (c) .14
[C] $.2 + .8 = \blacksquare$ (a) .10   (b) .010   (c) 1.0
★ [D] $3.7 + .8 = \blacksquare$ (a) 45   (b) 4.5   (c) .45

Teaching Pages 320 and 321

- **PURPOSE**

  To provide additional experiences in work with decimals

  To introduce addition and subtraction of rational numbers using decimal notation

  To provide additional experiences in reading decimals

  To introduce percent notation

Percents

The first two rows of the table will help you understand **percent** names for rational numbers. Give the missing names for the rest of the table.

Region	Lowest-terms fraction name	Other fraction names	Decimal name	Percent name
	$\frac{1}{2}$	$\frac{2}{4}, \frac{3}{6}, \frac{4}{8}, \ldots, \frac{50}{100}, \ldots$	.50	50%
	$\frac{1}{4}$	$\frac{2}{8}, \frac{3}{12}, \frac{4}{16}, \ldots, \frac{25}{100}, \ldots$	.25	25%
	$\frac{3}{4}$	$\frac{6}{8}, \frac{9}{12}, \text{[A]} \frac{12}{16}, \ldots, \frac{75}{100}, \ldots$	.75	[B] 75%
	[C] $\frac{4}{5}$	$\frac{8}{10}, \frac{12}{15}, \frac{16}{20}, \ldots, \frac{80}{100}, \ldots$	[D] .80	80% [E]
	$\frac{3}{10}$	[F] $\frac{6}{20}, \frac{9}{30}, \frac{12}{40}, \ldots, \text{[G]} \frac{30}{100}, \ldots$	.30	30% [H]
	[I] $\frac{1}{10}$	$\frac{2}{20}, \frac{3}{30}, \frac{4}{40}, \ldots, \text{[J]} \frac{10}{100}, \ldots$	[K] .10	10% [L]

We read "fifty **percent**" for 50%. 50% = $\frac{1}{2}$
We read "twenty-five **percent**" for 25%. 25% = $\frac{1}{4}$

EXERCISES

1. Write the percent for each decimal.

[A] .35 [B] .60 [C] .20 [D] .10 [E] .98 [F] .28 [G] .25 [H] .80
35%   60%   20%   10%   98%   28%   25%   80%

2. Write the decimal for each percent.

[A] 30% [B] 20% [C] 75% [D] 90% [E] 50% [F] 58% [G] 25% [H] 10%
.30   .20   .75   .90   .50   .58   .25   .10

★3. Tell which symbols in each row stand for the number in the blue screen.

[A] $\frac{1}{2}$ $\frac{2}{4}$; 30%; $\frac{50}{100}$; $\frac{5}{100}$; 50%; $\frac{5}{10}$; $\frac{4}{5}$; .50

[B] 25% $\frac{1}{4}$; .27; $2 + \frac{5}{10}$; .25; $\frac{2}{8}$; $\frac{3}{15}$; 2.5; 25

[C] 2.3 $\overline{23}$; $2 + \frac{3}{10}$; $\frac{23}{100}$; 23%; $2 + \frac{3}{100}$; $2\frac{3}{10}$; 2.3%; $2 + \frac{6}{20}$

[D] $\frac{4}{10}$ $\frac{40}{100}$; .45; 40%; $\frac{2}{5}$; 50%; .40; 4%; $\frac{6}{15}$

Explain to the students that on this page they are going to learn a new form of notation for rational numbers—percent notation.

Read through the chart with the students and have them supply the missing entries as an oral, class activity.

Have the class work exercises 1 and 2. After the more able students have completed starred exercise 3, involve the whole class in a discussion of the answers.

PREPARATION

Provide the class with a short oral practice session on the reading of various decimals. List several decimals on the chalkboard and have the students take turns reading them.

You can use the chart on page 321 to prepare the students for the percent exercises.

During the discussion which accompanies the checking of papers, you might have the students present some parts of exercises 4 and 5 on the chalkboard and demonstrate the working of these for the class. For example, it may be meaningful for the students to see how the borrowing involved is the same in work with these numbers which represent money as it is in the usual work with addition and subtraction. It might also be good practice during this particular discussion to dictate some amounts of money to the students and have them write the corresponding addition or subtraction problem on the chalkboard. This activity will be particularly beneficial if the students require further work in lining up the decimal points, or the periods, which separate the dollars and the cents.

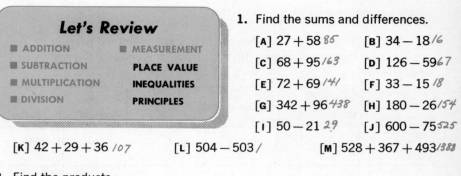

322   RATIONAL NUMBERS

Let's Review
- ADDITION
- SUBTRACTION
- MULTIPLICATION
- DIVISION
- MEASUREMENT

PLACE VALUE
INEQUALITIES
PRINCIPLES

1. Find the sums and differences.

[A] 27 + 58 *85*   [B] 34 − 18 *16*

[C] 68 + 95 *163*   [D] 126 − 59 *67*

[E] 72 + 69 *141*   [F] 33 − 15 *18*

[G] 342 + 96 *438*   [H] 180 − 26 *154*

[I] 50 − 21 *29*   [J] 600 − 75 *525*

[K] 42 + 29 + 36 *107*   [L] 504 − 503 *1*   [M] 528 + 367 + 493 *1388*

2. Find the products.

[A] 38 × 6 *228*   [C] 54 × 2 *108*   [E] 327 × 6 *1962*   [G] 621 × 3 *1863*   [I] 702 × 5 *3510*

[B] 57 × 8 *456*   [D] 68 × 5 *340*   [F] 438 × 5 *2190*   [H] 754 × 6 *4524*   [J] 860 × 3 *2580*

3. Find the quotients and remainders.

[A] 36 ÷ 4 *9*   [C] 68 ÷ 4 *17*   [E] 728 ÷ 5 *145 R3*   [G] 52 ÷ 3 *17 R1*   [I] 726 ÷ 1 *726*

[B] 75 ÷ 5 *15*   [D] 93 ÷ 6 *15 R3*   [F] 436 ÷ 9 *48 R4*   [H] 148 ÷ 2 *74*   [J] 343 ÷ 8 *42 R7*

4. Find the total amounts.

[A] $6.23
      5.37
   $11.60

[B] $13.24
       .67
   $13.91

[C] $33.02
      67.00
   $100.02

[D] $ 31.26
       5.48
     126.50
   $163.24

[E] $ 76.38
     142.50
       5.78
   $224.66

5. Find the difference of the amounts.

[A] $9.28
      5.07
   $4.21

[B] $68.80
       5.43
    $63.37

[C] $39.89
      29.59
    $10.30

[D] $128.46
       54.37
    $74.09

[E] $99.98
      75.24
    $24.74

6. Give the area for each figure.

[A] 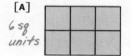 *6 sq units*

[B] *4 sq units*

[C] *4 sq units*

7. Which is more?

[A] (3 cups) or 1 pint   [C] 7 pints or (1 gallon)   [E] (3 gallons) or 10 quarts

[B] (3 pints) or 1 quart   [D] (1 pint) or 15 ounces   [F] (50 cups) or 3 gallons

Teaching Pages 322 and 323

- **PURPOSE**

  To provide a cumulative review of the material covered thus far in the text

  To provide review word problems

- **PREPARATION**

  Conduct a review of any algorithms with which the students have had difficulty in previous parts of the text. In particular, you might focus attention on finding the total amount when notation for money is used. You may choose to review the fact that the period, or dot, in money notation is to separate the dollars from the cents, but do

Add, subtract, multiply, or divide?

In these short-story problems no numbers are given. Use **A**, **S**, **M**, or **D** to tell which operation or operations (**A**ddition, **S**ubtraction, **M**ultiplication, **D**ivision) you would use to find the answers if numbers were given. For a problem where two operations, say addition and division, are needed, you would answer **A, D**.

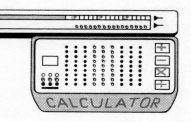

1. ▓ girls' bikes. ▓ boys' bikes. How many bikes? *A*

2. ▓ girls in the choir. ▓ moved away. How many girls in the choir now? *S*

3. Bob, ▓ years old. Don, ▓ years old. How much older is Bob than Don? *S*

4. ▓ girl-scout cookies in each box. ▓ boxes. How many cookies? *M*

5. Coin collection. ▓ coins in all. ▓ on each page. How many pages? *D*

6. Hiked ▓ miles in the morning, ▓ miles in the afternoon. How many miles? *A*

7. ▓ skirts. ▓ sweaters. How many different outfits? *M*

8. Butterfly collection. ▓ butterflies. ▓ boxes. How many in each box? *D*

9. Had ▓ baseball cards. Gave ▓ away. Bought ▓. How many cards now? *S, A*

10. ▓ boy scouts now. ▓ boy scouts needed for a full troop. How many more needed? *S*

11. ▓ nickels. How many cents? *M*

12. ▓ nickels. ▓ dimes. How many cents? *M, A*

13. ▓ large bottles of soda. ▓ ounces in each. ▓ small bottles of soda. ▓ ounces in each. How many ounces in all? *M, A*

14. Have ▓ cents. How many ▓ cent stamps can you buy? *D*

15. ▓ green marbles. ▓ red marbles. Each boy gets ▓ marbles. How many boys? *A, D*

Read the directions with the students and then instruct them to do the exercises. Some students may have difficulty arriving at an operation for exercise 7. This, of course, expresses the idea of product sets. With each skirt, the girl could wear one of her sweaters; hence, the idea of multiplication comes to mind with respect to this type of word problem. Note that in exercise 10, the students could say either addition or subtraction. That is, a student could think of a missing addend or he could simply think of a subtraction equation. Of course, either way of thinking should be counted as correct.

When the students have finished these exercises, be sure to allow time for discussion of each exercise. You might also give the students an opportunity to tell what they would add, subtract, multiply, and divide in these exercises.

not indicate anything concerning the meaning of the decimal point or of the relationship of this type of notation to rational-number notation.

For their work at this stage, the only thing the students need keep in mind is that it is convenient to line up the dots or periods separating the dollars and cents so that they can keep straight whether they are adding numbers that represent cents or adding numbers that represent dollars. Note that we speak of finding the total amount or the difference in the amounts rather than finding the sum or the difference. Addition and subtraction are operations reserved for numbers.

If time permits, have the students make up their own word problems for a given operation. You might have some students make up addition word problems; other

students, subtraction word problems; and so on. Ask the students to present their problems to the class for solving. Instruct the students to use small numbers so that their problems do not become too complicated. Should the students present some problems using large numbers, simply ask the students to decide what operation should be used to solve the problem and do not require that they do actual computing.

Give the students an opportunity to study the map. As an oral exercise, have them read from the map several distances between cities. Following this, have the students do the exercises.

Exercise 3 is starred since it is primarily for the more able students. When the explanation to this problem is given, note that the first leg of the trip is 300 miles; hence, Mr. Brown started either at St. Louis or at Chicago. In order to find out which city he started from, we must do the second part of the exercise and observe that on the second leg of his trip he traveled 272 miles; therefore, he must have started from St. Louis since the only 272-mile trip listed on the map is from Chicago to St. Louis.

As a follow-up activity to these exercises, you might have the students write problems of their own concerning some of the mileages given on the map.

Touring mileages

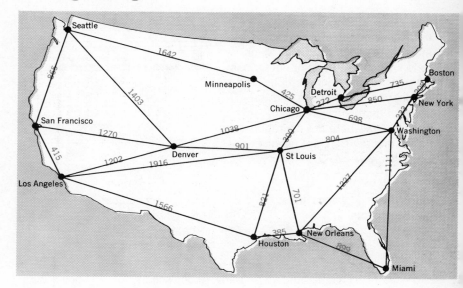

1. Give the total distance for each trip.
   [A] Chicago to New York to Boston *1058*
   [B] Los Angeles to Denver to Chicago to Detroit *2512*
   [C] Miami to Washington to New Orleans to Miami *3237*
   [D] San Francisco to Seattle to Minneapolis to Chicago *2932*
   [E] Houston to St. Louis to Chicago to Detroit to Boston *2128*
   [F] Seattle to Denver to St. Louis to New Orleans to Miami *3904*

2. Use the map to plan each of these trips for the smallest number of miles.
   [A] Denver to Washington *via St. Louis*   [D] Los Angeles to New York *via St. Louis, Wash.*
   [B] Chicago to Seattle *via Mpls.*   [E] Houston to Boston *via New Orleans, Wash., N.*
   [C] Miami to Chicago *via. Wash.*   [F] New Orleans to Seattle *via St. Louis, Denver*

★3. Mr. Brown had driven his new car 1247 miles before leaving for a trip. When he got to one of the cities on the map, he had driven his car a total of 1547 miles. He went from this city to another city on the map, and by then he had driven 1819 miles. From what city on the map did Mr. Brown start? *St. Louis*

Teaching Pages 324 and 325

● **PURPOSE**

To provide review word-problem experiences involving addition

To provide further practice in finding sums

● **PREPARATION**

Give the students further practice in working with the addition algorithm. It may be helpful to have several column-addition exercises presented on the chalkboard and explained by the students.

Airline distances

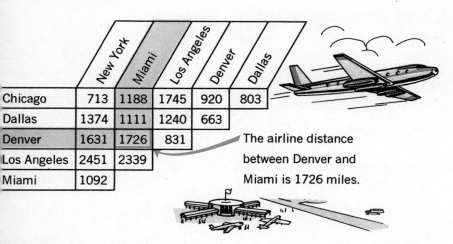

	New York	Miami	Los Angeles	Denver	Dallas
Chicago	713	1188	1745	920	803
Dallas	1374	1111	1240	663	
Denver	1631	1726	831		
Los Angeles	2451	2339			
Miami	1092				

The airline distance between Denver and Miami is 1726 miles.

EXERCISES

1. Use the chart to give the following airline distances.

[A] between Chicago and Denver *920*

[B] between New York and Dallas *1374*

[C] between Miami and Dallas *1111*

[D] between New York and Miami *1092*

[E] between Miami and Los Angeles *2339*

[F] between Chicago and Los Angeles *1745*

[G] between Denver and New York *1631*

[H] between Los Angeles and New York *2451*

2. How much farther is it from Chicago to Los Angeles than it is from Chicago to Denver? *825 mi*

3. A salesman flew from New York to Miami, then from Miami to Denver and from Denver back to New York. How far did he travel? *4449 mi*

4. An airliner made 7 round trips between Chicago and New York. How far did it fly? *9982 mph*

5. If a plane takes 3 hours to fly from Chicago to Miami, what is its average speed in miles per hour? *396 mph*

6. How much farther is it to go from Denver to Chicago to New York than it is to go from Denver to New York? *2 mi*

As you discuss the chart on the page, have the students explain how they read the chart in order to determine that the airline distance between Denver and Miami is 1726 miles. Elicit from the students that the blue tint on the row containing the name *Denver* and the blue tint on the column containing the name *Miami* meet at 1726, and this tells them the airline distance between Denver and Miami. Similarly other airline distances are found by looking for the intersection of a particular column and row. It might be helpful to have the students read one or two more airline distances from the chart before having them do the exercises.

Give the students an opportunity to do the exercises. When they have finished, allow time for discussion and checking papers. Although exercises 4, 5, and 6 are primarily for the more able students, you may want to have all the students participate in discussing the answers. Exercise 6 has been starred simply because it involves large numbers. Therefore, it is quite possible that the less able students will understand the problem, even though they may make a mistake in organizing the numbers or in performing the two operations necessary to find the answer.

Have the students do the exercises. If you use this as a test page, you will want to check the papers yourself. However, no matter how the page is used, you should allow time for discussion following the working of the page.

Chapter review

1. Match each set of fractions with a number-line picture.

   [A] $\{\frac{1}{8}, \frac{2}{16}, \frac{3}{24}, \frac{4}{32}, \ldots\}$ *2*

   [B] $\{\frac{3}{4}, \frac{6}{8}, \frac{9}{12}, \frac{12}{16}, \ldots\}$ *1*

   [C] $\{\frac{1}{4}, \frac{2}{8}, \frac{3}{12}, \frac{4}{16}, \ldots\}$ *4*

   [D] $\{\frac{2}{3}, \frac{4}{6}, \frac{6}{9}, \frac{8}{12}, \ldots\}$ *3*

   (1) [number line 0 to 1 with arrow near 3/4]

   (2) [number line 0 to 1 with arrow near 1/8]

   (3) [number line 0 to 1 with arrow near 2/3]

   (4) [number line 0 to 1 with arrow near 1/4]

2. Give the missing numerators and denominators.

   [A] $\frac{1}{2}=\frac{5}{}$ *10*   [C] $\frac{}{15}=\frac{1}{5}$ *3*   [E] $\frac{3}{4}=\frac{30}{}$ *40*   [G] $\frac{}{100}=30\%$ *30*   [I] $\frac{6}{7}=\frac{}{14}$

   [B] $\frac{4}{}=\frac{1}{3}$ *12*   [D] $\frac{1}{8}=\frac{}{40}$ *5*   [F] $\frac{}{50}=\frac{2}{5}$ *20*   [H] $\frac{2}{9}=\frac{}{36}$ *8*   [J] $\frac{5}{}=\frac{50}{80}$

3. Copy the number line on your paper and give the missing fractions. Use only lowest-terms fractions.

   [number line: 0 1/4 1/2 3/4 1 5/4 3/2 7/4 2 9/4 5/2 11/4 3 13/4 7/2 15/4 4]

4. Answer **T** (true) or **F** (false).

   [A] $\frac{1}{2}>50\%$ *F*   [B] $\frac{5}{8}>.5$ *T*   [C] $\frac{1}{4}<\frac{1}{3}$ *T*   [D] $\frac{3}{8}>\frac{3}{4}$ *F*   [E] $\frac{8}{3}<\frac{8}{2}$

5. Give a lowest-terms fraction or a whole number for each sum or difference.

   [A] $\frac{1}{2}+\frac{1}{2}$ *1*   [B] $\frac{1}{4}+\frac{1}{4}$ *½*   [C] $\frac{1}{4}+\frac{1}{2}$ *¾*   [D] $\frac{5}{6}-\frac{2}{6}$ *½*   [E] $\frac{7}{8}-\frac{1}{8}$ *¾*

6. Find each sum, difference, or product.

   [A] $5+\frac{1}{3}$ *5⅓*   [B] $\frac{1}{2}\times\frac{2}{3}$ *⅓*   [C] $\frac{2}{5}\times\frac{3}{4}$ *³/₁₀*   [D] $.3+.4$ *.7*   [E] $.9-.3$ *.6*

7. Give the correct sign (>, =, or <) for each ●.

   [A] 3 ● $3\frac{1}{4}$ *<*   [B] $2\frac{7}{8}$ ● 3 *<*   [C] $\frac{5}{4}$ ● $\frac{6}{4}$ *<*   [D] $\frac{5}{4}$ ● $\frac{5}{3}$ *<*

8. Give the length of the segment.

   6¾

   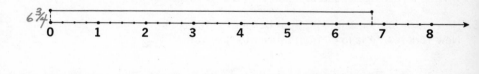

   [number line 0 to 8, segment from 0 to about 6¾]

Teaching Page 326

● **PURPOSE**

To provide a chapter review

To provide a sample evaluation instrument for this chapter

● **PREPARATION**

Review any topics with which the students have had difficulty in the chapter. In particular, review the rational number exercises in which the students were asked to associate exactly one number idea and one point on the number line with a given set of equivalent fractions.

Periodically throughout the year, you may find it helpful to have additional exercises to supplement those provided in the body of the text. Supplementary exercises have been prepared for key areas in the text and are found on pages 329 through 352. These same exercises, with answers printed in blue, are reproduced in this section of the manual. For your convenience in assigning the exercises throughout the year, each set of supplementary exercises bears two captions: one gives the page in the pupils' text after which the set may be used (a corresponding note appears in the page directions to refer you to sets that may be assigned), and the other describes the kinds of examples contained in each set.

Each set of supplementary exercises is divided into Part A and Part B, except those sets containing the basic facts (Sets 1, 2, 3, 4, 38, and 40) and reconstructions (Sets 34 and 35) and Sets 53 and 55. Answers in code are given for Part A at the end of the set in the pupils' text and also in the Teachers' Edition. The code for deciphering the answers is given only in the Teachers' Edition. There are nine different codes, in which the digits are represented by letters of the alphabet. For example, if a coded answer is CA, and C is 2 and A is 5, then the answer is 25. For a specific example, see Set 20, exercise 3(d). The pupil is given the coded answer BJHD for this problem, using the code given in the Teachers' Edition,

A	B	C	D	E	F	G	H	I	J
5	1	3	7	0	9	8	4	2	6

you decipher BJHD as 1647.

The use of coded answers makes it possible for pupils to check their work for Part A before proceeding to Part B. Since pupils can receive immediate feedback regarding the correctness of their work, the harm that can come from practicing incorrect procedures is considerably reduced.

We recommend using the code in the following ways: (1) Copy on the chalkboard the appropriate deciphering code from the Teachers' Edition and have the students check the answer to each exercise in Part A as soon as they have obtained it. (2) Assign Part A without giving out the deciphering code and let the students use their answers and the coded answers to try to discover what the code is. This will provide an interesting break for the students.

Although each set of supplementary exercises is marked with the page in the text after which it can be used, do not assign all of the supplementary exercises immediately following that page. Instead, plan your assignments of supplementary exercises in such a way that the practice will be distributed, throughout the remaining use of the text, only as necessary for review and maintenance of skills and abilities. You should also make sure that the students will clearly benefit from the extra practice and that these exercises are not assigned until the prerequisite material in the text has been carefully introduced, developed, and mastered. The supplementary exercises may also be used as diagnostic test material and as review exercises.

Supplementary Exercises

Set 1 *For use after page 35* — Addition facts: sums 10 or less

	a	b	c	d	e	f	g	h	i	j
1.	0 +1 = 1	3 +5 = 8	0 +3 = 3	1 +2 = 3	0 +4 = 4	1 +5 = 6	4 +2 = 6	4 +1 = 5	6 +2 = 8	5 +0 = 5
2.	2 +4 = 6	0 +2 = 2	7 +0 = 7	6 +1 = 7	0 +6 = 6	1 +7 = 8	7 +1 = 8	9 +0 = 9	2 +1 = 3	1 +3 = 4
3.	2 +6 = 8	2 +5 = 7	4 +4 = 8	1 +8 = 9	2 +0 = 2	0 +5 = 5	5 +3 = 8	2 +2 = 4	0 +7 = 7	3 +3 = 6
4.	3 +4 = 7	1 +1 = 2	0 +8 = 8	1 +6 = 7	3 +6 = 9	5 +2 = 7	8 +1 = 9	0 +0 = 0	3 +0 = 3	2 +7 = 9
5.	6 +3 = 9	7 +2 = 9	8 +0 = 8	1 +4 = 5	3 +2 = 5	4 +5 = 9	3 +1 = 4	1 +0 = 1	0 +9 = 9	4 +3 = 7
6.	5 +4 = 9	4 +0 = 4	5 +1 = 6	2 +3 = 5	6 +0 = 6	9 +1 = 10	2 +8 = 10	7 +3 = 10	4 +6 = 10	5 +5 = 10

Set 2 *For use after page 38* — Addition facts: sums 10–18

	a	b	c	d	e	f	g	h	i	j
1.	9 +2 = 11	3 +7 = 10	6 +5 = 11	8 +4 = 12	6 +6 = 12	4 +9 = 13	1 +9 = 10	6 +4 = 10	8 +6 = 14	9 +4 = 13
2.	9 +3 = 12	8 +2 = 10	2 +9 = 11	5 +7 = 12	6 +8 = 14	8 +7 = 15	9 +8 = 17	8 +3 = 11	7 +4 = 11	5 +9 = 14
3.	7 +7 = 14	9 +5 = 14	5 +6 = 11	3 +9 = 12	7 +8 = 15	8 +9 = 17	9 +7 = 16	4 +7 = 11	9 +9 = 18	7 +9 = 16
4.	8 +8 = 16	7 +6 = 13	3 +8 = 11	5 +8 = 13	6 +9 = 15	4 +8 = 12	6 +7 = 13	9 +6 = 15	8 +5 = 13	7 +5 = 12

Set 3   *For use after page 35*

Subtraction facts: differences related to sums 10 or less

	a	b	c	d	e	f	g	h	i	j
1.	3 −0 *3*	5 −1 *4*	8 −7 *1*	4 −4 *0*	1 −0 *1*	2 −2 *0*	2 −1 *1*	8 −2 *6*	3 −2 *1*	7 −5 *2*
2.	6 −6 *0*	6 −4 *2*	2 −0 *2*	1 −1 *0*	4 −3 *1*	7 −1 *6*	4 −2 *2*	5 −0 *5*	8 −8 *0*	6 −2 *4*
3.	3 −1 *2*	4 −0 *4*	7 −7 *0*	7 −6 *1*	4 −1 *3*	7 −2 *5*	6 −3 *3*	9 −4 *5*	8 −6 *2*	9 −7 *2*
4.	8 −1 *7*	9 −2 *7*	5 −3 *2*	3 −3 *0*	6 −1 *5*	7 −0 *7*	5 −4 *1*	8 −0 *8*	8 −5 *3*	9 −9 *0*
5.	9 −5 *4*	6 −5 *1*	9 −3 *6*	9 −6 *3*	0 −0 *0*	9 −8 *1*	5 −2 *3*	9 −1 *8*	8 −3 *5*	5 −5 *0*
6.	9 −0 *9*	7 −4 *3*	7 −3 *4*	6 −0 *6*	8 −4 *4*	10 −9 *1*	10 −2 *8*	10 −7 *3*	10 −4 *6*	10 −5 *5*

Set 4   *For use after page 41*

Subtraction facts: differences related to sums 10–18

	a	b	c	d	e	f	g	h	i	j
1.	14 −7 *7*	10 −6 *4*	13 −8 *5*	11 −8 *3*	12 −9 *3*	15 −7 *9*	13 −4 *9*	11 −2 *9*	10 −1 *9*	11 −3 *8*
2.	10 −3 *7*	11 −7 *4*	11 −9 *2*	10 −8 *2*	11 −4 *7*	12 −3 *9*	13 −5 *8*	14 −6 *8*	15 −8 *7*	17 −9 *8*
3.	12 −7 *5*	12 −8 *4*	11 −6 *5*	12 −5 *7*	13 −7 *6*	13 −9 *4*	12 −6 *6*	14 −5 *9*	18 −9 *9*	14 −9 *5*
4.	11 −5 *6*	15 −6 *9*	12 −4 *8*	16 −8 *8*	13 −6 *7*	16 −7 *9*	14 −8 *6*	16 −9 *7*	17 −8 *9*	15 −9 *6*

A

	a	b	c	d	e	f	g	h	i	j
1.	4 1 +2 *7*	2 4 +3 *9*	1 5 +2 *8*	2 5 +3 *10*	3 1 +0 *4*	6 2 +2 *10*	5 1 +2 *8*	3 1 +6 *10*	4 3 +2 *9*	3 4 +3 *10*
2.	6 2 +4 *12*	3 7 +6 *16*	5 3 +5 *13*	2 6 +8 *16*	9 4 +1 *14*	7 3 +7 *17*	2 8 +8 *18*	4 7 +6 *17*	5 5 +9 *19*	8 2 +5 *15*

B

	a	b	c	d	e	f	g	h	i	j
1.	5 2 +1 *8*	1 5 +1 *7*	2 3 +4 *9*	2 1 +7 *10*	3 0 +5 *8*	1 6 +2 *9*	5 3 +2 *10*	3 2 +2 *7*	6 3 +0 *9*	2 4 +2 *8*
2.	6 4 +3 *13*	7 3 +6 *16*	9 1 +8 *18*	2 8 +7 *17*	5 5 +4 *14*	6 8 +2 *16*	7 2 +3 *12*	1 5 +9 *15*	8 9 +2 *19*	5 8 +5 *18*

CODED ANSWERS, SET 5, PART A: 1. (a) D, (b) E, (c) G, (d) AF, (e) I, (f) AF, (g) G, (h) AF, (i) E, (j) AF; **2.** (a) AJ, (b) AH, (c) AB, (d) AH, (e) AI, (f) AD, (g) AG, (h) AD, (i) AE, (j) AC

CODE:
A	B	C	D	E	F	G	H	I	J
1	3	5	7	9	0	8	6	4	2

A

	a	b	c
1.	$2+5+3=$ *10*	$6+2+4=$ *12*	$3+2+9=$ *14*
2.	$3+4+6=$ *13*	$5+9+5=$ *19*	$6+7+4=$ *17*
3.	$5+7+6=$ *18*	$9+6+3=$ *18*	$8+7+2=$ *17*
4.	$9+4+1+3=$ *17*	$6+2+4+8=$ *20*	$2+7+8+1=$ *18*
5.	$8+4+2+6=$ *20*	$5+3+4+3=$ *15*	$1+0+6+8=$ *15*

B

	a	b	c
1.	$3+4+1=$ *9*	$5+4+1=$ *10*	$4+3+5=$ *12*
2.	$6+3+6=$ *15*	$4+8+4=$ *16*	$2+8+7=$ *17*
3.	$5+8+0=$ *13*	$6+7+4=$ *17*	$6+6+3=$ *15*
4.	$3+2+4+1=$ *10*	$5+4+5+5=$ *19*	$8+7+2+1=$ *18*
5.	$9+1+6+1=$ *17*	$8+3+2+3=$ *16*	$9+6+3+0=$ *18*

CODED ANSWERS, SET 6, PART A: 1. (a) DE, (b) DA, (c) DJ; **2.** (a) DB, (b) DC, (c) DG; **3.** (a) DI, (b) DI, (c) DG; **4.** (a) DG, (b) AE, (c) DI; **5.** (a) AE, (b) DH, (c) DH

CODE:
A	B	C	D	E	F	G	H	I	J
2	3	9	1	0	6	7	5	8	4

Set 7 *For use after page 41* Addition and subtraction equations

A

	a	**b**	**c**	**d**
1.	$5 + \boxed{n} = 9$ *4*	$9 = \boxed{n} - 4$ *13*	$\boxed{n} + 2 = 11$ *9*	$12 - \boxed{n} = 6$ *6*
2.	$5 + 9 = \boxed{n}$ *14*	$15 - 7 = \boxed{n}$ *8*	$9 = \boxed{n} - 6$ *15*	$7 = 15 - \boxed{n}$ *8*

B

	a	**b**	**c**	**d**
1.	$\boxed{n} + 3 = 7$ *4*	$14 = 9 + \boxed{n}$ *5*	$15 - 9 = \boxed{n}$ *6*	$8 + 5 = \boxed{n}$ *13*
2.	$13 - \boxed{n} = 8$ *5*	$\boxed{n} - 3 = 10$ *13*	$\boxed{n} = 16 - 7$ *9*	$8 = 14 - \boxed{n}$ *6*

CODED ANSWERS, SET 7, PART A: **1.** (a) C, (b) AI, (c) G, (d) F; **2.** (a) AC, (b) D, (c) AH, (d) D

CODE: A B C D E F G H I J
       1 0 4 8 7 6 9 5 3 2

Set 8 *For use after page 47* 2-digit addend plus a 1-digit addend, no carrying

A

	a	**b**	**c**	**d**	**e**	**f**	**g**	**h**	**i**
1.	16 +2 = *18*	13 +5 = *18*	4 +14 = *18*	11 +7 = *18*	23 +4 = *27*	5 +31 = *36*	56 +3 = *59*	37 +2 = *39*	7 +52 = *59*

	a	**b**	**c**	**d**
2.	$35 + 4 = \boxed{n}$ *39*	$27 + 0 = \boxed{n}$ *27*	$5 + 23 = \boxed{n}$ *28*	$20 + 8 = \boxed{n}$ *28*

B

	a	**b**	**c**	**d**	**e**	**f**	**g**	**h**	**i**
1.	13 +4 = *17*	12 +7 = *19*	12 +3 = *15*	4 +15 = *19*	26 +3 = *29*	51 +4 = *55*	37 +1 = *38*	84 +4 = *88*	72 +5 = *77*

	a	**b**	**c**	**d**
2.	$33 + 4 = \boxed{n}$ *37*	$55 + 4 = \boxed{n}$ *59*	$54 + 5 = \boxed{n}$ *59*	$98 + 1 = \boxed{n}$ *99*

CODED ANSWERS, SET 8, PART A: **1.** (a) EI, (b) EI, (c) EI, (d) EI, (e) AB, (f) CD, (g) HF, (h) CF, (i) HF; **2.** (a) CF, (b) AB, (c) AI, (d) AI

CODE: A B C D E F G H I J
       2 7 3 6 1 9 4 5 8 0

Set 9 *For use after page 57* Addend a multiple of 10, no carrying

A

	a	**b**	**c**	**d**	**e**	**f**	**g**	**h**	**i**
1.	20 +40 = *60*	30 +30 = *60*	50 +20 = *70*	30 +60 = *90*	10 +40 = *50*	30 +40 = *70*	70 +20 = *90*	40 +40 = *80*	90 +10 = *100*

	a	**b**	**c**	**d**
2.	$30 + 80 = \boxed{n}$ *110*	$90 + 60 = \boxed{n}$ *150*	$70 + 60 = \boxed{n}$ *130*	$60 + 40 = \boxed{n}$ *100*

B

	a	**b**	**c**	**d**	**e**	**f**	**g**	**h**	**i**
1.	30 +50 = *80*	10 +20 = *30*	60 +20 = *80*	80 +10 = *90*	60 +30 = *90*	20 +50 = *70*	50 +50 = *100*	40 +20 = *60*	50 +40 = *90*

	a	**b**	**c**	**d**
2.	$60 + 50 = \boxed{n}$ *110*	$70 + 60 = \boxed{n}$ *130*	$40 + 90 = \boxed{n}$ *130*	$60 + 80 = \boxed{n}$ *140*

CODED ANSWERS, SET 9, PART A: **1.** (a) DA, (b) DA, (c) GA, (d) FA, (e) HA, (f) GA, (g) FA, (h) EA, (i) JAA; **2.** (a) JJA, (b) JHA, (c) JIA, (d) JAA

CODE: A B C D E F G H I J
       0 2 4 6 8 9 7 5 3 1

Set 10 *For use after page 57*   Column addition: addends a multiple of 10, no carrying

A
a	b	c	d	e	f	g	h	i
1. 30	50	60	40	90	60	80	90	90
20	40	40	30	40	50	70	60	20
+40	+30	+70	+80	+30	+40	+30	+10	+80
90	120	170	150	160	150	180	160	190

a	b	c	d
2. $50+20+10=$ 80	$40+30+30=$ 100	$80+40+20=$ 140	$60+70+70=$ 200

B
a	b	c	d	e	f	g	h	i
1. 20	60	30	10	50	40	20	30	80
10	20	30	80	40	50	60	70	60
+50	+20	+70	+90	+50	+70	+50	+90	+60
80	100	130	180	140	160	130	190	200

2. $50+60+20=$ 130 $60+50+40=$ 150 $80+70+50=$ 200 $90+20+90=$ 200

CODED ANSWERS, SET 10, PART A: 1. (a) IB, (b) ECB, (c) EFB, (d) EDB, (e) EAB, (f) EDB, (g) EGB, (h) EAB, (i) EIB; **2.** (a) GB, (b) EBB, (c) EJB, (d) CBB

CODE: A B C D E F G H I J
       6 0 2 5 1 7 8 3 9 4

Set 11 *For use after page 59*   2-digit addends, no carrying

A
a	b	c	d	e	f	g	h	i
30	37	50	32	24	35	61	25	11
+46	+22	+27	+56	+63	+54	+18	+42	+62
76	59	77	88	87	89	79	67	73

B
a	b	c	d	e	f	g	h	i
31	45	18	12	37	49	20	80	42
+24	+31	+51	+86	+61	+40	+68	+13	+46
55	76	69	98	98	89	88	93	88

CODED ANSWERS, SET 11, PART A: (a) DJ, (b) AF, (c) DD, (d) GG, (e) GD, (f) GF, (g) DF, (h) JD, (i) DC

CODE: A B C D E F G H I J
       5 1 3 7 0 9 8 4 2 6

Set 12 *For use after page 60*   3-digit addends, no carrying

A
a	b	c	d	e	f	g	h
432	507	326	856	750	513	472	635
+264	+462	+453	+133	+108	+264	+516	+344
696	969	779	989	858	777	988	979

B
a	b	c	d	e	f	g	h
238	340	279	345	718	256	808	456
+421	+640	+420	+534	+271	+623	+190	+522
659	980	699	879	989	879	998	978

CODED ANSWERS, SET 12, PART A: (a) BGB, (b) GBG, (c) FFG, (d) GIG, (e) IDI, (f) FFF, (g) GII, (h) GFG

CODE: A B C D E F G H I J
       4 6 0 5 2 7 9 1 8 3

Set 13 *For use after page 60* 2-digit addends, 3-digit sums

A	a	b	c	d	e	f	g	h
	36	27	13	45	34	72	73	51
	+92	+81	+94	+84	+74	+66	+73	+75
	128	*108*	*107*	*129*	*108*	*138*	*146*	*126*
B	24	76	64	83	91	72	94	82
	+85	+32	+85	+76	+67	+97	+94	+95
	109	*108*	*149*	*159*	*158*	*169*	*188*	*177*

CODED ANSWERS, SET 13, PART A: (a) EIH, (b) EDH, (c) EDC, (d) EIJ, (e) EDH, (f) EAH, (g) EFG, (h) EIG

CODE: A B C D E F G H I J
        3 5 7 0 1 4 6 8 2 9

Set 14 *For use after page 62* Subtraction: 1-digit from 2-digit numbers, no borrowing

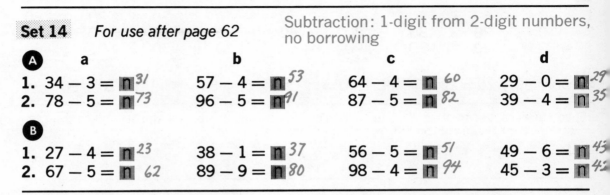

A   a   b   c   d

1. $34 - 3 =$ ▣ *31* $57 - 4 =$ ▣ *53* $64 - 4 =$ ▣ *60* $29 - 0 =$ ▣ *29*
2. $78 - 5 =$ ▣ *73* $96 - 5 =$ ▣ *91* $87 - 5 =$ ▣ *82* $39 - 4 =$ ▣ *35*

B

1. $27 - 4 =$ ▣ *23* $38 - 1 =$ ▣ *37* $56 - 5 =$ ▣ *51* $49 - 6 =$ ▣ *43*
2. $67 - 5 =$ ▣ *62* $89 - 9 =$ ▣ *80* $98 - 4 =$ ▣ *94* $45 - 3 =$ ▣ *42*

CODED ANSWERS, SET 14, PART A: 1. (a) BA, (b) CB, (c) HF, (d) JE; 2. (a) DB, (b) EA, (c) GJ, (d) BC

CODE: A B C D E F G H I J
        1 3 5 7 9 0 8 6 4 2

Set 15 *For use after page 63* Subtraction: 2-digit numbers, no borrowing

A	a	b	c	d	e	f	g	h	i
	43	60	67	59	47	56	83	90	46
	−10	−20	−30	−32	−13	−20	−40	−50	−41
	33	*40*	*37*	*27*	*34*	*36*	*43*	*40*	*5*
B	68	70	49	94	90	68	78	93	68
	−30	−40	−30	−20	−20	−33	−52	−53	−62
	38	*30*	*19*	*74*	*70*	*35*	*26*	*40*	*6*

CODED ANSWERS, SET 15, PART A: (a) BB, (b) JE, (c) BG, (d) AG, (e) BJ, (f) BF, (g) JB, (h) JE, (i) H

CODE: A B C D E F G H I J
        2 3 9 1 0 6 7 5 8 4

Set 16 *For use after page 63* Subtraction: 3-digit numbers, no borrowing

A	a	b	c	d	e	f	g	h
	460	463	872	768	952	638	846	794
	−150	−322	−541	−306	−340	−414	−313	−510
	310	*141*	*331*	*462*	*612*	*224*	*533*	*284*
B	390	576	898	792	856	984	649	977
	−240	−215	−344	−410	−313	−753	−132	−377
	150	*361*	*554*	*382*	*543*	*231*	*517*	*600*

CODED ANSWERS, SET 16, PART A: (a) IAB, (b) ACA, (c) IIA, (d) CFJ, (e) FAJ (f) JJC, (g) HII, (h) JDC

CODE: A B C D E F G H I J
        1 0 4 8 7 6 9 5 3 2

A

	a	b	c	d
1.	$64 + 3 = n$ *67*	$35 + 4 = n$ *39*	$30 + 6 = n$ *36*	$22 + 4 = n$ *26*
2.	$62 + n = 68$	$73 + n = 78$	*5* $n + 44 = 49$	*8* $n + 71 = 79$
3.	$72 + 8 = n$ *80*	$56 + 4 = n$ *60*	$83 + 7 = n$ *90*	*5* $n + 45 = 50$
4.	$47 + 9 = n$ *56*	$8 + 53 = n$ *61*	$6 + 86 = n$ *92*	$37 + 8 = n$ *45*
5.	*42* $n = 33 + 9$	*62* $n = 54 + 8$	$76 + 9 = n$ *85*	*47* $n = 39 + 8$
6.	$68 + 8 = n$ *76*	*103* $n = 94 + 9$	$17 + 9 = n$ *26*	$46 + 5 = n$ *51*

B

	a	b	c	d
1.	$36 + 3 = n$ *39*	$47 + 2 = n$ *49*	$50 + 7 = n$ *57*	$38 + 1 = n$ *39*
2.	$32 + n = 38$	$24 + n = 29$	*4* $n + 54 = 58$	*8* $n + 31 = 39$
3.	$58 + 2 = n$ *60*	$37 + 3 = n$ *40*	$84 + 6 = n$ *90*	*5* $n + 65 = 70$
4.	$56 + 9 = n$ *65*	$67 + 4 = n$ *71*	$5 + 39 = n$ *44*	$56 + 8 = n$ *64*
5.	*51* $n = 43 + 8$	*93* $n = 86 + 7$	$45 + 8 = n$ *53*	*92* $n = 84 + 8$
6.	$47 + 7 = n$ *54*	*94* $n = 85 + 9$	$19 + 6 = n$ *25*	$29 + 7 = n$ *36*

CODED ANSWERS, SET 17, PART A: 1. (a) DB, (b) CF, (c) CD, (d) AD; **2.** (a) D, (b) H, (c) H, (d) I; **3.** (a) IJ, (b) DJ, (c) FJ, (d) H; **4.** (a) HD, (b) DE, (c) FA, (d) GH; **5.** (a) GA, (b) DA, (c) IH, (d) GB; **6.** (a) BD, (b) EJC, (c) AD, (d) HE

CODE: A B C D E F G H I J
        2 7 3 6 1 9 4 5 8 0

Set 18 *For use after page 67*   Addition equations

A

	a	b	c	d
1.	$46 + n = 51$ *5*	$83 = 75 + n$ *8*	$96 = 9 + n$ *87*	$34 = n + 25$ *9*
2.	$176 + 4 = n$ *180*	$324 + 8 = n$ *332*	$657 + 9 = n$ *666*	$432 + 9 = n$ *441*
3.	$7 + 366 = n$ *373*	$9 + 238 = n$ *247*	*661* $n = 657 + 4$	*351* $n = 8 + 343$
4.	$434 + 9 = n$ *443*	$7 + 367 = n$ *374*	$n = 847 + 6$ *853*	$369 + 5 = n$ *374*
5.	$630 + 10 = n$ *640*	$586 + 6 = n$ *592*	$987 + 8 = n$ *995*	$683 + 8 = n$ *691*
6.	$867 + n = 871$ *4*	$934 + n = 942$ *8*	$586 = 578 + n$ *8*	$947 = n + 938$ *9*

B

	a	b	c	d
1.	$54 + n = 61$ *7*	$95 = 87 + n$ *8*	$47 = 9 + n$ *38*	$68 = n + 59$ *9*
2.	$187 + 5 = n$ *192*	$356 + 8 = n$ *364*	$477 + 7 = n$ *484*	$369 + 9 = n$ *378*
3.	$3 + 428 = n$ *431*	$972 + 9 = n$ *981*	$8 + 367 = n$ *375*	$9 + 485 = n$ *494*
4.	*877* $n = 868 + 9$	*752* $n = 742 + 10$	$867 + 9 = n$ *876*	$3 + 239 = n$ *242*
5.	*75* $n = 744 + 8$	$637 + 6 = n$ *643*	$896 + 7 = n$ *903*	*993* $n = 988 + 5$
6.	$563 + n = 572$ *9*	*7* $n + 638 = 647$	$892 + 9 = n$ *901*	$977 + n = 983$ *6*

CODED ANSWERS, SET 18, PART A: 1. (a) H, (b) E, (c) EG, (d) F; **2.** (a) JEA, (b) IIB, (c) DDD, (d) CCJ; **3.** (a) IGI, (b) BCG, (c) DDJ, (d) IHJ; **4.** (a) CCI, (b) IGC, (c) EHI, (d) IGC; **5.** (a) DCA, (b) HFB, (c) FFH, (d) DFJ; **6.** (a) C, (b) E, (c) E, (d) F

CODE: A B C D E F G H I J
        0 2 4 6 8 9 7 5 3 1

Set 19   *For use after page 69*   1-digit addend plus a 2-digit addend, carrying

A

	a	b	c	d	e	f	g	h	i
1.	37 +8	56 +26	87 +36	43 +9	68 +24	76 +76	58 +4	47 +17	56 +79
	45	82	123	52	92	152	62	64	135
2.	22 +9	68 +26	85 +79	67 +5	14 +69	58 +69	59 +4	18 +79	44 +66
	31	94	164	72	83	127	63	97	110

B

	a	b	c	d	e	f	g	h	i
1.	26 +6	54 +29	45 +98	54 +6	37 +38	66 +78	38 +4	29 +19	38 +97
	32	83	143	60	75	144	42	48	135
2.	73 +8	69 +25	76 +74	86 +5	48 +46	75 +99	67 +8	77 +19	89 +56
	81	94	150	91	94	174	75	96	145

CODED ANSWERS, SET 19, PART A: **1.** (a) JD, (b) GC, (c) ECH, (d) DC, (e) IC, (f) EDC, (g) AC, (h) AJ, (i) EHD; **2.** (a) HE, (b) IJ, (c) EAJ, (d) FC, (e) GH, (f) ECF, (g) AH, (h) IF, (i) EEB

CODE:
A	B	C	D	E	F	G	H	I	J
6	0	2	5	1	7	8	3	9	4

Set 20   *For use after page 69*   3-digit addends, carrying

A

	a	b	c	d	e	f	g	h
1.	326 +468	534 +259	421 +309	319 +146	573 +152	390 +469	376 +452	293 +486
	794	793	730	465	725	859	828	779
2.	467 +368	379 +123	378 +147	638 +287	456 +269	289 +376	193 +537	329 +396
	835	502	525	925	725	665	730	725

	a	b	c	d
3.	536 + 587 = 1123	947 + 589 = 1536	654 + 878 = 1532	948 + 699 = 1647
4.	677 + 388 = 1065	666 + 666 = 1332	385 + 769 = 1154	562 + 949 = 1511

B

	a	b	c	d	e	f	g	h
1.	629 +153	406 +279	384 +455	293 +563	425 +395	157 +285	476 +389	748 +197
	782	685	839	856	820	442	865	945
2.	763 +578	637 +895	666 +444	858 +564	647 +886	123 +998	746 +368	578 +839
	1341	1532	1110	1422	1533	1121	1114	1417

CODED ANSWERS, SET 20, PART A: **1.** (a) DFH, (b) DFC, (c) DCE, (d) HJA, (e) DIA, (f) GAF, (g) GIG, (h) DDF; **2.** (a) GCA, (b) AEI, (c) AIA, (d) FIA, (e) DIA, (f) JJA, (g) DCE, (h) DIA; **3.** (a) BBIC, (b) BACJ, (c) BACI, (d) BJHD; **4.** (a) BEJA, (b) BCCI, (c) BBAH, (d) BABB

CODE:
A	B	C	D	E	F	G	H	I	J
5	1	3	7	0	9	8	4	2	6

A

a	b	c	d
1. $54 - 3 = \blacksquare$ *57*	$68 - 5 = \blacksquare$ *63*	$37 - 6 = \blacksquare$ *31*	$45 - 0 = \blacksquare$ *45*
2. $40 - 2 = \blacksquare$ *38*	$20 - 4 = \blacksquare$ *16*	$80 - 3 = \blacksquare$ *77*	$90 - 6 = \blacksquare$ *84*
3. $42 - 4 = \blacksquare$ *38*	$61 - 2 = \blacksquare$ *59*	$32 - 3 = \blacksquare$ *29*	$24 - 6 = \blacksquare$ *18*
4. $56 - 8 = \blacksquare$ *48*	$74 - 9 = \blacksquare$ *65*	$37 - 8 = \blacksquare$ *29*	$22 - 7 = \blacksquare$ *15*
5. $67 - 8 = \blacksquare$ *59*	$45 - 9 = \blacksquare$ *36*	$36 - 8 = \blacksquare$ *28*	$54 - 7 = \blacksquare$ *47*
6. $54 - \blacksquare^{3} = 51$	$65 - \blacksquare^{2} = 63$	$37 - \blacksquare^{5} = 32$	$46 - \blacksquare^{5} = 41$

B

a	b	c	d
1. $87 - 4 = \blacksquare$ *83*	$56 - 6 = \blacksquare$ *50*	$98 - 3 = \blacksquare$ *95*	$66 - 5 = \blacksquare$ *61*
2. $60 - 1 = \blacksquare$ *59*	$50 - 3 = \blacksquare$ *47*	$70 - 5 = \blacksquare$ *65*	$40 - 8 = \blacksquare$ *32*
3. $31 - 2 = \blacksquare$ *29*	$73 - 5 = \blacksquare$ *68*	$84 - 5 = \blacksquare$ *79*	$17 - 9 = \blacksquare$ *8*
4. $64 - 9 = \blacksquare$ *55*	$72 - 7 = \blacksquare$ *65*	$43 - 6 = \blacksquare$ *37*	$56 - 9 = \blacksquare$ *47*
5. $95 - 6 = \blacksquare$ *89*	$96 - 5 = \blacksquare$ *91*	$84 - 7 = \blacksquare$ *77*	$76 - 7 = \blacksquare$ *69*
6. $47 - \blacksquare = 42$ *5*	$56 - \blacksquare = 50$ *6*	$65 - \blacksquare = 64$ *1*	$78 - \blacksquare = 78$ *0*

CODED ANSWERS, SET 21, PART A: **1.** (a) DH, (b) BJ, (c) JH, (d) AD; **2.** (a) JI, (b) HB, (c) FF, (d) IA; **3.** (a) JI, (b) DG, (c) EG, (d) HI; **4.** (a) AI, (b) BD, (c) EG, (d) HD; **5.** (a) DG, (b) JB, (c) EI, (d) AF; **6.** (a) J, (b) E, (c) D, (d) D

CODE: A   B   C   D   E   F   G   H   I   J
       4   6   0   5   2   7   9   8   1   3

A

a	b	c	d
1. $56 - \blacksquare^{7} = 49$	$42 - \blacksquare^{4} = 38$	$73 - \blacksquare^{6} = 67$	$85 - \blacksquare^{9} = 76$
2. $139 - 4 = \blacksquare$ *135*	$537 - 6 = \blacksquare$ *531*	$965 - 2 = \blacksquare$ *963*	$879 - 3 = \blacksquare$ *876*
3. $564 - 6 = \blacksquare$ *558*	$713 - 9 = \blacksquare$ *704*	$675 - 7 = \blacksquare$ *668*	$863 - 8 = \blacksquare$ *855*
4. $416 - \blacksquare^{2} = 414$	$537 - \blacksquare^{3} = 534$	$879 - \blacksquare^{6} = 873$	$465 - \blacksquare^{4} = 461$
5. $586 - 9 = \blacksquare$ *577*	$374 - \blacksquare^{8} = 366$	$657 - 8 = \blacksquare$ *649*	$876 - \blacksquare^{9} = 867$
6. $43 - 39 = \blacksquare$ *4*	$52 - 48 = \blacksquare$ *4*	$63 - 59 = \blacksquare$ *4*	$86 - 78 = \blacksquare$ *8*

B

a	b	c	d
1. $22 - \blacksquare^{5} = 17$	$35 - \blacksquare^{6} = 29$	$64 - \blacksquare^{7} = 57$	$56 - \blacksquare^{9} = 47$
2. $167 - 3 = \blacksquare$ *164*	$365 - 2 = \blacksquare$ *363*	$977 - 5 = \blacksquare$ *972*	$839 - 3 = \blacksquare$ *836*
3. $376 - 8 = \blacksquare$ *368*	$427 - 8 = \blacksquare$ *419*	$568 - 9 = \blacksquare$ *559*	$327 - 7 = \blacksquare$ *320*
4. $236 - \blacksquare^{6} = 230$	$329 - \blacksquare^{7} = 322$	$465 - \blacksquare^{0} = 465$	$827 - \blacksquare^{6} = 821$
5. $347 - 9 = \blacksquare$ *338*	$763 - \blacksquare^{7} = 756$	$465 - 7 = \blacksquare$ *458*	$863 - \blacksquare^{9} = 854$
6. $32 - 29 = \blacksquare$ *3*	$43 - 26 = \blacksquare$ *17*	$55 - 49 = \blacksquare$ *6*	$66 - 58 = \blacksquare$ *8*

CODED ANSWERS, SET 22, PART A: **1.** (a) C, (b) F, (c) G, (d) J; **2.** (a) EAB, (b) BAE, (c) JGA, (d) HCG; **3.** (a) BBH, (b) CDF, (c) GGH, (d) HBB; **4.** (a) I, (b) A, (c) G, (d) F; **5.** (a) BCC, (b) H, (c) GFJ, (d) J; **6.** (a) F, (b) F, (c) F, (d) H

CODE: A   B   C   D   E   F   G   H   I   J
       3   5   7   0   1   4   6   8   2   9

Set 23 *For use after page 74*

A

	a	b	c	d	e	f	g	h	i
1.	32 −8 = 24	51 −9 = 42	36 −8 = 28	22 −5 = 77	47 −8 = 39	83 −9 = 74	91 −3 = 88	44 −7 = 37	65 −7 = 58
2.	73 −27 = 46	42 −15 = 27	75 −39 = 36	60 −54 = 6	34 −28 = 6	26 −17 = 9	58 −29 = 29	97 −68 = 29	80 −47 = 33

B

	a	b	c	d	e	f	g	h	i
1.	30 −6 = 24	41 −8 = 33	66 −7 = 59	84 −8 = 76	40 −2 = 38	73 −4 = 69	57 −8 = 49	92 −5 = 87	32 −5 = 27
2.	53 −18 = 35	71 −42 = 29	84 −29 = 55	36 −18 = 18	97 −49 = 48	86 −29 = 57	57 −28 = 29	43 −17 = 26	94 −35 = 59
3.	82 −76 = 6	92 −66 = 26	63 −45 = 18	40 −29 = 11	81 −12 = 69	65 −39 = 26	88 −19 = 69	76 −37 = 39	57 −28 = 25

CODED ANSWERS, SET 23, PART A: 1. (a) JI, (b) IJ, (c) JG, (d) AD, (e) BE, (f) DI, (g) GG, (h) BD, (i) CG; **2.** (a) IH, (b) JD, (c) BH, (d) H, (e) H, (f) E, (g) JE, (h) JE, (i) BB

CODE: A B C D E F G H I J
      1 3 5 7 9 0 8 6 4 2

Set 24 *For use after page 76*

Find the difference of the amounts given and check your work.

A

	a	b	c	d	e	f	g
1.	$8.56 3.21 = $5.35	$7.74 4.53 = $3.21	$4.83 4.53 = $.30	$3.90 1.30 = $2.60	$6.38 .24 = $6.14	$9.74 4.34 = $5.40	$5.36 1.15 = $4.21
2.	$6.72 1.37 = $5.35	$8.65 2.26 = $6.39	$9.44 7.19 = $2.25	$4.36 .84 = $3.52	$7.29 4.93 = $2.36	$6.14 .39 = $5.75	$5.26 2.57 = $2.69

B

	a	b	c	d	e	f	g
1.	$5.81 2.30 = $3.51	$4.75 .21 = $4.54	$7.46 3.15 = $4.31	$6.66 4.24 = $2.42	$5.98 3.13 = $2.85	$8.72 5.72 = $3.00	$2.67 1.52 = $1.15
2.	$9.48 .19 = $9.29	$8.74 2.37 = $6.37	$5.46 2.49 = $2.97	$9.78 .94 = $8.84	$4.82 1.92 = $2.90	$6.34 2.87 = $3.47	$7.65 4.98 = $2.67

CODED ANSWERS, SET 24, PART A: 1. (a) H.BH, (b) B.AD, (c) .BE, (d) A.FE, (e) F.DJ, (f) H.JE, (g) J.AD; **2.** (a) H.BH, (b) F.BC, (c) A.AH, (d) B.HA (e) A.BF, (f) H.GH, (g) A.FC

CODE: A B C D E F G H I J
      2 3 9 1 0 6 7 5 8 4

Find the total amount.

A	a	b	c	d	e	f	g
1.	$1.36 7.54 $8.90	$4.25 3.57 $7.82	$3.44 5.39 $8.83	$5.65 .16 $5.81	$4.37 2.91 $7.28	$7.81 1.46 $9.27	$6.09 3.35 $9.44
2.	$8.34 6.79 $15.13	$4.53 .88 $5.41	$5.64 8.97 $14.61	$3.75 7.29 $11.04	$1.18 9.84 $11.02	$9.26 6.97 $16.23	$2.78 9.89 $12.67

B							
1.	$8.36 1.26 $9.62	$3.58 5.15 $8.73	$9.46 .37 $9.83	$5.61 3.09 $8.70	$6.84 2.41 $9.25	$4.72 4.92 $9.64	$3.86 3.72 $7.58
2.	$9.67 .43 $10.10	$10.83 3.59 $14.42	$14.47 2.97 $17.44	$11.63 4.88 $16.51	$8.64 5.99 $14.63	$16.27 3.86 $20.13	$17.48 1.84 $19.32

CODED ANSWERS, SET 25, PART A: **1.** (a) D.GB, (b) E.DJ, (c) D.DI, (d) H.DA, (e) E.JD, (f) G.JE, (g) G.CC;
2. (a) AH.AI, (b) H.CA, (c) AC.FA, (d) AA.BC, (e) AA.BJ, (f) AF.JI, (g) AJ.FE

CODE: A B C D E F G H I J
       1 0 4 8 7 6 9 5 3 2

Set 26 *For use after page 78*   Subtraction: 2-digit and 3-digit
                                                       numbers, borrowing

A	a	b	c	d	e	f	g	h
1.	123 −29 94	164 −77 87	186 −98 88	152 −73 79	285 −37 248	636 −58 578	347 −59 288	460 −75 385
2.	860 −158 702	356 −137 219	843 −539 304	691 −522 169	963 −692 271	707 −372 335	876 −481 395	559 −482 77

	a	b	c	d
3.	526 − 178 = ▥ 348	646 − 249 = ▥ 397	357 − 168 = ▥ 189	521 − 268 = ▥ 253
4.	734 − 365 = ▥ 369	846 − 289 = ▥ 557	447 − 138 = ▥ 309	956 − 387 = ▥ 569

B								
1.	153 −69 84	174 −89 85	216 −89 127	741 −53 688	580 −233 347	634 −126 508	727 −282 445	856 −373 483
2.	441 −159 282	672 −288 384	933 −797 136	764 −686 78	875 −276 599	586 −177 409	357 −258 99	928 −589 339

CODED ANSWERS, SET 26, PART A: **1.** (a) FG, (b) IB, (c) II, (d) BF, (e) AGI, (f) HBI, (g) AII, (h) CIH; **2.** (a) BJA,
(b) AEF, (c) CJG, (d) EDF, (e) ABE, (f) CCH, (g) CFH, (h) BB; **3.** (a) CGI, (b) CFB, (c) EIF, (d) AHC; **4.** (a) CDF,
(b) HHB, (c) CJF, (d) HDF

CODE: A B C D E F G H I J
       2 7 3 6 1 9 4 5 8 0

Set 27 *For use after page 78* Subtraction: 3-digit numbers, borrowing

A

	a	b	c	d	e	f	g	h
1.	671 −252 *419*	362 −133 *229*	437 −242 *195*	612 −136 *476*	906 −174 *732*	751 −227 *524*	628 −192 *436*	873 −618 *255*
2.	747 −288 *459*	535 −237 *298*	496 −369 *127*	368 −179 *189*	417 −254 *163*	925 −287 *638*	735 −369 *366*	626 −448 *178*

	a	b	c	d
3.	564 − 289 = ▉ *275*	936 − 687 = ▉ *249*	852 − 496 = ▉ *356*	691 − 193 = ▉ *498*
4.	746 − 599 = ▉ *147*	418 − 349 = ▉ *69*	736 − 717 = ▉ *19*	874 − 495 = ▉ *379*

B

	a	b	c	d	e	f	g	h
1.	635 −128 *507*	524 −327 *197*	816 −348 *468*	943 −544 *399*	747 −665 *82*	932 −763 *169*	543 −297 *246*	921 −875 *46*
2.	520 −398 *722*	885 −149 *736*	730 −591 *139*	861 −762 *99*	621 −274 *347*	526 −339 *187*	772 −494 *278*	681 −568 *113*

	a	b	c	d
3.	533 − 446 = ▉ *87*	963 − 255 = ▉ *708*	858 − 269 = ▉ *589*	896 − 317 = ▉ *579*
4.	722 − 348 = ▉ *374*	685 − 426 = ▉ *259*	542 − 467 = ▉ *75*	961 − 860 = ▉ *101*

CODED ANSWERS, SET 27, PART A: **1.** (a) CJF, (b) BBF, (c) JFH, (d) CGD, (e) GIB, (f) HBC, (g) CID, (h) BHH; **2.** (a) CHF, (b) BFE, (c) JBG, (d) JEF, (e) JDI, (f) DIE, (g) IDD, (h) JGE **3.** (a) BGH, (b) BCF, (c) IHD, (d) CFE; **4.** (a) JCG, (b) DF, (c) JF, (d) IGF

CODE: A B C D E F G H I J
       0 2 4 6 8 9 7 5 3 1

Set 28 *For use after page 78* Mixed practice: carrying and borrowing

A

	a	b	c	d	e	f	g	h
	476 +59 *535*	671 −346 *325*	537 +283 *820*	528 −141 *387*	628 +177 *805*	430 +398 *828*	732 −496 *236*	974 −876 *98*

B

	a	b	c	d	e	f	g	h
1.	813 −174 *639*	516 +694 *1210*	876 +427 *1303*	765 −379 *386*	657 −288 *379*	837 +999 *1836*	940 −333 *607*	777 +567 *1344*

	a	b	c	d
2.	503 − 261 = ▉ *242*	765 + 879 = ▉ *1644*	636 − 386 = ▉ *250*	638 + 597 = ▉ *1235*
3.	347 − 158 = ▉ *189*	767 + 967 = ▉ *1734*	294 − 195 = ▉ *99*	965 − 487 = ▉ *478*

CODED ANSWERS, SET 28, PART A: (a) DHD, (b) HCD, (c) GCB, (d), HGF, (e) GBD, (f) GCG, (g) CHA, (h) IG

CODE: A B C D E F G H I J
       6 0 2 5 1 7 8 3 9 4

Set 29 — Part A

	a	b	c	d	e	f	g	h	i	j
A	4	9	7	5	6	9	3	7	9	7
	8	5	6	9	9	9	9	8	8	9
	+9	+8	+8	+7	+8	+7	+8	+7	+6	+5
	21	22	21	21	23	25	20	22	23	21
B	5	9	8	6	8	7	5	6	9	7
	7	7	8	7	9	8	8	7	9	7
	+8	+8	+8	+9	+6	+8	+9	+8	+9	+7
	20	24	24	22	23	23	22	21	27	21

CODED ANSWERS, SET 29, PART A: (a) IB, (b) II, (c) IB, (d) IB, (e) IC, (f) IA, (g) IE, (h) II, (i) IC, (j) IB

CODE: A B C D E F G H I J
5 1 3 7 0 9 8 4 2 6

Set 30 *For use after page 78* Column addition: four 1-digit addends, carrying

Set 30 — Part A

	a	b	c	d	e	f	g	h	i	j
A	3	4	9	3	7	8	9	2	8	7
	8	6	6	7	5	6	7	3	6	6
	6	7	9	6	9	4	8	7	6	4
	+4	+9	+5	+8	+4	+2	+3	+9	+5	+8
	21	26	29	24	25	20	27	21	25	25
B	4	3	6	4	7	6	4	3	9	8
	7	6	8	9	5	8	6	8	9	7
	6	5	7	3	8	3	5	9	4	7
	+8	+8	+5	+6	+4	+7	+7	+7	+9	+6
	25	22	26	22	24	24	22	27	31	28

CODED ANSWERS, SET 30, PART A: (a) EH, (b) EB, (c) EG, (d) EA, (e) ED, (f) EC, (g) EF, (h) EH, (i) ED, (j) ED

CODE: A B C D E F G H I J
3 5 7 0 1 4 6 8 2 9

Set 31 *For use after page 78* Column addition: three 2-digit addends, carrying

Set 31 — Part A

	a	b	c	d	e	f	g	h	i
A	23	17	46	35	59	70	59	68	77
	35	36	29	48	48	49	36	48	88
	+14	+24	+24	+62	+61	+67	+17	+97	+99
	72	77	99	145	168	186	112	213	264
B	30	25	18	63	56	64	52	48	99
	57	39	27	29	74	39	87	67	79
	+14	+35	+43	+38	+58	+65	+36	+87	+96
	101	99	88	130	188	168	175	202	274

CODED ANSWERS, SET 31, PART A: (a) CI, (b) CC, (c) JJ, (d) EFB, (e) EGH, (f) EHG, (g) EEI, (h) IEA, (i) IGF

CODE: A B C D E F G H I J
4 6 0 5 2 7 9 1 8 3

Set 32 *For use after page 78* Column addition: three 2-digit addends

A

	a	b	c	d	e	f	g	h	i
1.	23	4	5	34	25	34	7	42	54
	5	17	6	9	17	6	16	29	9
	+7	+6	+18	+6	+5	+29	+53	+6	+26
	35	27	29	49	47	69	76	77	89
2.	15	34	43	51	26	67	73	82	91
	49	53	82	68	70	26	83	37	28
	+12	+54	+76	+94	+57	+68	+95	+94	+19
	76	141	201	213	153	161	251	213	138
3.	19	19	28	73	23	49	67	38	81
	99	76	23	54	45	18	66	43	67
	+16	+85	+57	+48	+26	+54	+75	+79	+23
	134	180	108	175	94	121	208	160	171

B

	a	b	c	d	e	f	g	h	i
1.	18	9	41	67	63	43	6	37	37
	+5	+12	+5	+8	+7	+29	+68	+8	+5
	23	21	46	75	70	72	74	45	42
2.	92	90	18	37	54	69	38	54	67
	58	17	43	90	78	54	73	12	80
	+46	+53	+76	+82	+97	+62	+26	+49	+51
	196	160	137	209	229	185	137	115	198
3.	97	46	29	76	78	76	19	54	67
	89	95	63	25	97	44	65	18	58
	+75	+83	+81	+43	+68	+58	+37	+92	+54
	261	224	173	144	243	178	121	164	179

CODED ANSWERS, SET 32, PART A: **1.** (a) BC, (b) JD, (c) JE, (d) IE, (e) ID, (f) HE, (g) DH, (h) DD, (i) GE; **2.** (a) DH, (b) AIA, (c) JFA, (d) JAB, (e) ACB, (f) AHA, (g) JCA, (h) JAB, (i) ABG; **3.** (a) ABI, (b) AGF, (c) AFG, (d) ADC, (e) EI, (f) AJA, (g) JFG, (h) AHF, (i) ADA

CODE: A B C D E F G H I J
1 3 5 7 9 0 8 6 4 2

Set 33 *For use after page 78* Addition equations

A

	a	b	c
1.	$25 + 6 + 3 = \blacksquare\ 34$	$36 + 9 + 24 = \blacksquare\ 69$	$64 + 32 + 7 = \blacksquare\ 103$
2.	$324 + 6 + 25 = \blacksquare\ 355$	$953 + 7 + 46 = \blacksquare\ 1006$	$6 + 707 + 46 = \blacksquare\ 759$

B

	a	b	c
1.	$43 + 8 + 7 = \blacksquare\ 58$	$27 + 8 + 53 = \blacksquare\ 88$	$75 + 67 + 8 = \blacksquare\ 150$
2.	$614 + 9 + 32 = \blacksquare\ 655$	$876 + 9 + 28 = \blacksquare\ 913$	$7 + 808 + 59 = \blacksquare\ 874$

CODED ANSWERS, SET 33, PART A: **1.** (a) BJ, (b) FC, (c) DEB; **2.** (a) BHH, (b) DEEF, (c) GHC

CODE: A B C D E F G H I J
2 3 9 1 0 6 7 5 8 4

Copy the problems. Write the missing digits instead of the ▦.

	a	b	c	d	e	f	g	h	i
1.	23 +▦6 = 69	▦4 −22 = 42	▦6 +3▦ = 88	6▦ +▦5 = 89	8▦ −▦3 = 36	49 +▦▦ = 89	▦9 −18 = 71	▦▦ −12 = 80	22 +▦▦ = 69
2.	36 +2▦ = ▦2	▦7 +13 = 6▦	▦9 −2▦ = 26	32 −▦▦ = 14	4▦ +▦5 = 89	85 −▦▦ = 55	▦▦ −36 = 14	6▦ +▦9 = 92	4▦ −▦3 = 6
3.	5▦ +▦2 = 115	▦▦ −17 = 26	▦4 +7▦ = 159	5▦ −13 = ▦▦7	▦8 −8▦ = 9	1▦ +94 = 1▦7	36 +▦▦ = 135	6▦ −▦9 = 28	7▦ +89 = 165

Copy the problems. Write the missing digits instead of the ▦.

	a	b	c	d	e	f	g	h
1.	11▦ −54 = ▦2	3▦2 +▦3▦ = 879	▦▦▦ +315 = 999	▦▦6 −7▦ = 75	146 +▦▦▦ = 648	63▦ +▦1 = ▦58	1▦▦ −82 = 96	▦▦▦ −73 = 96
2.	7▦5 −▦2▦ = 342	586 −▦▦▦ = 445	▦3▦ +3▦2 = 788	8▦7 −▦2▦ = 556	7▦▦ −▦42 = 47	8▦▦ +▦57 = 1489	▦96 +▦▦▦ = 263	47▦ −▦4 = ▦65
3.	15▦ +7▦7 = 893	377 −26▦ = 1▦9	▦6▦ −138 = 722	23▦ +6▦9 = 883	▦32 −39▦ = 140	282 +▦▦4 = 876	8▦2 +▦90 = 1042	▦53 +6▦5 = 928
4.	92▦ +▦78 = 11▦1	94▦ +▦▦9 = 1284	▦39 −46▦ = 477	8▦▦ +▦94 = 1574	7▦3 −32▦ = 434	7▦7 +▦64 = 1301	4▦2 −▦6▦ = 17	▦67 +84▦ = 1413

Set 36   *For use after page 78*   Addition equations: three and four addends

Ⓐ

	a	b	c
1.	54 + 6 + 3 = ▨ *63*	8 + 57 + 9 = ▨ *74*	6 + 27 + 8 = ▨ *41*
2.	34 + 9 + 43 = ▨ *86*	35 + 6 + 59 = ▨ *100*	86 + 27 + 4 = ▨ *117*
3.	465 + 7 + 9 = ▨ *481*	8 + 362 + 6 = ▨ *376*	9 + 8 + 274 = ▨ *291*
4.	367 + 5 + 26 = ▨ *398*	8 + 293 + 56 = ▨ *357*	93 + 4 + 389 = ▨ *486*
5.	536 + 24 + 56 = ▨ *616*	9 + 397 + 4 = ▨ *410*	413 + 657 + 28 = ▨ *1098*
6.	5 + 29 + 34 + 7 = ▨ *75*	4 + 93 + 467 + 8 = ▨ *572*	398 + 7 + 29 + 48 = ▨ *482*

Ⓑ

	a	b	c
1.	66 + 4 + 5 = ▨ *75*	7 + 63 + 9 = ▨ *79*	4 + 38 + 6 = ▨ *48*
2.	57 + 4 + 36 = ▨ *97*	42 + 9 + 63 = ▨ *114*	97 + 31 + 8 = ▨ *136*
3.	576 + 8 + 5 = ▨ *589*	5 + 639 + 7 = ▨ *651*	8 + 8 + 685 = ▨ *701*
4.	346 + 7 + 34 = ▨ *387*	6 + 647 + 39 = ▨ *692*	47 + 5 + 366 = ▨ *418*
5.	654 + 32 + 91 = ▨ *777*	8 + 466 + 37 = ▨ *511*	416 + 879 + 34 = ▨ *1329*
6.	5 + 42 + 39 + 3 = ▨ *89*	7 + 84 + 328 + 6 = ▨ *425*	347 + 6 + 38 + 52 = ▨ *443*

CODED ANSWERS, SET 36, PART A: 1. (a) FI, (b) EC, (c) CA; **2.** (a) DF, (b) ABB, (c) AAE; **3.** (a) CDA, (b) IEF, (c) JGA; **4.** (a) IGD, (b) IHE, (c) CDF; **5.** (a) FAF, (b) CAB, (c) ABGD; **6.** (a) EH, (b) HEJ, (c) CDJ

CODE:

A	B	C	D	E	F	G	H	I	J
1	0	4	8	7	6	9	5	3	2

Set 37   *For use after page 78*   Mixed practice, carrying and borrowing

Ⓐ

	a	b	c	d	e	f	g	h
1.	72 +65 = *137*	90 +47 = *137*	63 −23 = *40*	57 +84 = *141*	96 −37 = *59*	453 +236 = *689*	613 −252 = *361*	530 −224 = *306*
2.	513 +888 = *1401*	416 −126 = *290*	780 +57 = *837*	32 +499 = *531*	653 −283 = *370*	716 +24 = *740*	876 +347 = *1223*	924 −676 = *248*

Ⓑ

	a	b	c	d	e	f	g	h
1.	64 +36 = *100*	79 −48 = *31*	83 +49 = *132*	117 −28 = *89*	356 +241 = *597*	572 −148 = *424*	629 −598 = *31*	340 +960 = *1300*
2.	823 +799 = *1622*	962 −897 = *65*	430 +980 = *1410*	651 −279 = *372*	365 +376 = *741*	888 −499 = *389*	777 +666 = *1443*	367 −276 = *91*

CODED ANSWERS, SET 37, PART A: 1. (a) ECB, (b) ECB, (c) GJ, (d) EGE, (e) HF, (f) DIF, (g) CDE, (h) CJD; **2.** (a) EGJE, (b) AFJ, (c) ICB, (d) HCE, (e) CBJ, (f) BGJ, (g) EAAC, (h) AGI

CODE:

A	B	C	D	E	F	G	H	I	J
2	7	3	6	1	9	4	5	8	0

	a	b	c	d	e	f
1.	2 × 1 = 2	2 × 2 = 4	3 × 3 = 9	3 × 4 = 12	4 × 0 = 0	4 × 1 = 4
2.	4 × 3 = 12	5 × 5 = 25	4 × 4 = 16	6 × 6 = 36	8 × 7 = 56	8 × 9 = 72
3.	4 × 5 = 20	9 × 0 = 0	1 × 8 = 8	3 × 2 = 6	3 × 5 = 15	3 × 6 = 18
4.	5 × 3 = 15	6 × 5 = 30	4 × 6 = 24	7 × 6 = 42	9 × 1 = 9	9 × 7 = 63
5.	1 × 3 = 3	4 × 2 = 8	0 × 0 = 0	2 × 9 = 18	6 × 3 = 18	4 × 7 = 28
6.	7 × 3 = 21	3 × 7 = 21	7 × 5 = 35	7 × 7 = 49	1 × 1 = 1	5 × 2 = 10
7.	6 × 2 = 12	8 × 1 = 8	8 × 3 = 24	0 × 3 = 0	8 × 5 = 40	9 × 9 = 81
8.	4 × 8 = 32	6 × 9 = 54	1 × 9 = 9	7 × 9 = 63	9 × 8 = 72	9 × 3 = 27
9.	2 × 8 = 16	7 × 2 = 14	6 × 8 = 48	4 × 9 = 36	5 × 0 = 0	7 × 8 = 56
10.	0 × 6 = 0	5 × 4 = 20	5 × 1 = 5	1 × 5 = 5	8 × 2 = 16	2 × 7 = 14
11.	6 × 4 = 24	2 × 6 = 12	6 × 7 = 42	5 × 6 = 30	3 × 8 = 24	1 × 4 = 4
12.	3 × 1 = 3	2 × 5 = 10	9 × 2 = 18	1 × 2 = 2	7 × 4 = 28	5 × 7 = 35
13.	8 × 4 = 32	0 × 8 = 0	3 × 9 = 27	5 × 8 = 40	9 × 6 = 54	6 × 1 = 6
14.	1 × 7 = 7	8 × 6 = 48	1 × 6 = 6	0 × 1 = 0	8 × 8 = 64	9 × 5 = 45
15.	5 × 9 = 45	7 × 1 = 7	2 × 4 = 8	9 × 4 = 36	2 × 3 = 6	7 × 0 = 0

Set 39   For use after page 104   Multiplication equations

A

	a	b	c	d
1.	9 × 6 = ▨ 54	5 × ▨(7) = 35	▨(7) × 4 = 28	▨(0) × 5 = 0
2.	56 = 7 × ▨(8)	6 × ▨(4) = 24	▨(4) × 8 = 32	9 × ▨(4) = 36
3.	8 × ▨(1) = 8	▨(7) × 3 = 21	4 × ▨(5) = 20	30 = 6 × ▨(5)
4.	72 = 8 × ▨(9)	56 = ▨(7) × 8	▨(7) × 9 = 63	7 × ▨(7) = 49

B

	a	b	c	d
1.	8 × ▨(5) = 40	7 × 6 = ▨ 42	30 = 5 × ▨(6)	▨(4) × 7 = 28
2.	▨(5) × 5 = 25	21 = 7 × ▨(3)	24 = ▨(4) × 6	▨(8) × 8 = 64
3.	9 × ▨(8) = 72	▨(6) × 9 = 54	48 = ▨(8) × 6	7 × ▨(6) = 42
4.	35 = 7 × ▨(5)	8 × ▨(0) = 0	▨(5) × 9 = 45	24 = 3 × ▨(8)

CODED ANSWERS, SET 39, PART A: **1.** (a) CI, (b) D, (c) D, (d) F; **2.** (a) G, (b) I, (c) I, (d) I; **3.** (a) A, (b) D, (c) C, (d) C; **4.** (a) E, (b) D, (c) D, (d) D

CODE: A B C D E F G H I J
       1 3 5 7 9 0 8 6 4 2

Set 40   *For use after page 130*   Division facts

	a	b	c	d	e	f
1.	4 ÷ 2 *2*	9 ÷ 3 *3*	1 ÷ 1 *1*	2 ÷ 2 *1*	6 ÷ 3 *2*	16 ÷ 4 *4*
2.	12 ÷ 3 *4*	25 ÷ 5 *5*	20 ÷ 5 *4*	6 ÷ 2 *3*	2 ÷ 1 *2*	42 ÷ 6 *7*
3.	20 ÷ 4 *5*	15 ÷ 3 *5*	0 ÷ 1 *0*	24 ÷ 6 *4*	36 ÷ 6 *6*	8 ÷ 2 *4*
4.	10 ÷ 2 *5*	3 ÷ 1 *3*	48 ÷ 8 *6*	18 ÷ 3 *6*	27 ÷ 9 *3*	3 ÷ 3 *1*
5.	24 ÷ 4 *6*	54 ÷ 9 *6*	21 ÷ 3 *7*	12 ÷ 2 *6*	49 ÷ 7 *7*	48 ÷ 6 *8*
6.	24 ÷ 8 *3*	42 ÷ 7 *6*	28 ÷ 7 *4*	4 ÷ 1 *4*	24 ÷ 3 *8*	32 ÷ 8 *4*
7.	35 ÷ 5 *7*	18 ÷ 9 *2*	0 ÷ 9 *0*	56 ÷ 7 *8*	28 ÷ 4 *7*	8 ÷ 8 *1*
8.	9 ÷ 1 *9*	14 ÷ 2 *7*	4 ÷ 4 *1*	54 ÷ 6 *9*	21 ÷ 7 *3*	63 ÷ 7 *9*
9.	63 ÷ 9 *7*	32 ÷ 4 *8*	40 ÷ 5 *8*	16 ÷ 2 *8*	56 ÷ 8 *7*	45 ÷ 9 *5*
10.	18 ÷ 2 *9*	6 ÷ 6 *1*	8 ÷ 1 *8*	40 ÷ 8 *5*	18 ÷ 6 *3*	16 ÷ 8 *2*
11.	64 ÷ 8 *8*	35 ÷ 7 *5*	36 ÷ 4 *9*	14 ÷ 7 *2*	5 ÷ 5 *1*	7 ÷ 1 *7*
12.	15 ÷ 5 *3*	72 ÷ 8 *9*	12 ÷ 6 *2*	0 ÷ 5 *0*	30 ÷ 5 *6*	45 ÷ 5 *9*
13.	30 ÷ 6 *5*	6 ÷ 1 *6*	72 ÷ 9 *8*	36 ÷ 9 *4*	10 ÷ 5 *2*	27 ÷ 3 *9*
14.	12 ÷ 4 *3*	7 ÷ 7 *1*	81 ÷ 9 *9*	8 ÷ 4 *2*	5 ÷ 1 *5*	9 ÷ 9 *1*

Set 41   *For use after page 130*   Division equations

A

	a	b	c	d
1.	27 ÷ 3 = ■ *9*	48 ÷ ■ = 6 *8*	■ ÷ 4 = 4 *16*	72 ÷ 8 = ■ *9*
2.	■ = 63 ÷ 7 *9*	48 ÷ 8 = ■ *6*	32 ÷ ■ = 4 *8*	■ ÷ 9 = 5 *45*
3.	■ ÷ 7 = 7 *49*	54 ÷ ■ = 6 *9*	7 = ■ ÷ 3 *21*	72 ÷ ■ = 8 *9*
4.	3 = 21 ÷ ■ *7*	81 ÷ ■ = 9 *9*	40 ÷ 8 = ■ *5*	■ ÷ 7 = 3 *21*

B

	a	b	c	d
1.	20 ÷ 4 = ■ *5*	■ = 42 ÷ 6 *7*	■ ÷ 6 = 4 *24*	72 ÷ ■ = 9 *8*
2.	■ = 36 ÷ 4 *9*	■ ÷ 3 = 8 *24*	30 ÷ ■ = 6 *5*	40 ÷ ■ = 5 *8*
3.	5 = 15 ÷ ■ *3*	■ ÷ 8 = 0 *0*	42 ÷ 7 = ■ *6*	9 ÷ ■ = 9 *1*
4.	56 ÷ 8 = ■ *7*	■ = 24 ÷ 4 *6*	28 ÷ ■ = 4 *7*	■ ÷ 3 = 4 *12*
5.	48 ÷ ■ = 8 *6*	81 ÷ ■ = 9 *9*	■ = 63 ÷ 9 *7*	■ ÷ 6 = 9 *54*

CODED ANSWERS, SET 41, PART A: 1. (a) E, (b) G, (c) AH, (d) E; **2.** (a) E, (b) H, (c) G, (d) IC; **3.** (a) IE, (b) E, (c) JA, (d) E; **4.** (a) D, (b) E, (c) C, (d) JA

CODE:

A	B	C	D	E	F	G	H	I	J
1	3	5	7	9	0	8	6	4	2

(A)

	a	b	c	d	e	f
1.	10 × 10 *100*	8 × 10 *80*	10 × 7 *70*	6 × 10 *60*	10 × 4 *40*	5 × 10 *50*
2.	0 × 10 *0*	3 × 10 *30*	12 × 10 *120*	15 × 10 *150*	10 × 18 *180*	10 × 17 *170*
3.	23 × 10 *230*	10 × 61 *610*	34 × 10 *340*	52 × 10 *520*	65 × 10 *650*	10 × 39 *390*
4.	20 × 10 *200*	53 × 10 *530*	10 × 81 *810*	40 × 10 *400*	10 × 80 *800*	85 × 10 *850*
5.	38 × 100 *3800*	41 × 100 *4100*	56 × 100 *5600*	65 × 100 *6500*	100 × 73 *7300*	89 × 100 *8900*

(B)

	a	b	c	d	e	f
1.	9 × 10 *90*	7 × 10 *70*	10 × 8 *80*	10 × 0 *0*	2 × 10 *20*	10 × 5 *50*
2.	10 × 6 *60*	1 × 10 *10*	14 × 10 *140*	10 × 16 *160*	19 × 10 *190*	13 × 10 *130*
3.	32 × 10 *320*	10 × 58 *580*	36 × 10 *360*	58 × 10 *580*	76 × 10 *760*	10 × 57 *570*
4.	40 × 10 *400*	62 × 10 *620*	10 × 93 *930*	80 × 10 *800*	10 × 30 *300*	93 × 10 *930*
5.	39 × 100 *3900*	53 × 100 *5300*	67 × 100 *6700*	100 × 27 *2700*	43 × 100 *4300*	78 × 100 *7800*

CODED ANSWERS, SET 42, PART A: 1. (a) JAA, (b) EA, (c) GA, (d) DA, (e) CA, (f) HA; **2.** (a) A, (b) IA, (c) JBA, (d) JHA, (e) JEA, (f) JGA; **3.** (a) BIA, (b) DJA, (c) ICA, (d) HBA, (e) DHA, (f) IFA; **4.** (a) BAA, (b) HIA, (c) EJA, (d) CAA, (e) EAA, (f) EHA; **5.** (a) IEAA, (b) CJAA, (c) HDAA, (d) DHAA, (e) GIAA, (f) EFAA

CODE: A B C D E F G H I J
　　　　0 2 4 6 8 9 7 5 3 1

Set 43 *For use after page 179* — Multiplication: 1-digit multiple times a multiple of 10

(A)

	a	b	c	d	e
1.	3 × 40 *120*	60 × 4 *240*	50 × 9 *450*	8 × 70 *560*	2 × 30 *60*
2.	8 × 50 *400*	20 × 9 *180*	7 × 30 *210*	4 × 80 *320*	50 × 6 *300*
3.	9 × 90 *810*	4 × 70 *280*	80 × 6 *480*	60 × 6 *360*	8 × 60 *480*
4.	7 × 70 *490*	80 × 8 *640*	90 × 6 *540*	7 × 90 *630*	90 × 7 *630*
5.	275 × 10 *2750*	10 × 832 *8320*	653 × 10 *6530*	10 × 976 *9760*	8345 × 10 *83,450*
6.	8 × 100 *800*	100 × 9 *900*	18 × 100 *1800*	100 × 34 *3400*	100 × 76 *7600*

(B)

	a	b	c	d	e
1.	4 × 50 *200*	70 × 3 *210*	60 × 8 *480*	7 × 90 *630*	3 × 20 *60*
2.	7 × 60 *420*	30 × 9 *270*	6 × 30 *180*	5 × 80 *400*	6 × 60 *360*
3.	8 × 90 *720*	5 × 60 *300*	70 × 8 *560*	80 × 7 *560*	4 × 90 *360*
4.	7 × 30 *210*	90 × 5 *450*	60 × 9 *540*	90 × 6 *540*	90 × 9 *810*
5.	343 × 10 *3430*	10 × 976 *9760*	729 × 10 *7290*	10 × 834 *8340*	7638 × 10 *76,380*
6.	6 × 100 *600*	100 × 4 *400*	13 × 100 *1300*	71 × 100 *7100*	100 × 57 *5700*

CODED ANSWERS, SET 43, PART A: 1. (a) ECB, (b) CJB, (c) JDB, (d) DAB, (e) AB; **2.** (a) JBB, (b) EGB, (c) CEB, (d) HCB, (e) HBB; **3.** (a) GEB, (b) CGB, (c) JGB, (d) HAB, (e) JGB; **4.** (a) JIB, (b) AJB, (c) DJB, (d) AHB, (e) AHB; **5.** (a) CFDB, (b) GHCB, (c) ADHB, (d) IFAB, (e) GHJDB; **6.** (a) GBB, (b) IBB, (c) EGBB, (d) HJBB, (e) FABB

CODE: A B C D E F G H I J
　　　　6 0 2 5 1 7 8 3 9 4

Set 44 *For use after page 190*   Multiplication: 1-digit times a 2-digit number

A

	a	b	c	d	e	f	g	h	i
1.	13 ×4 = 52	16 ×2 = 32	22 ×4 = 88	11 ×3 = 33	22 ×5 = 110	53 ×4 = 212	43 ×6 = 258	51 ×3 = 153	24 ×7 = 168
2.	13 ×3 = 39	32 ×5 = 160	34 ×4 = 136	45 ×2 = 90	67 ×7 = 469	81 ×6 = 486	60 ×5 = 300	79 ×8 = 632	85 ×9 = 765

B

	a	b	c	d	e	f	g	h	i
1.	19 ×2 = 38	62 ×4 = 248	35 ×3 = 105	41 ×4 = 164	28 ×5 = 140	37 ×3 = 111	32 ×2 = 64	16 ×4 = 64	45 ×5 = 225
2.	29 ×6 = 174	43 ×7 = 301	78 ×3 = 234	65 ×8 = 520	56 ×2 = 112	43 ×9 = 387	27 ×4 = 108	81 ×5 = 405	90 ×3 = 270
3.	53 ×5 = 265	45 ×4 = 180	76 ×6 = 456	98 ×3 = 294	21 ×9 = 189	79 ×2 = 158	84 ×4 = 336	52 ×7 = 364	63 ×8 = 504

CODED ANSWERS, SET 44, PART A: 1. (a) AI, (b) CI, (c) GG, (d) CC, (e) BBE, (f) IBI, (g) IAG, (h) BAC, (i) BJG; **2.** (a) CF, (b) BJE, (c) BCJ, (d) FE, (e) HJF, (f) HGJ, (g) CEE, (h) JCI, (i) DJA

CODE:
A	B	C	D	E	F	G	H	I	J
5	1	3	7	0	9	8	4	2	6

Set 45 *For use after page 196*   Multiplication: 1-digit times a 3-digit number

A

	a	b	c	d	e	f	g	h
1.	123 ×2 = 246	564 ×3 = 1692	345 ×4 = 1380	153 ×5 = 765	254 ×6 = 1524	416 ×4 = 1664	325 ×3 = 975	513 ×5 = 2565
2.	243 ×3 = 729	563 ×5 = 2815	674 ×7 = 4718	755 ×2 = 1510	486 ×9 = 4374	327 ×8 = 2616	908 ×6 = 5448	219 ×4 = 876

B

	a	b	c	d	e	f	g	h
1.	413 ×3 = 1239	525 ×2 = 1050	334 ×4 = 1336	242 ×5 = 1210	453 ×3 = 1359	264 ×2 = 528	151 ×4 = 604	640 ×5 = 3200
2.	563 ×9 = 5067	652 ×3 = 1956	741 ×6 = 4446	835 ×8 = 6680	496 ×7 = 3472	347 ×4 = 1388	528 ×5 = 2640	679 ×5 = 3395

CODED ANSWERS, SET 45, PART A: 1. (a) EAB, (b) HBGE, (c) HJIC, (d) FBD, (e) HDEA, (f) HBBA, (g) GFD, (h) EDBD; **2.** (a) FEG, (b) EIHD, (c) AFHI, (d) HDHC, (e) AJFA, (f) EBHB, (g) DAAI, (h) IFB

CODE:
A	B	C	D	E	F	G	H	I	J
4	6	0	5	2	7	9	1	8	3

Set 46 *For use after page 198*

	a	b	c	d	e	f	g	h	i
A 1.	163 ×2 = 326	228 ×4 = 912	74 ×6 = 444	435 ×3 = 1305	58 ×4 = 232	365 ×5 = 1825	451 ×7 = 3157	67 ×7 = 469	57 ×9 = 513
2.	76 ×8 = 608	92 ×3 = 276	71 ×5 = 355	391 ×7 = 2737	28 ×9 = 252	485 ×3 = 1455	93 ×7 = 651	98 ×9 = 882	516 ×8 = 4128
B	23 ×6 = 138	169 ×2 = 338	548 ×4 = 2192	92 ×6 = 552	872 ×4 = 3488	67 ×7 = 469	48 ×5 = 240	825 ×6 = 4950	936 ×3 = 2808

CODED ANSWERS, SET 46, PART A: **1.** (a) BJH, (b) EAJ, (c) III, (d) ABFC, (e) JBJ, (f) AGJC, (g) BACD, (h) IHE, (i) CAB; **2.** (a) HFG, (b) JDH, (c) BCC, (d) JDBD, (e) JCJ, (f) AICC, (g) HCA, (h) GGJ, (i) IAJG

CODE: A B C D E F G H I J
          1 3 5 7 9 0 8 6 4 2

Set 47 *For use after page 201*

	a	b	c	d	e	f
A 1.	1542 ×2 = 3084	3361 ×3 = 10,083	5782 ×5 = 28,910	7954 ×3 = 23,862	8321 ×4 = 33,284	6765 ×6 = 40,590
2.	1738 ×3 = 5214	2138 ×5 = 10,690	3279 ×6 = 19,674	4960 ×9 = 44,640	6851 ×7 = 47,957	5742 ×4 = 22,968
B	4189 ×5 = 20,945	7498 ×6 = 44,988	5276 ×7 = 36,932	1556 ×8 = 12,448	2377 ×9 = 21,393	3648 ×4 = 14,592

CODED ANSWERS, SET 47, PART A: **1.** (a) ADHF, (b) EDDHA, (c) IHJED, (d) IAHGI, (e) AAIHF, (f) FDBJD; **2.** (a) BIEF, (b) EDGJD, (c) EJGCF, (d) FFGFD, (e) FCJBC, (f) IIJGH

CODE: A B C D E F G H I J
          3 5 7 0 1 4 6 8 2 9

Set 48 *For use after page 209*

	a	b	c	d	e
A 1.	560 ÷ 10 = 56	240 ÷ 8 = 30	350 ÷ 7 = 50	720 ÷ 9 = 80	630 ÷ 7 = 90
2.	3600 ÷ 4 = 900	4200 ÷ 100 = 42	4800 ÷ 6 = 800	2800 ÷ 7 = 400	2100 ÷ 3 = 700
B 1.	330 ÷ 10 = 33	180 ÷ 9 = 20	450 ÷ 9 = 50	560 ÷ 7 = 80	540 ÷ 9 = 60
2.	2400 ÷ 6 = 400	3800 ÷ 100 = 38	4200 ÷ 7 = 600	2700 ÷ 9 = 300	4900 ÷ 7 = 700

CODED ANSWERS, SET 48, PART A: **1.** (a) HF, (b) BE, (c) HE, (d) IE, (e) CE; **2.** (a) CEE, (b) JA, (c) IEE, (d) JEE, (e) GEE

CODE: A B C D E F G H I J
          2 3 9 1 0 6 7 5 8 4

Set 49   *For use after page 229*   Division: 1-digit divisors

A
a	b	c	d	e	f
1. 2)24	3)63	4)48	5)60	6)72	7)91
2. 3)78	5)75	7)98	6)78	8)96	9)108
3. 2)108	4)92	6)204	7)301	9)585	5)415
4. 5)470	3)222	2)134	8)368	6)342	4)384

B
a	b	c	d	e	f
1. 4)52	2)32	3)48	6)96	7)84	5)80
2. 7)112	8)176	9)207	4)144	2)88	3)138
3. 3)171	4)272	5)235	6)564	5)445	4)308
4. 7)385	8)752	6)588	7)483	8)312	9)666

CODED ANSWERS, SET 49, PART A: 1. (a) AJ, (b) JA, (c) AJ, (d) AJ, (e) AJ, (f) AI; 2. (a) JF, (b) AH, (c) AC, (d) AI, (e) AJ, (f) AJ; 3. (a) HC, (b) JI, (c) IC, (d) CI, (e) FH, (f) DI; 4. (a) GC, (b) EC, (c) FE, (d) CF, (e) HE, (f) GF

CODE: A B C D E F G H I J
       1 0 4 8 7 6 9 5 3 2

Set 50   *For use after page 237*   Division: 1-digit divisors with remainders

Find the quotients and remainders.

A
a	b	c	d	e	f
1. 2)57	3)46	5)82	4)77	7)98	6)86
2. 5)142	7)35	2)163	3)274	5)385	7)496
3. 8)572	6)189	2)138	3)249	4)354	9)665
4. 2)187	6)496	6)576	4)284	8)791	9)823

B
a	b	c	d	e	f
1. 2)69	3)92	4)58	5)76	6)69	7)87
2. 5)235	2)146	5)478	6)379	7)598	4)192
3. 3)163	6)475	3)286	4)379	4)281	2)192
4. 9)654	7)463	8)355	3)264	8)789	9)237

CODED ANSWERS, SET 50, PART A: (r stands for remainder) 1. (a) AIrE, (b) EHrE, (c) EDrA, (d) EFrE, (e) EGrJ, (f) EGrA; 2. (a) AIrA, (b) HrJ, (c) IErE, (d) FErE, (e) BBrJ, (f) BJrD; 3. (a) BErG, (b) CErC, (c) DFrJ, (d) ICrJ, (e) IIrA, (f) BCrI; 4. (a) FCrE, (b) IArG, (c) FDrJ, (d) BErJ, (e) FIrB, (f) FErG

CODE: A B C D E F G H I J
       2 7 3 6 1 9 4 5 8 0

(A)

	a	**b**	**c**
1.	$15 + \boxed{n} = 22$ *7*	$24 + 7 + 5 = \boxed{n}$ *36*	$37 - 9 = \boxed{n}$ *28*
2.	$78 \div 6 = \boxed{n}$ */13*	$16 \times 4 = \boxed{n}$ *64*	$24 - \boxed{n} = 16$ *8*
3.	$25 + 38 = \boxed{n}$ *63*	$57 - 29 = \boxed{n}$ *28*	$8 + 7 + 9 + 4 = \boxed{n}$ *28*
4.	$136 \div 4 = \boxed{n}$ *34*	$27 \times 6 = \boxed{n}$ *162*	$5 \times 93 = \boxed{n}$ *465*
5.	$376 - 29 = \boxed{n}$ *347*	$216 \div 6 = \boxed{n}$ *36*	$875 + 49 = \boxed{n}$ *924*
6.	$324 \times 7 = \boxed{n}$ *2268*	*476*$\boxed{n} = 572 - 96$	$216 \div 8 = \boxed{n}$ *27*

(B)

	a	**b**	**c**
1.	$24 + \boxed{n} = 32$ *8*	$6 + 37 + 4 = \boxed{n}$ *47*	$86 - 8 = \boxed{n}$ *78*
2.	$132 \div 4 = \boxed{n}$ *33*	$27 \times 4 = \boxed{n}$ *108*	$56 - \boxed{n} = 48$ *8*
3.	$87 + 93 = \boxed{n}$ *180*	$73 - 49 = \boxed{n}$ *24*	$6 + 9 + 4 + 7 = \boxed{n}$ *26*
4.	$258 \div 6 = \boxed{n}$ *43*	$63 \times 9 = \boxed{n}$ *567*	$6 \times 87 = \boxed{n}$ *522*
5.	$854 - 57 = \boxed{n}$ *797*	$456 \div 8 = \boxed{n}$ *57*	$686 + 37 = \boxed{n}$ *723*
6.	$636 \times 5 = \boxed{n}$ *3180*	$342 \div 9 = \boxed{n}$ *38*	*142*$\boxed{n} = 431 - 289$

CODED ANSWERS, SET 51, PART A: **1.** (a) G, (b) ID, (c) BE; **2.** (a) JI, (b) DC, (c) E; **3.** (a) DI, (b) BE, (c) BE; **4.** (a) IC, (b) JDB, (c) CDH; **5.** (a) ICG, (b) ID, (c) FBC; **6.** (a) BBDE, (b) CGD, (c) BG

CODE: A B C D E F G H I J
     0 2 4 6 8 9 7 5 3 1

Set 52 *For use after page 243*   Mixed practice

(A)

	a	**b**	**c**	**d**	**e**	**f**
1.	365 $+478$ ―― *843*	654 -276 ―― *378*	*53* $9\overline{)477}$	364 $\times7$ ―― *2548*	*64* $7\overline{)448}$	719 -263 ―― *456*
2.	846 $\times5$ ―― *4230*	923 -357 ―― *566*	*74 r4* $8\overline{)596}$	539 $+885$ ―― *1424*	*44* $9\overline{)396}$	396 $\times6$ ―― *2376*

(B)

	a	**b**	**c**	**d**	**e**	**f**
1.	790 -377 ―― *413*	466 $\times8$ ―― *3728*	*94* $6\overline{)564}$	927 $+878$ ―― *1805*	*93 r4* $4\overline{)373}$	832 -578 ―― *254*
2.	379 $\times3$ ―― *1137*	394 $+934$ ―― *1328*	*55* $8\overline{)440}$	971 -796 ―― *175*	*87* $3\overline{)261}$	356 $\times8$ ―― *2848*

CODED ANSWERS, SET 52, PART A: (*r* stands for remainder) **1.** (a) GJH, (b) HFG, (c) DH, (d) CDJG, (e) AJ, (f) JDA; **2.** (a) JCHB, (b) DAA, (c) FJrJ. (d) EJCJ, (e) JJ, (f) CHFA

CODE: A B C D E F G H I J
     6 0 2 5 1 7 8 3 9 4

Set 53   *For use after page 305*   Rational numbers: equalities and inequalities

Write the symbol (>, <, =) for each ▦.

	a	**b**	**c**	**d**	**e**
1.	$\frac{1}{2}$ ▦ $\frac{2}{4}$	$\frac{1}{4}$ ◁ $\frac{1}{2}$	$\frac{1}{3}$ ▷ $\frac{1}{6}$	$\frac{1}{3}$ ▦ $\frac{2}{6}$	$\frac{1}{4}$ ◁ $\frac{1}{3}$
2.	$\frac{5}{8}$ ▷ $\frac{3}{8}$	$\frac{4}{12}$ ▦ $\frac{3}{9}$	$\frac{2}{3}$ ◁ $\frac{5}{6}$	$\frac{4}{8}$ ▦ $\frac{8}{16}$	$\frac{1}{12}$ ◁ $\frac{1}{2}$
3.	$\frac{1}{3}$ ◁ $\frac{4}{6}$	$\frac{1}{5}$ ◁ $\frac{1}{2}$	$\frac{1}{4}$ ▷ $\frac{1}{8}$	$\frac{1}{4}$ ▦ $\frac{2}{8}$	$\frac{5}{6}$ ◁ $\frac{1}{1}$
4.	$\frac{3}{4}$ ▷ $\frac{3}{8}$	$\frac{1}{10}$ ◁ $\frac{1}{5}$	$\frac{3}{4}$ ▦ $\frac{15}{20}$	$\frac{4}{4}$ ▦ $\frac{5}{5}$	$\frac{7}{8}$ ◁ $\frac{15}{16}$

Set 54   *For use after page 311*   Rational numbers: addition

Ⓐ

	a	**b**	**c**	**d**
1.	$\frac{1}{2}+\frac{1}{2}=$ ▦ 1	$\frac{2}{5}+\frac{1}{5}=$ ▦ $\frac{3}{5}$	$\frac{5}{2}+\frac{4}{2}=$ ▦ $\frac{9}{2}$	$3+\frac{1}{3}=$ ▦ $\frac{10}{3}$
2.	$2\frac{1}{5}+1\frac{2}{5}=$ ▦ $3\frac{3}{5}$	$5\frac{2}{6}+3\frac{1}{6}=$ ▦ $8\frac{3}{6}$	$4\frac{2}{3}+6\frac{1}{3}=$ ▦ 11	$3\frac{1}{12}+5\frac{3}{12}=$ ▦ 8

Ⓑ

	a	**b**	**c**	**d**
1.	$\frac{2}{4}+\frac{2}{4}=$ ▦ 1	$\frac{3}{7}+\frac{2}{7}=$ ▦ $\frac{5}{7}$	$\frac{6}{8}+\frac{5}{8}=$ ▦ $1\frac{3}{8}$	$\frac{1}{5}+5\frac{1}{5}=$ ▦ $5\frac{2}{5}$
2.	$3\frac{3}{4}+2\frac{2}{4}=$ ▦ $6\frac{1}{4}$	$7\frac{1}{8}+6\frac{3}{8}=$ ▦ $13\frac{4}{8}$	$4\frac{1}{2}+7\frac{3}{2}=$ ▦ 13	$\frac{3}{8}+4\frac{5}{8}=$ ▦ 5

CODED ANSWERS, SET 54, PART A: 1. (a) I, (b) B/C, (c) J/H, (d) ID/B; **2.** (a) B B/C, (b) A B/G, (c) II, (d) A F/IH

CODE: A B C D E F G H I J
          8 3 5 0 7 4 6 2 1 9

Set 55   *For use after page 316*   Rational numbers: mixed practice

	a	**b**	**c**	**d**
1.	$\frac{1}{8}+\frac{6}{8}=$ ▦ $\frac{7}{8}$	$\frac{7}{8}-\frac{4}{8}=$ ▦ $\frac{3}{8}$	$\frac{3}{10}+\frac{6}{10}=$ ▦ $\frac{9}{10}$	$\frac{7}{10}-\frac{4}{10}=$ ▦
2.	$9\times\frac{1}{10}=$ ▦ $\frac{9}{10}$	$\frac{1}{2}\times\frac{1}{3}=$ ▦ $\frac{1}{6}$	$\frac{2}{3}\times\frac{3}{4}=$ ▦ $\frac{1}{2}$	$\frac{1}{5}\times\frac{3}{8}=$ ▦ $\frac{3}{4}$
3.	$\frac{3}{8}\times\frac{1}{2}=$ ▦ $\frac{3}{16}$	$\frac{5}{6}\times\frac{1}{5}=$ ▦ $\frac{1}{6}$	$\frac{2}{5}\times\frac{3}{4}=$ ▦ $\frac{3}{10}$	$\frac{5}{8}\times\frac{5}{8}=$ ▦ $\frac{2}{3}$
4.	$.6+.3=$ ▦ $.9$	$.7-.2=$ ▦ $.5$	$.6+.1=$ ▦ $.7$	$.9-.8=$ ▦

Tables of Measures

English System LENGTH Metric System	
12 inches (in.) = 1 foot (ft)	10 centimeters (cm) = 1 decimeter (dm)
3 feet = 1 yard (yd)	10 decimeters = 1 meter (m)
5280 feet = 1 mile (mi)	1000 meters = 1 kilometer (km)
1760 yards = 1 mile	

TIME	
60 seconds (sec) = 1 minute (min)	52 weeks = 1 year (yr)
60 minutes = 1 hour (hr)	12 months (mo) = 1 year
24 hours = 1 day	365 days = 1 year
7 days = 1 week (wk)	366 days = 1 leap year

LIQUID	DRY
8 fluid ounces (oz) = 1 cup	2 pints = 1 quart
2 cups = 1 pint (pt)	8 quarts = 1 peck (pk)
2 pints = 1 quart (qt)	4 pecks = 1 bushel (bu)
4 quarts = 1 gallon (gal)	

English System WEIGHT Metric System	
16 ounces (oz) = 1 pound (lb)	1000 grams (g) = 1 kilogram (kg)
2000 pounds = 1 ton	1000 kilograms = 1 metric ton

Table of Addition

+	0	1	2	3	4	5	6	7	8	9
0	0	1	2	3	4	5	6	7	8	9
1	1	2	3	4	5	6	7	8	9	10
2	2	3	4	5	6	7	8	9	10	11
3	3	4	5	6	7	8	9	10	11	12
4	4	5	6	7	8	9	10	11	12	13
5	5	6	7	8	9	10	11	12	13	14
6	6	7	8	9	10	11	12	13	14	15
7	7	8	9	10	11	12	13	14	15	16
8	8	9	10	11	12	13	14	15	16	17
9	9	10	11	12	13	14	15	16	17	18

Table of Multiplication

×	0	1	2	3	4	5	6	7	8	9
0	0	0	0	0	0	0	0	0	0	0
1	0	1	2	3	4	5	6	7	8	9
2	0	2	4	6	8	10	12	14	16	18
3	0	3	6	9	12	15	18	21	24	27
4	0	4	8	12	16	20	24	28	32	36
5	0	5	10	15	20	25	30	35	40	45
6	0	6	12	18	24	30	36	42	48	54
7	0	7	14	21	28	35	42	49	56	63
8	0	8	16	24	32	40	48	56	64	72
9	0	9	18	27	36	45	54	63	72	81

Basic Principles for Addition of Whole Numbers

0 Principle

When you choose a whole number and add 0, the sum is the number you chose.

Examples: $5 + 0 = 5$ $987 + 0 = 987$

Commutative principle

You can change the order of the addends and the sum is the same.

Examples: $5 + 7 = 7 + 5$
$863 + 92 = 92 + 863$

Associative principle

You can change the grouping of the addends and the sum is the same.

Examples: $(2 + 7) + 4 = 2 + (7 + 4)$
$(18 + 68) + 51 = 18 + (68 + 51)$

Since you can change both the order and grouping of the addends, you can arrange addends any way that is convenient.

Examples: $8 + 7 + 2 + 3 = 8 + 2 + 7 + 3$
$27 + 58 + 73 = 73 + 27 + 58$

Principles for Multiplication of Whole Numbers

1 Principle

When you choose a whole number and multiply by 1, the product is the number you chose.

Examples: $9 \times 1 = 9$ $834 \times 1 = 834$

Commutative principle

You can change the order of the factors and the product is the same.

Examples: $5 \times 7 = 7 \times 5$
$863 \times 92 = 92 \times 863$

Associative principle

You can change the grouping of the factors and the product is the same.

Examples: $(2 \times 7) \times 4 = 2 \times (7 \times 4)$
$(18 \times 68) \times 51 = 18 \times (68 \times 51)$

Since you can change both the order and grouping of the factors, you can arrange factors any way that is convenient.

Examples: $6 \times 5 \times 7 \times 2 = 6 \times 7 \times 5 \times 2$
$25 \times 38 \times 4 \times 10 = 25 \times 4 \times 10 \times 38$

Basic Principle for Multiplication and Addition of Whole Numbers

Distributive principle

The distributive principle can be described as follows:

You can "break apart" either factor when you multiply.

This principle can be illustrated best by using sets. Example A illustrates "breaking apart" the first factor. Example B illustrates "breaking apart" the second factor.

A

$$5 \times 4 = (3 + 2) \times 4 = (3 \times 4) + (2 \times 4)$$

B

$$5 \times 4 = 5 \times (3 + 1) = (5 \times 3) + (5 \times 1)$$

GLOSSARY

abacus A device used for calculating, usually involving sliding beads or counters along a wire.

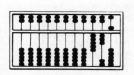

addend Any one of a set of numbers to be added. In the equation $4 + 5 = 9$, the numbers 4 and 5 are addends.

addition An operation that combines a first number and a second number to give exactly one number. The two numbers are called addends, and the one number which is the result of combining the two numbers is called the sum of the addends.

angle Two rays from a single point.

approximation One number is an approximation of another number if the first number is suitably "close" (according to context) to the other number.

area The area of a closed figure or region is the measure of that region as compared to a given selected region called the unit, usually a square region in the case of area.

associative principle *See* grouping principle.

average (arithmetic mean) The arithmetic mean of a set of numbers is the quotient resulting when the sum of the numbers in the set is divided by the number of addends.

bisect To divide in half or find the midpoint.

borrow A commonly used term for the regrouping process involved in certain types of subtraction. Example:

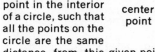

$$\begin{array}{r} 3\overset{1}{4}13 \\ -1\ 7 \\ \hline 2\ 6 \end{array} \rightarrow \begin{array}{r} 30 + 13 \\ -(10 + 7) \\ \hline 20 + 6 = 26 \end{array}$$

carry A commonly used term for the regrouping that is involved in addition. Example:

$$\begin{array}{r} {}^{1}57 \\ +26 \\ \hline 83 \end{array} \rightarrow \begin{array}{r} 50 + 7 \\ 20 + 6 \\ \hline 70 + 13 = 83 \end{array}$$

center point A given point in the interior of a circle, such that all the points on the circle are the same distance from this given point.

center point

centimeter A unit of length. One centimeter is $\frac{1}{100}$ meter.

central angle In the figure below, angle *BAC* illustrates a central angle with respect to a given circle with center *A*.

chord A line segment that has its end points on a given circle.

circle A set of points, all of which are a specified distance from a given point called the center or center point.

circumference The distance around a circle.

circumscribed circle A circle is circumscribed about a polygon when each vertex of the polygon is a point of the circle. In the figure, the circle is circumscribed about the triangle.

common factor When a number is a factor of two different numbers, it is said to be a common factor of the two numbers.

common multiple A number is a common multiple of two numbers if it is a multiple of each of the numbers.

commutative principle *See* order principle.

compass A device for drawing models of a circle.

composite number Any whole number greater than 1 that is not prime.

congruent angles Two angles are congruent if they are the "same size."

congruent segments Two segments are congruent if they are the "same size."

construction Used in this program relative to drawing models of particular geometric figures, using ruler and compass only.

count To name numbers in regular succession.

cube A rectangular prism (box) such that all faces are squares.

decimal Any base ten numeral that uses place value to represent a rational number.

decimal point The dot that is used in the decimal symbol.

decimeter One tenth of a meter. Ten centimeters.

denominator The number indicated by the numeral below the line in a fraction symbol.

diagonal A segment joining two nonadjacent vertices of a polygon. In the figure, the diagonal is segment *AB*.

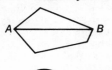

diameter A chord that passes through the center point of the circle.

difference The number resulting from the subtraction operation.

digits The basic Hindu-Arabic symbols used to write numerals. In the base ten system, these are the digits 0, 1, 2, 3, 4, 5, 6, 7, 8, 9.

dimensions The lengths of the various sides or parts of a particular geometric figure.

distributive principle *See* multiplication-addition principle.

division An operation related to multiplication as illustrated:

$$3 \times 4 = 12 \begin{cases} 12 \div 3 = 4 \\ 12 \div 4 = 3 \end{cases}$$

divisor In the problem $33 \div 7$, 7 is called the divisor.

$$\begin{array}{r} 4 \\ 7)\overline{33} \\ \underline{28} \\ 5 \end{array}$$

divisor

edge An edge of a space figure is one of the segments making up any one of the faces of the space figure.

equality (equals, or =) A mathematical relation of being exactly the same.

equation A mathematical sentence involving the use of the equality symbol. Examples: $5 + 4 = 9$; $7 + \square = 8$; $n + 3 = 7$.

equivalent fractions Two fractions are equivalent when it can be shown that they each can be used to represent the same amount of a given object. Also, two fractions are equivalent if these two products are the same:

$$\to 4 \times 6$$
$$\to 3 \times 8$$

equivalent sets Two sets that may be placed in a one-to-one correspondence.

estimate To find an approximation for a given number. (Sometimes a sum, a product, etc.)

even numbers The whole-number multiples of 2 (0, 2, 4, 6, 8, 10, 12, . . .).

exponent In the symbol 10^3, the "3" is an exponent. It indicates that 10 is used as a factor three times. Thus:

$$10^3 = 10 \times 10 \times 10 = 1000$$
$$5^4 = 5 \times 5 \times 5 \times 5 = 625$$
$$2^5 = 2 \times 2 \times 2 \times 2 \times 2 = 32$$

face The face of a given space figure is any one of the plane geometric figures (regions) making up the space figure. For example, in a cube each of the square regions is a face of the cube.

factor *See* multiplication. The equation $6 \times 7 = 42$ illustrates that both 6 and 7 are factors of 42.

factor tree The example shows two factor trees for the number 30.

$$2 \times 3 \times 5 \qquad 2 \times 3 \times 5$$
$$6 \times 5 \qquad 2 \times 15$$
$$30 \qquad 30$$

formula A general fact or rule expressed using symbols. Example: $\mathbf{A = l \times w}$ ($\mathbf{A}$ = area of rectangle, $\mathbf{l}$ = length of rectangle, $\mathbf{w}$ = width of rectangle).

fraction A symbol for a rational number. Examples: $\frac{2}{3}, \frac{5}{8}, \frac{7}{2}$.

graph (1) A set of points associated with a given set of numbers or set of number pairs.

(2) A picture used to illustrate a given collection of data. The data might be pictured in the form of a bar graph, a circle graph, a line graph, or a pictograph. (3) To draw the graph of.

greater than (>) One of the two basic inequality relations. Examples: $8 > 5$, $28 > 25$, $80 > 50$.

greatest common factor The largest, or greatest, number that is a factor of each of two numbers.

grouping principle (associative principle) When adding (or multiplying) three numbers, you can change the grouping and the sum (or product) is the same.
    Example: $2 + (8 + 6) = (2 + 8) + 6$.

hexagon A six-sided polygon.

higher terms A first fraction is in higher terms than a second fraction if the first fraction is equivalent to the second fraction and if the denominator of the first fraction is greater than the denominator of the second fraction.
    Example: $\frac{9}{12}$ is in higher terms than $\frac{6}{8}$.

hypotenuse The side opposite the right angle in a right triangle.

hypotenuse

improper fraction A fraction in which the numerator is greater than or equal to the denominator. Examples: $\frac{8}{5}, \frac{6}{6}, \frac{12}{3}$.

inch A unit of length. One inch is $\frac{1}{12}$ foot.

inequality ($<, \neq, >$) In arithmetic, a relation indicating that the two numbers are not the same.

inscribed angle Angle ABC in the figure illustrates an angle inscribed in a given circle.

integers, the set of The whole numbers together with their negatives:
    $\{. . . , -3, -2, -1, 0, 1, 2, 3, . . .\}$.

intersection of two sets The set containing those objects and only those objects which are in both of two sets. Example: Set A = $\{c, d, e, f\}$; Set B = $\{e, f, g\}$. The intersection of the two sets is the set $\{e, f\}$. We write: $A \cap B = \{e, f\}$.

least common denominator The least common multiple of two denominators. For $\frac{1}{4}$ and $\frac{5}{6}$, the least common denominator is 12.

least common multiple The smallest number that is a multiple of each of two numbers. For 4 and 6, the least common multiple is 12.

legs of a right triangle The two sides of a right triangle other than the hypotenuse.

legs

length (1) A number indicating the measure of one line segment with respect to another line segment, called the unit. (2) Sometimes used to denote one dimension (usually the greater) of a rectangle.

less than ($<$) One of the two basic inequality relations.   Examples: $5 < 8$, $25 < 28$, $50 < 80$.

lower terms A first fraction is in lower terms than a second fraction if the first fraction is equivalent to the second fraction and if the denominator of the first fraction is less than the denominator of the second fraction.
Example: $\frac{6}{8}$ is in lower terms than $\frac{9}{12}$.

lowest terms A fraction is in lowest terms if the numerator and denominator of the fraction have no common factor greater than 1.

matching lines Lines used to indicate the correspondence between the objects in two sets.

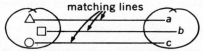

matching lines

measure (1) A number indicating the relation between a given object and a suitable unit. (2) The process of finding the number described above.

meter A unit of length that is slightly more than a yard.   A meter is approximately 39.37 inches.

minus ($-$) Used to indicate the subtraction operation, as in $7 - 3 = 4$ (read, "7 minus 3 equals 4").

mixed numeral A symbol given for a rational number greater than 1 that is a combination of a whole-number symbol and a fraction symbol.   Examples: $2\frac{1}{2}$, $3\frac{2}{3}$, $5\frac{1}{4}$.

multiple A first number is a multiple of a second number if there is a whole number that multiplies by the second number to give the first number. Example: 24 is a multiple of 6 since $4 \times 6 = 24$.

multiplication An operation that combines a first number and a second number to give exactly one number. The two numbers are called factors, and the one number which is a result of combining the two numbers is called the product of the two numbers.

multiplication-addition principle (distributive principle) This principle is sometimes described in terms of "breaking apart" a number before multiplying.
Example: $6 \times (20 \times 4) = (6 \times 20) + (6 \times 4)$.

negative integer An integer other than those integers which are the whole numbers.

number line A line on which specified points are given number labels or names. The following example illustrates the whole-number line.

0 1 2 3 4 5 6 7 8 9 10 11

number pair Any pair of numbers. In this program, usually a pair of whole numbers.

numeral A symbol for a number.

numerator The number indicated by the numeral above the line in a fraction symbol.

odd number Any whole number that is not even.

one-to-one correspondence A one-to-one correspondence exists between two sets when the elements of one can be matched with the elements of the other in such a way that each element of the first set is matched with exactly one element of the second set and each element of the second set is matched with exactly one element of the first set.

opposite Referring to the relation between two integers whose sum is zero. Example: 2 is the opposite of -2; -8 is the opposite of 8.

order principle (commutative principle) When adding (or multiplying) two numbers, the order of the addends (or factors) does not affect the sum (or product).   Example: $4 + 5 = 5 + 4$.

parallel lines Two lines which lie in the same plane and do not intersect.

parallelogram A quadrilateral with its opposite sides parallel.

parentheses (( )) Symbols used to indicate grouping or order of performing operations. Examples:
$(5 \times 4) - 2 = 18$; $5 \times (4 - 2) = 10$.

pentagon A five-sided polygon.

percent (%) Per 100; for each 100; $\frac{1}{100}$.

perfect number A number that is half the sum of its factors. Examples: 6, 28, and 496.

perimeter The sum of the lengths of the sides of a given polygon.

perpendicular Two lines that intersect in right angles are perpendicular to each other.

pi (π) The ratio of the circumference to the diameter of a circle; approximately 3.14.

placeholder In this program, this term is used to indicate the small box in which you write the solutions to equations.

place value A system used for writing numerals for numbers, using only a definite number of symbols or digits. In the numeral 3257 the 5 stands for 50; in the numeral 36,289 the 6 stands for 6000.

plus ($+$) Used to indicate the addition operation, as in $4 + 3 = 7$ (read, "4 plus 3 equals 7").

polygon A closed geometric figure made up of line segments.

positive integer Any whole number other than zero.

power The following examples illustrate powers of 10: 10^2, 10^5, 10^3, 10^7. These are powers of 7: 7^2, 7^4, 7^3, 7^5.

prime factor A factor that is a prime number.

prime number A number greater than 1 whose only factors are itself and 1.

product The result of the multiplication operation. In $6 \times 7 = 42$, 42 is the product of 6 and 7.

protractor A device used for measuring angles.

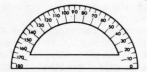

Pythagorean Theorem For any right triangle, the sum of the squares of the lengths of the two legs is equal to the square of the length of the hypotenuse.

quadrilateral A four-sided polygon.

quotient The number (other than the remainder) that is the result of the division operation. It may be thought of as a factor in a multiplication equation.

radian A unit for measuring angles. A radian is approximately 57.3 degrees.

radius (1) Any segment from the center point to a point on the circle. (2) The distance from the center point to any point on the circle.

ratio A pair of numbers used for certain types of comparisons.

rational number The number associated with a set of equivalent fractions.

ray A point on a line and all the points on one side of that point that are on that line.

reciprocal Two numbers are reciprocals of one another if their product is 1. Example: $\frac{4}{7}$ and $\frac{7}{4}$.

rectangle A quadrilateral that has four right angles.

reducing to lowest terms The process of finding the lowest-terms fraction that is equivalent to a given fraction. Example:

$$\frac{9}{12} \longrightarrow \frac{3 \times 3}{3 \times 4} \longrightarrow \frac{3}{4}.$$

regrouping A procedure commonly used in manipulating place-value symbols in adding or subtracting.

remainder Example:

$$\begin{array}{r} 6 \\ 7\overline{)47} \\ \underline{42} \\ 5 \end{array} \longleftarrow \text{remainder}$$

repeated addition Finding the sum of a set of numbers, each of which is the same. Example: $5 + 5 + 5 + 5$.

repeated subtraction Starting with a number and repeatedly subtracting the same given number from each difference that is obtained.

repeating decimals A decimal that repeats a given digit or group of digits over and over without end. Example: .333 . . . .

right angle An angle that has the measure of 90 degrees.
90° A right angle

right triangle A triangle that has one right angle.

Roman numerals Numerals used by the Romans. Used primarily to record numbers rather than for computing. Examples: IV, IX, XIV.

rounding Giving an approximation for a number.

scale drawing One constructed in such a way that the ratio of all the dimensions in the drawing to those of the actual object is the same.

scientific notation A number is said to be written in scientific notation if it is indicated as a number between 1 and 10 times a power of 10. Example: Speed of light in miles per second, $186,000 = 1.86 \times 10^5$.

segment Two points on a line and all the points on that line that are between the two points.

sequence A collection or set of numbers given in a specific order. Such numbers are commonly given according to some rule or pattern.

set A group or collection of objects.

similar triangles Two triangles are similar to each other if their sides can be matched so the ratio of the length of each pair of sides is the same.

skip count To count by multiples of a given number. Example: Counting by fives — 0, 5, 10, 15, 20, ...

solution The number or numbers which result from solving an equation or a given problem.

solve To find the number or numbers which, when substituted for the variable or place-holder, make the given equation true.

square A quadrilateral that has four right angles and four sides that are the same length.

subtraction An operation related to addition as illustrated:
$$7 + 8 = 15 \begin{cases} 15 - 8 = 7 \\ 15 - 7 = 8 \end{cases}$$

surface area The sum of the area of each face of a figure.

times (×) Used to indicate the multiplication operation, as in $3 \times 4 = 12$ (read, "3 times 4 equals 12").

triangle A three-sided polygon.

union of two sets The set consisting of those objects which are in one or the other or both of two sets. Example: Set A = {c, d, e, f}; Set B = {e, f, g}. The union of the two sets is the set {c, d, e, f, g}. We write: A ∪ B = {c, d, e, f, g}.

unit An amount or quantity adopted as a standard of measurement.

vertex The point that the two rays of an angle have in common.

volume The measure, obtained using an appropriate unit (usually a cube), of the interior region of a space figure.

whole number Any number in the set {0,1,2,3,4,5,6,7,8,9,10,11,12,13,14, . . .}.